PLANT PHYSIOLOGY

PLANT PHYSIOLOGY

With Reference to the Green Plant

2nd Edition

– Volume 2 –

EDWIN CYRUS MILLER

Professor, of Plant Physiology,
Kansas State College of Agriculture and Applied Science, and Plant Physiological, Kansas,
Agricultural Experimental Station

BIOTECH

2005

Biotech Books
Delhi - 110 035

ISBN 81-7622-154-6 (SET)
ISBN 81-7622-155-4 (Volume 1)
ISBN 81-7622-156-2 (Volume 2)
ISBN 81-7622-157-0 (Volume 3)

Published by : **BIOTECH BOOKS**
1123/74, Tri Nagar,
DELHI – 110 035
Phone: 27382765
e-mail: biotechbooks@yahoo.co.in

Showroom : 4762-63/23, Ansari Road, Darya Ganj,
NEW DELHI - 110 002
Phone: 23245578, 23244987

Printed at : **Chawla Offset Printers**
New Delhi – 110 052

PRINTED IN INDIA

To my wife

DELLA SLYE MILLER

PREFACE TO THE SECOND EDITION

In the preparation of this edition, various topics have been enlarged or revised to include the investigations and findings that have been made since the publication of the first edition. Certain topics that were overlooked in the preparation of that edition have been added. New material has been presented under appropriate headings.

Although no claim to completeness is made, it has been the effort of the author to present the more important citations relating to each subject. He has tried to present impartially the data that have been reported. He does not feel qualified to speak with authority on a majority of the topics, and his own ideas, if presented, thus would be of little consequence.

In order to conserve space, the questions that concluded each chapter in the first edition have been omitted.

The author is indebted in various ways to several of his associates at the Kansas State College of Agriculture and Applied Science, and he takes this occasion to thank them. He wishes to thank especially Hugh G. Gauch, for his invaluable aid in assembling and typing the bibliographies and other portions of the manuscript, and for aid in editing it; John C. Frazier, for aid in editing the manuscript, for helpful advice, and for unselfish service in many ways; Dr. Fritz Moore, head of the Department of Modern Languages, and Mrs. Irene Moore, for checking, respectively, the German and the French references; and Miss Esther Lewis, for clerical help in preparing the last half of the manuscript.

The author is especially indebted to Professor L. E. Melchers, head of the Department of Botany and Plant Pathology, Kansas State College of Agriculture and Applied Science, for his kindness in allotting clerical and stenographic help for the revision of this text.

EDWIN C. MILLER.

KANSAS STATE COLLEGE OF AGRICULTURE AND APPLIED SCIENCE,

PREFACE TO THE FIRST EDITION

There has existed for some time a need for an advanced text in plant physiology. The various texts by European investigators and teachers, although summarizing the work that has been done on the Continent, have failed to cover adequately the contributions of American and English plant physiologists. These contributions during the past two decades have been outstanding and dominate in many cases the work along certain lines. A summary of these contributions should be available to students, teachers, and investigators in the field of plant physiology.

It has been the intention of the author to bridge this gap in the literature and to summarize in this book the more important findings of English, American, and Continental plant physiologists. The material has been assembled in such form as to be available as a text for upperclassmen and graduate students and at the same time to be sufficiently comprehensive as a reference book for investigators in plant physiology.

The work has been confined entirely to the physiology of the green plant, as it has been thought that the processes and phenomena of the fungi belong, at present at least, to the province of plant pathology and allied fields. The discussions and summaries of the various investigators have been used freely, and in many cases their phraseology has been altered but little. The author has tried, however, in each instance to indicate the source of the information presented. Some topics are discussed more thoroughly than others. This, however, is to be expected as an author naturally is more familiar with those subjects which are in the field of his research.

With but few exceptions the references cited at the end of each chapter have been mentioned or discussed in the text. It is considered that these references will be of value to those who desire to familiarize themselves more thoroughly with any of the topics than they are herein discussed. The questions following each chapter cover all the topics discussed in that portion of the text. It has been the experience of the author that these are valuable to the student as an aid in guiding him to a mastery of the subject matter.

This text is the outgrowth of twenty years' experience as a teacher of plant physiology in the Kansas State Agricultural College and as plant physiologist of the Kansas Agricultural Experiment Station. The material included herein has been presented to classes composed for the most part of juniors, seniors, and graduate students. The favorable manner in which the subject matter and its method of presentation have been received in the classroom has prompted the author to present this volume to the public.

I am indebted to many of my associates for assistance in the preparation of this text. Most of the drawings were made by Mr. S. Fred Prince, formerly biological artist at the Kansas State Agricultural College. I am indebted to Miss Nora E. Dalbey, associate professor of botany in the Kansas State Agricultural College, for certain drawings and for helpful suggestions in the arrangement of the illustrations. I wish to thank Dr. Frank M. Schertz of the U. S. Bureau of Chemistry and Soils, Dr. John W. Shive of the New Jersey Agricultural Experiment Station, Dr. W. E. Tottingham of the University of Wisconsin, Dr. F. F. Blackman of Botany School, Cambridge, England, and Professor W. E. Davis of the Kansas State Agricultural College for permission to use certain figures as indicated in the text.

I am grateful to Mr. J. C. Frazier, formerly of the Department of Botany and Plant Pathology, Kansas State Agricultural College, for helpful advice in the preparation of the manuscript and to Dr. R. P. White, formerly of the same department, for criticism and advice in the preparation of Chap. II. I wish to thank Dr. J. V. Cortelyou, professor of modern languages at Kansas State Agricultural College, and Miss Madge Wardell, instructor in French at the same institution, for checking respectively the German and French references. I wish also to acknowledge the most valuable aid and advice of Miss Nellie Jacobs, clerk in the Department of Botany and Plant Pathology, Kansas State Agricultural College, in the preparation of the manuscript.

I am especially indebted to the following of my colleagues in the Kansas State Agricultural College for their constructive criticism in the preparation of the text: S. C. Salmon, professor of farm crops; Dr. P. L. Gainey, professor of bacteriology; R. J. Barnett, professor of horticulture; Dr. H. H. Haymaker, professor of plant pathology; W. E. Davis, professor of plant physiology; Dr. F. C. Gates, professor of taxonomy and ecology; Dr. F. L. Duley, professor of soils; Dr. C. W. Colver, professor of organic chemistry; and Dr. E. L. Tague, associate professor of chemistry. The author alone, however, is responsible for the statements in the text.

EDWIN C. MILLER.

KANSAS STATE AGRICULTURAL COLLEGE,

CONTENTS

CHAPTER II

CHAPTER III

CHAPTER IV

CHAPTER V

CHAPTER VII

CHAPTER VIII

CHAPTER IX

CHAPTER X

CHAPTER XI

CHAPTER XII

CHAPTER XIV

CHAPTER VII

THE LOSS OF WATER FROM PLANTS

I. GENERAL NEED OF WATER BY PLANTS

It is common knowledge that water is absolutely essential to animal life, and that if it is withheld for a relatively short period from animal organisms death ensues. Water is just as essential to plant life, and if a plant is deprived of water it will perish, perhaps not so quickly as an animal but just as surely nevertheless. Let us now consider the relationship of water to the life of the plant in order to ascertain the need of a continuous water supply by a plant that is normally carrying on its various functions.

A. The Protoplasm

A large amount of water is necessary to the proper functioning of the protoplasm, so that it has been said that "All living matter lives in water." The younger, the more vigorous, the more impressionable, the more active, and the more rapidly growing protoplasm is the more water it contains. As an example of the large amount of water in the actively growing regions of plants, the tip of a young stalk of corn or the base of the growing leaves of the same plant may be cited. These regions of the corn plant are composed of 92 to 93 per cent of water, most of which is directly associated with the protoplasm, which completely fills the cells of these portions of the plant. When we consider that the flesh of a ripe watermelon contains no higher percentage of water than the growing regions just mentioned, we can realize the relatively large amount of water that is required in the protoplasm of plant cells to bring about normal growth and development.

If the normal amount of water in the protoplasm is removed, it becomes less and less active until a point is reached where death ensues. The case of seeds is a good example of what takes place when water is withdrawn from the protoplasm. The protoplasm in the cells that make up the seed is living, but so much water has been withdrawn from it in the process of curing that it is very inactive or dormant. If water, however, is supplied to the seed, the protoplasm obtains the amount necessary to carry on its functions actively, and the seed begins to grow.

B. Vacuoles of Cells

The relationship of the vacuole to the plant cell has been discussed in Chap. I. A certain amount of water in the vacuole is necessary to maintain the normal condition of turgor essential for the growth of the cells and for the erectness of the plant. The amount of water in the various parts of plants will depend upon the type of plant and the conditions under which it is examined. The following list shows the amount of water in the leaves of plants grown at Manhattan, Kans. These leaves were fully developed and in full vegetative vigor. The samples were collected at 10 A.M.

Kind of leaf	Percentage of water	Kind of leaf	Percentage of water
Cabbage	86	Pumpkin	80
Tomato	84	Corn	77
Cowpea	82	Apple	60

C. For Continual Translocation of Materials from One Part of Plant to Another

As far as is known, all foods and materials translocated in a plant move from cell to cell in a watery solution.

D. For Chemical Combination

Many of the various organic compounds found in plants are formed by the combination of water with certain materials that enter the plant from the soil and the air.

The water needed by any plant during its growing season for the purposes that have just been mentioned amounts to very little. Thus, for example, a normal corn plant that reached a height of 10 to 12 ft. and produced a good yield of grain had, including the stem, leaves, grain, cob, and roots, a moist weight of 2,707 g. at the height of its full vegetative growth when the vegetative parts were all intact and the grain was in the late dough stage and was well glazed and dented. The total weight of dry matter of this plant was 835 g. The water content of the plant was thus 1,872 g. This means that the water in this plant, which was needed for the vacuoles of the cells, for the protoplasm, and for the translocation of materials, did not exceed this amount. The amount of water necessary for chemical combination in this case would not amount to over 250 g. even if we consider that all the hydrogen and oxygen in the dry matter was obtained by the plant from water. According to these figures, a corn plant would thus need during its entire growing season only 2,122 g. (a little over 2 l. or approximately 2⅕ qt.) of water to supply it with a sufficient amount for the four uses that have just been mentioned. It is well known, however, that a single corn plant requires during its growing season a much greater quantity of water than that which has just been stated. A single corn plant during the growing season of 1924 at Manhattan, Kans., removed from the soil 54 gal. or 1⅘ bbl. of water. This is approximately ninety-eight times more than is needed for the cell vacuoles, translocation, protoplasm, and chemical combination. What,

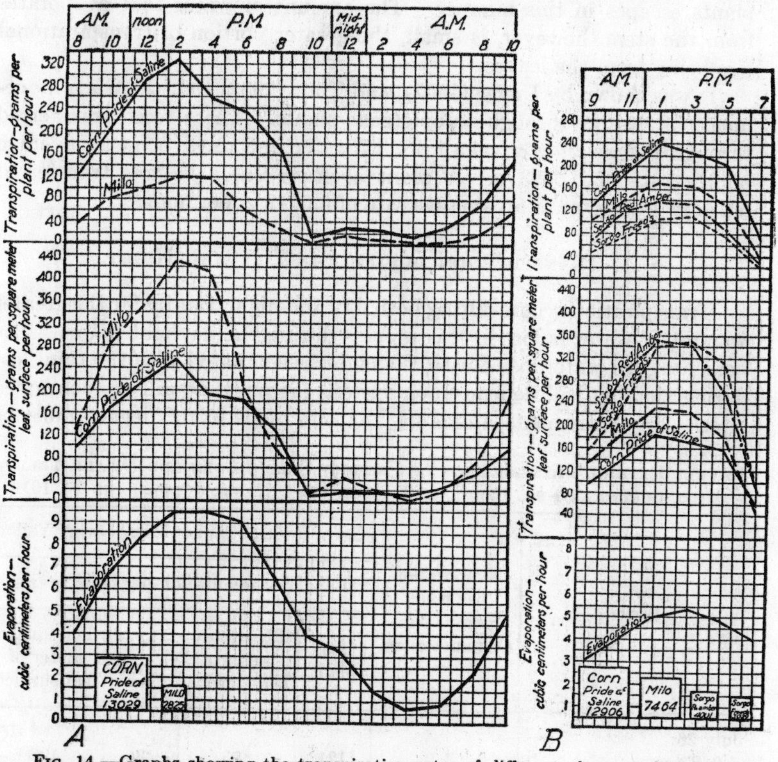

Fig. 14.—Graphs showing the transpiration rates of different plants under the same conditions and the distribution of their water loss during the day. The evaporation from a porous cup atmometer for the corresponding periods is also shown. The squares at the bottom of the figure represent the extent of the leaf surface of each plant expressed in square centimeters. *A*, the transpiration rates of Pride of Saline corn and Dwarf Yellow milo. *B*, the transpiration rates of Pride of Saline corn, Dwarf Yellow milo, Red Amber sorgo, and Freed's sorgo.

then, is the need of such a large supply of water for a plant during its growing season?

E. Replacement

A supply of water in the soil is needed by a plant at all times during its growing season to replace that which is being lost continuously from its stem and leaves by transpiration and by guttation.

II. THE EVAPORATION OF WATER FROM PLANTS. TRANSPIRATION

Transpiration is the loss of water in the form of vapor from the stem and leaves of the living plant. Practically all the water that is lost from plants escapes in this manner. The amount of water that evaporates from the stem, however, is small, the greater portion of transpirational loss being from the leaves.

It was shown by Unger (1862), and Thut (1932) that there is a movement of water through submerged plants. There was transferred through *Potamogeton crispus* 1.6 g. of water in 8 days, or at an average hourly rate of 0.0083 g. A plant of *Ranunculus fluitans* transferred 0.8 g. in 8 days, or at an average rate of 0.0042 g. per hour.

A. Transpiration during the Day and Night

Transpiration occurs during both day and night, but by far the greater amount of water is lost in this process during the daylight hours. The percentage of water lost during the night as compared with the total lost during the day will depend upon various factors that will be mentioned later. Any statements, therefore, that are made in this regard must be

Hourly Rate of Transpiration of Pride of Saline Corn and Dwarf Yellow Milo, during a 24-hr. Period at Garden City, Kans., July 26 and 27, 1916

Period	Evaporation per hour, porous cup atmometer, cc.	Corn, Pride of Saline		Milo, Dwarf Yellow	
		Rate of transpiration per hour, grams			
		Per plant	Per square meter of leaf surface	Per plant	Per square meter of leaf surface
July 26:					
6–8 a.m.	3.9	121	93	35	126
8–10 a.m.	6.7	212	163	79	281
10–12 noon	8.2	291	223	99	350
12–2 p.m.	9.5	329	253	122	432
2–4 p.m.	9.5	259	198	117	413
4–6 p.m.	9.1	236	181	58	206
6–8 p.m.	6.7	164	126	27	94
8–10 p.m.	3.9	11	8	3	12
10–12 mid.	3.4	25	19	13	44
July 27:					
12–2 a.m.	1.6	25	19	5	19
2–4 a.m.	0.8	18	14	2	6
4–6 a.m.	0.9	31	24	5	19
6–8 a.m.	2.7	71	55	21	75

general and relative only to the conditions prevailing at the time the observations were made.

The general distribution of the water loss during a 24-hr. period can be shown by an experiment selected from the work of Miller and Coffman (1918), as shown in Fig. 14 and in the table on page 410.

They found that from 94 to 96 per cent of the water transpired was lost during the daylight hours under the climatic conditions prevailing at Garden City, Kans. Briggs and Shantz (1916) observed at Akron, Colo., that the transpirational loss from various crop plants from sunset to sunrise amounted to only 3 to 6 per cent of the total transpiration for the 24-hr. period, according to the following table:

Plant	Percentage of total transpiration	
	Daylight	Darkness
Wheat	96	4
Oats	94	6
Rye	95	5
Sorghums	95	5
Alfalfa	97	3
Pigweed (*Amaranthus*)	97	3

Under the climatic conditions that prevail in the Great Plains area of the United States less water is transpired by plants during the forenoon than during the afternoon. The percentage of water transpired during the forenoon hours is, as a rule, from 40 to 50 per cent of the total water transpired during the daylight hours. As a general rule, the maximum rate of transpiration is reached somewhere between 11 A.M. and 3 P.M. Miller and Coffman (1918) found in 30 experiments with corn that the maximum rate of transpiration occurred eighteen times between 11 A.M. and 1 P.M. and twelve times between 1 P.M. and 3 P.M. In the case of 52 observations of various varieties of the sorghums, the maximum rate of transpiration occurred twenty-eight times between 11 A.M. and 1 P.M. and twenty-four times between 1 P.M. and 3 P.M.

Meyer (1932) noted that the peak of transpiration of young tulip trees (*Liriodendron tulipifera*) occurred shortly before noon. Of the 148 species of plants, in 16 plant associations in Ohio and Indiana, studied by Blaydes (1935), 93 per cent had their maximum rate of transpiration between 7 A.M. and 12 noon, over 89 per cent between 7 and 11 A.M., and 52 per cent between 9 and 11 A.M.

B. Amount of Water Lost

The total amount of water that is evaporated from plants during a growing season will depend primarily upon the prevailing climatic conditions, but the following data will serve as an example of the relatively large amount that escapes from the plant by transpiration. The data here presented were obtained by the author at Manhattan, Kans., in 1924 to 1925. The plants were grown in sealed containers and the soil was kept in good moisture tilth by the daily addition to it of the water that had been removed by the plants during that time (Fig. 21).

As shown in the table below, a single Kansas Sunflower corn plant during its growing season in 1924 lost 54 gal. of water. Let us consider how much water would thus be evaporated by an acre of corn plants during the growing season if the soil were supplied with sufficient moisture for normal growth and development.

Plant	Length of season	Total water lost during the season per plant, gallons
Cowpea	May 19 to Sept. 2, 1924	13
Potato, Irish cobbler, 1 hill, 2 to 3 plants	April 18 to July 30, 1924	25
Tomato, Louisiana Pink, pruned to 1 stem	May 19 to Sept. 2, 1924	34
Corn, Kansas Sunflower	May 5 to Sept. 8, 1924	54
Winter wheat, Kanred, 1 plant 15 stalks	Oct. 15 1924 to June 28, 1925	25
Sunflower, Russian	May 26 to Aug. 23, 1925	123
Sunflower, wild	May 24 to Aug. 23, 1925	130
Giant ragweed (*Ambrosia trifida*)	May 24 to Aug. 23, 1925	140

If the corn were in 44-in. rows, the plants 2 ft. apart in the row, with one plant per hill, we should have about 6,000 plants per acre if a perfect stand were obtained. The total amount of water that would be evaporated from the leaves and sheaths of an acre of corn during the growing season under these conditions would be 324,000 gal. or 1,296 tons of water. Since 1 in. of rainfall per acre weighs 113.25 tons, this is equivalent to approximately 11 acre in. of rainfall. A single corn plant that has reached its full leaf development has been observed to transpire as much as 32 qt. of water during a single week under the summer conditions of the Great Plains. This means an average of approximately 4½ qt. per plant per day. When the body weight of the plant is considered it is found that the plant during each day of the 7-day period that has just been mentioned evaporated a quantity of water equal to twice its body weight.

The question naturally arises as to what is the cause of such a large loss of water from plants. In order to understand this, we must consider the general structure of the leaves, and it is to that topic that we shall now devote our attention.

C. Factors That Influence the Rate of Transpiration

1. Leaf Structure.—It is not the intention here to enter into any detailed discussion of the anatomy of the leaf but only to mention in a general way those characteristics of its structure that are conducive to the loss of water by evaporation. The structure of leaves varies

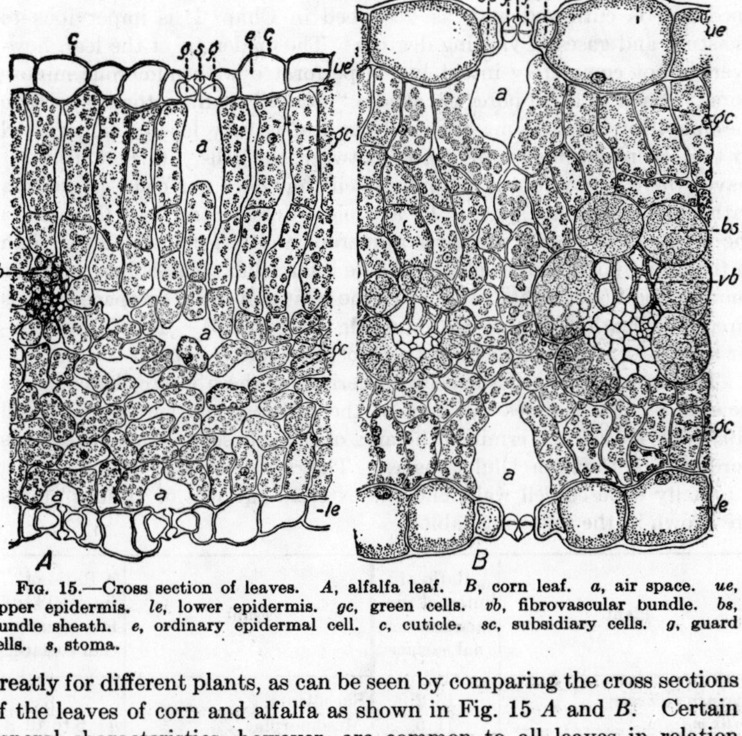

Fig. 15.—Cross section of leaves. *A*, alfalfa leaf. *B*, corn leaf. *a*, air space. *ue*, upper epidermis. *le*, lower epidermis. *gc*, green cells. *vb*, fibrovascular bundle. *bs*, bundle sheath. *e*, ordinary epidermal cell. *c*, cuticle. *sc*, subsidiary cells. *g*, guard cells. *s*, stoma.

greatly for different plants, as can be seen by comparing the cross sections of the leaves of corn and alfalfa as shown in Fig. 15 *A* and *B*. Certain general characteristics, however, are common to all leaves in relation to water loss, and it is these facts that we wish to consider here.

The leaf of most angiosperms is a relatively broad, flat, thin organ with a large amount of surface in proportion to its mass. A better conception of the large amount of surface exposed by leaves may be had by citing one or two examples. The leaf and sheath surface of an ordinary variety of corn plant grown under the conditions of the corn belt amounts to from 30 to 35 sq. ft. or is from four to six times as extensive as the surface of the soil in which the plants are growing. A wild sunflower plant growing under favorable conditions may have as much as 40 to 50 sq. ft. of leaf surface.

The ordinary leaf is composed, for the most part, of thin-walled parenchyma tissue through which numerous finely divided vascular bundles permeate and end free so that as many as 6,000 of these minute veins may end in a square centimeter of leaf. The entire leaf is covered by a layer of cells, generally only one cell in thickness, called the "epidermis." The outer wall of the epidermis is generally somewhat thickened and is cutinized and, as described in Chap. I, is impervious to moisture and gases in varying degrees. The epidermis of the leaf, however, is not completely intact but is perforated with numerous minute pores. Each of these pores is called a "stoma" (plural, stomata). The mesophyll or parenchyma tissue of the leaf is very loosely constructed so that there are many air spaces between the cells. In fact, in most leaves there is scarcely a mesophyll cell that does not come in contact with an intercellular space. In a typical dorsiventral leaf (Fig. 15*A*) the intercellular spaces are more numerous and larger in the lower than in the upper portion of the leaf. These intercellular spaces join with one another and finally unite with one of the relatively large air spaces that is directly beneath each pore or stoma (Fig. 15 *A* and *B*). These intercellular spaces form from 3 to 70 per cent of the total volume of the leaf.

The area of the cell surfaces bordering on these intercellular spaces exceeds by many times the area of the external leaf surface. Turrell (1933, 1934, 1936) determined the area of the exposed portion of the cells bordering on the intercellular spaces. The ratios between the area of the internally exposed cell walls and the external surfaces of various plants are shown in the following table:

Plant	Ratio of internal surface to external surface	Plant	Ratio of internal surface to external surface
Syringa vulgaris	13.2	Succulents	7.8
Vitis vulpina	11.6	Mesomorphic	11.6 to 16.3
Citrus limonia	22.2	Xeromorphic (in sun)	22.2 to 31.3
Berberis nervosa	9.8	Xeromorphic (in shade)	8.2 to 9.9

It is seen that the thin-walled cells of the mesophyll are in direct contact with the fibrovascular bundles, which, in turn, are in direct connection with the water supply of the roots and the soil. These cells, on the other hand, have a portion of their moist surface exposed to the intercellular air cavities which are connected either directly or indirectly with the atmosphere through the stomata of the leaf. The leaf structure thus is such that conditions are very favorable for the loss of water by evaporation. A moist porous cell-wall surface is exposed to the air on at least one side and is in contact on the other side under favorable conditions with a continuous water supply. The facts that have just been mentioned in regard to the leaves apply also in a more limited sense to the young stems of plants. Although the amount of water lost from the young stem parts is often considerable, the amount is negligible in comparison with the amount lost from the leaves. The large loss of water from plants by transpiration is thus due primarily to the structure of the leaf. The structure of the leaf is apparently an adaptation for the absorption of gases that it needs (Bessey, 1898) or for the excretion of those that arise in its metabolism, but it is poorly adapted for the retention of water, so that the continuous loss of water from it is a constant menace to the life of the plant.

It should be mentioned here that different plants exposed to the same environmental conditions do not have the same rate of transpiration. This may be illustrated, for example, by the experimental data obtained by Miller (1925) at the Kansas Agricultural Experiment Station in observations of corn, milo, pumpkin, cowpea, and soybean plants grown under field conditions, as shown in the table on page 416.

Blaydes (1928, 1935) collected data by means of the cobalt chloride-paper method on the transpiration rate of 148 species of plants growing under a wide range of conditions. The average standard water loss for all the species on which data were collected was 1.150 g. of water vapor per hour per 100 sq. cm. of leaf surface. On the same basis the greatest water loss was from *Plantago major*, *Polygonum amphibium*, and *Iris versicolor* with a rate of 3.802, 3.661, 3.452 g. per square decimeter per hour, respectively. The lowest transpiration rates were 0.074, 0.076, and 0.085 g. per 100 sq. cm. per hour, respectively, for *Juglans nigra*, *Bromus inermis*, and *Silphium perfoliatum*.

Weaver and Mogensen (1919) noted that the autumnal transpiration losses from conifers were as high per unit of surface or even higher than those from broad leaves. The winter losses from conifers were found to be only $\frac{1}{251}$ to $\frac{1}{55}$ as great as those in the autumn. The winter losses from conifers were scarcely greater than those from defoliated stems of broad-leaved trees.

Kelley (1930) in a study of the rate of transpiration of 21 species of deciduous fruit plants stated that *Ribes vulgare*, *Corylus maxima*, *Rubus occidentalis*, *Pyrus malus*, *Pyrus communis*, and *Cydonia maxima* showed a high rate of transpiration; *Fragaria chiloensis*, *Ribes grossularia*, and *Prunus domestica* a medium rate; and *Juglans nigra*, *Prunus amygdalus*, and *Prunus persica* the lowest rate of the plants examined. It was

Relative Transpiration of Corn, Milo, Pumpkin, Cowpeas and Soybeans under the Same Environmental Conditions in the Field at Manhattan, Kans.

Date	Corn, Kansas Sunflower		Milo, Dwarf Yellow		Pumpkin, Cheese		Cowpeas, New Era		Soybeans, Midwest		Evaporation
	Per plant	Per square meter of leaf surface	Per plant	Per square meter of leaf surface	Per plant	Per square meter of leaf surface	Per plant	Per square meter of leaf surface	Per plant	Per square meter of leaf surface	Porous cup atmometer, cc.
July 7–8:											
9 a.m.–4 p.m.	222	146	142	167	126	177	54	129	68	136	35.4
4 p.m.–9 a.m.	22	14	10	12	13	18	7	16	9	18	23.1
July 8–9:											
9 a.m.–4 p.m.	240	158	178	210	168	234	65	156	81	161	41.5
4 p.m.–9 a.m.	18	12	5	6	9	13	7	17	6	12	17.5
July 9–10:											
9 a.m.–4 p.m.	227	150	183	216	165	230	78	188	90	179	30.0
4 p.m.–9 a.m.	19	12	9	10	12	17	6	13	6	12	14.0

observed by Haas and Halma (1932) that the transpiration rate was highest for the lemon trees, less for grapefruit, and least for the orange. Ashby (1932) reported that transpiration from the wilting shoots of the creosote bush was greater than that from the privet. Compared with privet, the creosote stem offered twice the resistance to the passage of water under pressure. The root suction pressure of the latter was three times that of the former. Sperry (1936) noted in the Rocky Mountain National Park that the different species of pine varied markedly in their transpiration rates.

It was shown by Dowd (1931) that each variety of apple twigs has a distinct transpiration rate. These differences amounted to as much as 50 per cent in some cases. Markley and Sando (1931) found with but few exceptions that the skins of apples from New York were more permeable to water than those from Washington.

A striking example of the different effects of the changes in the environmental conditions upon the rate of transpiration of different plants is offered by the observations of Sayre (1919), who found that an increase in temperature of 23°F. and a decrease in humidity of 35 per cent increased the transpiration rate of the mullein plant only twenty-five times as compared to forty times for the tobacco plant. The two main factors that may contribute to these differences in response to the environment are the differences in anatomical structure and the specific ability of the plant to bring about changes in itself. Of the anatomical differences that apparently contribute to variation in the transpiration rate of different plants, the structure of the leaves is probably the most important. On account of their variation in structure, the leaves differ in their response to solar energy. Their absorption coefficients may not be the same, and the dissipation of the absorbed energy may be very different for different plants. We shall now discuss the more important structural differences in the anatomy of the leaves and the influence of the structural differences upon the rate of transpiration.

a. The Stomata.—The stomata or stomates (singular, stoma or stomate) are minute more or less elongated openings through the epidermis of plants. They occur in the epidermis of any part of the plant (Anderson, 1897; Jivanna Rao, 1923; and Barrett, 1929) except the root but are found in the greatest numbers in the leaves. A stoma or stomate is simply an intercellular opening between two specialized epidermal cells that are termed "guard cells." (Fig. 16*A*, *B*, and *C*.) In the most simple development, the stoma is formed by the division of a young epidermal cell, which has become ellipsoidal in outline, into two daughter cells. The dissolution of the middle lamella of the walls separating these two cells then occurs and the stoma or intercellular passage is formed by the splitting of two walls. The

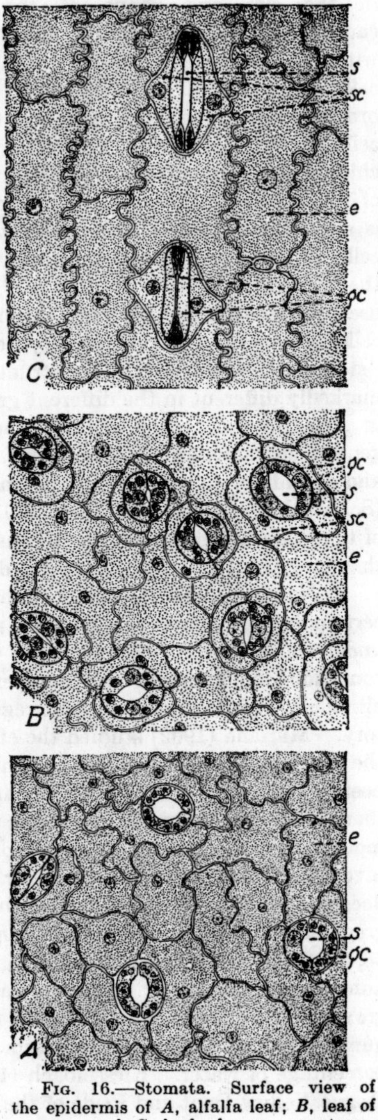

FIG. 16.—Stomata. Surface view of the epidermis of *A*, alfalfa leaf; *B*, leaf of cowpea; and *C*, leaf of corn. *s*, stoma. *gc*, guard cells. *sc*, subsidiary cells. *e*, ordinary epidermal cells.

stoma may be opened and closed in varying degrees by changes in the size and shape of the guard cells. The changes are caused by the variation of the turgor of the cells in connection with the structure of their cell walls. In some cases, the epidermal cells that border on the guard cells are also different from the ordinary epidermal cells and are called "subsidiary" or "accessory cells." The guard cells are richer in protoplasmic material, contain chloroplasts, are different in form, and have a higher concentration of the cell sap than the ordinary epidermal cells. The term "stoma" is also used to denote collectively the intercellular opening, the guard cells, and the subsidiary cells. In that case, the orifice is known as the "stomatal pore." In this text, however, the term stoma will be used to denote only the pore through the epidermis, while the guard cells and accessory or subsidiary cells will be collectively termed the "stomatal apparatus." The structure of the stomatal apparatus is markedly different in the different groups of plants. These peculiarities in structure may vary slightly under different conditions, but their general characteristics are constant. The peculiar type of guard cells and subsidiary cells of the grains and grasses is a good example of this (Schwendener, 1889). Rehfous (1917) considered that the structures of the stomatal apparatus are so constant within a given group of plants that they are of first importance in indicating phylogeny and relationships.

1. *Number.*—The number of stomata per unit of leaf surface is, within certain limits, a characteristic of the particular species or variety of plant under consideration. There seems to be evidence that environmental conditions do influence the number of stomata per unit of surface, although the information in that regard is rather meager and contradictory. Mariana (1902) studied the effect of the humidity of the air upon the development of the stomata on the cotyledonary leaves of buckwheat, beet, white lupine, crimson clover, and other plants and concluded that there were fewer stomata produced per unit of leaf area in a relatively moist than in a relatively dry atmosphere. He considered that humidity favors the development of the superficial areas of the leaves but that it does not increase the absolute number of the stomata. Duggar (1911) grew plants of wheat and corn in sand cultures containing, respectively, 38, 30, 20, 15, and 11 per cent of moisture and observed that the greatest number of stomata per unit area was found on the leaves of the plants growing in the sand with the highest moisture content, while the smallest number was on the leaves of plants grown in the sand with the lowest percentage of water. Kiesselbach (1916), however, in experiments with Hogue Yellow Dent and Pride of the North varieties of corn did not find any striking response in the relative number of stomata to variations in either soil moisture or soil fertility. Weiss (1866) also concluded from

extensive observations that the conditions under which plants are grown do not influence either the size or the number of their stomata.

It was noted by Reed and Hirano (1931) with *Citrus* that the density of the stomata varies in different portions of the leaf and between species. However, their density is decreased in all cases when the intensity of light is reduced. Tavčar (1926) believed that it is possible by crossing plants with larger and smaller numbers of stomata to change their density in the hybrid and thus alter to a certain degree the physiological processes that are concerned with them. Hirano (1931) noted that the species of *Citrus* in the tropics have more stomata per unit area than those growing in other regions. In studying barley, wheat, and corn, Van de Roovaart and Fuller (1935) found, with plants growing in a soil-moisture content ranging from 11 to 38 per cent, that there is a lower stomatal frequency under optimum conditions, because the ordinary epidermal cells are large, and hence there is a greater distance between the stomata. The ratio of the number of stomata to that of the ordinary cells, however, remains almost constant. The influence of a varying water content of the soil upon the number of stomata per unit of area is shown in the following table:

Soil moisture (wilting coefficient, 18 per cent), per cent	Stomata per unit area		
	Barley	Wheat	Corn
38	5.1	6.2	5.2
17	6.2	6.2	5.2
11	7.5	7.7	7.8

Niemann (1932) and Penfound (1932) also found that the number of stomata varied directly with the moisture content of the soil. Wood (1934) considered, however, that variations in stomatal frequency appear to be connected with generic and family characters to a greater extent than with environmental conditions.

Salisbury (1927) in an extensive study of the stomatal frequency of the woodland flora of England concluded that stomatal frequency is mainly dependent on the humidity of the environment, dry exposed conditions being associated with high frequencies and humid conditions with low frequencies. He noted also that the total pore space per unit area of leaf surface is greater in dry than in moist conditions, despite the larger size attained by the stomata in a humid environment. He makes the very important statement in this regard that there is a high positive correlation coefficient between the number of stomata and the number of epidermal cells per unit of area. The difference in frequency of stomata in wet and dry soil, small leaves as compared with large leaves, and different parts of the same leaf is due to differences in growth. Such differences in frequency are thus due to the spacing of the stomata and not to the differences in the number of stomata developed per number of epidermal cells in a unit area.

Salisbury proposed the stomatal index

$$I = \frac{S}{E + S} \times 100$$

where S equals the number of stomata per unit of area and E the number of ordinary epidermal cells in the same unit area. The stomatal index thus aims at expressing the percentage proportion of the ultimate divisions of the dermatogen of the leaf that have been converted into stomata. This infers that under a given set of conditions a species tends to form a definite proportion of stomatal initials. Salisbury considered that there is some evidence that high humidity tends to reduce the proportion of stomata formed, and aquatics would seem to have low stomatal indexes. Variations in the stomatal index appear to be due to internal factors, of which nutritional conditions are perhaps the most important. Hirano

Number of Stomata on the Leaves of Pride of Saline Corn, Dwarf Yellow Milo, and Blackhull Kafir during Nine Growing Seasons

Year	Number of stomata, thousands per square inch of leaf surface											
	Corn, Pride of Saline				Milo, Dwarf Yellow				Kafir, Blackhull			
	Upper	Lower	Total	Ratio lower to upper	Upper	Lower	Total	Ratio lower to upper	Upper	Lower	Total	Ratio lower to upper
Garden City, Kans.:												
1914	43	55	98	1.28	66	97	163	1.42	48	103	151	2.14
1915	40	50	90	1.25	64	76	140	1.17	44	89	133	2.02
1916	49	53	102	1.08	67	90	157	1.34				
1917	40	51	91	1.27	53	74	127	1.49	45	82	127	1.82
Manhattan, Kans.:												
1918	60	73	133	1.21	81	100	181	1.23	58	103	161	1.94
1919	39	51	90	1.51	59	85	144	1.27	55	91	146	1.65
1920	36	49	85	1.36	56	91	147	1.66	46	106	152	2.30
1922	43	56	99	1.30	61	87	148	1.42	51	98	149	1.92
1923	34	48	82	1.41	58	89	147	1.53	55	100	155	1.81
Average	42.6	54.0	96.6	1.27	62.8	87.6	150.4	1.40	50.2	96.5	146.7	1.92

(1931) noted in *Citrus*, that precipitation during the spring months, while the leaves were developing, showed a better correlation with the number of stomata than did the amount of annual rainfall.

Miller (1928) recorded the number of stomata per unit area for one variety each of corn, milo, and kafir during nine successive growing seasons. A summary of the data is given in the table on page 420.

The number was found to vary greatly from year to year. Thus for corn the number ranged from 82,000 in 1923 to 133,000 per square inch in 1918; for milo leaves from 140,000 in 1915 to 181,000 per square inch in 1918; and for kafir from 127,000 in 1917 to 161,000 per square inch in 1918. The number for each of the three plants was higher in 1918 than in any other of the growing seasons, but the variations in numbers during the other growing seasons were not consistent. Thus, for example, in 1923 the total number of stomata on corn leaves was only 82,000 per square inch, the lowest for corn of any of the nine seasons, while under the same conditions the leaves of kafir showed next to the highest number of stomata for that plant during the nine seasons.

The relative number of stomata on the lower and upper surfaces also showed marked fluctuations. For example, in corn the ratio of the number on the lower to that on the upper surface varied from 1.08 in 1916 to as much as 1.40 in 1923, and on kafir from 1.6 in 1919 to 2.3 in

Summary of the Observations on the Number of Stomata on the Leaves of Crop Plants

Plant	Number of years observed	Average number stomata, thousands per square inch of leaf surface			
		Upper	Lower	Total	Ratio lower to upper
Corn:					
Pride of Saline	9	43	54	97	1.255
Sherrod White Dent	4	48	60	108	1.250
Freed White Dent	6	44	57	101	1.295
Kansas Sunflower	5	49	59	108	1.204
Reid Yellow Dent	5	43	58	101	1.348
Sorghums:					
Sudan Grass	6	58	79	137	1.362
Feterita	6	71	98	169	1.380
Milo, Dwarf Yellow	9	63	88	151	1.396
Milo, White	4	65	86	151	1.322
Kafir, Blackhull	8	50	97	147	1.940
Kafir, Dawn	5	57	94	151	1.649
Kafir, Pink	4	53	100	153	1.886
Sorgo, Freed	5	65	98	163	1.507

SUMMARY OF THE OBSERVATIONS ON THE NUMBER OF STOMATA ON THE LEAVES OF CROP PLANTS.—(*Continued*)

Plant	Number of years observed	Average number stomata, thousands per square inch of leaf surface			
		Upper	Lower	Total	Ratio lower to upper
Sorghums: (*Continued*)					
Sorgo, Red Amber	5	51	86	137	1.686
Sorgo, Kansas Orange	4	53	86	139	1.622
Sorgo, Sumac	4	47	75	122	1.595
Broom Corn, Acme Dwarf	3	53	79	132	1.490
Wheat:					
Kanred	3	39	28	67	0.718
Blackhull	3	41	24	65	0.585
Triplet	2	40	28	68	0.700
Improved Turkey	2	45	28	73	0.622
Fulcaster	2	37	26	63	0.702
Harvest Queen	2	35	25	60	0.714
Rye:					
Abruzzi	3	33	30	63	0.909
Kansas	3	33	31	64	0.939
Rosen	3	32	28	60	0.875
Barley:					
Manchurian	3	37	39	76	1.054
Mariout	3	32	34	66	1.062
Kansas	3	36	35	71	0.972
Oats:					
Burt	3	25	27	52	1.080
Fulghum	3	27	28	55	1.036
Kherson	2	27	28	55	1.036
Texas	2	25	29	54	1.160
Alfalfa, common	3	109	89	198	0.816
Clover, white sweet	3	163	105	268	0.644
Clover, red	3	138	197	335	1.427
Cowpeas, New Era	3	74	157	231	2.121
Soybeans, Medium Yellow	2	95	107	202	1.126
Potato (several varieties)	3	33	104	137	3.151
Cabbage (several varieties)	3	91	146	237	1.604
Watermelon, Knobs Gem	3	127	234	361	1.842
Cucumber, Long Green	3	143	285	428	1.993
Squash, Hubbards	2	185	202	387	1.091
Tomato (several varieties)	3	62	131	193	2.112
Pumpkin, Cheese	2	135	182	317	1.348
Apple:					
Delicious	2	0	190	190	
Grimes Golden	2	0	266	266	
Jonathan	2	0	188	188	
Stayman Winesap	2	0	186	186	
Peach, Elberta	2	0	145	145	
Cherry, Early Richmond	2	0	161	161	

1920. The indications, from these observations, are that different plants may vary in their response to certain conditions as far as the number of stomata per unit of area is concerned.

Miller (1928) also observed the number of stomata of various other agricultural plants growing in the field during from two to nine growing seasons. The results of the observations, together with a summary of those just given, are shown in the tables on pages 421–422.

Of the plants observed, oats had the smallest number of stomata per unit of area—54,000 per square inch—while cucumber had the largest number—428,000 per square inch of leaf area. When stomata occur on both upper and lower surfaces, the majority of plants have more on the lower than on the upper surface. In these cases, the ratio of the number on the lower to that on the upper surface ranged from 1 in the case of barley and oats to 3 in the case of potato. The leaves of apple, peach, and cherry showed no stomata on the upper surface. Wheat, alfalfa, and white sweet clover consistently had more stomata on the upper surface of their leaves than on the lower, the ratio of the lower to the upper being 0.66, 0.82, and 0.64, respectively, while rye was found to have slightly more on the upper than on the lower surface.

Sawyer (1932) reported that the stomata on the leaves of the cranberry (*Vaccinium macrocarpon*) are confined entirely to the lower surface, and that in his observations their frequency was approximately 395,000 per square inch. The stomata of the strawberry are all on the lower surface, and, according to the observations of Darrow and Dewey (1934) ranged in number from 303 to 389 per square millimeter.

An interesting observation was made by Dodge (1923) in regard to the effect of orange rusts of blackberries and raspberries on the distribution of the stomata on the upper and lower surfaces of the leaves of these plants. In general, normal leaves of these plants had more stomata on the lower side of the leaves. Some few may be scattered singly or in groups of two or three on the upper surface along the large veins or near the edge of the leaf. Dodge found, however, that in blackberry plants which had been systemically infected with the orange rust for 2 or more years, from one-fourth to one-half of the total number of stomata were found on the upper surface.

It may be stated as a general rule (Eckerson, 1908) that there is an inverse relation between the number and size of stomata of a given type. Thus they are smallest where they occur in the largest numbers. For example, the stomata of oats are considerably larger than those of corn or the sorghums, while those of cucumber, squash, or watermelon are much smaller than the stomata of alfalfa, soybean, potato, or tomato. Reed and Hirano (1931), however, noted with *Citrus* that the size of the stomata seems to be influenced only slightly by the number per unit area.

The number of stomata vary on the different leaves of the same plant and on different parts of the individual leaf. Miller (1928) observed that the middle leaves of a mature corn plant have from 25 to 45 per cent more stomata per unit of surface than the lowest three or four leaves. The fact that the upper leaves have more stomata per unit area than the lower has been observed by Yapp (1912) for *Spiraea ulmaria*, L., by Rea (1921) for *Campanula rotundifolia*, and by Salisbury (1927) for a wide range of plants. The stomatal frequency in relation to the position of the leaf upon the plant is illustrated in the case of *Polygonatum multiflorum*, as shown by the data given by Salisbury in the table below.

The number of stomata per unit of area varies for different regions of the same leaf. Thus Salisbury (1927) found that the highest frequency was near the leaf tip and the lowest frequency toward the base, while the frequency for the middle region of the leaf was intermediate between the base and the apex. Salisbury also noted that, in some cases at least, the number of stomata per unit area increased from the midrib toward

RELATION OF HEIGHT OF LEAF ON THE PLANT TO THE STOMATAL FREQUENCY IN *Polygonatum multiflorum*

Height of leaf above ground, cm.	Number of stomata per square millimeter	Height of leaf above ground, cm.	Number of stomata per square millimeter
21.5	53.6	51.8	77.0
27.0	59.0	53.8	83.6
30.2	76.5	55.2	88.3
50.2	73.0	56.5	91.0

the margin. According to Maximow (1925), this is a part of the general law, first set forth by Zalenski, according to which the higher the leaf is attached to the stem the larger in comparison with the lower leaves are the total number and length of the vascular bundles per unit area, the smaller are the cells of the epidermis and mesophyll and also the cells of the stomata, but the more there are per unit of surface. Salisbury (1927) considered that the increase in the number of stomata on the leaves from the base of the plant toward the tip and from the base of an individual leaf toward its apex is determined by the water relations. Conditions favoring high rates of transpiration or a low rate of water intake favor high stomatal frequency. It was found that under constantly humid conditions the frequency gradient of stomata tends to disappear.

The total number of stomata per plant is enormous. Thus the number on the entire leaf surface of a fully grown corn plant ranges from 140,000,000 to 240,000,000, depending upon the variety and size of the plant, while a single fully developed pumpkin leaf of average size has from 50,000,000 to 60,000,000 of stomata.

Although the stomata occur in very large numbers, they occupy only a relatively small portion of the epidermal surface of the leaves. Kiesselbach (1916) found that the dimensions of the stomatal aperture of the leaves of corn under the conditions of his experiment were 3.5 by 25.6μ and that the area of the pore was approximately 90 sq. μ. He estimated that the area of the stomata was about 1.5 per cent of the total leaf surface. Brown and Escombe (1900) considered that the area of the stomata of the sunflower plant approximated 1 per cent of its leaf surface. Eckerson (1908) found the average dimension of the stomata of over 30 different species of plants grown in the greenhouse to be 6.7 by 17.7μ, and when fully open they occupied about one-ninetieth of the total leaf surface. From the various observations that have been made it may be stated, in general, that the area of the stomata may equal from 1 to 3 per cent of the leaf surface of plants.

2. *Opening and Closing.*—Since the time of Von Mohl (1856), the opening or closing of the stomata has been attributed to the changes in turgor of the guard cells. The opening is apparently brought about by an increase in the turgor of the guard cells and the closing by a decrease in their turgor. The changes in turgor result in the opening or closing of the stoma because of the uneven thickenings of the cell walls of the guard cells, a fact that was first pointed out by Schwendener (1881). These uneven thickenings in the walls vary in their arrangement but are fairly constant for large groups of plants. The structure of the different types of guard cells and its relation to the opening and closing of the stomata have been extensively described by Copeland (1902). The intention here is to mention only one type of structure to illustrate the relationship of turgor and the structure of the cell walls of the guard cells to the opening and closing of the stomata.

In one of the most common types of guard cells, the cell wall is much thinner where it borders on the epidermal cell than on the opposite side next to the stoma. When the turgor of the cell is increased, this thinner wall is stretched or dragged out farther than the other and pulls the more rigid and thicker wall bordering the stoma with it, thus increasing the size of the pore. This action is illustrated by a simple experiment that is described in practically all elementary textbooks of botany. Two pieces of rubber tubing are connected by a Y tube to a water faucet or an air pump and are placed parallel to each other. The lower end of the tubes are stoppered, tied securely together, and the exterior side of each piece of tubing is pared thin by means of a sharp knife. When the pressure is turned into the tubing, the thin exterior walls bulge and draw the pieces of tubing apart, producing an ellipsoidal opening between them.

(*a*) *The Physiology of the Guard Cells.*—It has just been stated that the opening or closing of the stomata is due primarily to changes in the turgidity of the guard cells, but no mention was made of the manner by which these changes in turgor might be brought about. In order to understand the explanations that are commonly offered to account for these changes in turgor, a certain knowledge of the anatomy and physiology of the guard cells is necessary; it is the intention here to discuss it briefly.

The guard cells always contain green plastids in contrast to the ordinary epidermal cells. These plastids have until recently commonly been called "chloroplasts" and considered similar to those of the mesophyll, but there seems to be considerable evidence that such is not the case. Sayre (1926) noted in the case of patience dock (*Rumex patientia*) that the chloroplasts of the mesophyll appear as single structures and do not vary in size with their starch content. The green plastids of the guard cells, on the other hand, have the appearance of compound structures, vary in size with their starch content, and are somewhat smaller than the chloroplasts of the mesophyll cells. Chlorophyll develops only in the chloroplasts of the mesophyll when exposed to light, while the green color of the plastids of the guard cells develops in either light or darkness. If a green plant is placed in continued darkness, the chlorophyll of the chloroplasts of the mesophyll disappears, while the green coloring matter of the plastids of the guard cells does not. Sayre (1926) could not obtain the microchemical tests for chlorophyll from the plastids of the guard cells, but he did not consider the proof conclusive due to the difficulty of making the test on such small bodies. On account of these differences, Sayre considered that the plastids of the guard cells are different structurally, physiologically, and genetically from the chloroplasts of the mesophyll cells of the leaf. Sawyer (1932) noted that chloroplasts do not occur in the guard cells of the leaves of *Vaccinium macrocarpon* but do occur in the other epidermal cells on both surfaces of the leaf. The stomata of this plant are poorly adjusted for response to the changing environmental factors of light, temperature, and moisture.

(1) *Osmotic Relations of the Guard Cells.*—It has been established by Iljin (1914), Wiggins (1921), and Sayre (1923, 1926) that the osmotic value of the cell sap of the guard cells is greater than that of the ordinary epidermal cells. Sayre also reported that the osmotic value of the cell sap of the subsidiary cells of *Rumex patientia* is higher than that of the ordinary epidermal cells. The osmotic value of the cell sap of the guard cells is not constant but is highest when the stomata are open and lowest when they are closed, while that of the epidermal cells remains practically constant throughout the day. Iljin (1914) reported that the osmotic value of the cell sap of the guard cells of the numerous plants with which he worked was 70 to 80 atmospheres higher than that of the epidermal cells. These results are perhaps too high, since Iljin used potassium

nitrate as a plasmolytic agent and Sayre (1926) has pointed out that the protoplasmic membrane of the guard cells is readily permeable to this salt. Wiggins (1921) used a solution of calcium chloride to plasmolyze the cells and substantiated the observations of Iljin, although he was unable to obtain such great differences. The results of Wiggins expressed in the table below show that the osmotic value of the guard cells averaged about 13 atmospheres higher than that of the epidermal cells.

Plant	Osmotic value, atmospheres			
	Ithaca, N. Y.		Columbia, Mo.	
	Epidermis	Guard cells	Epidermis	Guard cells
Zebrina pendula	5.4	11.3		
Cyclamen	9.5	12.6	10.1	29.5
Iresine	11.3	18.1	11.6	39.5
Beets	....	....	12.6	31.5

The osmotic values of the cell sap of the guard cells and epidermal cells of *Rumex patientia* were determined by Sayre (1926) by using sucrose, glucose, and calcium chloride as plasmolyzing agents. His results with all three agents were practically the same and showed the osmotic value of the cell sap of the guard cells to be higher than that of the epidermal cells and the differences to be greater when the stomata were open than when they were closed. The table that follows gives the data obtained by using sucrose as a plasmolytic agent:

Osmotic Value of the Cell Sap of the Guard, Subsidiary, and Epidermal Cells of Patience Dock

Items considered	8:30 a.m.	10:30 a.m.	1:30 p.m.	3:30 p.m.	7:30 p.m.
Size of stomata, microns	3 by 30	6 by 31	12 by 34	9 by 31	0 by 0
Osmotic value of the cell sap, atmospheres of guard cells	16.6	16.6	21.0	20.2	13.2
Subsidiary cells	16.6	16.6	16.6	17.8	15.5
Epidermal cells	14.4	14.4	14.4	14.4	13.2

The experimental evidence seems to show conclusively that during the daylight hours the osmotic value of the cell sap of the guard cells is greater than that of the epidermal cells, this difference rising to a maximum during the day and falling off in the afternoon, paralleling somewhat the opening and closing of the stomata. The difference between the osmotic value of the cell sap of the guard cells and the epidermal cells varies, no doubt, with different plants and with the different conditions under which the observations are made.

(2) *Changes in the Cell Contents.*—Almost without exception, starch occurs in the plastids of the guard cells under any condition where these cells are fully formed. It is found in the guard cells where the plant has been grown from the seed in complete darkness, in the white area of variegated leaves, in albino plants, and in the guard cells of numerous plants that never produce starch in the chloroplasts of their mesophyll cells. It was formerly supposed that this starch was synthesized by the green plastids of the guard cells, but the evidence at present indicates that the carbohydrate content of the guard cells may be obtained entirely from the green cells of the mesophyll. It has been noted by various observers that the starch content of the plastids of the guard cells changes during the opening and closing of the stomata. Darwin (1898), Lloyd (1908), Iljin (1914), and Sayre (1926) found, in general, that the starch content in the guard cells is greatest in the early hours of the morning and gradually disappears until the stomata are at their maximum opening. It, however, is never wholly depleted. After the stomata begin to close, there is a gradual accumulation of starch in the guard cells until the maximum content is again reached early in the evening, after which no marked changes can be detected during the night. It has been observed that, when the starch content decreases, the osmotic value of the cell sap increases, and the reverse is the case when the starch content increases. Hagen (1918) observed that, when the stomata are open, sugar is present in large amounts, while Sayre (1926) showed that in the guard cells of *Rumex patientia* there was 2 to 2½ times more sugar present when the stomata were open than when they were closed. Strugger and Weber (1926) in studying the stomata of *Galium mollugo* observed that as starch disappeared in the guard cells, it appeared in the companion cells, and vice versa. They concluded from this observation that the subsidiary cells cooperate in the movement of the stoma. This change of starch to sugar and sugar to starch seems to be a reversible reaction in which the total amount of carbohydrate material does not vary to any extent. This reaction has generally been assumed to be due to the enzyme diastase, but so far it has not been isolated from the guard cells, although Hagen (1918) by treating the guard cells with diastase converted the starch into sugar and thus caused the stomata to open.

The series of changes that result in the opening of the stomata of a turgid leaf are enumerated by Sayre (1926) and Loftfield (1921) as follows: In the morning, light initiates the action of diastase, probably by decreasing the acidity of the cell sap of the guard cells. The diastase changes the starch to sugar, which results in an increase of the osmotic value of their cell sap. This sauses water to enter the guard cells, since the osmotic value of the cell sap of the epidermal cells remains constant. A swelling of the guard cells results, and this causes the stoma to open. The procedure during the closing of the stomata is perhaps the reverse of that during the opening.

There are marked changes in the pH values of the guard cells under various conditions. Thus Sayre (1926) found that they were slightly more alkaline when the stomata were open than when they were closed, but no quantitative data could be secured. By using the pressed juice from the leaves as a buffer solution and varying its acidity he could cause the stomata to open or close in light or in darkness. When placed in a solution with a pH value of 4.2 to 4.4 they opened after 2 hr., but when placed in a solution with a pH of 3.6 to 4.0 and 4.6 to 5.0 they remained closed.

Scarth (1932) found that there was a wide change in the reaction of the guard cells from pH 6.0 to 7.4 in the light to less than pH 5.0 in the dark. He concluded that in the plants studied all the stomatal movements whether due to changes of leaf turgor, of illumination, or of temperature, are accompanied by reversible transformation of carbohydrates and by a pH change in the guard cells. When the stomata are opening or are open, the guard cells have a higher pH value than when they are closing or are fully closed. He considered that the carbohydrate balance in the guard cells depends strictly on the pH value. The origin of the pH change, when governed by the light factor, depends mainly on the relative rate of photosynthesis and respiration in the leaf tissue. The absence of carbon dioxide favors, if it does not of itself induce, stomatal opening. A certain concentration of carbon dioxide causes the closure of the stomata, but with a higher concentration—15 per cent—there is a hydrolysis of starch causing an increased osmotic value in the guard cells and stomatal opening.

It was noted by Linsbauer (1926) that there are marked differences in the physical and chemical state of the protoplasm of the guard cells depending on whether they are open or closed. When open the cells are more resistant to the toxic action of "Rongelit" and silver nitrate than when they are closed. Leick (1927, 1928) considered that when the stomata are open there is a change in the electrostatic condition of the molecules of the proteins of the guard cells. This is indicated by the increased viscosity and permeability of the protoplasm of the guard cells and by their resistance to higher temperatures.

The rapidity with which the stomata close or open, however, was considered by Scarth (1926) and others to be too rapid to be due entirely to the hydrolysis of starch or its condensation. They considered that the action of diastase is so slow that long before the starch can undergo any great amount of change, the movement of the guard cells is completed.

Scarth (1926) found that illuminated and open guard cells are alkaline in reaction, probably from the utilization of carbon dioxide in photosynthesis, and certain colloidal constituents of these cells become much swollen as the pH value increases. He considered that high turgidity in the guard cells is mainly caused by colloidal imbibition. Closure is accompanied by increased hydrogen-ion concentration due to the accumulation of carbon dioxide of respiration when photosynthesis ceases on account of low light intensity. The colloids are dehydrated as they approach their isoelectric point, the bound water is freed, the cells quickly lose their surplus water to the surrounding cells, and the guard cells close. Scarth considered that if hyperacidity develops due to prolonged darkness, the colloids of the guard cells may become more acid than the isoelectric point, produce an acid swelling of the colloids, and thus bring about night opening of the stomata. According to this theory, we have a mechanism whose response is almost instantaneous to light changes. In such a case, the sugar and starch reactions that are commonly associated with stomatal opening and closing may be subsidiary to the main regulatory mechanism. It is worthy of note in this connection that the guard cells have been observed in the case of *Carnegiea gigantea* to function in the opening and closing of the stomata for as long as a century (Long, 1928).

(*b*) *Methods of Measuring the Changes of Stomatal Apertures.*—Darwin (1898) considered that the amount of water vapor escaping from the leaf could be taken as an index of the condition of the stomata. He used shavings of horn and other materials as hygroscopes. The degree of curvature of these hygroscopes, which was an indication of the rate of water loss, was read on a graduated quadrant. This method measured the change in the transpiration rate but not necessarily the condition of the stomata. Another method reported by him in 1904 in which the degree of stomatal opening was measured by the changes in the temperature of the leaves is open to the same objections. Various types of porometers have been devised and used by Darwin and Pertz (1912), Balls (1912), Jones (1914), Laidlow and Knight (1916), and Knight (1915, 1916) to measure changes in stomatal apertures. The general procedure has been to use a constant-pressure aspirator to draw air through a leaf either intact or detached from the plant. The speed of the air stream is measured by the rate at which water flows from the aspirator and is considered to indicate the relative size of the stomatal openings. The main objections to such porometers are the unnatural condition of drawing air through the intercellular spaces of the leaf and the uncertainty as to what the results indicate. Trelease and Livingston (1916) made a comparative study of the porometer and standardized cobalt paper in regard to the transpiration rate. They obtained results that show a general agreement of data between the two methods during the morning hours but a lack of accord later in the day. The evidence indicates that the porometer measures the diffusive capacity of the stomata but fails to take into account other factors influencing transpiration. Darwin (1912) considered the porometer method to have an advantage over any microscopic method, since it strikes an average of the degree of opening of many hundreds of stomata at each reading instead of the comparatively few that can be observed through a microscope. Lloyd (1908) devised a method of stomatal observation that is the most applicable and the most widely used of any of the methods yet presented for stomatal study. His method consists of stripping the epidermis from the leaf and quickly plunging it into absolute alcohol. The effect of the alcohol is to dehydrate the cell wall and to cause it to become very stiff and hard before removing the water from the cell. As a result, the cell walls retain their original shape, and the size of the stoma is unaltered as long as the material is kept dehydrated. The specimens can thus be collected, preserved, stained and mounted, and studied at leisure. The reliability of this method was verified by Loftfield (1921), who compared the dimensions of the stomata of leaves in position and of those of the stripped epidermis treated with absolute alcohol and found that the measurements were practically identical. Lloyd (1913) used a specially arranged microscope to observe the stomata in position in their natural state. The microscope was provided with a condenser, a 4-mm. objective with a long working distance, and a cooling cell in the form of a flask wired beneath the substage apparatus. By this method it is possible to observe accurately the size of the stomata without injury, but it has its objections in that it cannot be used at night or in poor light and is more or less cumbersome and too slow to be used under the conditions that frequently occur in the field.

Ashby (1931) compared the sensitivity of the method of Knight with that of Lloyd for measuring the area of the stomatal apertures. There was a satisfactory agreement of the two methods on the leaves of *Geranium* and *Verbena* when the stomata were wide open. At the time the apertures were nearly closed, however, the porometer method of Knight was approximately ten times more sensitive than the method devised by Lloyd. Gregory and Pearse (1934) described a porometer that measures the changes in stomatal aperture by the amount of resistance recorded. Jones (1932) described a method for observing stomata by the use of the ultraopaque microscope. Long and Clements (1934) found that solutions of collodion can be used to study the number and distribution of stomata. The solution is applied with a camel's hair brush to the selected areas. After the films have dried they are removed, and the stomatal impressions are studied.

(*c*) *Factors Affecting Opening and Closing.*—Any statements that may be made in regard to factors that affect the opening and closing of the stomata must be considered only as very general in their application, since in this regard, as in many others, different plants may not only respond differently to the same factors, but the nature of the response may be greatly influenced by other environmental factors.

(1) *Light.*—In general, it can be stated that light is the factor to which the stomata most universally respond. As a rule, the stomata of the majority of plants open in light and close in darkness, but the light requirements for opening and closing are not identical, even for closely related plants (Kuyper, 1915; Livingston and Estabrook, 1912; Gray and Peirce, 1919; Smith, 1922; Hart, 1929; Magness and Furr, 1930; Paetz, 1930; Bartholomew, 1931; Sitton, 1932; Deen and Bruner, 1933; Scarth, Whyte, and Brown, 1933; and Yocum, 1935).

Light appears to induce the opening of the stomata by initiating conditions favorable to the conversion of the starch in the guard cells to sugar, which increases the osmotic value of their cell sap. The closing of the stomata at night is, however, by no means universal. Of the 75 species of plants examined by Darwin (1898), 13 per cent did not close their stomata at night. Burgerstein (1920) examined 48 species of herbaceous and 27 species of woody plants from 9 to 10 P.M. and found that the stomata of 15 species were fully open, 13 species partially open, 14 species only slightly open, and 33 species fully closed. The stomata of nyctitropic plants are frequently open at night, as are also those of some of the marsh and aquatic plants, and Loftfield (1921) has noted the same condition for the stomata of the potato plant. Although the closure of the stomata in darkness is the rule for the majority of plants, it is not necessarily so complete as entirely to prevent the interchange of gases between the interior of the leaf and the external medium, although it does greatly diminish it. In many cases, too, some stomata remain open, although the great majority of them on the same leaf are completely or partially closed, a fact which was first reported by Leitbeg (1868).

It was observed by Loftfield (1921) that the reduction of light to less than one-half of normal is usually necessary to produce any effect upon the stomata of plants growing in the open, and when stomata are closing they respond to a decrease in light more rapidly than when opening. Leick (1927, 1928) reported that light increased the permeability of the guard cells. Sayre (1929) found that the stomata of *Rumex patientia* do not open in light of longer wave lengths than 690mμ. He suggested that red light beyond 690mμ does not affect plants except as it may be absorbed and changed to heat. Paetz (1930) reported that red light, 760 to 620mμ, and blue light, 500 to 410mμ, had the greatest effect upon stomatal movement, the red rays being twice as effective as blue rays of the same intensity. Since it is the red and blue rays that are concerned in photosynthesis, it was suggested that the movement of stomata may be correlated with photosynthetic activity. The stomata of the variegated leaves of *Caladium*, whose guard cells are entirely free from chlorophyll, opened in a saturated atmosphere but were unresponsive to light. Scarth (1932) stated that the portion of the spectrum that is absorbed by chlorophyll affects stomatal movement. It acts primarily by its role in photosynthetic activity. Deen and Bruner (1933) found during the eclipse of the sun in 1932 that the stomata of the gray birch began to close 25 min. before the beginning of the eclipse. After it had passed, the stomata opened slightly. Ordinarily at the hour of the eclipse, most of these stomata were fully open. Loftfield (1921) stated that the stomata open at night as a result of moonlight or a strong artificial light of much less intensity than 1 per cent of the sunlight maximum. He also observed that in response to light they opened more readily toward morning than toward midnight.

The question of the periodicity or rhythm of the movement of stomata has received considerable attention, but the experimental results that have been obtained are very conflicting. Darwin (1898) found that artificial darkness is more effective in producing closure in the afternoon than in the morning and that illumination opens closed stomata more readily in the morning than later in the day. Sayre (1926) observed that if the plants of *Rumex patientia* growing under normal conditions were placed in a dark chamber in the late afternoon, the stomata began to open at the usual time in the morning, had opened to 10 to 15 per cent of their maximum width by the middle of the forenoon, and had closed by noon. Thus rhythm occurred to some extent the following day but was not noticeable the third and fourth days. Kuyper (1915) found that in sugar cane there is some indication that after prolonged darkness the stomata tend to open between 8 and 10 A.M. Hart (1929) found that the daily rhythm of stomatal movements differed in varieties of wheat. The stomata of some varieties open very soon after sunrise and remain open during the greater portion of the day, while those of other varieties remain open only a relatively short period of time.

(2) *Temperature.*—The temperature of the air affects the speed with which the stomata open. Loftfield (1921) observed that within the limits of temperature at which protoplasm functions, the length of time for opening is reduced one half for every 10°C. rise in temperature. Zalenski (1921) noted that when the temperature rises to 35 to 50°C. starch in the guard cells is transformed to maltose and the turgor of these cells increases, in consequence of which the stomata open widely, a fact also observed in the wilting of plants. Of the 50 species observed, only millet and succulents showed no opening of the stomata at high temperatures.

It was considered by Scarth, Whyte, and Brown (1933) that the night opening of stomata occurs when the concentration of oxygen inside the leaf reaches a certain minimum. The effect of temperature is primarily to hasten the onset of this shortage of oxygen by the acceleration. They suggested that a low oxygen tension reduces the rate of evolution of carbon dioxide, so that its concentration in the leaf falls. Thus opening at night is really a response to a low content of carbon dioxide, just as is opening in the light. It was noted by Clements and Martin (1934) in the sunflower that the stomata did not begin to close until the temperature of the soil was lowered to about 40°F., but that they were nearly closed when the soil reached 37°F.

(3) *Humidity.*—It is generally considered that high humidity of the air permits the stomata to open wider and remain open longer than a low humidity. This factor is especially important when the water content of the leaf is near the minimum point for normal stomatal behavior.

Paetz (1930) found that in *Tradescantia fluminensis, Oxalis losiandra, Zea mays*, and certain other plants, the stomata opened at different rates upon exposure to light after the plants had been kept in the dark at varying degrees of humidity. The plants that had been kept in the most humid atmosphere opened the most rapidly, and vice versa. It was observed by Overley, Overholser, and Haut (1931) that, with a high temperature and a low relative humidity, an early closing of the stomata might result for the leaves of the apple even though the soil moisture was above the wilting point.

The effect of relative humidity and temperature upon stomatal behavior is reflected in the results obtained from various methods of drying hay. Thus Jones and Palmer (1932, 1933, and 1934) found that a double windrowing of alfalfa 2 hr. after cutting produced a hay with a more desirable color, a larger percentage of leaves remaining on the stem, and a lower moisture content than hay that was cured in the swath. They observed that the stomata on the leaves remained open longer when the hay was windrowed than when it was allowed to remain in the swath. At the end of 2 hr. in the swath, the stomata were nearly all closed, and plasmolysis of the cells had occurred. At the end of the same period, the stomata of the windrowed hay were partially closed and began to reopen. This reopening was followed by an increased rate of water loss. The temperature inside the windrow 3 hr. after cutting was 5° to 8°C. lower than it was in the swath, while the relative humidity of the former was 10 per cent higher than in the latter. In the subdued light of the windrow, the chlorophyll was better preserved and thus made a brighter hay.

(4) *Moisture.*—Next to light, the moisture supply of the leaves is the factor that most universally affects the opening or closing of the stomata. The effect of wilting on the movement of the stomata will be discussed under subsequent topics. It will suffice here to state that, if the supply of water in the leaf reaches a certain minimum which causes the guard cells to lose their rigidity, the stomata close regardless of the influence of light or of any of the other factors that have been mentioned.

It was noted by Veihmeyer and Hendrickson (1927), Magness and Furr (1930), Furr and Magness (1930), Furr and Degman (1931), and Sitton (1932) that the stomata of apple, apricot, peach, prune, and pecan open in the morning and remain open until late afternoon or evening if the moisture content in the root zone is above the wilting percentage. According to Veihmeyer and Hendrickson (1927), if the moisture content is above the wilting coefficient, no difference can be detected in regard to the opening of the stomata of trees growing in relatively dry or saturated soils.

(5) *Chemical Agents.*—The effects of the amount of carbon dioxide on the behavior of stomata have already been noted. Sayre (1926) found that the stomata of *Rumex patientia* open to 50 per cent of their maximum in ammonia vapor in darkness and close in an acid atmosphere in light. According to Haas-Poetzl (1930) the effectiveness of ions in prolonging the hydrolysis of starch in the guard cells, and thus in promoting the opening of the stomata, stand in the following order for *Zebrina pendula* and *Vicia faba:* Li > Na > K > Mg > Ca > Sr > Ba and Cl > NO_3 > SO_4 > Br > tartrate > citrate > CNS. Pleasant (1930) found for plants of pea, bean, and radish that the application of nitrates increased the speed of the opening and closing of the stomata. Weber (1931) noted that in the actively growing leaves of *Ranunculus ficaria* the guard cells were very permeable to urea, while in the embryonic stage they were permeable only to a slight degree. It was considered by Scarth (1932) that the influence of chemicals upon the movement of stomata is conditioned by their effect upon the pH value of the cells.

(*d*) *Daily Movement.*—The general behavior of the stomata during the 24-hr. period has been studied extensively by Loftfield (1921) for about 60 species of cultivated, native herbaceous plants, shrubs, and trees. He found that there is a great variation in the behavior of the stomatal aperture of the different leaves of the same plant and even on the same leaf (see also Leick, 1928). The stomata on the upper surface may behave differently from those on the lower. Thus in alfalfa those on the lower surface open more slowly and close earlier than those on the upper. On all leaves there are a certain number of stomata that are functionless, while a certain portion are more or less inactive. Loftfield observed that 80 per cent of the stomata of alfalfa acted alike as far as movement was concerned and that 18 per cent behaved approximately as the majority, while 2 per cent were completely inactive. It was also noticed by Leick (1927, 1928), and by Veihmeyer and Hendrickson (1927) that the behavior of the stomata is influenced by their position on the leaf, by the position of the leaves on the plant, and by the intensity of sunlight. The closure of some stomata is frequently prevented by particles of sand or dust wedging in the opening. The general behavior of the movements may be greatly modified by the prevailing physical conditions, so that as many reactions may be observed as there are combinations of physical factors. Loftfield considered that the stomatal behavior of the plants he examined provided a basis for classifying the stomata into three general types as typified by alfalfa, potato, and barley.

(1) *The Alfalfa Type.*—The stomata of this type under favorable conditions are open all day and closed all night. In alfalfa they open in from 2 to 6 hr. after daylight, remain open from 3 to 6 hr., and then gradually close during a period about twice as long as that required for opening. When conditions become less favorable for moisture, the stomata close partially for a time during the middle of the day, this period of midday closure increasing to complete closure as the conditions become less and less

favorable. With the appearance of midday closure, night opening develops and increases with the increase of day closure, until finally there is a partial opening of the stomata all night and a complete closure all day. This type of stomata behavior Loftfield considered to be characteristic of most thin-leaved mesophytes and includes sweet, red, and white clovers; peas; beans; turnip; radish; muskmelon; cucumber; watermelon; carrot; parsnip; apple; peach; pear; and many others.

(2) *The Potato Type.*—The daily stomatal movement in potato was found to be markedly different from that of alfalfa under the same favorable conditions. The stomata of potato are open continuously except for about 3 hr. following sundown. Midday closure is observable in alfalfa before wilting is evident, but midday closure does not occur in potato until the plants are visibly wilted, and only after very extreme lack of moisture do the stomata open at dusk. The stomata of the cabbage, onion, tulip, salsify, plantain, squash, pumpkin, and leek show the general or modified behavior of those of the potato. The stomata of *Scirpus validus, Equisetum hyemale,* and *Equisetum palustre* were found to be continuously wide open under normal conditions and even during wilting or death from water loss.

(3) *The Barley Type.*—The behavior of the stomata of the barley is typical of the cereals. They show no opening during the night no matter how slight the day opening. Also, there are many closed stomata during the day occurring more or less in groups. They open and close comparatively rapidly, but even under favorable conditions they are fully open for an hour or two only.

The optimum conditions for the full opening of the stomata vary widely for different groups of cereals. Thus in the case of corn and the sorghums, very warm to hot weather, bright sunshine, and a high water content of the leaves seem to be the optimum conditions; while in the case of wheat, oats, and barley, cool, humid conditions with relatively mild sunlight are the best.

The examples that have been mentioned refer to the stomata of the leaves. According to Loftfield, the stomata that are found on the stem differ considerably in structure and water relations and consequently in their behavior from those that occur on the leaves.

3. *Capacity for the Diffusion of Gases.* (*a*) *The Stomata as Paths of Gaseous Exchange.*—It has been proved through the work of Blackman (1895), Stahl (1894), and Buscalioni and Pollacci (1902) that practically all the interchange of gases between the interior of the leaf and the atmosphere takes place through the stomata. Blackman found in leaves which have stomata only on the lower surface that on an average only 3 per cent of the total carbon dioxide exchange occurred through the upper surface. When stomata occur on both upper and lower surface, the amount of carbon dioxide diffusing through each epidermis was approximately proportional to the number of stomata on each side of the leaf. Stahl (1894) observed that the loss of water by transpiration is confined, for the most part, to the leaf surface that contains the stomata. By using the cobalt chloride-paper method to determine the transpiration rate, he observed in leaves with stomata only on the lower surface that the paper on this surface colored pink in a few minutes, while that on the upper surface did not change color until after several hours. The relative loss of water through the stomata and cuticle was observed by Buscalioni and Pollacci (1902) by placing a collodion film over the leaf and noting that the film clouded very quickly only just above the stomata. The water that evaporates through the stomata is termed "stomatal transpiration," while that which evaporates from the surface of the cuticle is termed "cuticular transpiration." Sayre (1920) in the case of the mullein leaf estimated that the cuticular transpiration amounted to only from one-fortieth to one-twentieth that of the total water loss. Darwin (1916) found in the case of the ivy leaf that during the day

the cuticular transpiration was one-thirtieth of the total but that at night it amounted to as much as one-twelfth of the entire water loss.

Rudolph (1925) found that the cuticle on the leaves of many plants permits a considerable water loss, inasmuch as a third of the water loss in still air is cuticular. He showed also that sulphuric acid could diffuse readily through the cuticle of some weeds. Kamp (1930) observed that the thickness of the cuticle does not seem to govern the amount of water that escapes through it. Aside from their layer of cutin, apparently the epidermal cells themselves are a factor in controlling the water loss. When the stomata were all on the ventral surface, as in the case of *Coffea arabica*, the loss of water from the ventral surface was only twice that from the upper one, while in other plants the transpiration rate from the ventral side was forty-five times greater than that from the dorsal surface. Bartholomew (1931) found that during the day 85 to 95 per cent of the water lost by mature *Citrus* leaves came from the ventral surface, which contains the stomata. During the night the loss of water from the ventral surface of these leaves was only 58 to 66 per cent of the total amount of water lost. Since practically all gaseous exchange between the leaf and the air takes place through the stomata, the question arises as to the capacity of the stomata for carrying gases to and from the interior of the leaf and whether their capacity might be a limiting factor for the maximum activity of its various functions.

(*b*) *Diffusion of Gases through Small Openings.*—In 1900 Brown and Escombe made certain observations in regard to the intake of carbon dioxide by the leaves of *Catalpa bignonioides*. They found that these leaves which have stomata only on the lower surface could extract from the air under favorable conditions for photosynthesis about 0.07 cc. of carbon dioxide per square centimeter of leaf surface per hour (measured at 0°C. and 760 mm. Hg). Assuming that all this gas entered the plant through the stomata, whose area equaled only 0.009 of the lower leaf surface, the rate of diffusion would be at the rate of 0.07 ÷ 0.009 or 7.77 cc. per square centimeter of the stomatal opening per hour. The surface of a strong solution of caustic soda when freely exposed to moderately still air, as is the surface of a leaf, absorbs carbon dioxide at ordinary temperatures at the rate of only 0.12 cc. per square centimeter per hour, and, even though the air current is increased, the maximum absorption is only about 0.177 cc. per square centimeter per hour. If all the carbon dioxide entered through the stomata of the lower surface of the leaf, the absorption per unit of area of these openings was from forty-three to sixty-four times or an average of more than fifty times as rapid as that of the surface of a constantly renewed concentrated solution of alkali. The observance of these facts led Brown and Escombe to take up the investigation of the free diffusion, especially of carbon dioxide and water vapor, through small apertures of known dimensions under conditions comparable to those existing in the leaf.

In the static diffusion of a gas, vapor, or solute, as the case may be, the amount of substances diffusing in a given time, all other conditions being the same, is directly proportional to the sectional area of the column. Brown and Escombe found, however, that by interposing at any point in the line of flow a thin septum pierced with a circular aperture, the rate of flow across unit area of the aperture is greater than it would be across an equal area of the unobstructed column at this point. When the size of the pore is diminished beyond a certain size relative to the cross section of the column, the amount of gas that passes becomes proportional to the linear dimensions of the aperture and not to the area. The following tables on page 438, giving data secured by Brown and Escombe (1900) and by Sayre (1926), will illustrate this point.

In order to understand more fully the diffusion of gases through small apertures let us consider experiments 3 and 5 in Table A. The diameters of the apertures are approximately 6 and 2 mm., respectively, and the ratio of their diameters is as 3:1, while the amount of carbon dioxide diffused in a unit of time stands in approximately the same ratio. The areas of the two openings, however, stand in the ratio of 9:1. Again let us consider experiments 3 and 5 in Table B. Here the diameters of the

TABLE A.—THE RELATION OF THE SIZE OF APERTURE TO DIFFUSION OF CARBON DIOXIDE
Brown and Escombe

No.	Diameter of aperture, mm.	CO_2 diffused per hour, cc.	Ratio of		
			Area of aperture	Diameter of aperture	CO_2 diffused in unit of time
1	22.70	0.238	1.00	1.00	1.00
2	5.86	0.055	0.068	0.25	0.23
3	6.03	0.062	0.07	0.26	0.26
4	3.23	0.039	0.023	0.14	0.14
5	2.00	0.023	0.0077	0.088	0.10

TABLE B.—DIFFUSION OF WATER VAPOR THROUGH SMALL OPENINGS UNDER UNIFORM CONDITIONS
After Sayre, 1926

No.	Diameter of aperture, mm.	Diffusion of H_2O vapor, grams	Ratio of		
			Area of aperture	Diameter of aperture	Diffusion of H_2O vapor
1	2.64	2.655	1.00	1.00	1.00
2	1.60	1.583	0.37	0.61	0.59
3	0.95	0.928	0.13	0.36	0.35
4	0.81	0.762	0.09	0.31	0.29
5	0.48	0.455	0.03	0.18	0.17
6	0.41	0.393	0.02	0.15	0.15

apertures are 0.95 and 0.48 mm., respectively, and their ratio is practically 2:1. The amount of water vapor diffusing through them in a unit of time is also in the ratio of 2:1. The areas of the two apertures, however, are in the ratio of 4:1. These data show another general law in regard to the diffusion of gases through small pores, *viz.*, that as the size of the openings decreases the velocity of flow through unit area increases, or, in other words, the velocity of flow varies inversely as the diameter of the pore.

Since the velocity of the diffusion flow of carbon dioxide and water vapor increases with the decrease in the diameter of the openings, it might reasonably be expected that a diaphragm could be so perforated with a series of very small holes that when interposed in the line of diffusive flow, diffusion could take place through such a partition approximately as rapidly as though no partition intervened at all, although the total area of the small holes might represent only a small fraction of the area of the partition.

Brown and Escombe investigated this question by using a thin celluloid kodak film 0.1 mm. in thickness, perforated at regular intervals with holes about 0.380 mm. in diameter. These films were placed over a solution of caustic potash 1 cm. from its surface, and the diffusion of carbon dioxide studied. The general results obtained are expressed in the following table:

No.	Diameter of holes, mm.	Distance of holes apart in terms of diameters	Number of holes per square centimeter	Percentage area of holes on unit area of septum	Observed flow expressed as percentage of septum diffusion on open-tube diffusion	Theoretical flow through porous septum expressed as percentage on open-tube diffusion
1	0.380	2.63	100.0	11.34	56.1	87.6
2	0.380	5.26	25.0	2.82	51.7	63.7
3	0.380	7.8	11.1	1.25	40.6	44.0
4	0.380	10.5	6.2	0.70	31.4	30.7
5	0.380	13.0	4.0	0.45	20.9	21.9

From the preceding table it is seen that the area of the pores in a diaphragm may be only a small percentage of the total area of the diaphragm, but that the amount of gas diffusing through them is much greater than the ratio of their area to that of the total area of the diaphragm. Thus in experiment 1 the total area of the pores is only 11.34 per cent of the area of the membrane, yet the flow of gas is equal to 56.1 per cent of the unobstructed tube. In experiment 4 the area of the perforations equals only 0.7 per cent of the area of the cross section, yet the flow is over 31 per cent of that of the unobstructed column. Brown and Escombe found in one case where the length of tube was 4 mm. that, with an area of pores totaling only 11.34 per cent of the total cross section, little obstructive influence on the flow of gas was produced, and the amount diffusing was practically equal to the open-tube diffusion. It may also be noted from the table that, when the pores are placed at least eight to ten times their diameter apart, the amount of diffusion approximates very closely the calculated rate, but that, when the holes are more closely spaced, the flow is less than that calculated. This is explained by assuming that in perfectly quiet air the lines of flux in a diffusive column are approximately parallel at some distance from the diaphragm but that as these stream lines approach the apertures they converge and gradually become parallel again on the other side of the diaphragm. This behavior is somewhat similar to the entrance and exit of water from a pipe. On entering the pipe it converges toward the opening and then again spreads out upon leaving it. In the case of gaseous diffusion, the rate of flow is slowed down if the pores are so close that the lines of flux of one pore interfere with those of another, but not if the apertures are so spaced that these lines of flow do not intercept one another, the maximum efficiency of flow being maintained. We shall now consider the application of these observations to the diffusion of carbon dioxide and water vapor through the stomata of the leaves.

(*c*) *The Stomata in Relation to Such Diffusion.*—Brown and Escombe (1900) considered that the ordinary green leaf has the structure for producing the phenomena of diffusion that is associated with a perforated diaphragm. They noted that the stomata on the lower side of the sunflower leaf are about 8 diameters apart, if they are regarded as circular openings, a distribution that allows each stoma to exercise its full efficiency for diffusion without any interference from the neighboring stomata. So far as is known to the author, however, it has never been determined how nearly the spacing of the stomata of all plants is within the limit for their maximum diffusion capacity. Jeffreys (1918) in a mathematical study of the laws of evaporation of water from circular surfaces calls into question the conclusions of Brown and Escombe in this regard. He concluded that the stomata in a leaf must close to one-fiftieth of that of their full aperture before they act independently of one another. The conclusions of Jeffreys have been adversely criticized by Lamour (1918), so that it would seem that a reinvestigation of the behavior of the stomata in this regard should be made.

The amount of gas that enters the leaf through an individual stoma will be conditioned by the gradient density of that gas between the exterior and interior of the leaf and by the linear dimensions of the stoma. In regard to the stoma of the leaf of the sunflower, Brown and Escombe found that, when fully opened, its depth was about 0.014 mm. and that it was elliptical in section. They determined that the area of this elliptical cross section was 0.0000908 sq. mm., which is about equal to that of a circle with a diameter of 0.0107 mm. They assumed from previous work in regard to diffusion through circular and elliptical openings (Stefan, 1873) that the elliptical stomatal tube would function the same as a cylindrical tube having the same area of cross section. Sayre (1926), however, considered that diffusion through an elliptical opening would be more nearly equal to that from a circular opening having the same perimeter rather than the same area.

Brown and Escombe considered that, if the stomata are wide open and the partial pressure of the carbon dioxide in the intercellular spaces is maintained practically at zero by the absorbent action of the parenchyma cells, the maximum amount of carbon dioxide that could pass into the sunflower leaf through the stomata would be 2.578 cc. per square centimeter per hour. The maximum rate of photosynthesis that has been recorded for the sunflower leaf by the weighing method of Sachs is approximately 1.8 g. of carbohydrate per square meter of leaf surface per hour. Such a rate of photosynthesis requires an intake of only 0.134 cc. of carbon dioxide per square centimeter per hour, or only about 5 per cent of that which could diffuse through the stomata of this leaf if they were wide open and the conditions for ideal diffusion were present. When the stomata of the sunflower are wide open, it would be necessary to have difference of pressure of carbon dioxide of only about 5 per cent between the inside of the leaf and the outer air in order to supply the gas needed by the leaf during maximum photosynthesis.

The theoretical carrying capacity of the stomata for water vapor was also determined by Brown and Escombe. At a temperature of 20°C. with the water vapor in the intercellular spaces maintained at 17.4 mm. of mercury—the maximum pressure corresponding to that temperature—with the pressure of the water vapor in the outer air at one-fourth this pressure, they considered that the maximum amount of water vapor which would diffuse through the open stomata of the sunflower leaf would amount to 1,730 cc. of water per square meter of leaf surface per hour. The maximum rates of transpiration that have been observed for the sunflower plant vary from 276 to 500 cc. per square meter of leaf per hour, according to the prevailing atmospheric conditions. Thus it appears that when the stomata of the sunflower are fully opened they are capable of carrying from three to six times as much water vapor as escapes from the plant at the maximum transpiration rate.

From the previous discussion it is seen that although the stomata occupy only from 1 to 3 per cent of the surface of the epidermis, they have, nevertheless, a carrying capacity for gases greatly in excess of that needed by the plant. Consequently they may close to a considerable degree and yet provide for all necessary gaseous exchange.

4. *Regulation or Control of Water Loss.*—After it had been observed by the earlier workers that the stomata are the main passageways for water vapor from plants, the general view came to be held that the stomata, by opening and closing, control or regulate the transpirational water loss from the plant. The opinions regarding the degree to which the stomatal apparatus may control transpiration have changed with increased knowledge of the stomata and the physiology of the guard cells. The earlier idea was that the stomata could close in anticipation of wilting and thus conserve the water supply of the leaf and prevent it from wilting. This has sometimes been called "active regulation." When it was found, however, that the stomata do not close until the leaf wilts to some extent, it was considered that stomatal regulation of water is passive, since under such conditions the stomatal closure is not due to any special activity of the guard cells but to a decrease in their turgor that is caused by the loss of water from the leaf cells being greater than the intake. It is now considered that passive regulation or hindrance of water loss is operative only after the stomata have closed to a considerable degree, since when they are fully open their carrying capacity for water vapor is from three to six times greater than that which escapes at the maximum rate of transpiration.

The question of stomatal regulation of water loss is complicated by several factors, the chief of which are the climatic conditions and the water supply of the soil. The actual rate of diffusion of water vapor through the stomata is not influenced alone by the size of the pore and the length of the tube but by the gradation of the density of the water vapor between the surface of the mesophyll cells and the outer air. This gradient is dependent upon the water-supplying power of the plant and upon the humidity of the outer air, which is, in turn, determined by the prevailing conditions. Thus the gradient of density of the water vapor from the inside of the leaf to the outside may vary independently of the size of the pores. The question of stomatal regulation of water loss has been considered along the three following general lines:

(*a*) *Stomatal Movement and the Water Content of the Leaf.*—The outgo of water from a leaf during the day is generally greater than the intake, while the reverse is generally true at night. The water content of the leaf thus may vary over a considerable range during a 24-hr. period even though no visible signs of wilting can be observed. This variation in water content may be demonstrated in various ways (Trelease, 1922) and will depend not only on the type and age of the plant but also to a large degree upon the prevailing atmospheric conditions. Livingston and Brown (1912) observed that the daily variation in the moisture content of a number of species of plants at Tucson, Ariz., was about 8 per cent on a moist basis. Lloyd (1913) noted for the leaves of the cotton plant grown under the conditions of Auburn, Ala., and Tucson, Ariz., that the loss of leaf water was from 7 to 15 per cent of the initial amount at sunrise. Shreve (1914) observed that the water content of the

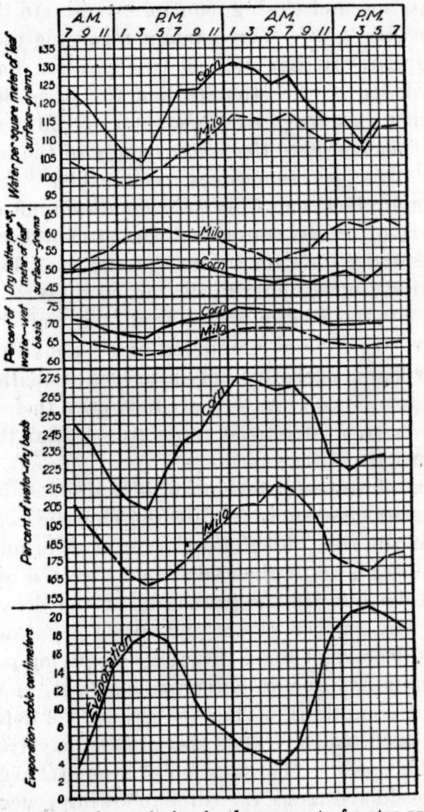

Fig. 17.—Graphs showing the variation in the amount of water and dry matter in the leaves of Pride of Saline corn and Dwarf Yellow milo during 24 hr. and the evaporation from a porous cup atmometer for the corresponding period.

leaves of *Parkinsonia microphylla* fluctuated as little as 2 per cent and as much as 9 per cent during the day at Tucson, Ariz. Knight (1922), however, found that the diurnal changes in leaf-water content in England amounted to not over 1 per cent. Miller (1917) studied extensively the daily variation of the water content of the leaves of corn and the two sorghums kafir and yellow milo growing under field conditions in the

Great Plains area of Kansas. The average difference between the maximum percentage of water in the leaves at night and the minimum percentage during the day was 5.4 for corn, 5.9 for kafir, and 6.0 for milo. The minimum percentage of water in the leaves during the day occurred from 11 A.M. to 5 P.M., but in the majority of cases it was reached between 1 and 3 P.M. The maximum percentage of water in the leaves occurred between 1 and 5 A.M., but in the majority of the 30 observations it occurred around 5 A.M. Hawkins (1927) reported that the lowest amount of water in the leaves of Acala and Pima cotton growing at Tucson, Ariz., occurred about 1:30 P.M. An example of the variation in the moisture content of the leaves of corn and milo during a 36-hr. period is shown in Fig. 17 and in the table on page 444.

Metzger, Holmes, and Bierman (1925) found in Maryland that the water content of the leaves of soybeans declined 7 per cent between 8 A.M. and noon. They recommended that on account of this lower moisture content these plants be cut for hay in the heat of the day so that they might cure more quickly. Willard (1931) from observations on alfalfa, and red, sweet, and alsike clovers concluded, however, that in Ohio there was not sufficient change in the water content of these plants to influence the time of day at which they should be cut for hay. Gilbert and Adams (1929) by withholding water from Swiss chard and barley caused a fall of 7.5 per cent in the water content of these plants. In the wheat plant, Hurd-Karrer and Taylor (1929) noted that the water content of the leaves gradually decreased from before flowering to maturity. For any one day Kiesselbach and Anderson (1931), in Nebraska, found a maximum difference of 4.4 per cent in the moisture content of alfalfa, and for all their observations an average difference of 2 per cent from 8 A.M. to 5 P.M. Yapp and Mason (1932) observed in the sunflower that the greatest quantity of water was in the lowest foliage and in the youngest leaves. Runyon (1936) noted that in the creosote bush the amount of moisture in the leaves differs with age, position on stem, habitat, and time of day. Isaac (1935) reported that between tides the decrease of water in *Laminaria digitata* was between 19.3 and 30.0 per cent, depending upon the prevailing atmospheric conditions.

Lloyd (1912) observed that the stomata continued to open when the water content of the leaves was decreasing and concluded, as did Knight (1917), that the stomata were ineffective in maintaining a constant water supply in the leaf and were thus of little or no value in controlling the water loss. Loftfield (1921) criticized these conclusions on the ground that there is a certain amount of the water present in a turgid leaf which may be regarded as a working margin and which may be lost without interfering with the opening of the stomata or the various other functions of the leaf. After the content of water has fallen below this working margin, the stomata begin to close owing to a fall in the turgor of the guard cells. Hendrickson (1926) noted in the case of peach trees that the decrease in moisture content of the leaves appeared at a period considerably in advance of the maximum opening of the stomata. Loftfield

VARIATION OF THE WATER AND DRY MATTER IN THE LEAVES OF PRIDE OF SALINE CORN AND DWARF MILO AT GARDEN CITY, KANS., AUG. 1 AND 2, 1916

Time	Water per square meter of leaf, grams		Dry matter per square meter of leaf, grams		Percentage of water, wet basis		Percentage of water, dry basis	
	Corn	Milo	Corn	Milo	Corn	Milo	Corn	Milo
Aug. 1:								
7 a.m.	123	105	49	51	72	68	251	206
9 a.m.	119	102	50	53	70	66	238	191
11 a.m.	112	100	51	56	69	64	219	179
1 p.m.	107	98	51	58	68	63	208	168
3 p.m.	104	99	51	61	67	62	203	162
5 p.m.	115	102	52	62	69	62	223	166
7 p.m.	123	107	51	60	71	63	241	177
9 p.m.	124	109	50	58	71	65	247	187
11 p.m.	129	113	49	58	72	66	262	195
Aug. 2:								
1 a.m.	131	117	48	56	73	68	275	210
3 a.m.	129	116	47	55	73	68	273	210
5 a.m.	125	115	47	52	73	69	268	221
7 a.m.	127	117	47	54	73	68	270	217
9 a.m.	120	112	47	55	72	67	258	205
11 a.m.	116	110	50	60	70	65	230	183
1 p.m.	115	110	52	62	69	64	224	176
3 p.m.	108	107	47	62	70	63	230	173
5 p.m.	115	113	50	63	70	64	232	180
7 p.m.	...	114	..	62	...	65	...	184

observed that plants may wilt during the early forenoon to such an extent that the stomata completely close but may again regain their turgor, during that part of the day when the evaporation is the highest, to such an extent that the stomata again open. He attributed this recovery of turgor to the influence of the stomata in retarding water loss so that the cells of the leaf again accumulate a supply of water above the working margin.

(*b*) *Number of Stomata and Transpiration.*—Kuyper (1915) could establish no relationship between the transpiration rate and the number of stomata per unit area of different varieties of sugar cane. Muenscher

(1915) studied the relation of the number and size of stomata to the rate of transpiration of sunflower, bean, wheat, and corn among others. He found no constant relation between the amount of transpiration and the number of stomata per unit of leaf surface or between the amount of water lost and the number of linear units of stomatal pore, *i.e.*, the number of stomata per unit of leaf surface multiplied by the average length of the pore. Kelley (1930) also found no correlation between the stomatal number per unit area of leaf surface and the rate of transpiration. The species with the greatest density of stomata were in the group of plants having the lowest rate of transpiration.

In comparing different species of plants for transpiration rates, it should not be overlooked that they possess structural differences, other than the number of stomata which may greatly influence transpirational loss. The length of time the stomata are open is also a very important factor, and Loftfield (1921) pointed out that only when the stomata are open for comparable periods can we draw conclusions in regard to the number of stomata and the transpiration rate of different plants. Thus, for example, Muenscher (1915) found that the ratio of the linear units of the stomatal pore of the sunflower to that of corn was 4:3, while the transpiration rate for a 24-hr. period was 2:1. He concluded that there is no relationship between the number and size of the stomata and the transpiration rate. Loftfield (1921), however, found that the stomata of corn are open 8 hr., while those of sunflowers are open for 12 hr. Thus the water lost by the sunflower plant was during a 12-hr. period and by corn during an 8-hr. period, so that the hourly loss would stand in the ratio of 4:3, which is the same as the ratio of the linear units of the stomatal pores.

(*c*) *Changes in Stomatal Openings.*—It would be expected that the rate of transpiration could undergo sudden and relatively wide fluctuations with little or no alteration in the size of the stomata provided their full diffusion capacity for water vapor at the stage of observation is greater than the prevailing transpiration rate. This fact was observed by Lloyd (1908) for the cut stems of *Fouquieria splendens*, *Verbena ciliata*, and other plants placed in potometers for transpiration experiments. He noted that the rate of transpiration frequently continued to increase for a considerable period of time after the maximum stomatal opening had been reached and that in the later part of the day there were increases in transpiration without any increase in the size of the stomata. It was concluded from these observations that the stomata are nonregulatory in regard to the loss of water by transpiration. Loftfield (1921) considered that the evidence obtained by Lloyd in this regard is of doubtful value as relating to plants growing under natural conditions, since he found that the stomatal movements and rates of water loss from cut stems in potometers differed greatly from those of field or potted plants. Kuyper (1915) found that the maximum transpiration rate in sugar cane was frequently reached after the stomata had begun to close, so that the rate of transpiration under the conditions of his observations was independent of stomatal behavior. Knight (1917) found that the interrelationship of stomatal aperture and transpiration was not consistent. In some cases the graphs of transpiration and stomatal openings ran closely parallel, but in other cases there appeared to be no relationship at all between the two. Zhemchuznikov (1922, 1924) found in the case of sunflowers, corn, and sorghums growing in soil with 60 per cent of complete saturation that the curves of transpiration usually, but not always, paralleled those of the dimensions of the stomatal pore. He considered that this datum indicates a relationship between stomatal aperture and the rate of transpiration, although meteorological factors may modify it. The prevailing atmospheric conditions without doubt determine to a great extent the correlation between the degree of stomatal opening and the rate of transpiration. Thus Livingston (1909) and Darwin (1916) found in diffuse light and under relatively mild atmospheric conditions that the variation in the size of stomatal openings was parallel with the changes in the rate of transpiration. As the intensity of the sunlight increases, the stomata apparently respond more quickly in their opening than does the transpiration rate to the increasing intensity of the atmospheric conditions, so that they reach their maximum opening ahead of the maximum transpiration rate.

The general opinion concerning the relation of stomatal opening to the rate of transpiration can be summed up in the words of Loftfield (1921), and Walter (1925, 1926) to the effect that when the stomata are fully opened or nearly so, the transpiration rate is determined by the factors of evaporation alone, since the diffusion capacity of the stomata is so great as to interfere in no way with their action. As the stomata close, the influence of the evaporation factors is lessened, but even after the size of the apertures has been reduced over 50 per cent, stomatal regulation is still largely overshadowed by the influence of atmospheric conditions. When the stomata are almost closed, they begin to exert a controlling influence on the water loss regardless of the evaporating factors prevailing at the time. Jeffreys (1918) considered that nearly all the reduction due to the closure of the stomata occurs in the last 2 per cent reduction of the aperture.

The degree of closure of the stomata would appear to have an influence on the moisture content of the air of the intercellular spaces of the leaf. As the stomata close, the degree of saturation of the air in the intercellular spaces increases, so that there would be an increase in the gradient of density of water vapor between the interior of the leaf and the atmosphere. This would increase the rate of diffusion outwardly, so that it is conceivable that as a stoma closes, the rate of transpiration through it may decrease little or none at all over what it was before it began to close. When the closure of the stomata is complete, the air within the leaf must reach saturation. It is not known, however, how completely transpiration is prevented by the apparent complete closure of the stomata.

b. Hairy and Waxy Coverings.—In most plants certain of the young epidermal cells grow out either singly or in groups to form appendages of various shapes, which are termed "hairs" or "trichomes" (Haberlandt, 1914). These epidermal hairs are readily divided into two classes: those that contain protoplasm and sometimes chlorophyll, which are termed "glandular hairs," and those that have lost their protoplasmic contents and are filled with air. The glandular hairs evidently affect transpiration only by adding to the evaporating surface of the leaf, but the influence which the dead, air-containing hairs have on transpiration is considerably in doubt, although numerous textbooks state that the hairy covering of leaves reduces transpiration. Haberlandt (1914) stated that the transpiration rate of leaves of *Stachys lanata* was increased by 20 per cent in the shade and as much as 50 per cent in bright sunlight by shaving off the hairs from the upper surface. He considered that a dense woolly coat of hairs reduces transpiration considerably when the leaf is exposed to direct sunlight and to a much lesser extent in diffuse light.

Weigand (1910) studied the effect of artificial hairy coverings on the rate of evaporation, since he considered that such experiments would throw some light on the function that such coverings play in transpiration. He used as an evaporating surface a good quality of blotting paper saturated with water and then rolled with a pencil and placed tightly on a glass surface. The edges of the paper were dipped in paraffin and pressed down tightly upon the glass. The loss of water was determined by weighing. Cotton, made waterproof by paraffin in gasoline, was used for protective coverings of various degrees of thickness. The experiments were performed in still air and in air in motion, the wind being produced by an electric fan. The results showed that porous coverings like cotton, wool, or hair must be very thick to produce any appreciable effect in retarding evaporation if the air is still but become very efficient even in thin layers when the air is in motion.

Rhine (1924) noticed in the stomata of the juniper, fir, and Austrian pine a deposit of wax that apparently retarded the gaseous exchange between the leaf and its surroundings. Emerson and Hildreth (1933) applied various waxes, gums, resin oils, paraffin emulsions, and commercial nursery waxes to young evergreens to prevent excessive transpiration during transplanting. Heavy coatings of these various compounds reduced the transpiration almost to zero but caused severe injury to the plants. Since the temperature of the material applied is a limiting factor, pure oils and emulsions of oils and waxes were tried because they could be applied as sprays at ordinary temperatures. It was found that when applied in the pure form castor oil and corn oil were the only ones that did not injure the conifer needles. The emulsification of some of the injurious oils, however, greatly reduced or entirely removed their toxicity. In practice these sprays are best applied to the seed beds or nursery rows before transplanting. It is believed that this practice will also protect coniferous seedlings from excessive drying in winter.

The leaves of the mullein plant (*Verbascum thapsus*) have one of the most dense coverings of dead hairs of any of the more common plants, these hairs being many-celled structures much branched and having the branches both parallel and perpendicular to the leaf surface. Sayre (1919, 1920) studied the influence of these hairs upon transpiration. Three plants, which may be designated as M^{1+h}, M^{2+h}, and M^{3+h}, with the hairs of the leaves intact were exposed to the desired conditions and their rates of transpiration determined. The ratios of the daily transpiration rates of these three plants in the greenhouse in the light and in still air were as follows:

$$\frac{M^{1+h}}{M^{2+h}} = 0.98 \text{ and } \frac{M^{1+h}}{M^{3+h}} = 0.82.$$

The hairs were than removed from the upper surface of M^{2+h} and from the lower surface of M^{3+h}, after which the plants were designated as M^{2-h} and M^{3-h}, respectively. The plant M^{1+h} was left intact as a check. These three plants were placed in the greenhouse in the light and in still air, and their daily transpiration rates obtained. The ratios of the rates of the treated plants to the check were as follows:

$$\frac{M^{1+h}}{M^{2-h}} = 0.99 \text{ and } \frac{M^{1+h}}{M^{3-h}} = 0.83$$

These were practically the same ratios as were obtained when the hairs were intact.

In the light and in a gentle breeze produced by an electric fan the ratios of the water loss were

$$\frac{M^{1+h}}{M^{2-h}} = 0.91 \text{ and } \frac{M^{1+h}}{M^{3-h}} = 0.78$$

In a dark room in still air the ratios were

$$\frac{M^{1+h}}{M^{2-h}} = 0.56 \text{ and } \frac{M^{1+h}}{M^{3-h}} = 0.65$$

These data indicate that the removal of hairs from the mullein leaves does not appreciably alter their resistance to water loss in still air and light but does slightly decrease the resistance of the leaves to water loss in wind and light as compared with still air and light. The removal of the hairs, however, greatly decreases the resistance of the leaves to water loss in still air and darkness as compared with still air and light. The removal of the hairs affects the transpiration rate most noticeably when the plants are placed in the dark. The stomata are then closed and the transpiration is practically all cuticular. Sayre concluded that the effect of the hairs of the mullein leaf on transpiration in ordinary intensities of wind and light may be disregarded, since the removal of these hairs affects only the cuticular transpiration which is not over one-fortieth to one-twentieth of the stomatal transpiration upon which the removal of hairs apparently has no effect. Shapiro and de Forest (1932) found in southern California that *Salvia apiana*, which has a thick covering of hairs on each surface, lost the most water of any of the eight species studied. The effect of hairs upon transpiration of the leaf will no doubt vary according to their number and arrangement, and it must be admitted, in the words of Cowles (1910), that the known uses of the hairs of plants are small in comparison with their abundant development, and it is probable that most of them are of little or no advantage to the plant.

c. General Structure and Composition of the Leaf.—Little work is available to indicate the relation of the transpiring power of the leaf to its general structure or composition. It has always been assumed that the structural characteristics of the leaves of xerophytic plants are useful in reducing the loss of water by transpiration. The structural characters that are commonly associated with the xerophytic leaf are stated by Pool (1923) as follows: "The leaf is, as a rule, relatively thick and sometimes without chlorophyll at the center. The epidermis is frequently very thick and waxy, resinous, or heavily cutinized, and the stomata-bearing surface is often hairy. The stomata are sometimes protected by being enclosed and are frequently structurally rigid. Xerophytic leaves generally have prominent palisade cells often in very densely packed layers, extending from one epidermis to the other. Frequently the palisades in the lower part of the leaf are less prominently developed or less densely packed than in the upper portion of the leaf. When the sponge or lower chlorenchyma is present, it is, as a rule, comparatively densely packed with a relatively small amount of intercellular space. As a rule, the fibrovascular elements are more copiously developed in the xerophytic leaf than in the mesophytic one. Of all the structural differences between the xerophytic leaf and the mesophytic one, the most striking are the relative development of the palisade and sponge tissue and the relative proportion of the intercellular spaces. The entire chlorenchyma of the mesophyte is likely to be much more open and, as a whole, thinner than the xerophyte."

Pool (1923) studied by means of the cobalt chloride-paper method the transpiring power of some 40 representative species from the various plant communities from the short-grass mesas and plateaus east of Colorado Springs up through the foothills to an altitude of 12,000 ft. It was found that there was some correlation between the transpiring power and the leaf anatomy, leaves of the xerophytic types being found generally to have the lowest transpiring power. The indications were that the compactness of the chlorenchyma of the xerophytic leaves has a marked effect in preventing the evaporation of water in the interior of the leaf and thus reduces the ability to give off water in the form of vapor (see also Lesage, 1894). Pool, however, found many apparent exceptions to this rule. Thus, for example, the leaf of *Pentstemon unilateralis* showed a more xerophytic structure than that of *Populus angustifolia,* yet the index of transpiring power of the latter was 0.641 while that of the former was 0.908. Miller and Coffman (1918) made a somewhat similar observation in regard to the relationship of the leaf structure of corn and the sorghums and the rate of transpiration. The leaves of the sorghums show a marked xerophytic structure in comparison with the leaves of corn, yet the transpiration rate in numerous cases was over twice that of the corn.

Shapiro and dé Forest (1932) studied the rate of transpiration of eight species of plants in the chaparral of southern California. The "relative transpiration indexes," or the ratios of the average rate of transpiration to that from an atmometer of moist blotting paper, were as follows:

Plant	Relative transpiration index	Plant	Relative transpiration index
Rhus integrifolia..........	0.066	*Quercus dumosa*........	0.148
Rhus laurina............	0.076	*Adenostema fasiculatum*..	0.275
Salvia mellifera..........	0.102	*Pentstemon spectabilis*....	0.427
Ceanothus cuneatus.......	0.119	*Salvia apiana*..........	0.483

With the possible exception of *Rhus integrifolia,* the general structural arrangement of the leaf furnished very little reliable information as to the relative loss of water.

Pool (1923) stated that he was unable to explain the discrepancies between leaf anatomy and the index of foliar transpiring power. He suggested that in his experiments it might be possible that the cobalt chloride-paper method was not sufficiently accurate to differentiate accurately between the more nearly similar forms. He believed also that the stomatal behavior should be considered in a study of this kind, since it is to be expected that such behavior would modify the transpiring power to a marked degree. Shreve (1924) considered that the differences in the anatomical structure of the mesophytic and xerophytic leaves do not account for the difference in resistance to water loss by plants in arid regions. Blaydes (1935) stated that according to the indications the standard water-vapor loss of a species is not necessarily correlated with the xerophytism as indicated by the usual habitat of that species. Many xerophytic species have relatively high rates of water loss, while many mesophytic species have low rates. A complete summary of the studies on the relation of leaf structure to transpiration is to be found in Burgerstein (1904, 1920).

It appears evident that internal factors other than the general structure of the leaf may influence the transpiration rate, although the extent to which they may do so is in most cases not definitely known. It has frequently been suggested that the osmotic value of the cell sap of the leaf cells might have some influence on the rate of water loss from the plant. The concentration of the cell sap, however, must vary over a wide range in order to have any appreciable effect upon the transpiration rate, as can be illustrated by the examples mentioned by Drabble and Drabble (1907). In these observations they found that osmotic concentration of the cell sap of plants growing in three different habitats was respectively equivalent to 3,728, 8,812, and 14,958 mm. of mercury.

They considered that the evaporation of water from the surfaces of these three solutions would be in the ratio of 1.011:1.005:1, respectively. The influence of the osmotic value upon the rate of water loss would thus be slight, since an increase in concentration of 400 per cent would reduce the rate of evaporation of water by only 1 per cent. Since the osmotic value of the cell sap varies with the accumulation or disappearance of osmotically active substances within the cells of the leaf, the metabolic changes that use or produce these substances must be taken into consideration for slight modifications of the transpiration rate.

Variations in the water-holding capacity of the internal tissues of the leaf may also influence the transpiring power of the plant. The emulsoid colloids of the protoplasm and the component compounds of the cell wall have an imbibitional attraction for water that varies with the changes in structure and composition of these two parts of the plant cell or of the structures with which they come in contact (Shreve, 1916). It is well known that acids, bases, and neutral salts affect the distribution of water between the dispersed and continuous phases of emulsoids. On that account, the alternation of the chemical constituents causes variations in the distribution of water among the cell wall, cell sap, and the protoplasmic membrane, so that the water-holding capacity of the tissues may be altered. The imbibitional forces of the cell walls are especially important factors in influencing the rate of transpiration and will be discussed under the following heading.

2. Incipient Drying or Incipient Wilting.—It has been observed in many cases when the hourly rate of transpiration is plotted that the graph shows a marked flattening in its slope as the evaporating power of the air increases. This flattening of the graph appears to be due to some change in the plant that causes a reduction in the transpiration rate below that which would be expected from the form of the curve during the earlier hours. This reduction in the increase of the transpiration rate has sometimes been interpreted to mean that the plant initiates certain changes, under conditions of increasing transpiration, which retard the loss of water and thus protect the plant against excessive water loss.

The causes of this retardation of the increase in the transpiration rate are apparently to be found in certain physical phenomena which were pointed out by Renner (1910) and by Livingston and Brown (1912). They suggested that the internal retardation in water loss which frequently occurs prior to the maximum rate of transpiration may be due largely to an increase in the rate of water loss itself. This fact can be illustrated, as shown by Livingston and Brown (1912), by mounting two filter-paper disks saturated with water over glass tubes in such a manner that one will be in continuous contact with water while the other will be deprived of a water supply. When these disks are exposed to conditions favoring evaporation, the one that is in contact with a water supply will maintain a moisture content that is practically constant, while the moisture content of the one mounted over the empty tube will become less and less. An experiment of this type was performed by Livingston and Brown and it was found that a fall in the moisture content of the paper of 6 per cent produced a corresponding decrease in the rate of evaporation of 5 per cent. A fall of 17 per cent in water content produced a rate of evaporation 8 per cent lower than when the paper was saturated, the effect becoming more and more pronounced as the paper dried out. The conditions that prevail in the leaf as the transpiration rate increases are apparently in some cases similar to those which prevail in the paper-disk experiment, since if at any time the rate of water loss from the leaf surpasses the rate of supply, the tissues of the leaf bordering on the intercellular spaces would become less moist after the manner of the filter paper above mentioned.

This drying out of the cell walls that border on the internal atmosphere of the leaf has been termed "incipient drying" or "incipient wilting" and is substantiated by experiments that have shown a decrease of the water content of the leaves as the evaporating power of the air increases. As incipient drying progresses, the water films gradually retreat into the pores or capillaries of the cell walls bordering on the intercellular spaces and thus increase the surface tension of these water surfaces. This increase of the surface tension of the water films decreases their vapor tension, which causes a fall in the rate of the vaporization of water from them. This means that the retardation of the increase of the transpiration rate under an increasing evaporating power of the air may, in some cases at least, be due to a rate of transpirational loss slightly greater than the rate of water intake by the leaves.

It is generally accepted that the water content of the leaf is one of the principal factors controlling the transpiration rate. According to Haines (1935) the content of water in the leaf depends partly upon the conditions of pressure or tension in the conducting tracts supplying the water. The amount of water in the leaf is thus only a sort of passive intermediary through which the transpiration rate might be affected indirectly by changes in the pressure or tension of the tracts. The operating factor is the "pressure deficit," which may be defined as the difference between the pressure in the conducting tracts and the pressure at the leaf surfaces. With *Acer pseudoplatanus*, Haines (1936) found that by increasing the pressure deficit the rate of transpiration was reduced. A decrease in this deficit caused a very large and immediate increase in the transpiration rate. These pressure deficits alone apparently cannot reduce transpiration by their effects upon the vapor pressure at the leaf cell surfaces but must also cause an increase in the resistance to the flow of water through the protoplasts of the cells of the leaf. When the transpiration of different plants is observed, it is seen that certain plants do not manifest this flattening of the transpiration graph. Thus Briggs and Shantz (1916) found that wheat, oats, and rye showed a flattening of their transpiration graph, while alfalfa and the sorghums under like conditions showed no such behavior. Huber (1923) noted that the transpiration of the lower twigs of *Sequoia gigantea* was six times that of the higher ones. If, however, they are allowed to stand in water for 24 hr., this transpiration difference disappears, which fact he considered proves that these observed differences are the result of unequal water saturation. Zalenski (1923), however, found in the plants that he studied that the intensity of transpiration per unit of surface increased from the lower to the upper leaves notwithstanding the more xeromorphous structure of the lower leaves.

We want now to inquire what internal factors may influence the imbibitional action on the transpiration rate. Two of the factors that apparently may greatly influence the degree of incipient drying in the leaf and thus influence its rate of transpiration are the leaf surface and the nature of the root system. We shall now consider the effect of these two factors.

a. Leaf Surface of the Plant.—In transpiration experiments with corn and sorghum plants Miller and Coffman (1918) observed that, in general, if two or more of these plants were placed under the same conditions, the total amount of water lost by each stood in the same relative order as the leaf surfaces. The results of an experiment conducted from 7 A.M. to 9 P.M., as shown in the following table, illustrate this relation:

LEAF SURFACE AND THE AMOUNT OF WATER TRANSPIRED BY CORN AND SORGHUMS FROM 7 A.M. TO 7 P.M.

Plant	Leaf surface, square centimeters	Water transpired, cubic centimeters
Corn, Pride of Saline	16,943	3,853
Sorgo, Red Amber	4,844	1,702
Sorgo, Freed	2,973	989

Although the amount of water transpired per plant stood in the same relative order as the extent of the leaf surface, the loss of water was not exactly proportional to it, so it follows that the rate of transpiration per unit of leaf surface was not the same for each plant (see table, page 454).

It is to be observed from the table (page 454) that the rate of transpiration of the sorghums per unit of leaf surface was approximately twice as

THE RATE OF TRANSPIRATION OF CORN AND SORGHUM EXPRESSED AS G.M.[2] HR. FOR EACH 2-HR. PERIOD FROM 7 A.M. TO 7 P.M.

Time	Corn, Pride of Saline	Sorgo	
		Red Amber	Freed
7 to 9 a.m.	122	205	190
9 to 11 a.m.	165	293	304
11 to 1 p.m.	216	374	376
1 to 3 p.m.	199	483	379
3 to 5 p.m.	161	383	272
5 to 7 p.m.	94	124	147

high as that of the corn, while the leaf surface of the Red Amber sorgo and Freed sorgo was only 28.5 and 16.5 per cent, respectively, of that of the corn plant. This same fact also holds when two varieties of plants of different extent of leaf surface are used. For example, Miller and Coffman (1918) observed in the case of a plant of Pride of Saline corn with a leaf surface of 14,568 sq. cm. and a plant of Sherrod White Dent corn with a leaf surface of 12,989 sq. cm. that the actual amount of water lost by the larger plant during a 6-hr. period was 918 cc. as compared to 784 cc. for the smaller plant. The rate of transpiration, however, for the larger plant was only 629 g. per square meter per hour as compared to 723 g. per square meter per hour for the smaller one. Cullinan (1920) made a similar observation on severely pruned and unpruned 2-year-old apple trees. The unpruned trees transpired more water per plant than did the pruned, but the latter transpired more water per unit of leaf surface. It has been further observed that the differences in the transpiration rate per unit of leaf surface were more marked when the differences in the leaf surfaces were the greatest and when the evaporating power of the air was the highest. Darrow and Sherwood (1931) found that the loss by transpiration from strawberry plants with a leaf area of 126.6 sq. cm. was 446 cc., while the loss of water from the same number of plants with a leaf area of 599 sq. cm. was only 206 cc. for the given period. Kelley (1932) found that the removal of approximately half the leaves from the shoots of various fruit trees increased the rate of transpiration per unit area of the remaining leaves by 22 to 93 per cent.

One of the chief causes for the higher transpiration rate of the plants with the smaller leaf surface is apparently their ability to maintain a more saturated condition of the external cell walls of the leaves than the plant with the larger surface. If the facilities for absorption and translocation are approximately the same in two plants with unequal leaf surface, then it is apparent that incipient drying would progress faster and farther in the leaves with the greatest extent of surface. As a consequence of this, the rate of transpiration per unit of area of the plant with the larger leaf surface would be less than that of the plant with the smaller surface.

b. Nature of the Root System.—The ability of the root system to absorb water must exert a marked influence upon the degree of incipient drying and therefore the rate of transpiration. This fact is illustrated by the root systems of corn and the sorghums. Miller (1916) observed that plants of corn, kafir, and milo growing under the same conditions in the field had practically the same number of roots of the first order and that these penetrated vertically to the same depth and showed no difference in their lateral spread. The roots of the second order, however, were twice as numerous in the sorghums as in corn, as is shown in the following table:

Number of Roots of the Second Order per Unit of Length of Root of the First Order of Corn, Kafir, and Milo Growing in the Field

Plant	Number of observations	Number of roots of second order per inch of root of first order
Corn, Pride of Saline	127	15
Milo, Dwarf Yellow	147	26
Kafir, Blackhull	100	28

If the number of fine roots can be taken as a criterion of the efficiency of absorption, it would appear that the sorghum plants would be able to supply the leaves with more water and prevent incipient drying to a greater degree than in the corn plant. The sorghums illustrate how in some plants both the root system and the extent of leaf surface may be important factors in keeping the water supply in the leaves sufficient to retard incipient drying. Maximow and Rybin (1925) in experiments with magnolia and cherry laurel also came to the conclusion that transpiration may be regulated by the conditions of absorption as well as by the action of the stomata.

3. Aerial and Meteorological Conditions.—The conditions that affect the evaporation of water act directly to influence the transpiration rate. Our knowledge, however, concerning the influence of physical environmental factors upon the rate of transpiration is as yet very limited. Efforts to find algebraic formulas or equations by which transpiration can be estimated from observed environmental conditions have produced none that is satisfactory. These efforts are handicapped primarily because the experimental data at the present time are not sufficient to enable a proper evaluation of radiation, wind, light, temperature, and humidity in relation to transpiration and because the effect of stomatal movement is very little understood. The two main environmental factors that affect the evaporation of water are the evaporating power of impinging solar radiation and the evaporating power of the air.

a. Evaporating Power of Solar Radiation.—By impinging solar radiation is meant the total energy received from the sun by a given surface in a unit of time. The intensity of solar radiation is frequently expressed as the number of calories falling per minute upon a square centimeter of surface normal to the sun's rays. The known methods for measuring solar radiation, however, are not very satisfactory (Livingston, 1911; Briggs and Shantz, 1916; and Pulling, 1919). Solar radiation may be direct from the sun or indirect as from the sky, clouds, or earth. With no clouds or other shade intervening, direct solar radiation is predominant, but when the sun is obscured by clouds indirect radiation may be the more influential of the two upon evaporation (Livingston, 1923).

The influence of solar radiation on evaporation is always positive and is confined to the daylight hours. Briggs and Shantz (1915) found that the radiation graph always rises in advance of the other cyclic environmental factors. This is to be expected, however, since the change in radiation is the primary cause of the cyclic changes of these factors. These investigators observed that radiation rose in advance of transpiration in the case of wheat, oats, and rye and approximately with it in the case of the sorghums, alfalfa, and *Amaranthus*. In the afternoon, radiation fell off somewhat in advance of the transpiration of wheat and oats but approximately with it in the case of rye, alfalfa, sorghum and *Amaranthus*. Martin (1935), working with *Helianthus annuus* in full sunlight, found that the amount of transpiration due to the effects of radiation was 38 to 81 per cent, depending upon the evaporating power of the air. They found that the correlation coefficient of transpiration with radiation ranged from 0.82 to 0.89 for the plants under consideration; the correlation coefficient of transpiration with temperature ranged from 0.77 to 0.86; and the correlation coefficient of transpiration with relative humidity ranged from 0.75 to 0.85. Manzoni and Puppo (1934) found that for wheat the correlation of transpiration with radiation was 0.882, with evaporation was 0.796, with temperature was 0.660, and with relative humidity was 0.538. These figures show that intercorrelations exist among the environmental factors, since the sum of the squares of the coefficients of the independent causative factors influencing transpiration cannot exceed unity.

Briggs and Shantz (1916) in transpiration experiments with wheat, oats, millet, and alfalfa under shaded and unshaded conditions concluded that the energy consumed in transpiration is only partially attributable to direct radiation. They considered that indirect radiation from the sky and surrounding objects and the heat energy received directly from the air contribute materially to the heat energy dissipated through transpiration. If, however, the total energy necessary to evaporate all the water lost from an acre of crop plants is compared to the total radiant energy falling upon that area, it is found that less than one-half of it is necessary to evaporate the water lost from the plants even at the time of the maximum transpiration rate.

The primary influence of solar radiation in determining transpiration is indicated by a consideration of the changes in the physical environmental conditions and of transpiration at night when solar radiation is zero. These conditions were determined during the hour from 8 to 9 P.M. and again from 3 to 4 A.M., together with the corresponding transpiration rate. It was found that a simultaneous diminution in the wet-bulb depression of one-fourth its maximum range and in temperature of one-third its maximum range resulted in only a 3 per cent drop in the transpiration rate. This would seem to indicate that the high correlation obtained between transpiration and air temperature and wet-bulb depression is largely due to the direct correlation between radiation and temperature or wet-bulb depression.

The study of the effect of impinging radiation upon transpiration has for the most part been confined to a consideration of the influence of light intensity upon this process, and it has been definitely shown that light has a direct accelerating action on transpiration aside from any secondary effect brought about by stomatal movement (Sampson and Allen, 1909). In order to eliminate any influence of stomatal action, Darwin (1914) covered the leaves with vaseline or cocoa fat and then slit them in various places for the escape of water. Under such conditions the acceleration in transpiration in diffuse daylight was found in the case of *Prunus laurocerasus* and *Hedera helix* to be as much as 50 per cent of the rate in darkness. The figures obtained by Darwin were perhaps too high, since he took data directly after making incisions in the leaves and did not take into consideration the increased water loss due to wound stimulation. Henderson (1926), who followed the same method but allowed the leaf to recover from the wound stimulation before collecting data, could not obtain the large increases in the transpiration rate obtained by Darwin. Electric light of the intensity of diffuse daylight was found to increase the mesophyll water loss in *Hedera helix* and *Eupatorium adenophorum* by an average amount of 5 per cent, of which 1 per cent was due to the heating effect. Thus the direct effect of the light on the transpiration rate amounted to 4 per cent. This amount varied from 1.5 to 9.4 per cent, indicating that the increase in water loss from the mesophyll due to light varies greatly for different plants and for different leaves on the same plant.

Chodat (1931) noted that the rate of transpiration of alpine plants decreased in high light intensities. He attributed this depression to changes in cellular permeability induced by the intense light. Because no depression in the rate was observed at low altitudes, it was considered that this regulatory action was a function of the ultraviolet region. Montemartini (1932) found with *Myosporum serratum* that light stimulated transpiration independently of the effects of temperature. He considered light to modify the action of the stomata or the attraction of the protoplasm for water. Bader (1930) considered that light and soil moisture are the most important external factors in modifying the transpiration of pine trees.

Light may increase transpiration in one or more of the following ways: (1) higher temperature of the leaves, although the impinging light may give some of the molecules of water sufficient kinetic energy to escape as vapor without generally raising the temperature of the leaves. (2) Greater permeability of the protoplasmic membrane as suggested by the work of Iwanoff and Thielmann (1923), who found a great increase in transpiration of the living, but not the dead, leaves of *Bromus inermis* and *Cyperus alternifolius* by changing the illumination from red-yellow to blue-violet rays. If light thus reduces the resistance to the passage of water through the protoplasm, the supply available to the cell wall will be increased, its imbibition will be higher, and the vapor tension at the evaporating surface of the cell wall will tend to rise. (3) Imbibitional changes in the cell-wall colloids in such a manner as to render the cell wall more permeable to water.

b. Evaporating Power of the Air.—The term "evaporating power of the air" is used to designate the combined influences of air temperature, air humidity, and air movement upon the evaporation of water. In contrast to impinging solar radiation, the evaporating power of the air acts on the evaporation of water, not only during the day but also during the night. It generally acts in a positive manner but sometimes in a negative way, as, for example, when the plant absorbs some moisture from the air or when dew is formed upon its surfaces. We wish now to consider individually the effect of temperature, relative humidity, and air movements upon the rate of transpiration.

1. *Temperature.*—The transpiration rate increases, in general, as the temperature rises. Briggs and Shantz (1915) observed that the behavior of transpiration in regard to temperature varies to a considerable degree with different plants. Thus they found in the case of wheat, oats, and alfalfa that the transpiration graph rose in advance of the temperature but rose with the temperature for rye and sorghums and after the tem-

perature in the case of *Amaranthus*. In the afternoon the transpiration for all plants always fell off more rapidly than the temperature, and when the transpiration had reached its night level, the temperature was still above the minimum by an amount equal to about one-third the daily range. In considering the relation to temperature of the average hourly transpiration rates of the above plants on clear days for periods of from 10 to 15 days, they found that the correlation coefficient of transpiration with temperature varied from 0.77 to 0.86 depending upon the plant. When, however, the correlation between the physical environmental factors and the transpiration of over 20 different crop plants during the growing season was determined as one population, the correlation coefficient between temperature and transpiration was found to be 0.64. This means that in the former case if temperature is considered as the primary causative factor, from 59 to 73 per cent of the transpiration was due to temperature, while in the latter observation only 41 per cent was due to this factor (Briggs and Shantz, 1916).

Whitfield (1932) found in the Pike's Peak region that the curve of transpiration showed a closer correlation with the curves of air temperature and relative humidity than with any of the other factors that were measured. It was observed by Kosaka (1933), where anthocyanin pigments occurred in the leaves, that the more highly colored leaves showed a higher transpiration rate than the less highly colored ones. He believed that in all probability this difference in transpiration rates is connected with heat absorption by the anthocyanin pigments. Arthur and Stewart (1933) studied the transpiration rates of tobacco plants under both visible and infrared radiation with controlled temperature and humidity. They found that between 73 and 78°F. an increase of the energy by 2.3 times doubled the water loss. This temperature relation appeared to be independent of the moisture content of the air within the range of 50 to 80 per cent relative humidity. Clements and Martin (1934) found with the sunflower that transpiration varied only slightly when the soil temperature was between 55 and 100°F., but that it dropped rapidly when the soil temperature reached 55°F., reached half at 38°F., and approached zero when the soil temperature neared 32°F.

2. *Relative Humidity.*—In general, it is known that a decrease in the relative humidity will induce a higher transpiration rate, but the amount of quantitative data on the effect of this factor on transpiration is very meager. Montgomery and Kiesselbach (1912) and Kiesselbach (1916) grew corn plants in two greenhouses in which the physical environmental conditions were practically the same with the exception of the relative humidity. During three growing seasons the humidity averaged 22 per cent higher for one greenhouse than for the other. The evaporation from a free water surface in the more humid greenhouse was 54 per cent,

and the transpiration per unit of leaf area was 62 per cent as much as in the drier greenhouse. Darwin (1914) found that the relation between relative humidity and the magnitude of transpiration in most cases is a linear one and that the straight line representing this relation is approximately in the position giving it an angle of 45 deg. with the horizontal. In some cases, however, the change in the rate of transpiration lagged behind the change in relative humidity so that the experimental graph became a curve instead of a straight line. Darwin also observed that transpiration is not zero in saturated air and apparently would not reach that point until the hypothetical humidity was 105 per cent. This means that the vapor tension of the leaf is higher than that of a saturated atmosphere and is about what it should be if the temperature of the leaf was 0.8°C. higher than that of the surrounding air. Darwin concluded that the temperature of the leaf above that of the atmosphere is produced by respiration. Dixon (1898, 1914) also obtained evidence that plants may transpire in a saturated atmosphere. Briggs and Shantz (1915) found in the case of the plants studied by them that transpiration rose in advance of the depression of the wet-bulb thermometer. They found that the correlation coefficient between transpiration and the wet-bulb thermometer depression varied from 0.75 to 0.85 for 10- to 15-day periods in clear weather.

3. *Wind.*—The effects of wind upon transpiration may be twofold. In the first place, moving air tends to remove the blanket of more or less saturated air that surrounds the leaf and thus tends to reduce the distance that the escaped molecular water must move in order to find free air conditions. The movement of air thus helps to increase the diffusion gradient and so increases the rate of transpiration. This influence may be understood by considering the opinion of Renner (1910). He considered that the rate of diffusion from leaves will be inversely modified by an increase in the distance between the region of minimum density outside the leaf and the maximum density within the leaf. This distance is increased in still air by the water-vapor cap that forms over the surface of the leaf, and the larger the leaf the greater the average thickness of the vapor cap, so that if the air were perfectly still, transpiration would vary inversely as the diameter of the leaves. On this account, Renner considered that wind increases the transpiration of large mature leaves by a much greater percentage than it does the small ones. In the second place, wind may influence transpiration if its velocity is sufficient to agitate the leaves and bring about a circulation of air in the intercellular spaces.

Copeland (1906) in experimenting with the coconut palm in the Philippine Islands observed that transpiration in one case in direct sunshine was four times as great in a wind with a velocity of 5 m.p.h. as in a calm, but the increase usually was not over 100 per cent. Brown (1910) found that, although gentle air currents stimulate transpiration, strong air currents may check it. In observations on *Silphium laciniatum*, Giddings (1914) noted that wind velocity increased the activity of the leaves until a velocity of about 8 m.p.h. was reached. If the velocity, however, rose above this, the activity of the leaves was impaired and the rate of transpiration became less. Knight (1917) found that a wind velocity of 0.26 m.p.h. caused an increase of 50 per cent in the rate of transpiration. Wilson (1924) noted that certain Australian plants had their transpiration checked when the wind velocity reached 20 m.p.h.

Seybold (1929, 1931, 1933) stated that wind influences only cuticular transpiration. Thus only hydrophytes that have a relatively high cuticular transpiration showed an appreciable increase in transpiration due to wind. Shapiro and de Forest (1932) noted that wind did not seem to affect the transpiration rates of xerophytic plants, although it did increase the evaporation from the atmometer. With a wind velocity of 10 m. per minute, Stalfelt (1932) with detached leaves obtained a very rapid rise in transpiration over that in still air. There was a slow rise from this velocity to 30 m. per minute, after which there was no further increase in transpiration with an increase in the velocity of the wind. The maximal increase of transpiration due to the wind was 140 per cent over that in still air. Wrenger (1935) studied the effects of wind on the rate of transpiration of 38 species of plants of various morphological types. In 1-hr. experiments, a wind velocity of 1.85 m. per second always brought about a considerable increase in the rate of transpiration. The rate of transpiration during the first 10 to 15 min. was always higher than that during the remainder of the period. The observed increase in the rate of transpiration varied from 12 to 150 per cent of the rate in still air, depending on the species, the effect generally being greater in mesophytes than in xerophytes.

Martin and Clements (1935) studied the effect of wind on the transpiration of *Helianthus annuus* for a short period of 8 days and for long periods of 6 to 8 weeks. During the short period, the rate of transpiration increased with an increased velocity of wind to 2 m.p.h. The rate of transpiration increased 20 to 30 per cent at the onset of the wind, and this value was maintained as long as the wind acted. For velocities higher than 2 m.p.h., there was a relatively large increase in transpiration directly after the application of the wind. This was followed by a fall in the rate, which in turn was followed by a gradual increase. This initial increase amounted to as much as 138 per cent at 16 m.p.h. and was followed by a slight wilting closure of the stomata and a reduction in the rate of transpiration. In about ½ hr. the leaves regained their turgidity, and the transpiration rate rose. A wind of 1 m.p.h. increased the rate of transpiration 30 per cent, while one of 16 m.p.h. increased it as much as 50 per cent. They could observe no difference in the effects of the wind at night as compared to the day.

In the long-time series the plants were grown under continuous wind of velocities of 5, 10, and 15 m.p.h., from the first leaf stage to the 6 to 8 weeks' stage. For the first week the transpiration rates of all three sets were practically the same as those of the controls. Thereafter, however, the rate began to increase with increasing wind velocity so that by the end of the series the three test sets were using water at rates about 20, 35, and 50 per cent higher per unit area than the controls. In this long-time series, the effect of wind on the transpiration rate was greater during the night than during the day. During the day the plants under a 15 m.p.h. wind velocity transpired about 1.5 times as rapidly per unit area as the controls, while at night they transpired four to five times as rapidly. If wind influences the rate of transpiration independently of the other physical environmental factors, it should show a higher correlation with transpiration than with these factors. This, however, is not the case, according to the work of Briggs and Shantz (1915) and Manzoni and Puppo (1934), who found that the wind velocity showed the lowest correlation with transpiration of any of the other physical environmental factors that were studied. When the correlation between the environmental factors and transpiration is considered for the growing season for a large variety of plants, Briggs and Shantz (1916) considered that only from 2 to 6 per cent of the transpirational loss can be attributed directly to the action of the wind.

Although the experimental evidence in regard to the influence of wind on transpiration is somewhat confusing, the indications are that the rate of water loss does not increase as the wind velocity increases above a gentle breeze. A method for controlling the rate of air movement in transpiration experiments has been devised by Blackman and Knight (1917).

4. Water Content of the Soil.—From what has been previously mentioned in regard to the relation of incipient drying to the rate of transpiration, it should be expected that the rate of transpiration would be higher if there were an abundant supply of water in the soil than if it were limited. A rapid movement of water to the roots would greatly aid in preventing incipient drying and thus aid in keeping up the transpiration rate (Shreve, 1924). Shreve (1905) and Hendrickson (1921) mentioned that the transpiration rate of plants is considerably increased by adding water to the relatively dry soil but submitted no quantitative data either in regard to soil moisture or in regard to the transpiration rates. Yuncker (1916) found in growing corn plants in a loam soil with moisture contents of 25, 45, and 65 per cent of saturation that the rate of transpiration for a 24-hr. period was 4.9, 5.8, and 7.2 g. per square meter per hour, respectively, for each of these moisture contents. Miller and Saunders (1923) determined the rate of transpiration of wilted and turgid plants. The soil with a wilting coefficient of 12 per cent had in the case of the turgid plants a moisture content of 20 to 22 per cent and was in good tilth, while that of the wilted plants was depleted to slightly above the wilting coefficient at the beginning of the experiment and slightly below it at its close. The transpiration rate for the turgid and wilted plants of cowpeas and soybeans is shown in the following table:

TRANSPIRATION RATE OF TURGID AND WILTED PLANTS

Date	Rate of transpiration, g.m.^{2} hr.			
	Cowpeas		Soybeans	
	Turgid	Wilted	Turgid	Wilted
July 24:				
1 to 3 p.m.	69.8	32.0	82.6	26.2
3 to 5 p.m.	78.3	44.8	92.2	24.0
5 to 7 p.m.	57.9	25.6	37.6	13.0
July 25:				
7 to 9 a.m.	20.4	19.2	21.4	10.9
9 to 11 a.m.	71.5	12.8	64.3	15.3
July 26:				
11 a.m. to 1 p.m.	126.0	6.3	75.1	4.3
1 to 3 p.m.	165.2	9.6	92.9	4.3

It is a significant fact that when the evaporation rate is relatively low, as in the morning and evening, the differences in the transpiration rate of the turgid and wilted plants are the least. This is due evidently to the fact that incipient drying at these times has not progressed to such an extent as it does when the evaporating power of the air and solar radiation is high.

Frei (1924) grew plants of apple, sunflower, maize, and beans, among others, in a soil with an optimum water content of 60 to 70 per cent of the total moisture capacity and in the same type of soil with a minimum moisture content of 35 to 40 per cent of the water-holding capacity. The intensity of transpiration from the plants in the moist soil was always greater than in the dry soil. Also, an increase in the moisture content of the dry soil led to an increase in the intensity of transpiration until it equaled that of the plants growing in the soil of optimum moisture content. Plants, however, that were growing in the soil with the optimum water content showed a considerably lower transpiration rate when the soil moisture was reduced to the minimum (35 to 40 per cent) than was exhibited by the plant that had been grown in the soil with this water content. Dosdall (1919) grew *Equisetum fluviatile* in a soil with a moisture content of 35 per cent, in mud, and with the roots submerged in water and found that the plants growing in the mud lost the most water, while those in the soil of 35 per cent water content lost the least. Dole (1924) found, with young plants of *Pinus strobus* growing in a soil with a saturation point of 24 per cent, that the transpiration rate with a moisture content of 20 per cent was from two to six times greater than that from plants growing in a soil with a moisture content of 10 per cent.

Miller (1928) in 12 experiments, each of which extended over an 8-hr. period during the daylight hours, studied the rate of transpiration of corn plants in a water-saturated soil and in a soil in good tilth. The plants which had reached about one-half their vegetative growth were grown in soil in good tilth in sealed cans and, just previous to the experiment, water was added in an amount sufficient to saturate the soil. It was found that the average transpiration rate for the 12 plants growing in the soil in good tilth averaged 104 g. per square meter per hour, while the rate for the plants in the saturated soil averaged 107 g. per square meter per hour, a difference that is of little or no significance. It is apparent (Livingston, Hemmi, and Wilson, 1926) that after the water supply in the soil has increased to a certain degree, the effect of a deficiency in the oxygen-supplying power of the soil is manifest, so that factors other than the water-supplying power of the soil must be considered. Niemann (1932) found that sunflower plants transpired the maximal amount of water when the soil was 80 per cent saturated, while the plants of bean and wheat lost their maximal amount when the soil moisture was 60 per cent of saturation. Whitfield (1932) found that transpiration was the highest from plants growing in a soil with a medium water content, lower when growing in saturated soils, and least from those plants in the soils with a low water content. Penfound (1932) and Peterhänsel (1934) substantiated in general the observations of previous investigators along this line.

The experimental evidence in regard to the effect of the water content of the soil on transpiration thus seems to indicate that a plant will transpire the maximal amount of water when the soil has sufficient moisture for good tilth but that an increase above that amount has no effect. A decrease, however, below that for good tilth lowers the rate of transpiration so that when the water content has been reduced to the wilting coefficient or below and the plant is badly wilted, the rate of transpiration may be only one-twentieth to one-thirtieth of that which prevails when the optimum amount of moisture is present.

5. Chemicals.—The effect of chemicals on transpiration has been studied along two different lines: (*a*) their effect when applied to the soil or nutrient solution in which the plant is growing and (*b*) their effect when applied to the leaves in the form of sprays.

a. Chemicals Applied to the Soil.—The presence of any substance in the soil that will injure the absorbing parts, prevent their development, or decrease the permeability of the protoplasmic membrane to water will decrease the absorption of water and consequently lower the transpiration rate as compared with that of a control plant growing in a medium lacking this substance. The addition of chemicals to the soil may also diminish the transpiration rate, owing to the increased concentration of the soil solution, which lowers the diffusion gradient of water into the plant.

On the other hand, the presence in the soil of substances that increase the permeability of the cell membranes to water and stimulate the growth and development of absorbing organs, or act in an antagonistic way upon substances that would lower the transpiration, may greatly increase the rate of transpiration. Also, any substance that increases or hinders the growth of the plant in general increases or decreases the transpiration. It is thus seen that the relation of chemicals to transpiration is very complicated and is interwoven with changes in growth, nutrition, and permeability.

Burgerstein (1904) found, in general, that weak acids and extremely weak solutions of alkali accelerated transpiration, but that stronger solutions retarded it. He also found that corn plants growing in solutions of 0.1 and 0.25 per cent of calcium nitrate and magnesium sulphate increased their transpiration rates, while those in 0.5 and 1 per cent solutions decreased their rates as compared with the controls. Harter (1908) in the case of wheat plants found that, when sodium chloride was present in the soil in sufficient concentration to cause the modification of the structure of the plant, transpiration was considerably reduced, but that when sodium chloride was present in amounts too small to produce any measurable structural effect, the salt had a stimulating effect upon transpiration. Wheat plants grown in soils containing 0.06 to 0.08 per cent of sodium chloride showed an increased transpiration as compared with plants growing in a nonsaline soil, the lower concentration of salt inducing the higher rate of transpiration (Ricome, 1903). Sampson and Allen (1909) in experiments with *Zea mays* and *Helianthus annuus* studied the effect of the acids hydrochloric, nitric, and acetic and the alkalies potassium hydroxide, sodium carbonate, and ammonium hydroxide. For the plants growing in solutions, concentrations of 0.065 and 0.13 per cent were used, while concentrations of 1.0 and 1.5 per cent were added to the plants growing in the soil. In all cases the acids accelerated transpiration, while in most cases the alkalies retarded it. In some few cases the rate was increased. Reed (1910) noted the effect on transpiration of the wheat plant of the addition to 189 soils from different localities of 100 p.p.m. of sodium nitrate, potassium sulphate, and calcium hydrogen phosphate and 1,000 p.p.m. of calcium carbonate. Considering the transpiration from the control plants as 100, that for sodium nitrate was 90.4; for potassium sulphate, 94.8; for monocalcium phosphate, 100.8; and for calcium carbonate, 97.8. Similar experiments with solutions of various organic and inorganic acids ranging in concentration from 0.0004 N to 0.000025 N, however, showed very contradictory results. Bouyoucos (1911) in a very exhaustive study of the effect of saits on transpiration found that the transpiration rate was affected by different densities of nutrient and nonnutrient solutions, by different chemical salts, and by the ions of these salts. Reed made the observation that the addition of pyrogallol or tannic acid to soil extracts markedly increased the rate of transpiration. Large increases in transpiration were also obtained by treating soil extracts with absorbent compounds like carbon and ferric hydrate. The increased transpiration in this case is apparently due to the action of these substances upon the toxic or injurious compounds in the soil. Burgerstein (1885) found that solutions containing 1 part of camphor per 1,000 had an accelerating effect upon the transpiration of most plants. Newton (1925) performed experiments which show that the rate of root respiration is increased as related to transpiration when the concentration of the cultural solution is increased. The rate of transpiration is decreased when the concentration of the cultural solution is increased, but this is not accompanied by a corresponding decrease in the rates of root respiration. This indicates that as the concentration of the cultural solution is increased, the plant roots must expend more energy in absorbing a given volume of water. Schmucker (1928) noted that transpiration from leaves and branches was greatly depressed by narcotic vapors of relatively low tension. Heiling (1933) found that transpiration was increased by a low concentration of sulphur dioxide. Meyer (1931) applied various salts of sodium, potassium, and calcium to the soil in concentrations of 0.025, 0.05, 0.1, 0.2, and 0.4 per cent of its dry weight. In observations continued through 4 days, the addition of these salts resulted in nearly all cases in a decrease of transpiration. Williams (1935) observed with barley that the application of phosphorus to the soil had the effect of lowering the ratio of the amount of water transpired to the amount of dry matter produced. In some cases this was caused apparently by a decrease in transpiration and in others by its influence on growth.

b. Films from Sprays.—It has long been recognized that Bordeaux mixture applied as a spray exerts a marked influence upon the physiological functions of the plant aside from its action as an insecticide or fungicide. For example, spraying with Bordeaux mixture has been observed to prolong the life of the potato plant for 25 days and to increase the yield of tubers 100 bu. per acre over that of unsprayed plants during a season when no disease or insect pests were present. Considerable work has been done to determine the nature of the reactions of plants to Bordeaux mixture when applied as a spray, but it is the intention to consider here only its reaction upon the process of transpiration.

Prior to 1914, observations, for the most part, on the effect of Bordeaux mixture on the rate of transpiration were incidental to other experimental work, so that the reports on that subject previous to that date are very brief, with little or no information concerning the state of the plants or the conditions under which the observations were made. Rumm (1893) considered that Bordeaux mixture decreased the rate of transpiration, since he observed that the unsprayed abscised leaves of the grape wilted before the sprayed ones. Bayer (1902) and Schander (1904) also considered that decreased transpiration rates followed spraying with Bordeaux mixture. Schander suggested that the decreased rates might be due to the exclusion from the leaves of certain rays which in the unsprayed leaf tend to accelerate the process of transpiration. The increased vigor and yield of potato plants in the field when sprayed with Bordeaux mixture, even when no diseases and insects are a source of loss, were believed by Clinton (1909) to be largely due to the conservation of moisture in the leaves in dry seasons by the spray. This conservation of water he considered prevented tip burn. This theory was strengthened by the fact that the application of sprays with little sediment did not prolong the life of the plants or give increased yields as did Bordeaux mixture.

Frank and Krüger (1894) concluded that Bordeaux mixture applied to the leaves as a spray exerted an accelerating influence upon the rate of water loss by transpiration. These observations were later confirmed by Zucker (1896).

Since 1914 experimental work in considerable detail has been undertaken by various investigators to determine the effect of sprays and especially Bordeaux mixture upon the rate of transpiration. Duggar and Cooley (1914) instituted the method of procedure that has been generally followed by other workers along this line. The general plan has been to divide the plants under consideration into two groups, which may be designated test plants T and control plants C. These plants are then paired and the ratio $T:C$ of their units of transpiration during a given period is obtained. After this standardization period the plants T are sprayed and the ratio of the units of transpiration $T:C$ is again obtained for each pair of plants. If the ratio $T:C$ has increased over what it was during the standardization period, the transpiration rate has been increased by the spray. If the ratio has decreased, the transpiration rate has been lowered. Duggar and Cooley found that spraying abscised leaves of the castor bean with 4-6-50 Bordeaux mixture increased the rate of transpiration as much as 80 per cent. In the case of potted tomato plants 12 in. high growing in the greenhouse, the transpiration rate was increased as much as 40 and 25 per cent during a period from October 18 to November 4 by spraying with 4-6-50 and 2-3-50 Bordeaux mixtures, respectively. They also determined the effect upon the transpiration of tomato plants of calcium hydroxide, aluminum hydroxide, clay suspension, and lime sulphur as liquid sprays and powdered aluminum hydroxide, charcoal, and calcium carbonate as dust sprays. With the exception of calcium hydroxide during one period, all these applications produced during two 15-day periods an increase in the transpiration rate which varied from 8 to 15 per cent above that of the controls. In the case of potted potato plants, the effect of various sprays upon transpiration during two 5-day periods was as shown in the first table on page 467.

The lime-sulphur spray produced the least effect upon the transpiration rate. Lamp black added to Bordeaux mixture produced a higher

Spray used	Water transpired, cubic centimeters	
	May 6 to 11	May 11 to 15
Bordeaux mixture 4-6-50	5,266	4,633
Bordeaux mixture 2-3-50	6,424	5,740
Lime wash (60 g. CaO per liter)	5,845	6,136
Lime sulphur (1–25)	4,430	4,507
Bordeaux + lamp black	7,921	6,530
Lime wash + lamp black	5,966	5,856
Controls	4,138	4,333

rate of transpiration than the mixture alone. Martin (1916) at the New Jersey experiment station found that Bordeaux mixture (5-5-50) had a much more marked effect upon the rate of transpiration of abscised leaves than upon those of potted plants. Considering the ratio of $T:C$ before spraying as 1.00, the ratio of $T:C$ after spraying for abscised leaves was as follows:

Effect of Bordeaux Mixture upon the Rate of Transpiration of Abscised Leaves

Plant	Duration of experiment	$T:C$ after spraying
Ricinus communis	6 days	1.50
Datura meteloides	4 days	2.12
Phaseolus vulgaris	10 hr.	2.39
Beta cycla	10 hr.	1.57
Raphanus sativus	10 hr.	1.63
Hibiscus cardinalis	10 hr.	3.72

The average increase in transpiration due to this spray in these and other experiments was about 100 per cent over that of the standardization period. In the case of potted plants of cabbage, eggplant, pepper, and tomato, the increase in transpiration of the sprayed plants over that of the unsprayed plants was respectively 3, 11, 29, and 8 per cent. Martin also observed that a surface covering of dry powdered copper sulphate was less effective in the acceleration of transpiration than the film of Bordeaux mixture. Lutman (1916) found that the transpiration of potato plants was only slightly increased by spraying with Bordeaux mixture under the conditions of his experiments. The increase that he noted amounted to only 1 per cent, which is apparently insignificant. Shive and Martin (1917) determined the relative rate of transpiration of the sprayed and unsprayed leaves of tomato plants by means of the cobalt chloride method. They found that the rate of transpiration from the sprayed leaves was from 18 to 29 per cent higher than that of the unsprayed ones on the same plant.

Miller (1928) in a series of experiments during four growing seasons studied the effect on transpiration of Bordeaux mixture applied as a spray to tomato plants. The plants were grown in soil in large sealed containers under conditions of the field and were vegetatively normal and produced a normal crop of fruit. The data were collected during a period of 20 days when the plants were in full vegetative vigor. The method used was essentially that used by Duggar. The plants were arranged in pairs and the ratio of the transpiration rate of each pair was determined for a 10-day period. After this period one plant of each of the pairs was sprayed and their ratio obtained for another period of 10 days. The results for the 4 years are summarized in the following table:

EFFECT OF BORDEAUX MIXTURE UPON THE RATE OF TRANSPIRATION OF THE TOMATO PLANT

Year	Number of experiments performed	Spray used	Effect on transpiration, number		Transpiration of sprayed plants (unsprayed = 1)
			Increased	Decreased	
1924	6	4-8-50	4	2	0.990
1925	17	4-8-50	11	6	1.050
1926	47	4-8-50	20	27	0.994
1927	49	4-5-50	16	33	0.970

Miller thus was unable to obtain any of the striking results on transpiration from spraying as had been reported by other investigators. With the exception of Shive and Martin (1917), most of the experiments reported have been done under greenhouse conditions and under conditions, too, of relatively low transpiration as compared to the experiments at Manhattan, Kans. The results of Shive and Martin were obtained by the cobalt-paper method, while those of Miller were obtained by weighing. Whether the spray may in some way affect the reaction of the cobalt chloride paper is not known.

Anderson (1931) reported that the dusting of peanut plants with calcium sulphate influenced but little their rate of water loss. Childers (1935) found little or no alteration of the transpiration of tomato plants after spraying them with Bordeaux mixture. Cross (1927) found that butter fat and the emulsions of Wesson oil, of cotton oil, and of mineral oil reduced the rate of transpiration approximately 43 per cent. After spraying the twigs of the apple, peach, pear, plum, and sour cherry with saturated and unsaturated oils, Kelley (1930) noted the effects of the treatment upon the rate of transpiration. All the oils used retarded transpiration, this retardation ranging from 50 to 75 per cent. Spraying of the lower leaf surfaces retarded

INFLUENCE OF BORDEAUX MIXTURE ON THE TRANSPIRATION RATE OF VARIOUS PLANT SPECIES (WILSON AND RUNNELS, 1934)

Plant	Increase of transpiration due to application of 4-6-50 Bordeaux mixture		Portion of daily water loss that occurred during the night period (untreated plants), per cent
	Night period only (7 P.M. to 7 A.M.), per cent	24-hr. period, per cent	
Coleus	375	27	7
Bean	320	24	7
Tomato	250	24	8
Squash	186	29	11
Bean (lima)	183	19	7
Beet	171	9	4
Pepper	150	7	4
Castor bean	147	8	8
Chinese cabbage	141	32	17
Tobacco	136	12	6
Mustard	118	31	17
Muskmelon	114	16	14
Watermelon	100	23	17
Lettuce	82	16	19
Swiss chard	78	14	8
Cucumber	77	33	23
Parsnip	75	17	6
Chrysanthemum	75	13	10
Potato	67	11	11
Eggplant	64	15	5
Corn	60	12	6
Geranium	57	5	5
Cockscomb	56	6	5
Cauliflower	47	13	16
Carrot	43	18	13
Nasturtium	38	14	32
Onion	38	8	13
Sunflower	38	6	10
Cabbage	36	6	13
Hollyhock	35	10	11
Carnation	30	9	7
Spinach	28	11	22
Calendula	28	5	10
Soybean	27	10	18
Pea	25	20	8
Stock	25	−2	7
Snapdragon	18	6	20
Horseradish	17	8	24
Dill	11	5	17
Celery	8	3	37

transpiration, while spraying the upper leaf surfaces had no influence. The retarding effect of these sprays was noted within 30 min., and it continued for 3 days after their application.

Wilson and Runnels (1931 to 1935) studied extensively the action of sprays on the loss of water from plants. They applied 18 different spray solutions to *Coleus* and found that only a few of these caused an increase in the transpiration rate comparable to that caused by Bordeaux mixture. It was found that the sulphates of iron, nickel, and manganese, in combination with hydrated lime and water, caused nearly as great an increase in the rate of transpiration of *Coleus* as did Bordeaux mixture. They studied the effects of Bordeaux mixture upon 40 species of plants growing in the greenhouse. The most marked increases in transpiration due to this spray occurred from 7 P.M. to 7 A.M., and ranged from 8 to 375 per cent. For a 24-hr. period the increase ranged from −2 to 33 per cent. In the untreated plants the portion of the water loss which occurred during the night was 4 to 37 per cent. It appears, therefore, that this spray affects the cuticular rather than the stomatal transpiration, as shown in the table on page 469.

Tilford and May (1929) observed that the application of Bordeaux mixture and copper-lime dust to the leaves of potato lowered their temperature. A 4-4-50 Bordeaux mixture lowered the temperature of the leaves 1.45°C. below that of the controls, while a 4-6-50 mixture lowered their temperature 2.41°C. When the leaves were sprayed with a 4-4-50 Bordeaux mixture, plus lamp black, their temperature was 2.92°C. higher than that of the unsprayed ones. Rosen (1933) found in certain regions of Arkansas that spraying with Bordeaux mixture gave excellent control of tip burn of potato. He stated that around the sprayed plants there was in most instances a sudden drop in the air temperature ranging from 1.5 to 8.0°C.

6. Fungous Diseases.—Fungous diseases affect the rate of transpiration, in most cases, apparently in a manner that would be expected from the effect that the fungus has on the morphology of the host. In others the effect cannot be explained by any of the known reactions that the diseases have upon the plant. Müller-Thurgau (1894) seems to have been the first to note the effect of fungi upon the transpiration of the host. He noted by the use of hygrometric paper that, when pear leaves were infected with *Fusicladium pyrinum* (pear scab) and apple leaves with *Fusicladium dendriticum* (apple scab), the rate of transpiration was considerably increased, the transpiration of the diseased areas being higher than the healthy adjacent portions. Grape leaves infected with *Peronospora viticola* (downy mildew) showed a much lower rate of transpiration than the healthy leaves, and this was attributed to the fact that the conidiophores almost completely filled the stomata. Blodgett (1901) noted that leaves of *Rubus* which were infected heavily on the lower surface with *Gymnoconia interstitialis* transpired almost twice the amount of water as did the normal healthy leaves. Montemartini (1904) found in the case of 20 species of plants, each infected by a different fungus, that almost without exception the transpiration rate was higher for the diseased than for the healthy plants. Reed and Cooley (1913) by means of Freeman's method studied the effect of *Gymnosporangium* *juniperi-virginianae* upon the rate of transpiration of 8-year-old York Imperial and Ben Davis apple trees. The rate of transpiration per unit of surface of the diseased leaves was, in the majority of cases, less than that of the healthy ones. The average ratio of the transpirational loss of the diseased to the healthy leaves was 0.783 for the York Imperial and 0.742 for the Ben Davis. The ratios showed certain differences if they were grouped according to different stages in the development of the disease. The rate of transpiration was depressed to the greatest extent when the fungus had reached maturity and many of the cluster cups were open for the release of the aeciospores.

This fungus brings about certain changes in the morphology of the leaf which would apparently lower the transpiration rate. The apple leaves bearing the cluster cups are thicker by three or four times than the normal leaf. The large intercellular spaces in the spongy tissue disappear owing to the formation of columnar cells, while the stomata are scarce or lacking and the substomatal cavities are absent altogether.

Weaver (1916) made a study of the influence of the rusts of wheat, rye, oats, barley, corn, sunflower, cocklebur, and carnation upon the transpiration rate. In the case of wheat infected with *Puccinia graminis tritici*, the transpiration rate of the diseased plants was increased 30 per cent above that of the healthy plants. This difference in rate was produced by the fungus when the rust pustules amounted to only nine-tenths of 1 per cent of the leaf surface. A striking increase in transpiration was noticeable when the pustule area was increased by only two-tenths of 1 per cent. Rye infected with *Puccinia rubigo-vera secalis* showed the same increase in the rate of transpiration per unit of leaf area over that of the healthy plants as did wheat. Thus an increase of 20 per cent in the transpiration rate was noted when the pustules represented only 3.8 per cent of the leaf surface.

In oats infected with *Puccinia graminis avenae*, in which the pustules equalled only 0.5 per cent of the leaf surface, a transpiration rate 37 per cent higher than that of the healthy leaves was obtained. Corn, sunflower, and carnation plants infected with rust behaved in a similar manner to the cereals that have just been discussed. Cocklebur plants that were inoculated with *Puccinia xanthii*, however, showed a transpiration rate which was only 50 to 60 per cent that of the healthy plants. This behavior of the cocklebur seems to be due to a change in the tissue of the leaves similar to that which occurs in the apple leaf when infected with *Gymnosporangium juniperi-virginianae*.

In the case of the rusts of the cereals, the increase in the transpiration rate occurs about the time that the pustules break through the epidermis. After the pustules are for the most part broken out, no increase in the transpiration rate is apparent. The cause of this increased transpiration rate is not known. Dufrenoy (1918) considered that a number of fungi accelerate transpiration owing to localized necrosis, rupture of the epidermis, or changes in the permeability of the cells.

In the case of the cereal rusts, however, Weaver considered that the cause of the accelerated transpiration is not wholly due to the torn epidermis. The whitish areas around the pustules indicate that some striking change has occurred in the cells composing these regions. The mesophyll cells that are penetrated by the haustoria certainly do not function normally. It is conceivable, as was suggested by Weaver, that the fungi may excrete into these cells substances which may cause a change in the permeability of the protoplasmic membrane that accelerates water loss. Weiss (1924) considered that the infection of wheat by either leaf or stem rust resulted in a lowered water economy of the host, as indicated by the higher water requirement of the rust-infected plants as compared to the healthy ones.

Kourssanow (1928) found that the loss of water from wheat plants infected by *Ustilago tritici* was slightly higher than that from uninfected ones. Nicolas (1930) studied 10 different species of plants parasitized by as many different types of fungi, and found that with but few exceptions the infected plants showed increased transpiration rates. The ratio of transpiration of the infected to that of the healthy plants varied from 1.01:1.0 to as high as 2.1:1.0. It was observed by Graf-Marin (1934) that barley plants infected with *Erysiphe graminis* transpired 67 per cent more water than did healthy plants. The proportion of water transpired at night was greater for mildewed plants than for healthy ones. This increased transpiration of the infected plants could not be attributed to the rupture of the cuticle or to an increased number of stomata. He considered that the increase of transpiration was due to an increase in the opening of the stomata and to the loss of water from the aerial mycelium of the fungus.

D. Temperature of the Leaves

It is commonly stated that transpiration is beneficial to plants because it cools the leaves and thus prevents their temperature from becoming so high in bright sunlight as to cause their death or at least to hinder their normal activities. The temperature of a leaf, however, depends upon numerous and varied factors, so that in order to understand the influence of transpiration upon it, a general discussion of the subject is necessary. The most important factors that influence the temperature of leaves are the temperature of the air, the supply of available moisture in the soil, the evaporating power of the air, currents of air, the thermal emissivity of the leaf, the intensity of light, and the angle at which it is incident to the leaf surface. Under identical conditions the temperature of one kind of leaf is different from that of another kind, while different regions of the same leaf have different temperatures. Any data, therefore, that are presented upon this subject must be regarded as relative only to the various conditions that prevailed when the temperature determinations were made.

1. Methods of Measuring.—The earlier determinations of leaf temperatures were made by pressing the thermometer against the leaves or by wrapping the leaves about the thermometer. This method is still used when only approximate results are desired. It is not accurate, however, due primarily to the relatively slow response of the ordinary thermometers to changes in temperature and to the inability to get a proper contact of leaf and thermometer with the leaf in its normal position.

More accurate determinations of leaf temperatures are now made by means of thermocouples, with which it is possible to measure not only accurately but very quickly either the internal or the surface temperature of the leaf. The thermocouple method has been used by Blackman and Matthaei (1905), Ehlers (1915), and Clum (1926) for measuring the internal temperature of leaves and by Shreve (1919), Miller and Saunders (1923), Eaton and Belden (1929), and Curtis (1936) for measuring the surface temperature.

In the determination of leaf temperatures by means of the thermocouple method, the general procedure of each investigator has been very similar, although the methods have varied somewhat in detail. The method used by Miller and Saunders (1923)—a modification of that used by Shreve (1919)—for determining the surface temperature of leaves will serve as an illustration of the general procedure for the determination of plant temperatures by the thermocouple method. A diagram of the apparatus used is shown in Fig. 18. It consists of two thermo junctions *TC* and *T′C′* approximately 5 mm. in length, which are formed by braiding two wires and then uniting them by an acid-free solder. The wires generally used are No. 36 copper and No. 36 constantan with insulated connecting lengths *A*, *B*, and *B′* totaling approximately 3 ft. One of the thermocouples *T′C′* is placed with a thermometer graduated to 0.1°C. in a stoppered Dewar flask surrounded by any suitable insulating material as glass wool (GW), and water, in any convenient container. The air in the flask remains practically constant, since under the most severe conditions it does not fluctuate more than 0.1°C. during a 15- to 20-min. period. The other thermo junction *TC* is attached to a clamp *C* in such a way that it can be conveniently placed upon the surface of the leaf. This clamp may consist of a pair of crucible tongs 44 cm. in length, modified by filing their distal ends to narrow dimensions. One of these filed ends is inserted in a small wedge shaped piece of cork *CK*, the edge of which measures 1 by 5 mm. and holds the thermocouple *TC*. On the other tip of the tongs is inserted a small cube of cork *CK* 5 by 5 mm. which serves as a support to the leaf when the thermocouple is placed upon it. By means of a clamp of this kind, the thermo junction can easily be placed as desired in direct contact with either the upper or the lower surface of the leaf and the temperature determined. Similarly, the temperature of the air can readily be determined by holding the open clamp in the air and taking precautions to shield the thermo junction from the direct rays of the sun. A galvanometer *G* and a damping switch *K* are placed in the circuit. Since the temperature of the thermo junction *T′C′* is known and can be kept approximately constant, the difference in temperature *T′C′* and *TC* can be calculated from the swing of the galvanometer, which has previously been calibrated. By such an instrument a difference in temperature of 0.1°C. can be accurately detected. This apparatus when in use in the field with leaves that are some distance above ground is placed upon a small table, which is shaded by a piece of heavy canvas placed about 2 ft. above its surface. When vines and low plants are being investigated, the apparatus is placed on a low box and shaded with an umbrella.

Curtis (1936) threaded the thermocouple wires through the leaf so that the thermocouple junctions as well as that part of the wires back to the insulation would touch the leaf surface. He found this method far superior to the one used by Miller and Saunders (1923) and Eaton and Belden (1929). The electrical equipment used by him consisted of a Leeds and Northrup Type K-2 potentiometer, a portable galvanom-

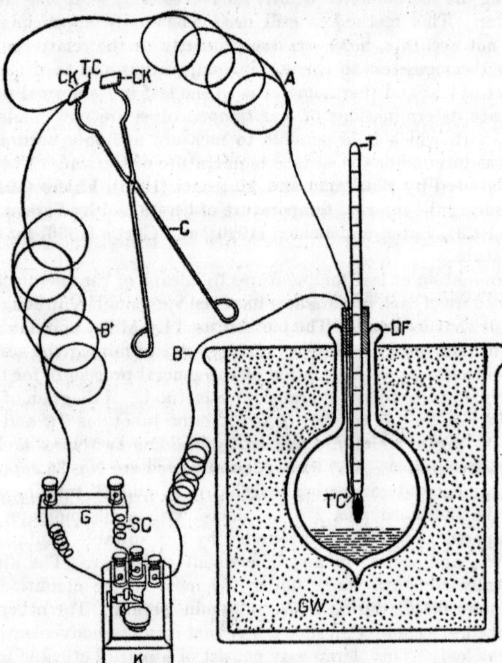

Fig. 18.—Apparatus used in measuring the surface temperature of the leaf by the thermocouple method. Description in the text.

eter, a standard cell, and two, ordinary 1.5-volt dry cells. These were all mounted in a shallow box that could be carried to the field. With such an outfit, temperatures could be read to approximately 0.05°C. Curtis considered that the method used by Miller and Saunders (1923) in measuring the temperature of the air gives readings that are too high. He found that the temperature of the air as measured by their method was 2 to 3°C. warmer than if the thermocouple was held in the shade at a distance of 1 to 2 cm. from the shading object.

2. Temperature. *a. Fluctuations in Temperature of the Air.*—In direct sunlight, when the temperature is relatively high and the air is in motion, the temperature of a leaf and the surrounding air is not constant but shows sudden and marked fluctuations even during so brief a period as a few seconds. These changes in temperature, which vary from a small fraction of a degree to as much as 4°C., are easily detected by the galvanometer through the thermo junctions but are of such short duration that as a rule they are not visibly recorded by a mercury-bulb thermometer, even when it is graduated to tenths of a degree. These rapid fluctuations in the temperature of the air are due, in all probability, to the fact that the air is not uniformly heated throughout but contains warmer or cooler pockets that suddenly replace the air surrounding the measuring instruments. The leaves of most crop plants respond very quickly to these changes in air temperature, since even a very slight increase or decrease in the temperature of the air is almost immediately followed by a corresponding change in the temperature of the leaves. When the air is still and when the temperature is relatively low, the fluctuations in the temperature are so few and so slight that they are seldom detected by the galvanometer. Curtis (1936) reported that leaves frequently change in temperature as much as 2.5°C. within a period of 10 to 15 sec. The rapid fluctuations of the temperature of the leaf and the surrounding air emphasize the necessity not only of having a rapid means of determining temperatures but also of making a large number of observations in order to obtain the relative temperature relations of a leaf and its surroundings. The thermocouple method for measuring temperatures is relatively rapid. The swing of the galvanometer for a temperature determination can be read in 2 or 3 sec. The time, however, that elapses during the recording of the deflection and the return of the galvanometer to equilibrium amounts to approximately 10 to 12 sec., so that an interval of about 15 sec. occurs between any two consecutive observations. Shull (1936), however, noted that it required from 1 to 2 min. for the leaves of *Pelargonium*, *Begonia*, and *Caladium* to reach thermal equilibrium after being transferred from diffuse light to direct illumination.

b. Temperature of Normal Turgid Leaves.—Miller and Saunders (1923) made numerous determinations of the temperature of the upper surface of the leaves of corn, sorghum, cowpeas, soybeans, watermelon, pumpkin, and alfalfa growing under field conditions in Kansas. The average of 1,000 determinations of the temperature of the air and of the upper surface of the turgid leaves of corn in direct sunlight between the hours of 9 A.M. and 4 P.M. and under a wide range of atmospheric conditions was 30.58°C. for the air and 30.64°C. for the leaves. The average of the same number of determinations made with the leaves of five varieties of sorghums under conditions of exposure similar to those of the corn leaves showed that the temperature of the leaves was 30.64°C., while the average of an equal number of determinations of the air temperature during the same period was 30.66°C. Five hundred observations on soybeans gave an average temperature of the air of 33.13°C. and an average of 33.66°C. for the temperature of the upper surface of the leaves. A similar number of determinations on the leaves of cowpeas showed an average temperature of 34.4°C., while the temperature of the air averaged 34.2°C. during the observations. These observations show that the temperature of the turgid leaves of corn, sorghum, pumpkin, watermelon, and soybean in direct sunlight under the general climatic conditions which prevail in Kansas fluctuates slightly above and below air temperatures but that their average temperature is essentially the same as that of the surrounding air. The temperature of the leaves of alfalfa under the same conditions as the plants above mentioned consistently showed less than 1°C. below that of the surrounding air. In the case of corn, sorghum, watermelon, pumpkin, soybean, and cowpeas, the heat absorbed by the leaves from the sun is quickly utilized in transpiration or rapidly disseminated into the surrounding air, so that the temperature of the leaves is always approximately that of the air. In the case of alfalfa the rate of transpiration is evidently rapid enough to reduce the temperature of the leaf slightly below that of the air. Eaton (1930) reported for cotton that the young leaves were cooler than the old ones. Thus the temperature of leaves 82 days old was 2.3°C. below that of the air, while those 20 to 26 days old had a temperature 4.1°C. below that of the atmosphere. Copeland (1932) reported from observations on chaparral in the Sierra Nevada that, in a breeze, leaves transpiring in the sun sometimes cooled below the shade temperature of the air. It was reported by Ezekiel and Taubenhaus (1932) that the leaves of cotton plants that had wilted from *Phymatotrichum* root rot were as much as 6.5°F. warmer than air, while the leaves of the control plants were usually cooler than the air.

However, Curtis (1936) in extensive experiments could find no case where the temperature of leaves in direct sunlight was below that of the surrounding air. He attributed the results obtained in this regard by Miller and Saunders (1923) to the fact that their method gave too high a reading for the temperature of the air.

The internal temperature of the leaves of *Fuchsia speciosa*, *Phaseolus vulgaris*, *Brassica oleracea*, and *Syringa vulgaris* was determined by Clum (1926) by means of thermocouples. The plants were in the direct sunlight in the open or in the greenhouse at Ithaca, N. Y. He found that the temperature of the leaves with which he worked was nearly always higher than the air during the day and that in direct sunlight it was 5 to 10°C. higher. The maximum difference observed between leaf and air temperature in the open was 13°C. and in the greenhouse, 16°C.

The type of leaf has an important bearing on its temperature in relation to the surrounding air. It seems reasonable to suppose that a thick, fleshy leaf will absorb and retain more heat than a thin one. This supposition is borne out generally in experimental observations. Thus Askenasy (1875) and Ursprung (1903) by placing thermometers in close contact with the surface of the fleshy leaves of *Sempervivum* found that the leaves attained a temperature in the sunlight of 18 to 25°C. above that of the surrounding air. Askenasy attributed the high temperature of these leaves primarily to the fact that the heat which they absorbed was not readily dissipated by air currents or radiation. As mentioned above, Clum (1926) obtained temperatures of leaves that were 5 to 10°C. higher than that of the surrounding air. The type of leaves with which he worked had, in general, a much greater mass in proportion to the surface exposed than did the leaves investigated by Miller and Saunders (1923), which in no case had temperatures appreciably different from that of the surrounding air. An example of the relation between the compactness and general mass of a plant organ and its temperature in relation to that of the air is afforded by the work of Brooks and Fisher (1926) with the apple. They found that the side of an apple exposed to the sun may have a temperature from 12 to 25°C. higher than the air temperature and from 10 to 16°C. higher than the shaded side of the same apple. In the case of the thin sunflower leaves, Brown and Escombe (1905) calculated their temperature to be only approximately 2° above or below that of the air.

Grainger and Allen (1936) by means of the thermocouple method found that apple buds were warmer than the air by day and usually cooler by night. When the buds were screened from the radiation of the sun, their temperature was cooler than that of the air by day as well as by night. The buds of black currants and raspberries were usually cooler than the air. The experiments that have just been discussed were conducted under summer conditions, but it is interesting to note that Ehlers (1915) found that evergreen conifer leaves under winter conditions maintain internal temperatures from 2 to 10°C. higher than that of the surrounding air.

In considering the temperature of a leaf, the air currents must be taken into consideration. A leaf in direct sunshine freely exposed to a breeze always has a lower temperature than one under like conditions of sunlight but in such a position as to be protected from air currents. Smith (1909) observed that breezes reduce the temperature of leaves in sunlight by amounts varying from 2 to 10°C. and that a thin leaf is much more noticeably affected than a thick one. Similar observations were also made by Miller and Saunders (1923) and by Ehlers (1915).

Miller and Saunders observed for the plants with which they worked that in diffuse light the temperature of attached turgid leaves is always consistently lower than the temperature of the surrounding air. The average temperature differences between the turgid leaves and the surrounding air under conditions of diffuse light varied from 0.1 to 3°C. In direct sunlight the temperature of a turgid leaf may be above the air temperature, but as soon as a cloud obscures the sun the temperature of the leaf almost immediately drops below the temperature of the air and remains there until the leaf is again exposed to direct sunlight (see the following table):

THE TEMPERATURE CHANGES OF THE AIR AND OF THE TURGID LEAVES OF SOYBEAN PLANTS IN DIRECT SUNSHINE AND IN DIFFUSE LIGHT CAUSED BY A HEAVY CLOUD OBSCURING THE SUN

Time, p.m.	Temperature, degrees centigrade, of	
	Air	Turgid leaf
In direct sunlight		
1:10	32.0	34.0
1:11	32.1	33.9
1:12	32.7	33.3
1:13	30.7	30.7
1:14	31.0	32.3
1:15	31.3	31.8
1:16	32.8	32.6
1:18	32.0	34.2
In diffuse light due to cloud passing over sun		
1:19	30.0	26.3
1:20	28.0	26.3
1:21	27.7	26.0
1:22	26.7	25.3
1:23	26.3	25.3
1:24	26.8	25.3
1:25	26.3	25.1
1:26	25.9	25.0

During the night the temperature of the leaves falls to the same level as that of the surrounding air or slightly below it.

c. Rate of Transpiration and the Temperature of the Leaf.—It has long been known that a wilted leaf has a higher temperature than a turgid one under the same conditions, but the actual differences in temperature and the correlation of the transpiration rate with this temperature difference have been but little studied. Darwin (1898) in the observation of withered detached leaves and normal attached leaves of *Tropaeolum majus* found in intermittent sunshine and relatively low humidity that the temperature of the withered leaves was from 1.2 to 3.9°C. higher than that of the attached leaf. Kiesselbach (1916) by inserting the bulb of a thermometer momentarily in the folds of corn leaves found that a transpiring leaf was uniformly cooler than a dry dead one, the difference in temperature amounting in one case to as much as 8.5°F. in direct sunshine and to 4.2°F. in the shade. Using a similar method, Loftfield (1921) made a few observations on the temperature of the leaves of alfalfa, potato, and sugar beet in relation to stomatal behavior. He found that usually the temperature of the leaves with stomata open was lower than that of the air, while the temperature of the leaves with closed stomata was higher than that of the air.

Rather extensive experiments in relation to transpiration and leaf temperature were conducted by Miller and Saunders (1923) and by Clum (1926). The former investigators measured the surface temperature of the leaves and the latter their internal temperature by means of the thermocouple method. The transpiration temperature experiments of Miller and Saunders were conducted with turgid and wilted plants of three varieties of corn, three varieties of sorghums, and one each of cowpeas and soybeans. The plants designated as turgid were those which showed no visible signs of wilting during the experiments. The soil in the containers in which the plants were growing was kept at a moisture content sufficient for good tilth by the frequent addition of water to replace that lost from the plants. In order to obtain wilted plants, certain containers were set aside to which no water was added to replace that lost by transpiration, and the plants were considered sufficiently wilted for the experiment when they did not regain their turgid condition during the night. The water content of the soil in which the wilted plants were rooted averaged about 2 per cent above the wilting coefficient. The rate of transpiration was determined at intervals of 2 hr., and the temperature determinations were made at times intermediate between these periods.

A typical response of the turgid and wilted leaves of plants in regard to temperature and the rate of transpiration is shown by the graphs in Fig. 19, representing the data obtained with corn leaves in direct sunlight. The data obtained from several thousand observations on corn, sorghum, soybeans, and cowpeas showed that the temperature of a wilted leaf in direct sunlight is always higher than the temperature of a turgid leaf exposed to the same conditions. The average temperature of the wilted leaves of corn, sorghum, soybeans, and cowpeas during the hours of 9 A.M. to 4 P.M. was respectively 1.85, 1.55, 2.8, and 4.6°C. higher than that of the turgid leaves. The maximum temperature difference observed between the turgid and wilted leaves of corn in direct sunlight was 4.3°C. when the temperature of the air was 32.3°C., and the transpiration rate of the turgid leaves was approximately five times that from the wilted leaves. The maximum temperature difference between the wilted and turgid leaves of cowpeas was 6.7°C. when the temperature of the air was 37.6°C., and the transpiration of the wilted leaves was approximately only one-sixteenth that of the turgid plants.

The observations of Miller and Saunders agree, in general, with the results obtained by Clum (1926) with *Fuchsia speciosa*, *Phaseolus vulgaris*, *Brassica oleracea*, and *Syringa vulgaris*. He reduced transpiration by allowing the soil to dry and in some cases by vaselining the surface of the leaves. In general, the vaselined leaves and the leaves of the plants in the dry soil were 2 to 4°C. warmer than the controls. In no case, however,

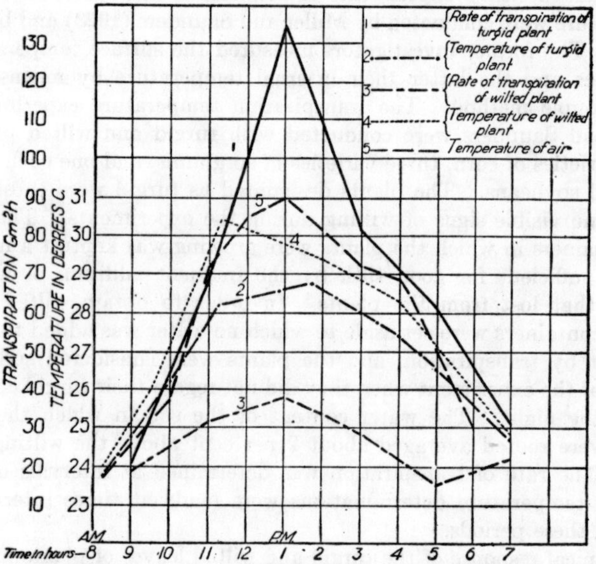

Fig. 19.—Graphs showing the transpiration rate of turgid and wilted corn plants and temperature of the leaves of these plants at different periods of the day.

did he find a definite correlation between the transpiration rate and the difference between the leaf and air temperatures or between differences in the transpiration rates of two leaves or plants and differences in their temperatures.

It was reported by Copeland (1932) that the transpiration of the chaparral in the Sierra Nevada cooled the leaves as much as 10°C., and he considered that a greater cooling effect would be recorded if more appropriate technique could be used.

Watson (1933) and Curtis (1936) considered that there are numerous factors other than transpiration which prevent the excessive heating of foliage leaves. The leaf may dissipate the absorbed energy by thermal emission, by conduction to internal tissues of a lower temperature, and by photochemical reactions. Curtis stated that the angle of exposure to incident radiation will greatly affect the absorption of radiant energy. Even when the light inception is normal to the leaf, 25 per cent of it may be reflected. When the leaf temperatures exceed that of the atmosphere, there may be considerable loss by conduction. There is also radiation to cooler objects near or far, and, when the sky is clear, to space, or to cold gases, especially carbon dioxide and water. Thus plant temperatures may be greatly influenced by water in the atmosphere, either as clouds or vapor, at a great distance from the plant, because of the influence of this water on the receipt or loss of infrared radiation. This effect may be totally independent of the effect on loss of water vapor close to the leaf and independent of the effects of clouds on the passage of visible radiation to the plant. The relative importance of these different methods of dissipating heat varies greatly with the environment of the plant as well as the conditions within the leaf, and its surface. Watson (1934) calculated the relative amounts of heat dissipated by thermal emission and transpiration for varying rates of transpiration and for varying temperature differences between the leaf and the air. The evidence thus obtained indicated that neither transpiration nor thermal emission can be called the more important factor.

d. The Thermal Death Point.—It has been observed by numerous investigators that the thermal death point of most plant cells lies between 45 and 55°C., although in extreme cases it may range between 62 and 105°C. for certain types of tissues (MacDougal, 1922; and Hopkins, 1936). In many cases at least, the fatal temperature must be prolonged some little time before death ensues. It has been shown that transpiration lowers the temperature of leaves even under severe conditions only to the extent of 2 to 5°C. with an average difference somewhat less than 3°C. This difference in temperature is not striking, and it would seem doubtful whether the increased temperature of the wilted leaves could to any marked degree injure the protoplasm or even retard its vital activities. Even if a leaf became heated to a critical temperature, the lowering of it from 2 to 3°C. by transpiration would not greatly prolong life. The temperature of a leaf does not long remain constant, due to rapid radiation, convection, and air currents, so that these factors may be more effective in protecting the leaves from overheating than is transpiration. The cause of the death of leaves under severe climatic conditions would thus seem to be due to the dehydration of the protoplasm rather than to a critical temperature induced by the lowering of the transpiration rate.

E. Evaporation

Since the days of Unger (1861), who regarded transpiration as a physical process modified by the nature or peculiarities of the plant, transpiration has frequently been defined as the evaporation of water from the plant altered to some extent by its structure and functions (see also Woods, 1893). Because of the similarity of evaporation and transpiration and because of the aim apparently to show that transpiration is a relatively simple physical process, the rate of evaporation has been frequently used as a standard to which transpiration is compared or referred. The rate of water loss from plant surfaces exposed to the air is always lower than the rate of evaporation from an equal area of water surface under the same environmental conditions (Livingston, 1906, 1913). Briggs and Shantz (1916) noted that the loss of water from wheat, oats, barley, sorghum, and alfalfa during a 10-day period of maximal transpiration at Akron, Colo., amounted to only 5 to 14 per cent of the loss during the same period from a free water surface. McLean (1919), however, stated that transpiration in the tropical rain forests was in his observations four-fifths of that from a free water surface. It is evident from these facts that certain internal factors exert a retarding influence upon the evaporation of water contained in the plant. This retardation or resistance to the evaporation of water will vary with the kind of plant, its age, the portion of the plant considered, and the changes of internal conditions.

Evaporation and transpiration are both determined largely by the same factors—solar radiation, temperature, saturation deficit, and wind—so that if transpiration is a purely physical process, then a high correlation between it and evaporation is to be expected. Briggs and Shantz (1916) found in comparing the rate of evaporation from a small shallow tank with the transpiration rate from wheat, oats, rye, alfalfa, and *Amaranthus* that the correlation coefficient ranged from 0.84 to 0.95. In the case of the highest correlation it would thus appear that nine-tenths of the transpiration was determined by the same factors that determine evaporation. They noted that the transpiration graph of these plants showed a tendency to rise somewhat earlier than the graph of evaporation from the small tank and to fall off somewhat later in the afternoon. Owing, however, to the greater slope of the transpiration graph in the late afternoon, they both reach the night level at the same time. These authors considered that the relation of transpiration to evaporation should be considered associative, both responding to the same environmental factors but not in the same way or to the same degree. The extent of this association, however, depends upon the manner in which evaporation is measured, so that a consideration of that subject is next in order.

1. Measurement. *a. Value of Data.*—A knowledge of evaporation in considering the water relations of plants is of importance in several ways. In the first place, the rate of evaporation from a free water surface or from a moist porous surface is considered the best single valued expression of the intensity of the weather factors influencing transpiration (Briggs and Shantz, 1917). Evaporation thus serves as a simple means of expressing the aerial conditions under which experimental work is performed. A study of the evaporating power of the environment prevailing in a given section during the growing season furnishes an approximate measure of the transpiration loss that would occur in that region. The intensity of evaporation thus gives a standard by which it is possible to correlate some of the general facts of plant distribution and to predict whether certain plants are adapted to the atmospheric conditions prevailing in the region under consideration. The rate of evaporation thus may be an indicator of the vegetative possibilities of a given region (Livingston, 1907, 1911).

b. Instruments for Measuring Evaporation.—Any instrument that is used for the measurement of evaporation is termed an "atmometer" or "evaporimeter." Numerous types of atmometers have been used, and one of the main handicaps in evaporation studies so far has been to obtain a standard instrument. It should be kept in mind that the water surface from which evaporation proceeds is as truly a control of the rate of water loss as are the atmospheric conditions. The loss of water from one instrument is thus different from the loss from another under the same conditions, and furthermore the evaporation from one instrument cannot be reduced to that of another. Thus suppose that under one set of conditions an instrument *A* loses twice the water per hour as an instrument *B*. If the environmental conditions are changed, this relation between the two rates of loss does not hold, and the instrument *A* does not lose twice the amount of water as does *B*. Hence the readings from any evaporating instrument cannot be reduced to the losses from another instrument of unlike form. It is of course impossible to produce two instruments that are exactly alike, but if their form and volume are approximately the same, they may be very accurately standardized, as will later be mentioned. The exposure of two instruments must be the same if the readings are to be at all comparable. If one of the two instruments that are alike in all details is placed 1 ft. from the level of the ground and the other 2 ft. from the ground, the evaporating rates will be different. The exposures thus need to be specific as well as the kind of instruments if the rates of evaporation are to be comparable (Livingston, 1915, 1917). These facts in regard to evaporation have in many cases been little appreciated or considered by those who have studied evaporation, so that the data are very confusing.

1. *Atmometers with a Free Water Surface.*—The two instruments of this type that have been the most extensively used have been designated the large tank and the small tank. The large open tank has been used extensively by the U. S. Department of Agriculture Office of Dry Land Agriculture. It is circular in form, made of galvanized iron, and is about 6 ft. in diameter and 2 ft. in depth, being sunk into the ground so that its surface and that of the ground are on approximately the same level. The loss in evaporation is measured in terms of depth by means of a vernier arrangement attached to the side of the tank, but a self-recording apparatus may also be attached. There are many objections to this means of measuring evaporation. The wind not only increases the surface exposed by waves or ripples but may frequently remove water by whipping it over the sides. There is no means of keeping the depth of the water constant, so that the evaporation alters the nature of the instrument. The removal of water by birds, insects, and toads and the addition of water by

rains and its loss by splashing also tend to make the data thus obtained less exact. Accurate readings for short periods have never been possible with the large tank, so that for hourly comparisons of evaporation with transpiration it is of little or no value. For a comparison of transpiration and evaporation for the entire growing season, however, it has proved very satisfactory (Briggs and Shantz, 1916).

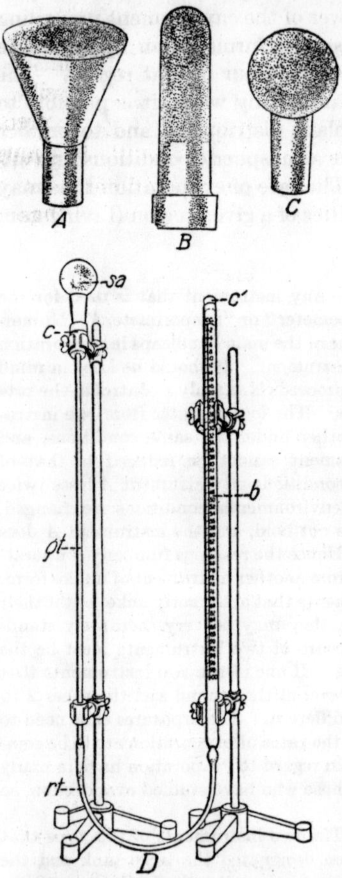

FIG. 20.—*A*, Bellani plate type of atmometer. *B*, cylindrical porous cup atmometer. *C*, spherical porous cup atmometer. *D*, apparatus for measuring the evaporation from an atmometer: *sa*, spherical porous cup atmometer; *c*, perforated rubber stopper; *c'*, notched cork; *b*, burette; *rt*, rubber tubing; *gt*, glass tubing.

The small tank type of atmometer was devised and perfected by Briggs and Shantz (1916, 1917) and consists of a shallow copper tank 91 cm. in diameter and 2.5 cm. high and blackened on the inside. It is supported on a wooden disk 4 cm. in thickness and mounted about 1 m. above the ground on an automatic scale sufficiently sensitive to record the loss of a layer of water 10μ in thickness. The depth of the water is automatically maintained at about 1 cm. by means of a mariotte apparatus mounted on the scale platform. This instrument is automatic, accurate, and has few of the disadvantages of the large tank. It is the best yet devised for determining the loss of evaporation from a free water surface.

Stark and Whitfield (1930) described an evaporimeter that maintains a constant water level in the evaporating pan by utilizing the principle of the mariotte flask. A rain overflow is provided, which permits any increase of water in the evaporation pan to escape automatically and to be measured in a standard rain gauge. Gates and Black (1931) found the dragoyle a child's toy, very useful to measure ecological conditions.

2. *Atmometers with a Moist Porous Surface.* The most widely used porous surfaces for evaporation studies are those of porous clay, although filter and blotting papers have sometimes been used. The first known porous-clay atmometer was the Bellani porous plate devised by Bellani in 1820 (Fig. 20*A*). It consists of a horizontal porous-clay disk forming the top of a container completely filled with water so that the lower surface of the disk is in contact with the liquid while the upper surface is exposed to the air. The porous-clay cup is now the most universally used of any of the porous-surface evaporimeters. This instrument was independently devised three times, first by Babinet (1848), then by Mitscherlich (1904), and finally by Livingston (1906, 1910). These atmometers as now used are hollow cylinders or spheres of unglazed porcelain and have a capacity of about 50 cc. They are pro-

vided with a neck or collar which is either glazed or shellacked and are so arranged that they may be connected with a water supply by means of a rubber cork carrying a glass tube (Fig. 20*B* and *C*). The porous-surface atmometers are filled with water and the porous unglazed portions of the walls absorb water by capillarity or by imbibition, so that a moist porous surface is exposed to the air. These atmometers may be connected with a relatively large container whose supply of water need not be replenished for a number of days or weeks, the evaporation being determined by noting the amount of water necessary to fill the reservoir to its original level. The porous atmometers may be connected with a burette as shown in Fig. 20*D* when accurate readings are required at brief intervals of a few minutes to several hours. The porous cup atmometers present to the action of the air a water surface that is held in position by surface tension, adhesion, and the rigidity of the material that composes the instrument. The form of the surface is thus not disturbed by wind, insects, or splashing, as is so frequently the case with free water surfaces. The intake of water by rains can be almost prevented by various rain-excluding attachments that have been described by Livingston (1910), Livingston and Thone (1920), Shive (1915), Johnston (1918), Nichols (1923), and Wilson (1930).

Sayre (1928) describes a recording atmometer. The porous-clay cup atmometers generally used are white in color, but in order to obtain responses to the atmospheric complex that more nearly correspond with those of the plant or to study the effect of solar radiation on water loss, atmometers of darker colors have been employed. These are either made from colored clay or are painted with lampblack (Livingston, 1911, 1923, 1926).

Stanley (1932) described a method of making permanently black atmometer bulbs from white ones by dipping them into a 3*N* solution of silver nitrate. Bates (1919) devised an atmometer with an impervious upper surface and a perforated lower surface, between which surfaces a porous moist material was placed. He found that this type of an instrument followed very closely the transpiration losses from small conifers.

Wilson and Welton (1935) stated that a Livingston black atmometer could be used as an indicator for the proper time to water lawn grasses. The application of 1 in. of water, as soon as the atmometer had lost 320 cc. of water without a rain of ½ in. or more intervening, produced the best and most uniform growth of grass.

Before setting up a porous-clay cup atmometer it should be soaked in water for several hours at least, so as to replace the air in the interstices with water. The atmometer and connecting tubes must be filled with water and connected with the water supply in such a manner that no air bubbles enter the apparatus. If any bubbles enter they will collect at the top of the cup on the inside and thus hinder evaporation from that portion of its surface. The cup must always be placed higher than the water level in the reservoir, otherwise water will be forced out of the atmometer by hydrostatic pressure. It has been found, however, that the cup may be placed several feet above the level of the water in the burette or reservoir without perceptibly influencing the rate of water loss.

Similar forms of porous-clay cup atmometers may be standardized by operating them along with a cup that has been checked to a given standard. The atmometers are mounted upon a rotating table so that they will all be similarly exposed (Nichols, 1913). The evaporation is determined for a given period of time and the reading of the standardized cup is then divided by the reading from the cup that is to be standardized to determine the coefficient of correction. The calculation of this coefficient K may be stated algebraically as follows (Livingston, 1918): $K = CR/r$ where R is the reading of the standardized cup that is being used and C is its coefficient of correction, while r is the reading of the instrument that is being standardized. K is thus the coefficient by which the reading from the instrument under consideration must be multiplied to reduce it to the loss of the standard cup with a coefficient of unity. The readings from similar atmometers can thus all be reduced to the same basis, and the atmospheric conditions under which the observations are made can thus be more correctly interpreted than if no such reduction could be made.

Thomas and Ferguson (1917) considered that an attempt should be made to realize a standard which should be invariable under given conditions and capable of replacement at any place or time. They concluded from rather elaborate experiments that the free water surface contained in a cylindrical vessel and protected by a rim 3 cm. in depth fulfills these conditions, although many factors must yet be considered before definite statements in this regard can be made.

2. The Ratio of Transpiration to Evaporation.—The term "absolute transpiration" is used to denote the observed rate of water loss from the plant. In a general way, the curve of absolute transpiration usually follows very closely the curve of evaporation and may give no indication of any retardation or acceleration of transpiration that is due to causes other than the evaporating power of the surrounding air.

The ratio of the rate of transpiration to evaporation was termed by Livingston (1906, 1907) "relative transpiration" and by Briggs and Shantz (1916), the "transpiration coefficient." It has also been called the "transpiring power" of the plant, a term used to denote the reciprocal of the resistance or acceleration manifested by plants to water loss by transpiration as compared to evaporation from an atmometer. It represents the group of internal conditions influencing the transpiration rate. If the plant and an atmometer responded alike to changes in the environment, the rate of relative transpiration would give a straight line when plotted hour by hour.

The graph of relative transpiration, however, is periodic in form and exhibits a marked minimum during the night hours. This fluctuation in the rate of transpiration has been interpreted by Livingston (1906, 1913), Shreve (1914, 1916), Livingston and Hawkins (1915), Burns (1915), Trelease (1922), and others to represent departures in the transpiration rate of the plant from that which would prevail if the plant responded freely to its environment. When considered in this light the curve of relative transpiration should thus indicate the magnitude of the physiological retardation or acceleration of the transpiration rate due to closure of the stomata or to reversible changes taking place within the plant. In making this interpretation, it is assumed that an evaporimeter responds freely to its environment and that the rate of evaporation from it affords a perfect summation of the environmental condition determining evaporation from the plant. It should be kept in mind, however, that all atmometers do not respond to their environment in the same manner, so that the particular atmometer used should make a great difference in determining relative transpiration. Its value, therefore, may not be so definite an indicator of internal changes in the plant as was formerly supposed.

Briggs and Shantz (1917) compared the hourly transpiration rate of alfalfa with the hourly evaporation rate from various types of atmometers. The comparison rate was made by superimposing the hourly transpiration graph on each of the hourly evaporation graphs, choosing the scale of ordinates of the transpiration graph so that the total area under the transpiration graph was equal to the total area under the evaporation graph. The average hourly departure of each of the evaporation graphs from the superimposed transpiration graph was expressed in percentage of the mean hourly evaporation for the day. The summation of the data obtained is shown in the following table:

AVERAGE-HOURLY DEPARTURE OF EVAPORATION RATE FROM TRANSPIRATION RATE FOR ALFALFA, PERCENTAGE OF THE MEAN EVAPORATION RATE FOR VARIOUS TYPES OF ATMOMETERS

Type of atmometer	Day periods, 6 a.m. to 6 p.m., per cent	24-hr. period, per cent
White cylinder	38	49
Brown cylinder	29	41
White sphere	31	43
Bellani plate	30	41
Filter-paper atmometer	22	31
Shallow tank	12	17
Large deep tank	93	39

Since the greater part of the transpiration and evaporation occurs during the daylight hours, calculations are made for that period as well as for the 24-hr. period.

These figures indicate, for example, in the case of the white sphere atmometer, that the average error in predicting the amount of transpiration at each hour in the day from the evaporation, when the ratio of daily transpiration of the plant to the daily evaporation of the atmometer under consideration is known, would amount to 43 per cent of the mean hourly value of the transpiration in the case of the alfalfa plant. The departure from the hourly transpiration rate and the hourly evaporation rate was the least when evaporation was measured by the small shallow tank.

It is evident from the foregoing that an atmometer has not yet been secured that responds in the same manner to its environment as the plant. The atmometers depart widely from the plant during the night hours—the rate of evaporation being relatively much higher than transpiration in all the cases that have been observed. Knight (1917) found that the porous-clay cup atmometer and the plants with which he worked responded unequally to changes of wind velocity but that changes in temperature and relative humidity acted upon the rate of evaporation and transpiration equally. Freeman (1920) concluded that changes in relative transpiration do not necessarily represent changes in the intrinsic transpiring power of a plant unless conditions of air movement are maintained constant. The transpiration rate of different plants varies under the same environmental conditions, owing to internal factors, so that when a comparison of the responses of transpiration and evaporation to the environment is made, the kind of plant as well as the type of atmometer must be taken into consideration.

F. Methods of Measuring Transpiration

The rate of transpiration may be measured by determining the amount of water lost per plant during a given period of time or the rate of loss per unit of leaf surface per unit of time. One of the most common ways of expressing the loss is in grams per square meter of leaf surface per hour. Comparative transpiration between different plants may also be obtained in a qualitative way by means of color standards, as will later be described.

The determination of the rate of water loss per unit of leaf surface per unit of time makes the measurement of the leaf surface of the plants necessary. This may be accomplished in any of the following ways: (1) by tracing the outlines of the leaves on paper and then at a convenient time measuring the enclosed areas by means of a planimeter, (2) by cutting out the traced areas and comparing the total weight of paper thus obtained with that of a known area of paper, (3) by obtaining the form of the leaf on sensitized paper and then either measuring or weighing the enclosed areas as above mentioned, (4) by rough measurement of the leaves and determining their area by direct calculations, and (5) by measurement with the photoelectric cell. The essentials of the apparatus used in the last method comprise a light-tight cabinet or photometer within which is mounted a selenium cell having at its upper surface a fairly large plate-glass window illuminated from above by means of a balopticon. The leaves to be measured are placed upon the glass window, and the change in the electrical resistance of the selenium cell occasioned by the reduced amount of light passing into the cabinet is measured by a suitable electrical device. Gerdel and Salter (1928) stated that this device is accurate to within 3 per cent for an area of 500 sq. cm. and 0.8 per cent for areas of 2,000 sq. cm. Withrow (1935), Frear (1935), and Mitchell (1936) have reported for the measurement of leaf areas improved photoelectric instruments that are accurate to approximately 2 to 3 per cent. Bolas and Melville (1933) devised a light method for measuring leaves that is accurate to 2.5 per cent. Vyvyan and Evans (1932) determined leaf area by the use of a sheet of glass divided into areas of one square centimeter. This glass was placed over the leaf, the number of squares in contact with it were counted, and the amount of surface in the portions of the squares at the margins was estimated. Lott and LeMert (1932) reported a modified method for obtaining rapidly the impression of leaves on blueprint paper. Darrow (1932) described three methods for determining leaf area that had not as yet been reported:

1. *Leaf-product Method.*—This method is based on the correlation between the extent of leaf surface and the linear measurements of leaves. The product of the length by the breadth in correlation with the surface is the most satisfactory.

2. *Matching Method.*—A pasteboard form equal in area to the largest leaf to be encountered in the experiment is cut out, and its area determined and written on the form. On this form are drawn outlines of successively smaller leaves each of which is measured and the area recorded on the corresponding outline. The leaves of the plant are then matched on these forms and their areas are thus determined.

3. *The leaf may be measured intact* on the plant by inserting it under cellophane on an adjustable stand and using the planimeter.

Marshall (1933) devised an apparatus for the quick determination of the area of compound leaves by translating width and length measurements of end leaflets into terms of leaf area. The apparatus is so arranged that as two wires are extended for the width and length of the leaflet, water is discharged into a calibrated tube and the area of the leaflets is read from the height of the water column.

One of the main things to be desired in measuring the rate of transpiration is that the plant be placed during the experiment as nearly as possible under the same conditions of the soil and atmosphere as prevail in the field. The accuracy, rapidity, and convenience of the method are factors that also must be considered. No method, however, has been devised for the measurement of transpiration that is entirely satisfactory in all these regards. Numerous methods for measuring transpiration have been reported, detailed descriptions of which have been given by Burgerstein (1904, 1920), but it is the intention here to describe only the four methods that have been the most universally used, especially in experiments with agricultural plants. These are the potometer method, the weighing method, the cobalt chloride-paper method, and Freeman's method.

1. The Potometer.—This method consists of placing the severed plant or branch thereof directly in water and after proper sealing determining by weight or volume the amount of water lost. One of the most common methods of procedure is to connect the severed branch or plant with a burette by means of rubber tubing and to note the loss of water volumetrically. This method was formerly used very extensively, but at present it is very little used. It has the very serious objection that the plant is placed under abnormal conditions, and it has been definitely shown that the rate of transpiration under these conditions is in most cases not comparable at all to that occurring where the plant is normally rooted in the soil. Thus, as an example, Freeman (1908) found that the rate of transpiration for the daisy, coleus, portulaca, and geraniums growing in the soil was, respectively, 7.21, 2.77, 1.72, and 0.65 mg. per square centimeter per hour, but that, from like plants which were severed and placed in potometers under like conditions, the rate of transpiration was 1.44, 0.37, 0.47, and 0.65 mg. per square centimeter per hour, respectively. Not only was the rate of transpiration much less, but the order of the transpiration rate was entirely different from what it was with the plants growing in the soil. Loftfield (1921) has also pointed out the difference in the behavior of stomata of plants in potometers as compared to those growing in the soil.

2. The Weighing Method.—For quantitative data the weighing method of measuring transpiration is the most convenient and satisfactory. The amount of transpiration from the entire plant is obtained, while the conditions under which the plant is placed previous to and during the experiment can be made very comparable to those which occur in the field. The method consists, in general, of growing the plants in soil in containers, which can be sealed so that no water escapes except that which evaporates from the plant (Fig. 21), and determining the loss by weighing. The containers that have been most frequently used for experiments with crop plants were cylindrical galvanized-iron cans with a capacity of from 250 to 1,000 lb. of soil, which is tightly packed therein. The cans are covered with galvanized-iron lids supplied with perforations for the plant and for the addition of water (Fig. 21). This lid is either sealed with tape that is waterproof (Briggs and Shantz, 1913, 1914) or rendered so by shellac (Miller, 1916, 1923) or is covered with oilcloth or other waterproof material (Kiesselbach, 1916). The escape of water around the plant is prevented by using as a seal a mixture of beeswax and paraffin (Briggs and Shantz, 1913, 1914), beeswax and a small amount of Venetian turpentine (Miller, 1916, 1923), or plastic modeling clay (Kiesselbach, 1916). One of the greatest difficulties experienced in growing plants in soil in large containers is to replace evenly throughout the soil the water that has been removed by the plant. Kiesselbach (1916) placed in each container 16 ft. of ¾-in. brass tubing made into a spiral coil perforated every 8 in. and obtained a good distribution of moisture through the soil by adding water to a container connected with this coil. Briggs and Shantz (1913, 1914) placed 5-in. flower pots over a small bed of gravel placed near the upper surface of the soil and obtained in this manner a good distribution of water. A modification of this method was used by Miller (1916, 1923), as shown in Fig. 21. Two more or less cone-shaped masses of soil 6 in. in diameter and 15 in. in depth are removed from the upper portion of the container. From the bottom of this cavity a hole 1.5 in. in diameter is made to the bottom of the can by means of a soil tube. The entire cavity is then filled with coarse sand and gravel to within 5 or 6 in. of the top of the can. A 5-in. clay flower pot with the bottom removed is placed directly on top of this sand so that the rim of the pot is flush with the metal lid of the can. A 1-in. hole for the addition of water is in the lid of the can directly over each flower pot. By this device not only is water evenly distributed through the soil, but sufficient aeration is apparently also provided, since the roots do not collect between the soil and the surface of the container, as is so frequently the case in pot experiments, but are evenly distributed throughout the soil.

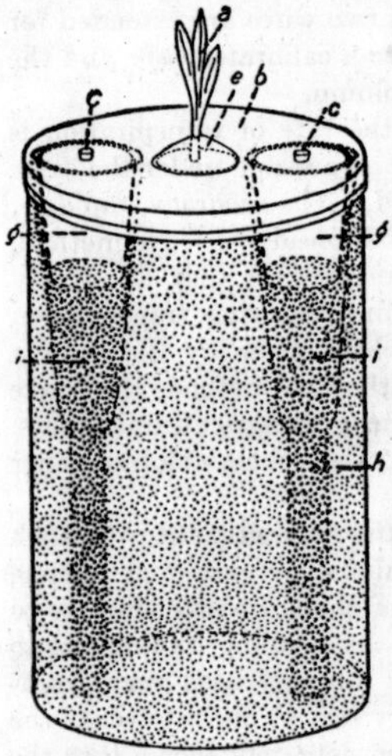

FIG. 21.—Diagram showing the method used in growing plants in soil in large metal containers for the determination of the loss of water by transpiration. *a*, plant. *b*, cover of galvanized iron. *c*, corks. *e*, wax seal. *g*, flower pots. *h*, soil. *i*, gravel beneath flower pots and extending to the bottom of the container.

When small plants and only a small quantity of soil are to be used, it has been found satisfactory to use unglazed porous-clay atmometers of the cylindrical, cone, or Bellani plate types as distributers of moisture. These are buried in the soil and connected with the surface by glass tubing so that water may be added directly or supplied automatically, as it is needed, from a reservoir (Livingston, 1908, 1918; Livingston and Hawkins, 1915). A small, inverted, porous flower pot buried in the soil and connected with the surface by means of glass tubes is also a very satisfactory watering device for small volumes of soil (Kiesselbach, 1916).

The plant containers are weighed at stated intervals by hand or on automatic scales connected with recording devices (Ganong, 1905; Briggs and Shantz, 1915; Transeau, 1911; and Blackman, 1914). By the latter method a continuous record of the water loss during the day and night is obtained. The use of automatic balances, however, is rather difficult in the field and is almost prohibited by price when a large number of plants must be considered. The most common method is to weigh the plants at certain stated intervals and in that manner determine their water loss for the period. The large containers may be lifted by means of a differential block and tackle and weighed with steelyard or spring balances (Kiesselbach, 1916; Briggs and Shantz, 1913, 1914), or they may be permanently mounted on small platforms provided with wheels or casters and pulled on and off the ordinary platform scales (Miller, 1916, 1923).

Since such a large mass of soil is required in many cases to grow normal plants, it is not possible to employ scales with a very high sensitivity, so that when the transpirational loss is desired for short intervals, the readings are not so accurate as are sometimes desired. The weighing method does not take into consideration the increased weight of the plant due to growth, but this increase in weight is very insignificant when compared to the large loss in weight due to transpiration.

3. The Cobalt Chloride Method.—Cobalt chloride ($CoCl_2.6H_2O$) occurs in the form of dark red crystals which may be dehydrated in different stages, forming successively red or violet $CoCl_2.4H_2O$, and $CoCl_2.2H_2O$, and finally the blue anhydrous $CoCl_2$. Taking advantage of this property of cobalt chloride, Stahl (1894) prepared a hygrometric paper by dipping filter paper in a solution of $CoCl_2.6H_2O$ and then drying it. Such a paper is blue when dry but changes its color to white or rose when moist. When this dry blue paper is placed upon the leaf and covered with glass or a thin piece of mica held firmly in place by a small spring clamp, it will in time become pink due to the escape of water vapor from the leaf surface. Stahl used this method to compare the rate of transpiration from the upper and lower leaf surfaces and from the leaves of different plants by comparing the time required for the paper to assume the pink color. He, however, did not attempt to standardize these readings to any standard physical evaporating surface. Livingston (1913) conceived the idea of comparing the power of a standard evaporating surface to give off water to the hygrometric cobalt chloride paper with that possessed by any leaf surface that might be considered. The method first devised by Livingston (1913) has been modified, improved, and studied by Bakke (1914), Bakke and Livingston (1916), Livingston and Shreve (1916), and Shreve (1917, 1919). The improved method of procedure is approximately as follows (Livingston and Shreve, 1916):

a. Preparation of the Hygrometric Paper.—Circular filter paper of a high grade of uniformity of texture is placed for 1 min. in an agitated solution of 3 g. of cobalt chloride in 100 cc. of water made distinctly acid by the addition of hydrochloric acid. It is then placed on a clean glass and the excess solution is squeezed out with a rubber roller. The paper is then partially dried in the oven between two filter papers, but while still pink it is removed from the oven and thoroughly pressed and dried between the two filter papers by means of a flatiron. The blue color of the paper must be more intense than that of the standard to be later mentioned, the intensity of color being varied by altering the time the paper remains in the solution. After the paper is dried, it is placed in a desiccator over a convenient dehydrating agent and left until needed.

b. Standard Colors.—Since the cobalt chloride paper takes up some moisture during the transfer from the desiccator to the leaf and since it is difficult to determine with any degree of accuracy the end point in color of the moist paper, Livingston and Shreve (1916) devised two permanent standard colors with which to mark the beginning and the end of the experiment. Both these colors are blue, one being just a little less intense than the color of the dried cobalt chloride paper while the other is much less intense but clearly blue. The permanent color standards are made by precipitating Prussian blue in the same type of filter paper as is used for the cobalt chloride paper. The paper is first dipped in a solution of ferric chloride, and after the excess solution is removed it is then dipped into a solution of potassium ferrocyanide, the excess solution removed, and the paper dried after the manner described for the preparation of the cobalt chloride paper. The two intensities of color are obtained by varying the concentration of the solutions and the time of treatment. The color-standard papers thus prepared do not alter their color when exposed to air and sunshine or with changes in the moisture content of the air. A composite strip of the cobalt paper and the two standard color papers is made by taping together pieces each 4 mm. square with the cobalt chloride square in the center.

These composite strips are taken from the desiccator and clamped upon the leaf as has previously been described. When the cobalt chloride paper matches in color that of the more intense standard, the experiment is considered started, and it is considered concluded when it reaches the intensity of the lighter color standard.

c. The Standard Evaporating Surface.—For a standard evaporating surface in this method, a free water surface (Livingston, 1913), a moist filter paper supplied from beneath with water (Bakke, 1914), and a porous-clay cup atmometer filed to a flat surface (Livingston and Shreve, 1916) have been used. In all cases, the cobalt chloride paper is held by suitable appliances at a distance of 1 mm. from the evaporating surface. The length of time that is required for the hygrometric paper to reach the color end point is determined after the same manner as when the paper is applied to the leaves.

d. The Index of Transpiring Power.—The time that is required for the hygrometric paper to reach its end point in color over the leaf is called the "leaf-test time" and over the evaporating surface the "water-test time." The ratio of the water-test time to the average leaf time is called the "index of transpiring power," a value that varies greatly at different times of the day; *e.g.*, Bakke (1916) found that within a single hour just after sunrise it increased 240 per cent in the case of sunflower. He also found (1914) that the younger leaves have a higher index of transpiring power than do the older ones. Let us consider a specific example to illustrate the application of the cobalt chloride method of determining the index of transpiring power. Let us assume that the water-test time is 15 sec. and the leaf-test time for the upper surface 300 sec. and for the lower surface 150 sec. The index of transpiring power for the upper surface would thus be $^{15}/_{300}$ or 0.05 and for the lower surface $^{15}/_{150}$ or 0.10. The average index of transpiring power for the whole leaf would thus be $\frac{0.05 + 0.10}{2}$ or 0.075. The evaporation from the leaf thus goes on at the rate of 0.075 times that from the standard evaporating surface under observation.

The cobalt chloride-paper method of determining transpiration is valuable since it makes possible the determination of the relative transpiring power of plants growing in the open soil under field conditions. The method thus is applicable and very convenient for determining the relation of the position of leaves on the plant to the rate of water loss, the xerophytism or mesophytism of plants, and the wilting point. Its chief disadvantage is that it is only a qualitative method and gives no quantitative data in regard to the amount of water actually lost from the plant.

Meyer (1927) used a modified method of procedure in the application of the cobalt chloride method so that the rate of water loss may be expressed in absolute units instead of only relative values. He determined the amount of water by weight that must be taken up by a given area of standardized cobalt chloride paper to reach the pink end point. From this datum it is thus possible to determine the number of units of water vapor being lost from a given area of leaf in a unit of time if the area of the paper used and the time required for it to reach the end point are known. In the method of Meyer the paper is so placed that the conditions of humidity, radiation, and air movement are practically constant beneath it, so that the only variable atmospheric factor is the temperature and thus all readings can be standardized to the same temperature. Meyer adopted the term "standard rate of water loss" for designating the amount of water vapor lost under the conditions of the experiment in terms of grams per hour per 100 sq. cm. of leaf surface at 20°C.

Blaydes (1932) determined the rates of water loss from *Helianthus tuberosus* simultaneously by the weighing and cobalt paper methods. He found that these methods do not correlate very closely because: (1) The weighing method measures the loss of water during an entire unit of time, while cobalt paper records the transpiration during a very short period of the unit of time interval; (2) the loss of water by the weighing method fluctuates with the environmental conditions, while with the cobalt chloride-paper method the direct effects of atmospheric environmental fluctuations are practically eliminated; (3) in the cobalt chloride method the diffusion gradient is much steeper at the beginning of the experiment than it is under the conditions of the weighing method.

Howes (1923) has devised a calcium chloride method for measuring the transpiring power of plants. Small tubes of calcium chloride are attached to the leaf by means of special clips. The calcium chloride retains its efficiency as a water absorber for a considerable period even when small amounts are used, and the results are not affected by the amounts of calcium chloride in the tubes.

Heinicke (1930) described a satisfactory means of studying the comparative transpiration rates, in which the water lost by the leaf is absorbed by calcium chloride contained in a small weighing bottle held to the leaf by a special clamp.

4. The Freeman Method.—This method was first used by Freeman in 1908 and is a modification and adaptation of the methods used by Ganeau de Lamarlière (1892) and E. and J. Verschaffelt (1890). The general details of the apparatus used in this method are shown in Fig. 22. The apparatus consists of a large glass cylinder of suitable size for a transpiration chamber for the twig or portion of the plant whose water loss is to be measured, two U tubes containing phosphorus pentoxide for absorption of moisture, and a water aspirator of known capacity. These are connected together by rubber tubing so that as water flows from the aspirator a known quantity of air may be drawn through the cylinder over the leaves under experiment and through the phosphorus pentoxide, which is loosely packed in order to allow the free passage of air. The glass cylinder containing the twig is closed at its distal end with a split cork, which fits tightly around the twig and carries a tube for the intake of air. The upper end of this cylinder is closed with a two-holed cork carrying a thermometer and a glass tube for connection with the rest of the apparatus.

In preparation for an experiment, the aspirator is filled with water, the U tubes containing phosphorus pentoxide are weighed and placed in the circuit with stopcocks closed, and lastly the stem of the plant is inserted in the cylinder. The stopcocks in the U tubes are then opened and the water started running from the aspirator, the speed with which the air is drawn over the twig being regulated according to its size and rate of transpiration. After all the water or a certain measured portion of it has flowed from the aspirator, the U tubes are closed, disconnected, and weighed, and the amount of moisture absorbed by them determined. This moisture, however, includes not only that which escapes from the plant but also that contained in the air that is drawn through the apparatus. The amount of moisture contained in the volume of air that has been drawn over the leaf is determined by running a control experiment at the same time with the transpiration experiment. The amount of water lost by transpiration is obtained by subtracting the increase in weight of the tubes used for the normal air from the increase in weight of those used with the plant. After the experiment, the leaf area may be determined by any convenient method and the rate of transpiration calculated. This method of measuring transpiration is adapted to cases where the plants are too large to be grown in containers or where the whole plant cannot be sacrificed for the experiment. It is adapted to give quantitative data on the comparative rate of transpiration of different plants. The method, however, has some serious objections. In the first place, the leaves are placed under very abnormal conditions of temperature in the transpiration cylinder—the temperature being much higher than that of the open air. In the second place, unless great care is exercised in the selection of a small amount of leaf surface and in the rate at which air is drawn through the apparatus, the moisture escaping from the leaves cannot be removed rapidly enough to prevent its condensation upon the walls of the cylinder. Such a collection of moisture of course renders the experiment void. The

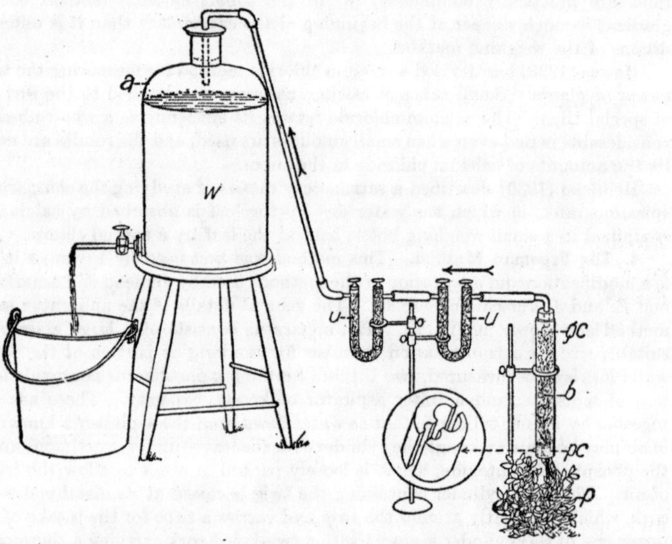

FIG. 22.—Apparatus for the determination of transpiration by the Freeman method. *a*, aspirator. *b*, branch of plant. *gc*, glass cylinder. *p*, plant. *pc*, perforated cork for the entrance of a portion of the plant and air. *u*, tubes containing phosphorus pentoxide. *w*, water.

period of time that must necessarily elapse in setting up the apparatus also tends to add considerable error.

Minckler (1936) used a modified Freeman method with an air pump and a gas meter to measure the flow of air. The maximum air flow in an ordinary Freeman experiment was 19.5 l. per hour, while with the modified method it was 5 to 10 l. per minute. This method permitted the use of a chamber sufficiently large to accommodate 20 to 30 or more relatively large leaves of trees. The duration of each experiment was only 6 min. As determined by this method, the daily transpiration of an American elm, 13 in. in diameter at a height of 4 to 5 feet from the ground, was 8.7 l., or 1,360 l. for a growing season of 150 days. The daily average for a red maple of similar size but with more foliage growing in a moist habitat was 51.7 l., or 7,770 l. for the growing season.

G. The Significance of Transpiration

Although transpiration has been studied, perhaps, more thoroughly than any other plant process, very little is yet known concerning the significance of this function in the life of the plant. The opinions that have been expressed in regard to the possible value of transpiration vary all the way from those which ascribe to this function benefits to the plant that are as important as photosynthesis and respiration to those which assume that transpiration brings nothing to the plant but harm (Curtis, 1926). When the present data in regard to transpiration are surveyed, it must be admitted that its obvious harmful effects outweigh any of the benefits that might be attributed to the process.

It has frequently been stated in texts that transpiration cools the leaves and prevents their death or injury by high temperatures. The change of water from the liquid to the vapor form within a leaf does absorb a considerable amount of heat and this vaporization would thus tend to lower the temperature of the leaf. As previously mentioned, however, the average leaves are cooled by transpiration rarely more than 2 to 5°C.—a difference which, so far as our knowledge of protoplasm goes, could be of no marked benefit in preventing injurious effects. The death of leaves during hot, dry weather is apparently due to the excessive loss of water from the protoplasm rather than to any injury caused by an excessive increase in temperature. Thus it would seem that the injury to leaves which frequently occurs on hot days is due chiefly to the injurious drying effects of transpiration itself. Transpiration thus apparently is more harmful than beneficial on hot days when the cooling effects are most needed (Curtis, 1926).

It has frequently been stated that transpiration increases the rate and amount of absorption of solutes from the soil, but, as stated in Chap. V, conclusive experimental evidence indicates that there is no relationship whatsoever between the rate of transpiration and the amount of nutrients absorbed.

It has also been claimed that transpiration plays an important part in transferring solutes from the roots to the leaves in the transpiration stream or current. As Curtis (1926), however, points out, if the rate of removal of nutrients from the roots were largely determined by transpiration, the removal of solutes from the absorbing organs should increase absorption. Increased transpiration should therefore increase absorption, but, as mentioned above, the experimental evidence indicates that it does not. The upward transpiration stream is in the xylem, so that if the transfer of solutes upward is in the phloem, as indicated by the work of Curtis, which will be discussed in Chap. XII, it seems apparent that transpiration can have little or no effect on their movement.

The loss of water by transpiration always results in a reduction of turgor of the cells, since the water lost cannot be instantaneously replaced. A slight reduction in turgor, however, has but little influence on the various processes of the plant, especially if there is an abundant supply of water in the soil to replace the loss from the plant. When, however, the moisture content of the soil is low, the decrease in turgor soon reaches a point where the reactions of the cells are greatly or completely retarded, so that death finally ensues.

It is estimated that more plants perish or are retarded in their development from a deficient water supply due primarily to its loss by transpiration than from all other factors combined, a fact which indicates that, if transpiration is of any benefit to a plant, it may be attended by very dangerous effects.

Barnes (1902) considered that the significance of transpiration is to be seen in its origin and in tracing its development. Thus it is considered that the most primitive plants lived in water and absorbed the carbon dioxide and oxygen needed in the process of photosynthesis and respiration directly from this medium. In the course of their development, plants have apparently not modified to any great extent the manner of obtaining these two gases, so that under the present organization of the plants, exposed wet cell walls cannot be waterproofed on that account. Thus, wherever moist cell surfaces are exposed to the atmosphere, evaporation of water must occur, so that transpirational loss must be considered unavoidable, although in itself it is a constant menace to the activity and life of the plant.

Clements (1934) believed that transpiration may play some important role. He stated that, although this process may cause the death of the plant under certain conditions, it is not due so much to the process itself as it is to the limiting factors that make the normal functioning of an essential process impossible.

H. The Water Requirement of Plants

The term "water requirement" in the most restricted sense is defined as the ratio of the number of units of water absorbed by the plant during the growing season to the number of units of dry matter produced by the plant during that time. In most cases, however, the dry matter considered in this relation is the amount harvested and in most instances includes all the plant except the roots. The water under consideration is in reality the amount lost through transpiration during the growing season, since of the total water absorbed the amount retained within the plant is very insignificant compared to the amount evaporated from it.

The term "water requirement" is a rather misleading one, since it seems to imply that it denotes the amount of water necessary for the growth of the plant. It merely, however, denotes that under certain conditions of climate, soil, and water supply, there was evaporated from the stem and leaves or retained within the plant and leaves water to the amount of so many times the number of units of dry matter produced. The water requirement of plants has been studied, for the most part, in those regions where water is a limiting factor in crop production, since it was formerly considered that there was a relationship between the ability of a plant to withstand drought and its water requirement. This relationship in the light of investigations, however, does not appear to exist.

1. Methods of Determining.—The methods of determining the water requirement of plants were, previous to 1910, not under very well-controlled conditions. A summary of the methods used previous to that time and the results thus obtained are discussed by Montgomery (1911), Briggs and Shantz (1913), and Kiesselbach (1916) in their review of the literature on the subject. Since 1910 the main work on water requirement has been reported by Briggs and Shantz (1913, 1914), Shantz and Piemeisel (1927) at Akron, Colo., Montgomery and Kiesselbach (1912), Kiesselbach (1916) in Nebraska, Miller (1916, 1923) in Kansas, and Khankoje (1914) and Thom and Holtz (1917) in Washington. The water requirement was determined by these investigators by growing the plants in large sealed containers after the manner described in the discussion of the weighing method for transpiration determinations. The containers are weighed at frequent intervals, and the amount of water that has been lost from the soil is replaced by adding a known amount of water to the container by means of the watering devices that have previously been described.

After the plant or plants in a given container have reached maturity, they are harvested and the amount of dry matter determined by drying to a constant weight at a temperature of 100 to 105°C. The amount of water taken from the soil is known from the weights of the container at the beginning of the experiment and at its close and from the amounts of water that have been added from time to time during the season. The water requirement is determined by dividing the number of units of water absorbed during the season by the number of units of dry matter produced. Thus, for example, if a plant absorbs from the soil 251,020 g. of water and produces 652 g. of dry matter during the season, its water requirement would be 251,020/652 or 385. The water requirement may be stated also in terms of the grain produced and is frequently determined in this manner when the plants under consideration are of importance in the production of grain. The measurement of the water requirement under field conditions has been attempted by Briggs and Shantz (1913),

Thom and Holtz (1917), and others. The general method is to determine the amount of water removed by the crop as shown by the difference between the initial and final water content combined with the rainfall entering the soil as determined by daily sampling. In some of the attempts, fallow plots are used to determine the loss of water from the soil by evaporation. Briggs and Shantz (1913) considered this method uncertain, owing to the difficulty of determining what proportion of the rainfall enters the soil and actually is used by the crop.

2. Factors Affecting the Water Requirement.—The water requirement of different plants varies greatly under the same conditions. Thus Briggs and Shantz (1913, 1914) and Shantz and Piemeisel (1927) found in their extensive work in Colorado that the water requirement of some 150 plants studied ranges from 216 for Kursk millet to 1,131 for *Franseria sp.*, a native weed. Thus *Franseria* evaporated five times as much water during the production of a unit of dry matter as did the millet. Shantz and Piemeisel (1927) summarized the variation in the water requirement in regard to the plants studied by them as follows: considering the water requirement of proso millet to be 1.00, the water requirement of the various crops would be: millets, 1.07; sorghums, 1.14; corn, 1.31; barley, 1.94; wheat, 2.09; oats, 2.18; rye, 2.37; legumes, 2.81; and grasses 3.10. In general, the millets, sorghums, and corns had the lowest water requirement, while the small grains, barley, wheat, oats, and rye lost almost twice as much water and the legumes almost three times as much per unit of dry matter produced as did the millets, sorghums, and corns.

Since the water requirement is the ratio between the amount of water taken up by the plant and the amount of dry matter produced, it is evident that its value will be affected by any factor that influences either transpiration or growth. Perhaps the most influential factor in this regard is the climatic complex that prevails during the growth of the plant.

a. Climatic Conditions.—The effect of air humidity on the water requirement is conclusively shown by the work of Montgomery and Kiesselbach (1912). Corn was grown in two greenhouses; in one the relative humidity was kept at 37 per cent during 12 hr. of the day, and in the other at 58 per cent for that time. The water requirement of the plants in the dry greenhouse was 340, while in the more humid greenhouse it was 191—the corn in the dry greenhouse having a water requirement 56 per cent higher than in the humid one. The range of the water requirement during different years due to prevailing climatic conditions is very great. Thus, for example, the lowest value for any one year at Akron, Colo., averaged only about 60 per cent of that of the highest value. Some idea of the variation in the water requirement due to climatic conditions may be obtained from the following table, which gives the water requirement of some of the more common crop plants and a summary of the weather conditions in terms of evaporation from a free water surface:

WATER REQUIREMENT FOR THE YEARS 1911 TO 1917 AT AKRON, COLO., AND THE EVAPORATION IN INCHES FROM A FREE WATER SURFACE FROM APR. 1 TO SEPT. 1

Plant	1911	1912	1913	1914	1915	1916	1917
Alfalfa	1,068	657	834	890	695	1,047	822
Oats, Burt	639	449	617	615	445	809	636
Barley, Hannchen	527	443	513	501	404	664	522
Wheat, Kubanka	468	394	496	518	405	639	471
Corn, N. W. Dent	368	280	399	368	253	495	346
Millet, Kursk	287	187	286	295	202	367	284
Sorghum, Red Amber	298	239	298	284	303	296	272
Evaporation, inches, April to September	48.8	37.7	43.0	41.8	33.4	47.1	42.7

Dillman (1931) reported that at Sewell, S. D., from 1912 to 1918, and at Mandan, N. D., from 1919 to 1922, the water requirement of alfalfa ranged from 602 to 1,036, of Kubanka wheat from 333 to 531, of Sudan grass from 272 to 347, of millet from 177 to 316, and of sorgo from 210 to 284. All the plants except sorgo and Sudan grass were highly responsive to seasonal changes.

Owing to changes in weather conditions, the loss of water from plants may vary as much as 600 per cent on successive days. Thus the weather conditions that prevail during a month or even so short a period as 10 days or a week may determine whether the water requirement is going to be high or low for that season. In this regard, Briggs and Shantz (1916) found that during a period of 10 days from July 7 to 16, 1914, many of the crop plants including wheat, barley, rye, corn, and Sudan grass lost 25 per cent of the total water transpired during the entire season. Richardson (1923) working in Australia found that in September to November, 80 per cent of the water lost from winter cereals was transpired, although the growing period was 7.5 months, while alfalfa in bloom transpired as much as 25 per cent of its total water in 3 days. The stage of development of the plant when certain climatic conditions occur also is an important factor in determining the value of the water requirement. If a high evaporating period occurs when the plant has as yet only a small leaf development, it may affect the water requirement but little, but if a high evaporation period of a week or 10 days should occur when the full leaf development has been attained, it will greatly increase the value of the water requirement for that season. An example from the work of Miller (1923) will illustrate that point. In 1920 the water requirement of Sudan grass at Manhattan, Kans., was only 81 per cent of what it was in the previcus year. The evaporation from a free water surface for May, June, July, and August during 1920 was 98.9 per cent of that in 1919. It would seem that the difference in the water requirement for the two years should be small. The evaporation, however, during August when the Sudan grass had reached its full leaf development was in 1920 only 83 per cent of that of 1919—a difference which is very comparable to the difference in the water requirement for the two years.

b. Soil Fertility.—Many investigations have been made concerning the effects of the fertility of the soil on the water requirement. Almost without exception, the application of fertilizers to the soil has shown a reduction of the water requirement. In very productive soils this reduction is extremely slight, but in poor soils the water requirement may be reduced one-half and sometimes as much as two-thirds by the application of nutrients. When the supply of nutrients in the soil approaches exhaustion, the rate of growth of the plant is greatly reduced, but no corresponding change occurs in the transpiration rate. This fact is evidence that transpiration is not a measure of growth. An example to illustrate the effect of soil fertility on the water requirement may be taken from the work of Kiesselbach (1916). He grew corn in an infertile soil *a*, a fertile soil *c*, and an intermediate soil *b* composed of equal parts of *a* and *c*. The amount of dry matter produced and the water requirement obtained were as follows:

Soil	Dry matter produced, grams	Water requirement
a.........	113	550
b.........	184	479
c.........	270	392

By the application of sheep manure in equal amounts to soils *a*, *b*, and *c*, the dry matter was increased 194, 79, and 41 per cent and the total water transpired 106, 43, and 29 per cent in the order named, but the water requirement by this treatment was reduced 29, 17, and 8 per cent, respectively.

The effect of the fertility of the soil is shown indirectly when the relation of the volume of soil in which the plants are growing is considered in relation to the water requirement. Many of the experimental data that have been reported in regard to water requirement are in error because the plants were grown in such a small volume of soil that they did not mature normally, owing primarily to an insufficient nutrient supply for the plant. In such cases, as the volume of soil is increased the water requirement is reduced within certain limits. Thus Kiesselbach

(1916) found that when he used various amounts of soil he obtained the following results with corn:

Amount of soil used, pounds	Dry matter produced, grams	Water requirement
32	97.5	411
85	205.7	362
150	316.0	341
239	442.0	277
583	627.0	290
956	728.0	240

In these cases when 1¾ lb. of sheep manure was added to each can, the water requirement was 322, 311, 304, 272, 269, and 252, respectively. These results indicate that the nutrients contained in the volumes of soil used were in most cases insufficient for the plant's needs.

c. Soil Moisture.—The experiments that have been reported in regard to soil moisture and the water requirement show, as a rule, an increase in the water requirement when the soil-moisture content approaches either extreme (Briggs and Shantz, 1913). Kiesselbach (1916) obtained in corn a maximum production of dry matter when the water content of the soil was at approximately 70 per cent of saturation. The average for 3 years showed that the reduction of the moisture content below the optimum reduced the water requirement 7.9 per cent but that this was accompanied by a 30.7 per cent lower yield of dry matter. An increase in the soil-moisture content above the optimum for the three years increased the water requirement 8.2 per cent, but this was accompanied by a 16.7 per cent lower yield of dry matter.

Flory (1936) reported a 3-year comparative study of the rate of transpiration, development of leaf area, and production of dry matter in the climax prairie and a field of maize at Lincoln, Neb. At maturity the prairie vegetation had a leaf area of 950, 1,050, and 1,014 sq. in. per square foot of soil surface, respectively, for each of the successive years. By maturity the corn had developed 437, 546, and 467 sq. in. of leaf surface per square foot of soil surface. The average daily loss of transpiration per square foot of soil surface for the 3-year period was 0.59 lb. in the prairie and 0.39 lb. in the corn field. It was greater in the corn, however, when the period of tasseling was accompanied by a high water content of the soil. The total amount of water lost in the production of 1 g. of dry matter in the prairie was 1,376 g. of which 445 g. or 32 per cent was lost in runoff and surface evaporation. The total amount of water used or lost in the corn field for the production of 1 g. of dry matter was 786 g. About 65 per cent of this was lost in runoff and evaporation from the soil surface. Approximately 52 per cent more dry matter was produced per square foot of soil in the corn field than in the prairie.

d. Plant Diseases.—It was found by Johnston and Miller (1934) that leaf-rust infection increased the water requirement of susceptible varieties of wheat 31.7 to 104 per cent, depending on the length of the rust period. The water requirement of the resistant varieties was only very slightly increased by rust infection. Murphy (1935) found that when infected in the seedling stage a variety of oats susceptible to crown rust used 290.8 per cent more water per unit of dry matter than rust-free plants. The resistant varieties that had been inoculated used only 40 per cent more water than the controls.

I. Drought Resistance

The term "drought" may be defined in various ways depending upon the point of view from which it is considered. Drought may be defined as a condition of the soil or atmosphere, or of both, that prevents or hinders the plant in obtaining sufficient water for its functions. Drought as thus defined may be caused in two ways: (1) By the inability of the plant to absorb water from the soil, although an abundance is present. This condition is frequently termed "physiological drought." Plants that grow in marshes and bogs frequently have difficulty obtaining sufficient water to supply their needs although the soil in which they grow is saturated with it. Many of the plants growing under these conditions have xeromorphic anatomical adaptations that resemble those of plants that grow in regions of limited rainfall. The inability of plants to absorb water from a frozen soil when there is an abundance therein and when the aerial parts of the plant are in need of water is another example of physiological drought. This is exemplified frequently by the winter cereals growing in the Great Plains. During the winter they are sometimes injured by the loss of water from their leaves due to a high evaporating power of the air. The water thus lost cannot be replaced by the roots because they are in a cold or frozen soil. (2) Drought is more frequently caused by a lack of sufficient water in the soil or by a high evaporating power of the air, which depletes both the soil and plant of moisture. These two factors generally accompany each other, although this is sometimes not the case. The term "soil or edaphic drought" is used to define the condition of a lack of water in the soil. "Atmospheric drought" refers to the desiccation of the plant to the point of injury under conditions of relatively high soil moisture.

Maximow (1925) believed that the ability of a plant to resist drought is due to a multiplicity of morphological and physiological characteristics which investigators have so far failed to separate into their component parts. Some of the general characteristics of plants that may aid them in withstanding drought are a small leaf surface, an exceptional root development, a short growing season, and the ability to become dormant. Certain agricultural plants have several or all of these characteristics. On this account the three plants that have done the most for agriculture in the Great Plains are the hard winter wheats, alfalfa, and the sorghums. One of the first principles in dry-farming is to conserve the largest possible supply of moisture for the crop that is to be grown. In order to obtain the best returns under conditions of drought, the soil must be kept free of weeds and a thin stand of the desired crop must be grown. A weed evaporates as much water and frequently much more than a crop plant so that in a weedy field the loss of water from the weeds may be as great as or greater than it is from the crop plants. Under dry conditions, the plants must be well spaced so that each individual has a large mass of soil from which to draw water.

It is well known that plants exhibit different capacities for enduring drought at various stages of their development. Thus Tumanov (1929) stated that in wheats the "shooting" and "soft dough" periods were the most critical in regard to the effects of drought. He believed that varieties should be selected whose critical periods of growth do not coincide with the greatest combination of adverse meteorological factors. Ivanov (1923) cites the example of Turkestan wheat in this regard, which develops very rapidly during early stages of growth and is drought-escaping because it comes in head long before other types. Vassiliev (1932) believed that it is not possible to breed plants that are resistant to soil drought but that the breeding of plants resistant to atmospheric drought might be accomplished. Martin (1930) and Aamodt and Johnston (1936) give thorough discussions of the nature of drought and of drought resistance by plants.

III. LOSS OF WATER FROM PLANTS IN THE LIQUID FORM. GUTTATION

The loss of water in the form of liquid from the uninjured leaf or stem of the plant is called "guttation." Guttation occurs, for the most part, under conditions that are favorable for the absorption of water by the roots but conducive to reduced evaporation from the leaves. Cool nights following warm days provide excellent conditions for this phenomenon. The soil retains warmth and absorption is very active, while the air is cool and humid, and transpiration is reduced almost to zero. Although guttation occurs, for the most part, at night, it may occur in daylight if the proper conditions prevail and may be caused in many plants at any time by artificial means. The water of guttation usually collects in drops along the edges and at the tips of leaves, but in some cases it appears over the entire leaf surface when conditions are very favorable. The water exuded in the case of the sorghums and sometimes corn is so abundant that it runs down the leaves and collects in the leaf axils. Under the conditions of the Great Plains it is not uncommon for the sorghum leaves to be very badly wilted during the day yet recover their turgidity at night and form abundant water of guttation.

In the tropics, guttation occurs to a greater extent than under conditions of the temperate region, since at night the air is very humid, while the soil is warm, making conditions ideal for absorption. The water of guttation, especially on the leaves of cereals and grasses, is frequently mistaken for dew. The process of guttation has been observed for a large range of plants, and Burgerstein (1920) lists 333 genera and 115 families of plants for which guttation has been reported.

The quantity of water lost by guttation is often considerable, the largest recorded amount being 100 cc. for a single night from a young leaf of *Colocasia nymphaefolia.* In this case, the water is exuded near the tip of the leaf and is actually forced out or ejected in drops, which follow one another in rapid succession. It is stated by some observers that in the tropics in the early morning the bamboos in dense growths produce a fine mist due to the loss of water by guttation.

The water of guttation in most cases escapes from the plant through more or less specialized organs called "hydathodes." These organs are generally located on the leaves and their structure is subject to a considerable amount of variation. There are two main types of hydathodes in their relation to the vascular system. The one type has no direct connection with the water-conducting system. The hydathodes of this group are purely epidermal structures such as specialized hairs, conical protrusions, and other forms of modified epidermal cells.

The other type, called generally the "epithem hydathode," is characterized by the fact that it is in direct communication with the water-conducting system. One of the most common forms of hydathodes of this type opens to the outside through a water stoma beneath which is located a mass of thin-walled cells, loosely arranged and called the "epithem," which border directly upon the xylem elements of the fibrovascular bundle. The main distinction between the water stomata or water pores and the ordinary stomata consists in the fact that the guard cells of water stomata have lost their power of adjustment to a large extent. They are located at the end of a fibrovascular bundle and are generally much larger. Haberlandt (1914) stated that they usually become stationary at a very early stage of development, although in some cases from the first they are incapable of movement.

Lepeschkin (1923) noted that when the edge of the leaf bearing the epithem hydathode is severed and laid with its cut surface in water, guttation does not occur. Flood (1919) noted that when the tip of the leaf of *Colocasia antiquorum* is anaesthetized, the exudation of water continues at the normal rate. Both these investigators concluded that their experimental results indicate that guttation in the case of epithem hydathodes is simply a process of filtration, the force being supplied by sap pressure, which in some cases may also force the water through the ordinary stomata.

The water exuded from the purely epidermal hydathodes is apparently purely water of excretion, the cells of the hydathode themselves developing the force necessary for such an excretion process. It seems, however, that an exudation pressure or sap pressure must be set up in the conducting system before this type of hydathode will function. The role that the sap pressure here plays seems to be that of a stimulus which sets the action of these hydathodes in motion.

The water excreted in guttation is not pure but contains a small amount of total solids. One of the most recent and thorough investigations on this subject was conducted by Wilson (1923). He found that the total solids in the water of guttation from corn plants growing under nonsterile conditions amounted to 1,030 p.p.m. The total solids in water from timothy plants growing under sterile conditions was 573 p.p.m. in one case and 220 p.p.m. in another. In all cases, the total solids were more than one-half organic matter. In the guttation water from corn, oats, and timothy, reactions were obtained indicating the presence of nitrates, nitrites, catalases, and peroxidases, but the presence of reductases was uncertain. Materials were also present which were capable of reducing methylene blue. The pH value of the exudate from young plants was found neutral, but the acidity increased as the plants became older.

It was shown by Pavilinova (1926) with seedlings of maize growing in water cultures that the concentration of calcium in guttation water was directly proportional to its concentration in the culture solution. The quantity of calcium excreted was approximately 17 per cent of the quantity absorbed. The water of guttation had an acid reaction with an average pH of 5.3. Shardakov (1928) collected water of guttation from the hydathodes of various plants and examined it for calcium, potassium, chlorine, and phosphate. The salt concentration of water of guttation changes with time. These ions were more concentrated in the water of guttation than in the soil solution. He believed that these ions are absorbed as the solution passes through the hydathodes, because when these organs are removed, the ion concentration in the bleeding sap is greater than it was before their removal.

Hiltner (1930) believed that dew is absorbed by the aerial parts of plants and that this reduces the salt concentrations of the solutions supplied by the roots. Arens (1934) found that the dew on leaves is generally slightly alkaline, while the water of guttation is slightly acid.

Distilled water with a pH of 5.6 becomes alkaline in a few hours after being sprayed on the leaves. The alkalinity of this water adhering to the leaf surfaces is caused by exosmosis of potassium, calcium, magnesium, phosphorus, and organic substances.

The physiological significance of the hydathodes and of the loss of water by guttation is not definitely known. This escape of water from the plant would seem to be a means of regulating the turgor of the leaves and prevent it from becoming so high as to interfere with the metabolism of the cells when transpiration is almost or completely suppressed. This, however, is purely an assumption and is based upon no experimental evidence whatsoever.

Bibliography

Aamodt, O. S., and J. H. Torrie, 1934: The relation between awns and yield in spring wheat, *Can. J. Res.*, **11**: 207–212.

——— and W. H. Johnston, 1936: Studies on drought resistance in spring wheat, *Can. J. Res.*, **14**: 122–152.

Anderson, A. P., 1897: Stomata on the bud scales of *Abies pectinata*, *Bot. Gaz.*, **24**: 294–295.

Anderson, D. B., 1931: Influence of $CuSO_4$ dusts upon the transpiration rate of peanuts and other plants, *N. C. Sta. Ann. Rept.*, **53**: 110.

Arends, J., 1925: Ueber den Einfluss chemischer Agenzien auf Stärkegehalt und osmotischen Wert der Spaltöffnungschliesszellen, *Planta*, **1**: 84–115.

Arens, K., 1934: Die kutikuläre Exkretion des Laubblattes, *Jahrb. wiss. Bot.*, **80**: 248–300; *Biol. Abst.*, **10**: 41.

Arthur, J. M., and W. D. Stewart, 1933: Transpiration of tobacco plants in relation to radiant energy in the visible and infrared, *Contr. Boyce Thompson Inst.*, **5**: 483–501.

Ashby, E., 1931: Comparison of two methods of measuring stomatal aperture, *Plant Physiol.*, **6**: 713–719.

———, 1932: Transpiratory organs of *Larrea tridentata* and their ecological significance, *Ecology*, **13**: 182–188.

Askenasy, E., 1875: Über die Temperatur, welche Pflanzen im Sonnenlicht annehmen, *Bot. Ztg.*, **33**: 441–444.

Avery, G. S., 1933: Structure and development of the tobacco leaf, *Am. J. Bot.*, **20**: 565–592.

Babinet, M., 1848: Note sur un atmidoscope, *C. R. Acad. Sci. Paris*, **26**: 529–530.

Bader, A., 1930: Vergleichende Transpirationsuntersuchungen in der Gattung Pinus, *diss., Eberhard-Karl Universität (Tübingen); Biol. Absl.*, **8**: 1138.

Bakke, A. L., 1914: Studies of the transpiring power of plants as indicated by the method of standardized hygrometric paper, *J. Ecol.*, **2**: 145–173.

——— and B. E. Livingston, 1916: Further studies on foliar transpiring power in plants, *Physiol. Res.*, **2**: 51–71.

Balls, W. L., 1912: The stomatograph, *Proc. Roy. Soc.*, B, **85**: 33–44.

Barnes, C. R., 1902: The significance of transpiration, *Sci.*, **15**: 460.

Barritt, N. W., 1929: The structure of the seed coat in *Gossypium* and its relation to the growth and nutrition of the lint hairs, *Ann. Bot.*, **43**: 483–489.

Barss, A. F., 1932: Effect of moisture supply on development of *Pyrus malus*, *Bot. Gaz.*, **90**: 151–177.

BARTHOLOMEW, E. T., 1926: Internal decline of lemons. III, Water deficit in lemon fruits caused by excessive leaf evaporation, *Am. J. Bot.*, **13**: 102–117.

———, 1931: Certain phases of citrus leaf transpiration, *Am. J. Bot.*, **18**: 765–783.

BATES, C. G., 1919: A new evaporimeter for use in forest studies, *Month. Weather Rev.*, **47**: 283–294.

BAYER, L., 1902: Beitrag zur pflanzenphysiologischen Bedeutung des Kupfers in der Bordeaux-Brühe, *Inaug. Diss., Königsberg.*

BELLANI, A., 1820: Descrizione di un mivo amidometro per servire di continuazione e fine alle reflessioni critiche intomo all' evaporazione, *Gior. Fis. Chim.*, **3**: 166–177.

BESSEY, C. E., 1898: Some considerations upon the functions of the stomata, *Sci.*, **7**: 13–16.

BIALOGLOWSKI, J., 1935: Effect of humidity on transpiration of rooted lemon cuttings under controlled conditions, *Proc. Am. Soc. Hort. Sci.*, **33**: 166–169.

BLACKMAN, F. F., 1895: Experimental researches on vegetable assimilation and respiration. I, On a new method of investigating the carbonic acid exchanges of plants, *Phil. Trans. Roy. Soc.*, **186**: 485–502.

———, 1895: Experimental researches on vegetable assimilation and respiration. II, On the paths of gaseous exchange between aerial leaves and the atmosphere, *Phil. Trans. Roy. Soc.*, **186**: 503–562.

——— and G. L. C. MATTHAEI, 1905: Experimental reseaches on vegetable assimilation and respiration. IV, A quantitative study of carbon-dioxide assimilation and leaf-temperature in natural illumination, *Proc. Roy. Soc.*, B, **76**: 402–460.

BLACKMAN, V. H., and S. G. PAINE, 1914: A recording transpirometer, *Ann. Bot.*, **28**: 109–113.

——— and R. C. KNIGHT, 1917: A method of controlling the rate of air movement in transpiration experiments, *Ann. Bot.*, **31**: 217–220.

BLAIKLEY, N. M., 1932: Absorption and conduction of water and transpiration in *Polytrichum commune*, *Ann. Bot.*, **46**: 289–300.

BLAYDES, G. W., 1928: A survey of rate of water loss from leaves, *Ohio J. Sci.*, **28**: 99–118.

———, 1932: Water loss and stomatal investigations, *Abst. Doctor's Diss.* 8, *Ohio State Univ.*

———, 1935: Water vapor loss from plants growing in various habitats, *Ohio J. Sci.*, **35**: 112–130.

BLODGETT, F. H., 1901: Transpiration of rust-infected *Rubus*, *Torreya*, **1**: 34–35.

BOLAS, B. D., and R. MELVILLE, 1933: The influence of environment on the growth and metabolism of the tomato plant. I, Methods, technique and preliminary results, *Ann. Bot.*, **47**: 673–688.

BOUYOUCOS, G. J., 1911: Transpiration of wheat seedlings as affected by soils, by solutions of different densities, and by various chemical compounds, *J. Am. Soc. Agron.*, **3**: 130–191.

BRIERLEY, W. G., 1930: Transpiration rates in old and new canes of the Latham raspberry as measured by non-toxic dyes, *Proc. Am. Soc. Hort. Sci.*, **27**: 152–157.

———, 1931: Transpiration in new and old canes of the Latham raspberry, *Proc. Am. Soc. Hort. Sci.*, **28**: 188–193.

BRIGGS, L. J., and H. L. SHANTZ, 1913: The water requirement of plants. I, Investigations in the Great Plains area in 1910 and 1911, *U. S. Plant Ind. Bull.* 284.

——— and ———, 1913: The water requirement of plants. II, A review of the literature, U. S. *Plant Ind. Bull.* 285.

——— and ———, 1914: The relative water requirement of plants, *J. Agr. Res.*, **3**: 1–65.

——— and ———, 1915: Influence of hybridization and cross-pollination on the water requirement of plants, *J. Agr. Res.*, **4**: 391–403.

——— and ———, 1915: An automatic transpiration scale of large capacity for use with freely exposed plants, *J. Agr. Res.*, **5**: 117–133.

——— and ———, 1916: Daily transpiration during the normal growth period and its correlation with the weather, *J. Agr. Res.*, **7**: 155–213.

——— and ———, 1916: Hourly transpiration rate on clear days as determined by cyclic environmental factors, *J. Agr. Res.*, **5**: 583–651.

——— and ———, 1917: Comparison of the hourly evaporation rate of atmometers and free water surfaces with the transpiration rate of *Medicago sativa*, *J. Agr. Res.*, **9**: 277–293.

Brooks, C., and D. F. Fisher, 1926: Some high-temperature effects in apples: Contrasts in the two sides of an apple, *J. Agr. Res.*, **32**: 1–17.

Brown, H. T., and F. Escombe, 1900: Static diffusion of gases and liquids in relation to the assimilation of carbon and translocation in plants, *Phil. Trans. Roy. Soc.*, B, **193**: 223–291; *Ann. Bot.*, **14**: 537–542; *Proc. Roy. Soc.*, B, **67**: 124–128.

——— and ———, 1905: Researches on some of the physiological processes of green leaves, with special reference to the interchange of energy between the leaf and its surroundings, *Proc. Roy. Soc.*, B, **76**: 29–111.

Brown, M. A., 1910: The influence of air currents on transpiration, *Proc. Iowa Acad. Sci.*, **17**: 13–15.

Burgerstein, A., 1885: Ueber einige physiologische und pathologische Wirkungen des Kampfers auf die Pflanzen, inbesonders auf Laubesprosse, *Verh. Zool.-bot. Ges. Wien*, **34**: 543.

———, 1904: "Die Transpiration der Pflanzen," 283 pp., Jena, Gustav Fischer.

———, 1920: "Die Transpiration der Pflanzen," II, 262 pp., Jena, Gustav Fischer.

———, 1920: Änderungen der Spaltöffnungsweite unter dem Einfluss verschiedener Bedingungen, *Verh. Zool.-bot. Ges. Wien*, 113–131.

Burns, G. P., 1915: The relative transpiration of white pine seedlings, *Plant World*, **18**: 1–6.

Buscalioni, L., and G. Pollacci, 1902: Alteriovi ricerche sull' applicazione delle pellicole di collodio allo studio di alcuni processi fisiologici dell piante ed in particolare modo delle transpirazione vegetale, *Att. Inst. Bot. Univ. Pavia*, 7.

Chapman, G. W., 1931: The cause of succulence in plants, *New Phytol.*, **30**: 119–128

Childers, N. F., 1935: Some effects of sprays on the growth and transpiration of tomatoes, *Proc. Am. Soc. Hort. Sci.*, **33**: 532–535.

Chodat, F., 1931: Influence de la lumière sur la transpiration végétale, *C. R. Séances Soc. Phys. et Hist. Nat. Genève*, **48**: 55–58.

Clapp, G. L., 1908: A quantitative study of transpiration, *Bot. Gaz.*, **45**: 254–267.

Clements, F. E., and E. V. Martin, 1934: Effect of soil temperature on transpiration in *Helianthus annuus*, *Plant Physiol.*, **9**: 619–630.

Clements, H. F., 1934: Significance of transpiration, *Plant Physiol.*, **9**: 165–172.

Clinton, G. P., 1909: Spraying potatoes in dry seasons, *Conn. Sta. Bien. Rept.*, 739–752.

Clum, H. H., 1926: The effect of transpiration and environmental factors on leaf temperatures. I, Transpiration, *Am. J. Bot.*, **13**: 194–216.

———, 1926: The effect of transpiration and environmental factors on leaf temperatures. II, Light intensity and the relation of transpiration to the thermal death point, *Am. J. Bot.*, **13**: 217–231.

Copeland, E. B., 1902: The mechanism of stomata, *Ann. Bot.*, **16**: 327–365.

———, 1906: On the water relations of the coconut palm, *Philippine J. Sci.*, **1**: 6–58.

———, 1932: Transpiration by chaparral and its effect upon the temperature of leaves, *Univ. Calif. Pub.* **17**: 1–21.

Cowles, H. C., 1910: "A Textbook of Botany," Vol. II, "Ecology," American Book Company, New York.

Cross, F. B., 1927: May water loss from plants be reduced by foliage sprays? *Proc. Okla. Akad. Sci.* (*Okla. Univ.*), **7**: 129–131.

Cullinan, F. P., 1920: Transpiration studies with the apple, *Proc. Am. Soc. Hort. Sci.*, **17**: 232–240; *Bot. Abst.*, **9**: 226.

Curtis, O. F., 1926: What is the significance of transpiration? *Sci.*, **63**: 267–271.

———, 1936: Leaf temperatures and the cooling of leaves by radiation, *Plant Physiol.*, **11**: 343–364.

———, 1936: Transpiration and the cooling of leaves, *Am. J. Bot.*, **23**: 7–11.

Darrow, G. M., and H. Sherwood, 1931: Transpiration studies on strawberries, *Proc. Am. Soc. Hort. Sci.*, **28**: 225–230.

———, 1932: Methods of measuring strawberry leaf areas, *Plant Physiol.*, **7**: 745–747.

——— and G. W. Dewey, 1934: Studies on the stomata of strawberry varieties and species, *Proc. Am. Soc. Hort. Sci.*, **32**: 440–447.

Darwin, F., 1898: Observations on stomata, *Proc. Roy. Soc.*, B, **63**: 413–417.

———, 1898: Observations on stomata, *Phil. Trans. Roy. Soc.*, B, **190**: 531–621.

———, 1904: On a self-recording method applied to the movements of stomata, *Bot. Gaz.*, **37**: 81–105.

——— and D. F. M. Pertz, 1912: On a new method of estimating the aperture of stomata, *Proc. Roy. Soc.*, B, **84**: 136–154.

———, 1914: The effect of light on the transpiration of leaves, *Proc. Roy. Soc.*, B, **87**: 281–299.

———, 1916: On the relation between transpiration and stomatal aperture, *Phil. Trans. Roy. Soc.*, B, **207**: 413–437.

Deen, J. L., and M. H. Bruner, 1933: The effect of the 1932 eclipse upon the width of stomatal openings in gray birch, *Ecology*, **14**: 76–77.

DeVilliers, F. J., 1926: Factors influencing the transpiration rate of grapes, *S. African J. Sci.*, **23**: 486–487; *Biol. Abst.*, **3**: 1078.

Dillman, A. C., 1931: The water requirement of certain crop plants and weeds in the northern Great Plains, *J. Agr. Res.*, **42**: 187–238.

Dixon, H. H., 1898: Transpiration into a saturated atmosphere, *Proc. Roy. Irish Soc.*, III, **4**: 627–635; *Bot. Cent.*, **76**: 135.

———, 1914: "Transpiration and the Ascent of Sap in Plants," The Macmillan Company, New York.

Dodge, B. O., 1923: Effect of the orange-rusts of *Rubus* on the development and distribution of stomata, *J. Agr. Res.*, **25**: 495–501.

Dole, E. J., 1924: Studies on the effect of air, temperature and relative humidity on the transpiration of *Pinus Strobus*, *Vt. Sta. Bull.* 238.

Dosdall, L., 1919: Water requirement and adaptation in *Equisetum*, *Plant World*, **22**: 1–13; 29–44.

Dowd, O. J., 1931: Studies in the transpiration rate of apple varieties, *Proc. Am. Soc. Hort. Sci.*, **28**: 590–593.

Drabble, E., and H. Drabble, 1907: The relation between the osmotic strength of cell sap in plants and their physical environment, *Biochem. J.*, **2**: 117–132.

Dufrenoy, J., 1918: Les facteurs physiques de la transpiration chez les plantes et la transpiration des feuilles parasitées, *Rev. Gén. Sci. Ann.*, **29**: 565–566.

Duggar, B. M., 1911: "Plant Physiology," 92–93 pp., The Macmillan Company, New York.

——— and J. S. Cooley, 1914: The effect of surface films and dusts on the rate of transpiration, *Ann. Mo. Bot. Gard.*, **1**: 1–23.

——— and ———, 1914: The effect of surface films on the rate of transpiration. Experiments with potted potatoes, *Ann. Mo. Bot. Gard.*, **1**: 351–357.

——— and W. W. Bonns, 1918: The effect of Bordeaux mixture on the rate of transpiration, *Ann. Mo. Bot. Gard.*, **5**: 153–176.

Eaton, F. M., and G. O. Belden, 1929: Leaf temperatures of cotton and their relation to transpiration and varietal differences and yields, *U. S. Dept. Agr. Tech. Bull.* 91.

———, 1930: Cell-sap concentration and transpiration as related to age and development of cotton leaves, *J. Agr. Res.*, **40**: 791–805.

Eckerson, S. H., 1908: The number and size of stomata, *Bot. Gaz.*, **46**: 221–224.

Ehlers, J. H., 1915: The temperature of leaves of *Pinus* in winter, *Am. J. Bot.*, **2**: 32–70.

Eidelman, Z. M., 1933: Principal results of experiments on the artificial reduction of the leaf surface in various geographical locations, *Bull. Plant. Protection*, **3**: 65–72; *Biol. Abst.*, **9**: 747.

Emerson, J. L., and A. C. Hildreth, 1933: Preliminary report on reducing transpiration on transplanted evergreens, *Sci.*, **77**: 433–434.

Ezekiel, W. N., and J. J. Taubenhaus, 1932: Leaf temperatures of cotton plants with *Phymatotrichum* root rot, *Sci.*, **75**: 391–392.

Finch, A. H., and C. W. Van Horn, 1936: The moisture relations of pecan leaves, *Sci.*, **83**: 260.

Finnell, H. H., 1928: Effect of wind on plant growth, *J. Am. Soc. Agron.*, **20**: 1206–1210.

Firbas, F., 1931: Die Wirkung des Windes auf die Transpiration, *Ber. bot. Ges.*, **49**: 443–452.

Flood, M. G., 1919: Exudation of water by *Colocasia antiquorum*, *Sci. Proc. Roy. Dublin Soc.*, **15**: 505–512.

Flory, E. L., 1936: Comparison of the environment and some physiological responses of prairie vegetation and cultivated maize, *Ecology*, **17**: 67–103.

Frank, A. B., and F. Krüger, 1894: Ueber den Reiz, welchen die Behandlung mit Kupfer auf die Kartoffelpflanze hervorbringt, *Ber. bot. Ges.*, **12**: 8–11.

——— and ———, 1894: Ueber den direkten Einfluss der Kupfervitriolkalkbrühe auf die Kartoffelpflanze, *Arb. landw. Ges.*, **1894**: 1046.

Frear, D. E. H., 1935: Photoelectric apparatus for measuring leaf areas, *Plant Physiol.*, **10**: 569–574.

Freeman, G. F., 1908: A method for the quantitative determination of transpiration in plants, *Bot. Gaz.*, **46**: 118–129.

———, 1920: Studies in evaporation and transpiration, *Bot. Gaz.*, **70**: 190–211.

Frei, L., 1924: Influence of soil moisture on the transpiration capacity of plants, (Russian) *Bull. Soc. Nat. Leningrad*, **53**: 179–210; *Bot. Abst.*, **15**: 164–165.

Furr, J. R., and J. R. Magness, 1930: Preliminary report on relation of soil moisture to stomatal activity and fruit growth of apples, *Proc. Am. Soc. Hort. Sci.*, **27**: 212–218.

——— and E. S. Degman, 1931: Relation of moisture supply to stomatal behavior of the apple, *Proc. Am. Soc. Hort. Sci.*, **28**: 547–551.

Ganeau de Lamarlière, L., 1892: Recherches physiologiques sur les feuilles, développées à l'ombre et au soleil. VI, Transpiration, *Rev. Gén. Bot.*, **4**: 529.

Ganong, W. F., 1905: New precision appliances for use in Plant Physiology. II, *Bot. Gaz.*, **39**: 145–152.

Gates, F. C., and R. L. Black, 1931: The dragoyle as an ecological instrument, *Ecology*, **12**: 448–451.

GERDEL, R. W., and R. M. SALTER, 1928: Measurement of leaf area using the photoelectric cell, *J. Am. Soc. Agron.*, **20**: 635–643.

GIDDINGS, L. A., 1914: Transpiration of *Silphium laciniatum*, *Plant World*, **17**: 309–328.

GILBERT, B. E., and W. L. ADAMS, 1929: Moisture fluctuations in extracted plant solutions and in leaf tissue, *Plant Physiol.*, **4**: 529–536.

GIRTON, R. E., 1932: An inexpensive recording transpirometer, *Proc. Ind. Acad. Sci.*, **41**: 127–132.

GRAČANIN, M., 1932: Contribution à l'étude de la relation entre la transpiration et la résorption des ions, *C. R. Acad. Sci. Paris*, **195**: 899–901.

GRAF-MARIN, A., 1934: Studies on powdery mildew of cereals, *N. Y. Sta.* (*Cornell*) *Mem.* 157.

GRAINGER, J., and A. L. ALLEN, 1936: The internal temperatures of fruit tree buds, *Ann. App. Biol.*, **23**: 1–10.

GRAY, J., and G. J. PEIRCE, 1919: The influence of light upon the action of stomata and its relation to the transpiration of certain grains, *Am. J. Bot.*, **6**: 131–156.

GREGORY, F. G., and H. L. PEARSE, 1934: The resistance porometer and its application to the study of stomatal movement, *Proc. Roy. Soc.*, B, **114**: 477–493.

GUSTAFSON, F. G., 1934: The effect of a decrease in the amount of transpiration on the growth of certain plants, *Mich. Acad. Sci.*, *Arts and Letters*, **19**: 65–83.

HAAS, A. R. C., and F. F. HALMA, 1932: Relative transpiration rates in citrus leaves, *Bot. Gaz.*, **93**: 466–473.

HAAS-POETZL, I., 1930: Die Wirkung von Salzen auf die Spaltöffnungsbewegung, *Beih. bot. Cent.*, **47**: 255–270.

HABERLANDT, G., 1914: "Physiological Plant Anatomy," Eng. transl., pp. 493–498.

HAGEN, F., 1918: Zur Physiologie des Spaltöffnungsapparates, *Beitr. Allg. Bot.*, **1**: 260–291; *Bot. Abst.*, **13**: 63–64.

HAINES, F. M., 1932: A self-recording potometer with a note on transpiration under pressure, *Ann. Bot.*, **46**: 1051–1060.

———, 1935: Transpiration and pressure deficit. I, Apparatus and preliminary experiments, *Ann. Bot.*, **49**: 213–238.

———, 1936: Transpiration and pressure deficit. III, Observations by the thermopile method, *Ann. Bot.*, **50**: 1–22.

———, 1936: Transpiration and pressure deficit. IV, The effects of small deficits: Apparatus and preliminary experiments, *Ann. Bot.*, **50**: 281–291.

HART, H., 1929: Relation of stomatal behavior to stem rust resistance in wheat, *J. Agr. Res.*, **39**: 929–949.

HARTER, L. L., 1908: The influence of a mixture of soluble salts, principally sodium chloride, upon the leaf structure and transpiration of wheat, oats, and barley, *U. S. Plant Ind. Bull.* 134.

HAWKINS, R. S., 1927: Variations of water and dry matter in the leaves of Pina and Acala cotton, *Ariz. Sta. Tech. Bull.* **17**: 417–444.

HEILING, A., 1933: Influence of gaseous atmospheric impurities on plant transpiration, *Phytopath. Z.*, **5**: 435–492; *Biol. Abst.*, **27**: 3971.

HEINICKE, A. J., 1930: A method for studying the relative rates of transpiration of apple leaves and fruits, *Proc. Am. Soc. Hort. Sci.*, **26**: 312–314.

HENDERSON, F. Y., 1926: On the effect of light and other conditions upon the rate of water-loss from the mesophyll, *Ann. Bot.*, **40**: 507–535.

HENDRICKSON, A. H., 1921: Transpiration rate of deciduous fruit trees as influenced by irrigation and other factors, *Proc. Am. Soc. Hort. Sci.*, **18**: 145–147.

———, 1926: Certain water relations of the genus *Prunus*, *Hilgardia*, **1**: 479–524.

HILTNER, E., 1930: Dew and its importance in plant growth, *Pflanzenbau*, **3**: 1–70; *Exp. Sta. Rec.*, **64**: 211.

HIRANO, E., 1931: Relative abundance of stomata in *Citrus* and some related genera, *Bot. Gaz.*, **92**: 296–311.

HOPKINS, C. Y., 1936: Thermal death point of certain weed seeds, *Can. J. Res.*, **14**: 178–183.

HOWES, F., 1923: Researches on the vegetation of Natal. Ser. I. Section II. A new calcium chloride method of measuring the resistance to water loss in leaves, *Mem. Bot. Survey S. Africa*, **5**: 23–33; *Bot. Abst.*, **13**: 925.

HUBER, B., 1923: Transpiration in verschiedener Stammhöhe. I, *Sequoia gigantea*, *Z. Bot.*, **15**: 465–501; *Bot. Abst.*, **14**: 1218.

HURD-KARRER, A. M., and J. W. TAYLOR, 1929: The water content of wheat leaves at flowering time, *Plant Physiol.*, **4**: 393–397.

ILJIN, W. S., 1914: Die Regulierung der Spaltöffnungen in Zusammenhang mit Veränderung des osmotischen Druckes, *Beih. bot. Cent.*, **32**: 15–35.

———, 1932: Ueber Öffnen der Stomata bei starkem Welken der Pflanzen, *Jahrb. wiss. Bot.*, **77**: 220–251.

ISAAC, W. E., 1935: A preliminary study of the water loss of *Laminaria digitata* during intertidal exposure, *Ann. Bot.*, **49**: 109–117.

IVANOV, L. A., 1923: The present state of the question of drought resistance, *Bull. App. Bot. Plant Breeding*, **13**: 1–32.

——— and M. M. THIELMANN, 1923: Über den Einfluss des Lichtes verschiedener Wellenlänge auf die Transpiration der Pflanzen, *Flora*, **116**: 296–311.

JEFFREYS, H., 1918: Some problems of evaporation, *Phil. Mag. J. Sci.*, 6 ser., **35**: 270–280.

JIVANNA RAO, P. S., 1923: Stomata in cotton flower, *J. Madras Agr. Student Union*, **11**: 40–42; *Bot. Abst.*, **13**: 886.

JOHNSTON, C. O., and E. C. MILLER, 1934: Relation of leaf-rust infection to yield, growth, and water economy of two varieties of wheat, *J. Agr. Res.*, **49**: 955–981.

JOHNSTON, E. S., 1918: A simple non-absorbing atmometer mounting, *Plant World*, **21**: 257–261.

———, 1920: A method of studying the absorption-transpiration ratio in nutrient media, *Sci.*, **52**: 517–518.

JONES, I. D., 1932: Ultropaque microscope equipment as an aid in stomatal studies, *Proc. Am. Soc. Hort. Sci.*, **29**: 78–79.

JONES, T. N., and L. O. PALMER, 1932: Field curing of hay as influenced by plant physiological reactions, *Agr. Eng.*, **13**: 199–200.

——— and ———, 1933: Field curing of hay as influenced by plant physiological reactions. II, The role of leaves in the dehydration of hay plants, *Agr. Eng.*, **14**: 156–158.

——— and ———, 1934: Hay curing. III, Relation of engineering principles and physiological factors, *Agr. Eng.*, **15**: 198–201.

JONES, W. N., 1914: A self recording porometer and potometer, *New Phytol.*, **13**: 353–364.

KAMP, H., 1930: Untersuchungen über Kutikularbau und kutikuläre Transpiration von Blättern, *Jahrb. wiss. Bot.*, **72**: 403–465.

KELLEY, V. W., 1930: A comparison of the transpiration rates of twenty-one deciduous fruit species, *Ill. Sta. Bull.* 341.

———, 1930: Effect of certain hydrocarbon oils on the transpiration rate of some deciduous fruits, *Ill. Sta. Bull.* 353.

———, 1932: The effect of pruning of excised shoots on the transpiration rate of some deciduous fruit species, *Proc. Am. Soc. Hort. Sci.*, **29**: 71–73.

KHANKOJE, P., 1914: Some factors which influence the water requirement of plants, *J. Am. Soc. Agron.*, **6**: 1–23.

KIESSELBACH, T. A., and A. M. MONTGOMERY, 1911: The relation of climatic factors to the water used by the corn plant, *Neb. Sta. Rept.*, **1911**: 91–107.

———, 1916: Transpiration as a factor in crop production, *Neb. Sta. Res. Bull.* 6.

——— and A. ANDERSON, 1931: Quality of alfalfa hay in relation to curing practice, *U. S. Dept. Agr. Tech. Bull.* 235.

KNIGHT, R. C., 1915: A convenient modification of the porometer, *New Phytol.*, **14**: 212–216.

———, 1916: On the use of the porometer in stomatal investigation, *Ann. Bot.*, **30**: 57–76.

———, 1917: The interrelations of stomatal aperture, leaf water-content and transpiration rate, *Ann. Bot.*, **31**: 221–240.

———, 1917: Relative transpiration as a measure of the intrinsic transpiring power of the plant, *Ann. Bot.*, **31**: 351–359.

———, 1922: Further observations on the transpiration, stomata, leaf water-content, and wilting of plants, *Ann. Bot.*, **36**: 361–385.

KONDO, J. N., 1931: The influence of external factors as well as stages of development on the resistance of plants to dehydration, *Bull. App. Bot. and Plant Breeding*, **27**: 129–156.

KOSAKA, H., 1933: The relationship between different physiological aspects of plants and the appearance of pigments in the different parts of the plants. V, The relationship between the presence of anthocyanin pigments and transpiration in some cultivated plants, *J. Dept. Agr. Kyushu Imp. Univ.*, **4**: 95–126; *Chem. Abst.*, **28**: 2390.

KOURSSANOW, A. L., 1928: De l'influence de l'*Ustilago tritici* sur les fonctions physiologiques du froment, *Rev. Gén. Bot.*, **40**: 350–353.

KUYPER, J., 1915: Contributions to the physiology of stomata in *Saccharum officinarum*, *Arch. Siukerindus. Nederland. Indie.*, **23**: 1673–1700; *Exp. Sta. Rec.* **35**: 330.

LACHENMEIER, J., 1932: Transpiration und Wasserabsorption intakter Pflanzen nach vorausgegangener Verdunkelung bei Konstanz der Lichtintensität und der übrigen Aussenfaktoren, *Jahrb. wiss. Bot.*, **76**: 765–827; *Biol. Abst.*, **8**: 1659.

LAIDLOW, C. G. P., and R. C. KNIGHT, 1916: A description of a recording porometer and a note on stomatal behavior during wilting, *Ann. Bot.*, **30**: 47–57.

LAMOUR, J., 1918: On transpiration through leaf stomata, *Phil. Mag. J. Sci.*, 6 ser., **35**: 350–352, 433–434.

LEICK, E., 1927: Untersuchungen über den Einfluss des Lichtes auf die Öffnungsweite unterseitiger und oberseitiger Stomata desselben Blattes, *Jahrb. wiss. Bot.*, **67**: 771–848.

———, 1928: Über das verschiedenartige Verhalten der unterseitigen und oberseitigen Stomata desselben Blattes, *Ber. bot. Ges.*, **45**: 28–42.

LEITBEG, H., 1868: Beiträge zur Physiologie der Spaltöffnungsapparate, *Graz. Bot. Inst. Mitt.*, **1**: 123.

LEPESCHKIN, W. W., 1923: Über aktive und passive Wasserdrusen und Wasserpalten. *Ber. bot. Ges.*, **41**: 298–300; *Bot. Abst.*, **13**: 925.

LESAGE, P., 1894: Sur les rapports des palissades dans les feuilles avec la transpiration, *C. R. Acad. Sci. Paris*, **118**: 255–258.

LINSBAUER, K., 1926: Beobachtungen an Spaltöffnungen, *Planta*, **2**: 530–536; *Biol. Abst.*, **2**: 865.

———, 1927: Weitere Beobachtungen an Spaltöffnungen, *Planta*, **3**: 527–561; *Biol. Abst.*, **3**: 1079.

LIVINGSTON, B. E., 1906: The relation of desert plants to soil moisture and to evaporation, *Carnegie Inst. Wash. Pub.* 50.

———, 1907: Relative transpiration in cacti, *Plant World*, **10**: 110–114.

———, 1907: Evaporation and plant development, *Plant World*, **10**: 269–276.

———, 1908: Evaporation and plant habitats, *Plant World*, **11**: 1–9.

———, 1908: A method for controlling plant moisture, *Plant World*, **11**: 39–40.

———, 1909: Stomata and transpiration in *Tradescantia zebrina*, *Sci.*, **29**: 269–270.

———, 1910: A rain-correcting atmometer for ecological instrumentation, *Plant World*, **13**: 79–82.

———, 1910: Operation of the porous cup atmometer, *Plant World*, **13**: 111–119.

———, 1911: A radio-atmometer for comparing light intensities, *Plant World*, **14**: 96–99.

———, 1911: A study of the relation between summer evaporation intensity and centers of plant distribution in the United States, *Plant World*, **14**: 205–222.

———, 1911: Paper atmometers for studies in evaporation and plant transpiration, *Plant World*, **14**: 281–289.

———, 1911: Light intensity and transpiration, *Bot. Gaz.*, **52**: 417–438.

——— and A. H. ESTABROOK, 1912: Observations on the degree of stomatal movement in certain plants, *Bull. Torrey Bot. Club*, **39**: 15–22.

——— and W. H. BROWN, 1912: Relation of the daily march of transpiration to variations in the water content of foliage leaves, *Bot. Gaz.*, **53**: 309–330.

———, 1913: The resistance offered by leaves to transpirational water loss, *Plant World*, **16**: 1–35.

———, 1915: Atmometry and the porous cup atmometer, *Plant World*, **18**: 21–30, 51–74, 95–111, 143–149.

——— and L. A. HAWKINS, 1915: The water relation between plant and soil, *Carnegie Inst. Wash. Pub.* 204.

——— and E. B. SHREVE, 1916: Improvements in the method for determining the transpiring power of plant surfaces by hygrometric paper, *Plant World*, **19**: 287–309.

———, 1917: Atmometric units, *Johns Hopkins Univ. Circ.*, **3**: 160–170.

———, 1918: Porous clay cones for the auto-irrigation of potted plants, *Plant World*, **21**: 202–208.

——— and F. THONE, 1920: A simplified non-absorbing mounting for porous porcelain atmometers, *Sci.*, **52**: 85–87.

———, 1923: Studies upon the influence of solar radiation on the rate of transpirational water-loss from plants, *Carnegie Inst. Wash. Yearbook*, **22**: 288–289.

———, 1923: Blackened spheres for atmometry, *Sci.*, **58**: 182–183.

———, 1926: A black collodion coating for atmometer spheres, *Sci.*, **63**: 362–363.

———, T. HEMMI, and J. D. WILSON, 1926: Growth of young wheat plants in auto-irrigated soils, as related to the water-supplying power of the soil and to the adjustment of the auto-irrigator, *Plant Physiol.*, **1**: 387–395.

———, 1927: Plant water relations, *Quart. Rev. Biol.*, **2**: 494–515.

LLOYD, F. E., 1908: The physiology of stomata, *Carnegie Inst. Wash. Pub.* 82.

———, 1912: The relation of transpiration and stomatal movements to the water content of the leaves in *Fouquieria splendens*, *Plant World*, **15**: 1–14.

———, 1913: Leaf-water, and stomatal movement in *Gossypium* and a method of direct visual observation of stomata *in situ*, *Bull. Torrey Bot. Club*, **40**: 1–26.

LOFTFIELD, J. V. G., 1921: The behavior of stomata, *Carnegie Inst. Wash. Pub.* 314.

LONG, F. L., 1928: Stomata which show functional movement for a century, *Sci.*, **69**: 218–219.

——— and F. E. CLEMENTS, 1934: The method of collodion films for stomata, *Am. J. Bot.*, **21**: 7–17.

LOTT, R. V., and H. W. LEMERT, 1932: A simple device for use in leaf area studies, *Proc. Am. Soc. Hort. Sci.*, **29**: 83–84.

LUTMAN, B. F., 1916: Some studies on Bordeaux mixture, *Vt. Sta. Bull.* 196.

MACDOUGAL, D. T., 1922: How plants endure heat and cold, *Gard. Mag.*, **36**: 152–154.

MAGNESS, J. R., and J. R. FURR, 1930: Stomatal activity in apple leaves, *Proc. Am. Soc. Hort. Sci.*, **27**: 207–211.

MANZONI, L., and A. PUPPO, 1934: Sur la transpiration du blé en fonction das facteurs du climat, *C. R. Acad. Sci. Paris*, **198**: 1066–1068; *Biol. Abst.*, **9**: 1966–1967.

MARIANA, G., 1902: The influence of humidity on the formation and development of stomata. *Separate from Att. Inst. Bot. Univ. Pavia*, 2 ser., **8**: 32; *Exp. Sta. Rec.* **14**: 943.

MARKLEY, K. S., and C. E. SANDO, 1931: Permeability of the skin of apples as measured by evaporation loss, *Plant Physiol.*, **6**: 541–547.

MARSHALL, R. E., 1933: An apparatus for the ready determination of areas of compound leaves, *J. Agr. Res.*, **47**: 437–439.

MARTIN, E. V., and F. E. CLEMENTS, 1935: Studies on the effect of artificial wind on growth and transpiration in *Helianthus annuus*, *Plant Physiol.*, **10**: 613–636.

MARTIN, J. H., 1930: The comparative drought resistance of sorghums and corn, *J. Am. Soc. Agron.*, **22**: 986–993.

MARTIN, W. H., 1916: Influence of Bordeaux mixture on the rates of transpiration from abscised leaves and from potted plants, *J. Agr. Res.*, **7**: 529–548.

MAXIMOW, N., and V. RYBIN, 1921: Non-stomatal regulation of transpiration, *J. Russ. Bot. Congress*, **1**: 25–26; *Bot. Abst.*, **14**: 287.

———, 1925: The physiological basis of drought resistance of plants, *Eng. Abst.*

———, 1929: "The Plant in Relation to Water," 451 pp., translated by R. H. Yapp, The Macmillan Company, New York.

MCLEAN, R. C., 1919: Studies in the ecology of tropical rain forests. I, Humidity. *Ecology*, **7**: 5–54; II, Illumination, 121–172.

METZGER, J. E., M. G. HOLMES, and H. BIERMAN, 1925: Soybeans, *Md. Sta. Bull.* 277.

MEYER, B. S., 1927: The measurement of the rate of water-vapor loss from leaves under standard conditions, *Am. J. Bot.*, **14**: 582–592.

———, 1931: Effects of mineral salts upon the transpiration and water requirement of the cotton plant, *Am. J. Bot.*, **18**: 79–93.

———, 1932: The daily periodicity of transpiration in the tulip poplar (*Liriodendron tulipifera*), *Ohio J. Sci.*, **32**: 104–114.

MILLER, E. C., 1916: Comparative study of the root systems and leaf areas of the corn and the sorghums, *J. Agr. Res.*, **6**: 311–333.

———, 1916: Relative water requirement of corn and the sorghums, *J. Agr. Res.*, **6**: 473–485.

———, 1917: Daily variation of water and dry matter in the leaves of corn and the sorghums, *J. Agr. Res.*, **10**: 11–47.

——— and W. B. COFFMAN, 1918: Comparative transpiration of corn and the sorghums, *J. Agr. Res.*, **13**: 579–605.

———, 1923: Relative water requirement of corn and sorghums, *Kans. Sta. Tech. Bull.* 12.

——— and A. R. SAUNDERS, 1923: Some observations on the temperature of the leaves of crop plants, *J. Agr. Res.*, **26**: 15–43.

———, 1925: Relative transpiration in crop plants, unpub. data, *Kans. Sta.*

———, 1928: Some observations on the number of stomata of crop plants, unpub. data, *Kans. Sta.*

———, 1928: The relation of soil moisture to transpiration, unpub. data, *Kans. Sta.*

———, 1928: The effect of Bordeaux mixture on the rate of transpiration, unpub. data, *Kans. Sta.*

MINCKLER, L. S., 1936: A new method of measuring transpiration, *J. Forestry*, **34**: 36–39.

MITCHELL, J. W., 1936: Measurement of the area of attached and detached leaves, *Sci.*, **83**: 334–336.

MITSCHERLICH, A., 1904: Ein Verdunstungsmesser, *Landw. Versuchs-Stat.*, **60**: 63–72.

MONTEMARTINI, L., 1904: Note di fisiopatologia vegetale, *Atti dell' Ist. Bot. di Pavia*, Ser. II, 63 pp., **9**: 1–66; *Bot. Cent.* **98**: 276–277.

———, 1932: Intorno all'azione della luce e di eccitanti chimici sopra la traspirazione, *Lavori R. Inst. Bot. Palermo*, **3**: 3–15; *Biol. Abst.*, **8**: 1138.

MONTGOMERY, E. G., 1911: Methods of determining the water requirements of crops, *Proc. Am. Soc. Agron.*, **3**: 261–283.

——— and T. A. KIESSELBACH, 1912: Studies in water requirements of corn, *Neb. Sta. Bull.* 128.

MUENSCHER, W. L. C., 1915: A study of the relation of transpiration to the size and number of the stomata, *Am. J. Bot.*, **2**: 487–504.

MÜLLER-THURGAU, H., 1894: Die Tätigkeit pilzkranker Blätter, 4 *Jahresb. der Vers. Stat. Obst. Wein- und Gartenbau Wadensweil*, **1894**: 54–57.

MURPHY, H. C., 1935: Effect of crown rust infection on yield and water requirement of oats, *J. Agr. Res.*, **50**: 387–412.

NEWTON, J. D., 1925: The relation of the salt concentration of the culture solution to transpiration and root respiration, *Sci. Agr.*, **5**: 318–320.

NEWTON, R., and W. M. MARTIN, 1930: Physicochemical studies on the nature of drought resistance in crop plants, *Can. J. Res.*, **3**: 336–383, 385–427.

NICHOLS, G. E., 1913: A simple revolving table for standardizing porous cup atmometers, *Bot. Gaz.*, **55**: 249–251.

———, 1923: The Musch rain-correcting mounting for porous porcelain atmometers. *Sci.*, **57**: 26–28.

NICOLAS, G., 1930: Sur la transpiration des plantes parasitées par des champignons, *Rev. Gén. Bot.*, **42**: 257–271.

NIEMANN, W., 1932: Über Beziehungen zwischen Blattgrösse und Spaltöffnungszahl in Abhängigkeit von der Bodenfeuchtigkeit, *Sonderabdruck Angew. Bot.*, **14**: Heft 1.

OVERLEY, F. L., E. L. OVERHOLSER, and I. A. HAUT, 1931: The relation of soil moisture and spray applications to stomatal behavior and growth of Jonathan apples, *Proc. Am. Soc. Hort. Sci.*, **28**: 543–546.

PAETZ, K. W., 1930: Untersuchungen über die Zusammenhänge zwischen stomatärer Öffnungsweite und bekannten Intensitäten bestimmter Spektralbezirke, *Planta*, **10**: 611–665; *Biol. Abst.*, **9**: 296–297.

PAVILINOVA, E., 1926: Physiological significance of guttation, *Bull. Inst. Rech. Biol. and Sta. Biol. Univ. Perm*, **4**: 471–478.

PENFOUND, W. T., 1932: The anatomy of the castor bean as conditioned by light intensity and soil moisture, *Am. J. Bot.*, **19**: 538–546.

PETERHÄNSEL, H., 1934: Experimental investigations on the relations between soil moisture and the use of water by plants, *Bot. Arch.*, **36**: 99–151; *Exp. Sta. Rec.*, **72**: 166.

PLEASANTS, A. L., 1930: The effect of nitrate fertilizer on stomatal behavior, *J. Elisha Mitchell Sci. Soc.*, **46**: 95–116; *Biol. Abst.*, **8**: 1659.

POOL, R. J., 1923: Xerophytism and comparative leaf anatomy in relation to transpiring power, *Bot. Gaz.*, **76**: 221–241.

PULLING, H. E., 1919: Sunlight and its measurement, *Plant World*, **22**: 151–172, 187–209.

REA, M. W., 1921: Stomata and hydathodes in *Campanula rotundifolia* L., *New Phytol.*, **20**: 56–72.

REED, H. S., 1910: The effect of certain chemical agents upon the transpiration and growth of wheat seedlings, *Bot. Gaz.*, **49**: 81–109.

——— and J. S. COOLEY, 1913: The transpiration of apple leaves infected with *Gymnosporangium*, *Bot. Gaz.*, **55**: 421–430.

——— and E. HIRANO, 1931: The density of stomata in citrus leaves, *J. Agr. Res.*, **43**: 209–222.

REHFOUS, L., 1917: Étude sur les stomates, *Univ. Genève Inst. Bot.* IX, No. 6, 110 pp.

RENNER, O., 1910: Beiträge zur Physik der Transpiration, *Flora*, **100**: 451–547.

RHINE, J. B., 1924: Clogging of stomata of conifers in relation to smoke injury and distribution, *Bot. Gaz.*, **78**: 226–232.

RICHARDSON, A. E. V., 1923: The water requirement of farm crops, *J. Dept. Agr. Victoria*, **21**: 193–212, 257–284, 321–339, 385–404, 449–481; *Exp. Sta. Rec.*, **50**: 733–735.

RICOME, H., 1903: Influence du chlorure de sodium sur la transpiration et l'absorption de l'eau chez les végétaux, *C. R. Acad. Sci. Paris*, **137**: 141–143.

RIPPEL, A., 1919: Der Einfluss der Bodentrockenheit auf den anatomischen Bau der Pflanzen insbesondere von *Sinapis alba*, etc., *Beih. bot. Cent.* I, **36**: 187–260.

ROSEN, H. R., 1933: Influence of spray applications on air temperatures surrounding sprayed potato plants, *Phytopath.*, **23**: 912–916.

RUDOLPH, K., 1925: Epidermis and epidermale Transpiration, *Bot. Arch.*, **9**: 49–94. Quoted by Crafts, 1933.

RUMM, C., 1893: Ueber die Wirkung der Kupferpräparate bei Bekämpfung der sogenannten Blattfallkrankheit der Weinrebe, *Ber. bot. Ges.*, **11**: 79–93.

RUNYON, E. H., 1936: Ratio of water content to dry weight in leaves of the creosote bush, *Bot. Gaz.*, **97**: 518–553.

SALISBURY, E. J., 1927: On the causes and ecological significance of stomatal frequency, with special reference to the woodland flora, *Phil. Trans. Roy. Soc.*, B, **216**: 1–65.

SAMPSON, A. W., and L. M. ALLEN, 1909–1916: Influence of physical factors on transpiration, *Minn. Bot. Studies*, **1–4**: 33–60.

SAWYER, W. H., 1932: Stomatal apparatus of the cultivated cranberry, *Vaccinium macrocarpon*, *Am. J. Bot.*, **19**: 508–513.

SAYRE, J. D., 1919: Comparative transpiration of tobacco and mullein, *Ohio J. Sci.*, **19**: 422–426.

———, 1919: Factors controlling variations in the rate of transpiration, *Ohio J. Sci.*, **19**: 491–509.

———, 1920: The relation of hairy leaf coverings to the resistance of leaves to transpiration, *Ohio J. Sci.*, **20**: 55–86.

———, 1923: Physiology of stomata of *Rumex patientia*, *Sci.*, **57**: 205–206.

———, 1926: Physiology of the stomata of *Rumex patientia*, *Ohio J. Sci.*, **26**: 233–267.

———, 1928: A recording atmometer, *Ecology*, **19**: 123–125.

———, 1929: Opening of stomata in different ranges of wave lengths of light, *Plant Physiol.*, **4**: 323–328.

SCARTH, G. W., 1926: The influence of the hydrogen-ion on the turgor and movement of the plant cells with especial reference to stomatal movement, *Proc. First Int. Cong. Plant Sci.*, Ithaca, N. Y., rev. by C. A. Shull, *Bot. Gaz.*, **82**: 453–454.

———, 1927: Stomatal movement: Its regulation and regulatory role—a review, *Protoplasma*, **2**: 498–511.

———, 1929: The influence of H-ion concentration on the turgor and movement of plant cells with special reference to stomatal behavior, *Proc. Int. Cong. Plant Sci.*, **2**: 1151–1162.

———, 1932: Mechanism of the action of light and other factors on stomatal movement, *Plant Physiol.*, **7**: 481–504.

———, J. Whyte, and A. Brown, 1933: On the cause of night opening of stomata, *Trans. Roy. Soc. Can.*, Section **5**: 115–117.

Schander, R., 1904: Über die physiologische Wirkung der Kupfervitriol-kalkbrühe, *Landw. Jahrb.*, **33**: 517–584.

Schertz, F. M., 1929: The origin of chlorophyll and its relation to the blood pigment, *Sci.*, **70**: 258–259.

Schmucker, T., 1928: Über den Einfluss narkotischer Stoffe auf Transpiration und Wasserleitung, *Jahrb. wiss. Bot.*, **68**: 771–800.

Schwendener, S., 1881: Ueber Bau und Mechanik der Spaltöffnungen, *Monatsber. Akad. Wiss. Berlin*, **1881**: 833.

———, 1889: Die Spaltöffnungen der *Gramineen* und *Cyperaceen*, *Sitzungsber. Akad. Wiss. Berlin*, **1**: 65–77.

Seybold, A., 1929: Die pflanzliche Transpiration, *Ergeb. Biol.*, **5**: 29–165.

———, 1931, 1932: Weitere Beiträge zur Kenntnis der Transpirationsanalyse, *Planta*, **13**: 18–28; **14**: 77–93, 386–410; **16**: 518–525.

———, 1933: Zur Klärung des Begriffes Transpirationswiderstand, *Planta*, **21**: 353–367.

Shantz, H. L., and L. N. Piemeisel, 1927: The water requirement of plants at Akron, Colorado, *J. Agr. Res.*, **34**: 1093–1190.

Shapiro, A. A., and H. deForest, 1932: A comparison of transpiration rates in chaparral, *Ecology*, **13**: 290–295.

Shardakov, S., 1928: The physiological significance of guttation, *Bull. Inst. Rech. Biol. et Sta. Biol. Univ. Perm*, **6**: 193–208.

Shive, J. W., 1915: An improved non-absorbing porous cup atmometer, *Plant World*, **18**: 7–10.

——— and W. H. Martin, 1917: The effect of surface films of Bordeaux mixture on the foliar transpiring power in tomato plants, *Plant World*, **20**: 67–86.

Shreve, E. B., 1914: The daily march of transpiration in a desert perennial, *Carnegie Inst. Wash. Pub.* 194.

———, 1916: An analysis of the causes of variations in the transpiring power of cacti, *Physiol. Res.*, **2**: 73–127.

———, 1917: The transpiring power of plants, *Carnegie Inst. Wash. Year Book*, **16**: 66–68.

———, 1919: A thermo-electrical method for the determination of leaf temperature, *Plant World*, **22**: 100–104.

———, 1919: The role of temperature in the determination of the transpiring power of leaves by hygrometric paper, *Plant World*, **22**: 172–180.

———, 1924: Factors governing seasonal changes in transpiration of *Encelia farinosa*. *Bot. Gaz.*, **77**: 432–439.

Shull, C. A., 1919: Transpiration as energy dispersal, *School Sci. and Math.*, **19**: 1–6.

———, 1934: Lateral water transfer in leaves of *Ginkgo biloba*, *Plant Physiol.*, **9**: 387–389.

———, 1936: Rate of adjustment of leaf temperature to incident energy, *Plant Physiol.*, **11**: 181–188.

Sideris, C. P., and B. H. Krauss, 1928: Water relations of pineapple plants, *Soil Sci.*, **26**: 305–313.

SITTON, B. G., 1932: Some observations on stomatal movements in *Hicoria pecan*, *Proc. Am. Soc. Hort. Sci.*, **29**: 80–82.

SMITH, A. M., 1909: On the internal temperature of leaves in tropical isolation with special reference to the effect of color on the temperature, *Ann. Roy. Bot. Gard. Peradniya*, **4**: 229–298.

SMITH, G. E., 1935: On the orientation of stomata, *Ann. Bot.*, **49**: 451–477.

SMITH, H. B., 1922: Stomatal behavior of plants in the greenhouse in winter, *Mich. Acad. Sci., Arts, and Letters*, pp. 109–117.

SMITH, H. F., 1936: The effect of light on transpiration, *Ann. Bot.*, **50**: 155–159.

SMITH, W. H., 1933: Evaporation of water from apples in relation to temperature and atmospheric humidity, *Ann. App. Biol.*, **20**: 220–235.

SPALDING, V. M., 1905: Soil water in relation to transpiration, *Torreya*, **5**: 25–27.

SPERRY, O. E., 1936: A study of the growth, transpiration, and distribution of the conifers of the Rocky Mountain National Park, *Bull. Torrey Bot. Club*, **63**: 75–103.

SPROAT, B. B., and G. M. DARROW, 1935: Relation of leaf area to berry production in the strawberry, *Proc. Am. Soc. Hort. Sci.*, **33**: 389–392.

STAHL, E., 1894: Einige Versuche über Transpiration und Assimilation, *Bot. Ztg.*, **52**: 117–146.

STÅLFELT, M. G., 1932: Der Einfluss des Windes auf die kutikuläre und stomatäre Transpiration, *Svensk. Bot. Tidsk.*, **26**: 45–69.

———, 1929: Die Abhängigkeit der Spaltöffnungsreaktionen von der Wasserbilanz, *Planta*, **8**: 287–340; *Biol. Abst.*, **6**: 681.

STANLEY, J., 1932: A method of making permanent black atmometer bulbs, *Ecology*, **13**: 218–219.

STARK, O. K., and C. J. WHITFIELD, 1930: An improved evaporimeter, *Ecology*, **11**: 288–292.

STEFAN, J., 1873: Versuche über die Verdunstung, *Sitzungsber. Akad. Wiss. Wien*, **68**: 385–428.

STEINBERG, R. A., 1930: An automatic watering system with recorder for use in growing plants, *J. Agr. Res.*, **40**: 233–241.

STRUGGER, S., and F. WEBER, 1926: Zur Physiologie der Stomata-Nebenzellen, *Ber. bot. Ges.*, **44**: 272–278.

TAVČAR, A., 1926: Die Vererbung der Anzahl von Spaltöffnungen bei *Pisum sativum*, *Z. Pflanzenzücht.*, **11**: 241–259.

THOM, C. C., and H. F. HOLTZ, 1917: Factors influencing the water requirements of plants, *Wash. Sta. Bull.* 146.

THOMAS, N., and A. FERGUSON, 1917: On the reduction of transpiration observations, *Ann. Bot.*, **31**: 241–255.

THUT, H. F., 1932: The movement of water through some submerged plants, *Am. J. Bot.*, **19**: 693–709.

TILFORD, P. E., and C. MAY, 1929: The effect of bordeaux mixture on the internal temperature of potato leaflets, *Phytopath.*, **19**: 943–949.

TRANSEAU, E. N., 1911: Apparatus for the study of comparative transpiration, *Bot. Gaz.*, **52**: 54–60.

TRELEASE, S. F., and B. E. LIVINGSTON, 1916: The daily march of transpiring power as indicated by the porometer and by standardized hygrometric paper, *J. Ecol.*, **4**: 1–14.

———, 1922: Incipient drying and wilting as indicated by movements of cocoanut pinnae, *Am. J. Bot.*, **9**: 253–265.

———, 1922: Foliar transpiring power of the cocoanut, *Philippine J. Sci.*, **20**: 167–176.

TUMANOV, J. J., 1927: Ungenügende Wasserversorgung und das Welken der Pflanzen als Mittel zur Erhöhung ihrer Dürreresistenz, *Planta*, **3**: 391–480.

———, 1929: Wilting and drought resistance, *Bull. App. Bot. and Plant Breeding*, **22**: 107–146.

TURRELL, F. M., 1933: The internal exposed surface of foliage leaves, *Sci.*, **78**: 536–537.

———, 1934: A method for the measurement of the internal exposed surface of foliage leaves, *Univ. Iowa Studies Nat. Hist.*, **16**: 119–126.

———, 1936: The area of the internal exposed surface of dicotyledon leaves, *Am. J. Bot.*, **23**: 255–264.

UNGER, F., 1861: Beiträge zur Anatomie und Physiologie der Pflanzen. XI, XII, Neue Untersuchungen über die Transpiration der Gewächse, *Sitzungsber. Akad. Wiss. Wien*, **44**: 181–227, 327–368.

———, 1862: Neue Untersuchungen über die Transpiration der Pflanzen, *Sitzungsber. Akad. Wiss. Wien*, **45**: 181–217.

URSPRUNG, A., 1903: Die physikalischen Eigenschaften der Laubblätter, *Bibl. Bot.*, **60**: 1–120.

VAN DE ROOVAART, E., and G. D. FULLER, 1935: Stomatal frequency in cereals, *Ecology*, **16**: 278–279.

VAN DE SANDE-BAKEHUYZEN, H. L., 1928: Studies upon wheat grown under constant conditions. I, II, *Plant Physiol.*, **3**: 1–31.

VASSILIEV, I. M., 1932: Plant physiology in relation to drought control, (Russian), *Soc. Zern. Khoz.*, **1-2**: 10–12. Quoted by Aamodt and Johnston, 1936.

VEIHMEYER, F. J., and A. H. HENDRICKSON, 1927: Soil-moisture conditions in relation to plant growth, *Plant Physiol.*, **2**: 71–82.

——— and ———, 1927: The relation of soil moisture to cultivation and plant growth, *Proc. Int. Cong. Soil Sci. Wash.*, **3**: 498–513.

VERSCHAFFELT, E. and J., 1890: De transpiratie der planten in koolzuurorije lucht, *Bot. Jaarboek* (*uitgegeven door het kruidkundig genootschap Dodonaea te Gent*), **2**: 305.

VON MOHL, H., 1856: Welche Ursachen bewirken die Erweiterung und Verengung der Spaltöffnungen? *Bot. Ztg.*, **14**: 697–704, 713–720.

VYVYAN, M. C., and H. EVANS, 1932: The leaf relations of fruit trees. I, A morphological analysis of the distribution of leaf surface on two nine-year-old apple trees (Laxton superb), *J. Pom. and Hort. Sci.*, **10**: 228–270.

WALTER, H., 1925, 1926: Die Verdunstung von Wasser in bewegter Luft und ihre Abhängigkeit von der Grosse der Oberfläche, *Z. Bot.*, **18**: 1–47.

WATSON, A. N., 1933: Preliminary study on the relation between thermal emissivity and plant temperatures, *Ohio J. Sci.*, **33**: 435–450.

———, 1934: Further studies on the relation between thermal emissivity and plant temperatures, *Am. J. Bot.*, **21**: 605–609.

WEAVER, J. E., 1916: The effect of certain rusts upon the transpiration of their hosts, *Minn. Bot. Studies*, **4**: 397–406.

——— and A. MOGENSEN, 1919: Relative transpiration of coniferous and broad-leaved trees in autumn and winter, *Bot. Gaz.*, **68**: 393–424.

WEBER, F., 1923: Enzymatische Regulation der Spaltöffnungsbewegung, *Natur. Wiss.*, **11**: 309–316.

———, 1931: Harnstoffpermeabilität ungleich alter Stomatazellen, *Protoplasma*, **14**: 75–82.

WEIGAND, K. M., 1910: The relation of hairy and cutinized coverings to transpiration, *Bot. Gaz.*, **49**: 430–444.

———, 1910: Some evaporation experiments in relation to excessive transpiration, *Sci.*, **31**: 434.

WEINBERGER, J. H., 1931: Growth of fruit and stomatal behavior of Elberta peaches as affected by weather conditions, *Proc. Am. Soc. Hort. Sci.*, **28**: 539–542.

WEISS, A., 1865–1866: Untersuchungen über die Zahlen- und Grössenverhältnisse der Spaltöffnungen, *Jahrb. wiss. Bot.*, **4**: 126–196.

WEISS, F., 1924: The effect of rust infection upon the water requirement of wheat, *J. Agr. Res.*, **27**: 107–118.

WHITFIELD, C. J., 1932: Ecological aspects of transpiration. I, Pike's Peak Region: Climatic aspects, *Bot. Gaz.*, **93**: 436–452.

———, 1932: Ecological aspects of transpiration. II, Pike's Peak and Santa Barbara regions: Endaphic and climatic aspects, *Bot. Gaz.*, **94**: 183–196.

WIGGINS, R. G., 1921: Variations in the osmotic concentrations of the guard cells during the opening and closing of stomata, *Am. J. Bot.*, **8**: 30–41.

WILLARD, C. J., 1931: The moisture content of forage at different times in the day, *J. Am. Soc. Agron.*, **23**: 853–859.

WILLIAMS, R. F., 1935: An analysis of the effect of phosphorus supply on the transpiration ratio in plants, *Australian J. Exp. Biol. and Med. Sci.*, **13**: 49–66.

WILSON, H. W., 1924: Studies on the transpiration of some Australian plants with notes on the structure of their leaves, *Proc. Roy. Soc. Victoria*, **36**: 175–237.

WILSON, J. D., 1930: A modified form of non-absorbing valve for porous-cup atmometers, *Sci.*, **71**: 101–102.

——— and H. A. RUNNELS, 1931: Bordeaux mixture as a factor increasing drought injury, *Phytopath.*, **21**: 729–738.

——— and ———, 1933: Some effects of Bordeaux mixture on transpiration, *Ohio Sta. Bimon. Bull.*, **18**: 147–151.

——— and ———, 1934: Influence of Bordeaux mixture and an oil emulsion on water requirement, *Ohio Sta. Bimon. Bull.*, **19**: 21–28.

——— and ———, 1934: The relative influence of calcium and magnesium in Bordeaux mixture on the transpiration rate. I, *Ohio Sta. Bimon. Bull.*, **19**: 158–163.

——— and ———, 1934: Influence of Bordeaux and oil sprays on the daily curve of transpiration, *Ohio Sta. Bimon. Bull.*, **19**: 179–186.

——— and ———, 1934: Transpirational response of various plants to Bordeaux mixture, *Ohio Sta. Bimon. Bull.*, **19**: 198–202.

——— and ———, 1935: Influence of certain sulfate-hydrated lime mixtures on transpiration, *Ohio Sta. Bimon. Bull.*, **175**: 143–146.

——— and ———, 1935: Influence of various sulfur-containing fungicides on transpiration, *Ohio Sta. Bimon. Bull.*, **175**: 146–148.

——— and F. A. WELTON, 1935: The use of an evaporation index in watering lawns, *Ohio Sta. Bimon. Bull.*, **20**: 112–119.

——— and H. A. RUNNELS, 1935: The relation of time to the effect of Bordeaux mixture on transpiration, *Ohio Sta. Bimon. Bull.*, **20**: 120–124.

WILSON, J. K., 1923: The nature and reaction of water from hydathodes, *N. Y. Sta. (Cornell) Mem.* 65.

WITHROW, R. W., 1935: A photoelectric device for the rapid measurement of leaf area, *J. Agr. Res.*, **50**: 637–643.

WOOD, J. G., 1934: The physiology of xerophytism in Australian plants. The stomatal frequencies, transpiration and osmotic pressures of sclerophyll and tomentose succulent-leaved plants, *J. Ecology*, **22**: 69–87.

WOODS, A. F., 1893: Some recent investigations of the evaporation of water from plants, *Bot. Gaz.*, **18**: 304–310.

WRENGER, M., 1935: Über den Einfluss des Windes auf die Transpiration der Pflanzen, *Z. Bot.*, **29**: 257–320.

YAPP, R. H., 1912: *Spirea Ulmaria*, L., and its bearing on the problem of xeromorphy in marsh plants, *Ann. Bot.*, **26**: 815–871.

——— and U. C. MASON, 1932: The distribution of water in the shoots of certain herbaceous plants, *Ann. Bot.*, **46**: 159–183.

YOCUM, L. E., 1935: The stomata and transpiration of oaks, *Plant Physiol.*, **10**: 795–801.

YUNCKER, T. G., 1916: A study of the relation of soil moisture to transpiration and photosynthesis in the corn plant, *Plant World*, **19**: 151–161.

ZALENSKI, V., 1921: Action of high temperature on the behavior of stomata, *J. Russ. Bot. Congress*, **1**: 62–63; *Bot. Abst.*, **14**: 287–288.

———, 1923: The intensity of transpiration in the upper and in the lower leaves, *Bull. Agr. Inst. Saratov*, **1**: 13–17; *Bot. Abst.*, **15**: 165–166.

ZHEMCHUZHNIKOV, E. A., 1922: To the question of stomatal regulation of plant's transpiration, *J. Agr. Res. Don and North Caucasus*, **(1922)**: 29–39; *Exp. Sta. Rec.*, **52**: 517.

———, 1924: Transpiration by the stomata, (Russian) *Trans. Agr. Exp. Inst. Don and Northern Caucasus*, 1–34; *Bull.* 164; *Bot. Abst.*, **15**: 166.

ZUCKER, A., 1896: Beitrag zur direkten Beeinflussung der Pflanzen durch die Kupfervitriol-Kalkbrühe, *Inaug. Diss., Stuttgart.*

CHAPTER VIII

THE FORMATION OF CARBOHYDRATES BY THE GREEN PLANT

I. THE SYNTHETIC POWER OF THE GREEN PLANT

The materials that enter the green plant from its environment are for the most part inorganic compounds of the most simple character. Thus, for example, the plant obtains carbon dioxide from the air; water and the nitrates, sulphates, and phosphates of potassium, sodium, magnesium, iron, calcium, among others, from the soil. From these simple compounds or in their presence the plant is able to synthesize a large variety of substances of varying degrees of complexity, the most important and abundant of which are the carbohydrates, fats and oils, amino acids, proteins, glucosides, chlorophyll, and various other pigments, enzymes, vitamins, tannins, alkaloids, and numerous organic acids. Some of the substances named may be degeneration products under certain conditions, but, if they are, they are derived from more complex compounds which, in turn, have been synthesized by the plant.

The first evident synthetic product that is formed by the green plant in any appreciable quantity from the simple inorganic compounds that are obtained from the air and soil is one of the more simple forms of carbohydrate. The first carbohydrate thus formed is the nucleus or foundation of most of the other organic compounds in the plant. A general knowledge of the carbohydrates is thus necessary for a clear understanding not only of their formation but also of the formation of other plant substances.

II. THE CARBOHYDRATES OF THE GREEN PLANT

The carbohydrates are the most abundant compounds in the plant and make up the greater portion of its dry weight. The term "carbohydrates" signifies or implies that these compounds are composed of carbon and water, and the name originated from the fact that they contain carbon, hydrogen, and oxygen with the two latter elements generally present in the same proportion as in water. Some few carbohydrates, however, *e.g.*, rhamnose ($C_6H_{12}O_5$) do not show this simple relation between the hydrogen and oxygen atoms, while certain other compounds, *e.g.*, acetic acid ($C_2H_4O_2$) and lactic acid ($C_3H_6O_3$), which are not carbohydrates, contain hydrogen and oxygen atoms in the same proportion as in carbohydrates. From the present knowledge of the structure of carbohydrates they may be defined more specifically as aldehyde alcohols, ketone alcohols, which contain an "ose" or sugar group, or compounds that are converted by hydrolysis into one or both of these two types of alcohol.

The green plant alone possesses the power to synthesize carbohydrates from inorganic compounds. Although the production of carbohydrates has been accomplished artificially, this has been done in only an extremely limited way as far as the number of compounds and the quantity of material obtained are concerned. The members of the animal kingdom lack the power to synthesize carbohydrates from inorganic material and are dependent either directly or indirectly upon plants for their supply of these energy-producing foods.

In addition to being the basis for the formation of numerous plant products, the carbohydrates make up the greater part of the plant's structural framework and are also one of the chief foods of the protoplasm and the main source of energy in the plant. The carbohydrates are stored in relatively large quantities as reserve food in various parts of the plant, and when present in the cell sap in the soluble form they increase its osmotic value and thus play a part in maintaining the turgidity of the cells.

There are various classifications of the carbohydrates, but, in the main, their classification rests upon their solubility, taste, number of carbon atoms, the number of sugar groups that they contain, their reaction toward various reagents, their products of hydrolysis, and other physical and chemical reactions. The principal carbohydrates that occur in the green plant may be classified according to the following diagram:

The principal carbohydrates that may occur in green plants

- **The sugars**
  - **Monosaccharoses**
    - **Pentoses** $C_5H_{10}O_5$
      - Arabinose (R.)[1]
      - Xylose (R.)
      - Rhamnose (R.)
    - **Hexoses** $C_6H_{12}O_6$
      - Dextrose, glucose, or grape sugar (R.)
      - Levulose, fructose, or fruit sugar (R.)
      - Mannose (R.)
      - Galactose (R.)
  - **Disaccharoses** $C_{12}H_{22}O_{11}$
    - Sucrose, saccharose or cane sugar (N. R.)[2]
    - Maltose or malt sugar (R.)
    - Gentiobiose (R.)
    - Melibiose (R.)
  - **Trisaccharoses** $C_{18}H_{32}O_{16}$
    - Raffinose (N. R.)
    - Gentianose (N. R.)
    - Melicitose (N. R.)
- **The non-sugars**
  - **Polysaccharoses**
    - **Hexosans**
      - Celluloses $(C_6H_{10}O_5)_n$ — See components of cell wall (Chap. I)
      - Amyloses or starches $(C_6H_{10}O_5)_n$
        - Starch (dextrosan)
        - Dextrins (dextrosans)
        - Inulin (levulosan)
      - Mannosans or Mannans $(C_6H_{10}O_5)_n$
      - Galactosans or Galactans $(C_6H_{10}O_5)_n$
    - **Pentosans** $(C_5H_8O_2)_n$
      - Araban
      - Xylan

[1] (R.) reducing sugars.
[2] (N. R.) nonreducing sugars.

From the preceding diagram it is observed that the carbohydrates may be divided into the sugars and the nonsugars and that, since each carbohydrate contains one or more sugar or saccharose groups, the term "saccharose" is used as a basis for the classification of the entire group of carbohydrates.

A. The Sugars

The sugars are the simplest carbohydrates. They are soluble in water and have a characteristic sweet taste that varies in degree according to the type of sugar.

1. Physical and Chemical Reactions.—The sugars give certain physical and chemical reactions that vary in number and degree according to the sugar under consideration. These reactions are in many cases specific and may be utilized as a means of identification of a given type of sugar. The most striking properties of sugars are their specific rotatory power, their reducing action, and their formation of osazones.

a. Specific Rotatory Power.—All the natural sugars are optically active in that they rotate the plane of polarized light when it passes through a solution of any one of these carbohydrates. The degree of rotation depends upon the kind of sugar, the kind of light, and the concentration and length of the column of solution through which the beam of light has to pass. The same amount of the same sugar dissolved in the same volume of water and placed in a tube of the same length, however, will always cause the same rotation of the plane of polarized light. The sugar is thus said to have a specific rotatory power. It is expressed as the number of degrees of angular deviation of the plane of polarized light caused by a column of the solution 100 mm. in length composed of 100 g. of the substance dissolved in 100 cc. of water at a temperature of 20°C. This deviation is expressed by the symbol $[\alpha]_D^{20}$, which indicates that the observation was made at 20°C. and with the D or sodium light. Sugars that rotate the beam of light to the right or in the direction in which the hands of the clock move are called "dextrorotatory," and the degree of rotation is preceded by the plus sign. Those sugars which rotate the beam of light to the left or in a direction counterclockwise are termed "levorotatory," and the nature of the rotation is indicated by the minus sign. Thus, for example, the specific rotation of d-glucose is $[\alpha]_D^{20} + 52.7°$ and d-fructose $[\alpha]_D^{20} - 92°$.

b. Reducing Action.—Any sugar that contains a potentially active "ose" or sugar group $\left(\begin{array}{cc} \mathrm{O} & \mathrm{OH} \\ \| & | \\ \text{—C—} & \text{C—} \\ & | \end{array}\right)$ in its structure will behave as a reducing agent. Certain of the metallic compounds when in alkaline solutions are reduced when boiled with sugars of this type. Thus, for example, when treated in this manner, an ammoniacal silver solution gives a silver mirror, an alkaline solution of cupric hydroxide forms cuprous oxide, and alkaline mercury salts are reduced to metallic mercury. Any sugar that possesses this power of reduction is known as a "reducing sugar." The structure of certain of the di- and trisaccharose sugars is such, however, that the aldehyde and ketone groups are linked in such a manner that they lose their reducing power. Such sugars are termed "non-reducing sugars," and saccharose, sucrose, or cane sugar is the most common of this type.

The reagent most commonly used to determine the reducing qualities of sugars is Fehling's solution. This is prepared in the following manner: Part *A* is made by dissolving 69.278 g. of pulverized cupric sulphate in distilled water and making up to 1 l. Part *B* is made by dissolving 346 g. of sodium potassium tartrate (Rochelle salts) in distilled water and making up to 500 cc. and by dissolving 100 g. of sodium hydroxide in distilled water, again making up to 500 cc. Both parts of solution *B* are then mixed and kept until needed. Fehling's solution is then made by mixing equal parts of solutions *A* and *B* just before using.

The active substance in this solution, as far as reducing sugars are concerned, is cupric hydroxide, which is held in alkaline solution by the presence of the Rochelle salts. When this solution is heated with a solution of reducing sugar, oxygen is withdrawn from the cupric hydroxide, and it is converted into cuprous oxide. The cuprous oxide thus formed is insoluble in the solution and is separated from it in the form of a reddish-brown precipitate. Advantage is taken of this reaction of sugars with the alkaline solution of cupric hydroxide for their detection and quantitative determination, since the amount of the cuprous oxide produced bears a definite relation to the amount and type of sugar used.

c. Formation of Hydrazones and Osazones.—When sugars with aldehyde or ketone groups in their molecules are treated with phenylhydrazine ($C_6H_5.NH.NH_2$), they yield condensation products called "hydrazones," just as do other aldehydes and ketones. The phenylhydrazones are characteristic crystalline solids and are usually very easily soluble in water, so that they do not serve for the identification of individual sugars. When, however, these sugars are heated in aqueous solution with an excess of phenylhydrazine over that required to form the phenylhydrazone, a reaction takes place in which 1 molecule of the carbohydrate reacts with 3 molecules of the phenylhydrazine to form a substance callled a "phenylosazone." The osazones of sugars are compounds that dissolve with difficulty in cold water, crystallize well, and have a characteristic form and a definite melting point. The osazones are thus very characteristic for certain sugars and afford a means for their identification.

2. Kinds or Types.—The most important groups of sugars that occur in green plants are the monosaccharoses, the disaccharoses, and the trisaccharoses.

a. The Monosaccharoses.—The monosaccharoses are the simplest of the sugars and cannot be hydrolyzed or changed into simpler compounds still retaining the property of sugar. They are so named because they contain only one sugar group. There are two classes of the monosaccharoses in plants—the pentoses and the hexoses.

1. *The Pentoses.*—The pentoses are sugars that contain five carbon atoms and have the formula $C_5H_{10}O_5$. These sugars occur in the free state in plants in only very small amounts. Davis and Sawyer (1914) determined the free pentoses in the alcoholic extract of the leaves of the mangold, turnip, *Tropaeolum majus, Helianthus annuus*, carrot, and potato and found that they amounted to from 0.3 to 1 per cent of the dry weight. VerHulst, Peterson, and Fred (1923) found in the leaves of corn that the free pentoses amounted to 0.69, 0.52, 0.39, and 0.47 per cent of the dry weight, respectively, at the tasseling, silking, milk, and dent stages. Apparently, one of the components of the nucleic acids of plants is pentose. Paracaoutchouc is considered to be composed of a large number of groups of the formula C_5H_8 that have been polymerized to form an exceedingly large molecule. These C_5H_8 groups are considered reduction products of the pentoses (Spoehr, 1917, 1919). The pentoses occur in the plant for the most part in the combined state in the form of pentosans, natural gums, and hemicelluloses. As stated in Chap. I the pentoses may be obtained in various amounts by the hydrolysis of the hemicelluloses of the cell walls of seeds, pods, straw, and the xylem elements of the plant. Cherry and peach gum and certain mucilages of plants also yield pentoses on hydrolysis. The two most common pentoses that are obtained from the hydrolysis of the materials above mentioned are arabinose and xylose. Both of these are reducing sugars. Rhamnose ($CH_3C_5H_9O_5$), is a pentose in which 1 atom of hydrogen has been replaced by a methyl group. This compound is of interest in that it has the characteristics of the sugars yet does not have the proportion of hydrogen and oxygen that ordinarily occurs in the carbohydrates.

2. *The Hexoses.*—The hexoses are the most abundant of the monosaccharoses in the plant. They contain six carbon atoms and have the formula $C_6H_{12}O_6$. The most important hexoses that are found in the green plant in the free state or in the form of condensation products are glucose, fructose, mannose, and galactose. All these hexoses are reducing sugars, and all are optically active.

(*a*) *Glucose, Dextrose, or Grape Sugar.*—This sugar is found in considerable abundance in fruits—especially in the grape, on which account it received the name "grape sugar." It also occurs in the seeds, roots, and leaves of plants and is thus found in varying quantities in practically every living cell of the plant. This sugar occurs in the combined state in sucrose, maltose, starch, and various other di-, tri-, and polysaccharoses and may be obtained by hydrolysis from these products. *d*-Glucose is dextrorotatory, its specific rotatory power being $[\alpha]_D^{20} + 52.7°$, and for this property it has been termed "dextrose." It is approximately three-fifths as sweet as cane sugar. Glucose is an aldehyde alcohol, and the structure of *d*-glucose is represented as shown on page 528.

(*b*) *Fructose, Lcvulose, or Fruit Sugar.*—Fructose is a ketone alcohol and has the structure shown below. Owing to the ketose group in its molecule, it is a strong reducing agent and reduces Fehling's solution more rapidly than does glucose. Fructose is strongly levorotatory and for that reason has also been termed "levulose." Its specific rotatory power is $[\alpha]_D^{20} - 92.5°$. It is slightly sweeter than cane sugar and is the sweetest of the ordinary sugars (Archbold and Barter, 1935). Fructose is widely distributed in the plant and occurs in considerable quantities in fruits, generally in excess of glucose and sucrose. It occurs in the combined form in sucrose, in the trisaccharoses, raffinose, gentianose, and melicitose and in the polysaccharose inulin. It may be obtained from these substances by hydrolysis with acids or enzymes.

d-glucose

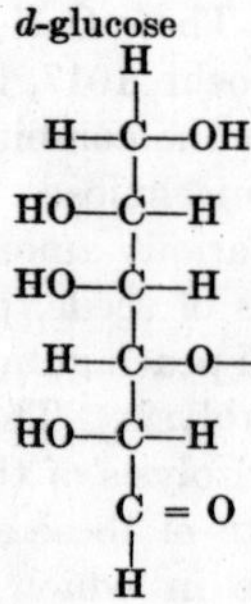

d-fructose

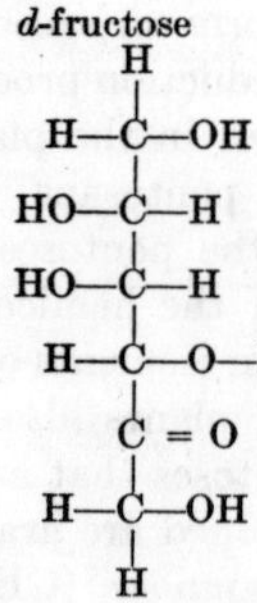

(*c*) *Mannose.*—Mannose is a sugar closely related to glucose and forms the same osazones as do that sugar and fructose. Mannose does not occur in the free state in plants but is readily obtained by hydrolysis from numerous compounds found in them. Thus the hemicelluloses of the cell wall of the date stone, ivory nuts, coffee, pea, and bean yield mannose among other sugars upon hydrolysis. The compounds in the plants which thus yield mannose are termed "mannans" or "mannosans." Mannose may also be obtained by the oxidation of mannitol, a hexatomic alcohol sometimes known as "mannite," which occurs in numerous plants. Mannose is dextrorotatory $[\alpha]_D^{20} + 14.3°$ and is a reducing sugar.

(*d*) *Galactose.*—Galactose very rarely occurs in the green plant in the free form and when so found is in only very small amounts. It exists in the plant almost entirely in the form of condensation products, which are sometimes collectively termed "galactans." This term includes the gums, mucilages, and hemicelluloses of the plant which yield galactose on hydrolysis. Galactose may thus be obtained from agar-agar, the pectins of carrot and pears, from gums occurring in peaches and plums, and from the cell walls of the seed coats of the seed of corn, lupine, bean, pumpkin, and many others. Galactose is also a constituent of the trisaccharose raffinose and may be obtained together with glucose and fructose from this source by hydrolysis. *d*-Galactose obtained from these sources just mentioned very closely resembles glucose in many of its properties, but it has one characteristic difference in that it forms mucic instead of saccharic acid when oxidized by concentrated nitric acid. Galactose is only very slightly sweet, reduces Fehling's solution more slowly than glucose, and is strongly dextrorotatory, $[\alpha]_D^{20} + 83.8°$.

Although galactose, mannose, and the pentose sugars, arabinose and xylose, are rarely found in the plant in the free form, they may nevertheless play an important part, in some cases at least, in plant nutrition. They are formed very slowly by hydrolysis and may thus be utilized by the cells almost as rapidly as they are produced, so no considerable amount ever accumulates.

b. The Disaccharoses.—A disaccharose sugar consists of two monosaccharoses or hexoses linked together with the elimination of 1 molecule of water. The molecular formula for disaccharoses is $C_{12}H_{22}O_{11}$. The manner in which the two monosaccharoses are joined together to form a sugar of this kind varies with the type of disaccharose. The linkage may be through the alcoholic groups of each monosaccharose, through the alcoholic group of one and the ketone or aldehyde group of another, or through the aldehyde or ketone groups of each of the two sugars. If the linkage is through the aldehyde or ketone group of both monosaccharose units, the reducing power of these groups is destroyed and the disaccharose thus resulting is a nonreducing sugar. The most important disaccharoses occurring in green plants are sucrose, maltose, gentiobiose, and melibiose.

1. *Sucrose, Saccharose, or Cane Sugar.*—Sucrose is the most abundant and the most widely distributed sugar in green plants, being found in varying amounts in practically all living plant cells. In the stalk of the sugar cane (*Saccharum officinarum*) it is present in quantities equal to from 12 to 20 per cent of the green weight and may compose as much as 90 per cent of the soluble material in the expressed juice of this plant. This sugar composes from 15 to 20 per cent or more of the fresh weight of sugar beets and is present in quantities ranging from 2 to 4 per cent in the sap of the sugar maple and in the stalks of the saccharine sorghums (*Sorghum saccharatum*), amounting to as much as 12 per cent of the green weight or 40 per cent on a dry basis. Sucrose is the sugar present in the greatest amount in most leaves, is the principal sugar in the nectar of flowers, and is found in most sweet fruits in amounts varying from 1 to 12 per cent.

Widdowson and McCance (1935) determined the glucose, fructose, sucrose, and starch in 41 different fruits. The results for some of the more common fruits are shown in the following table:

Fruit	Carbohydrates			
	Glucose, per cent	Fructose, per cent	Sucrose, per cent	Starch, per cent
Apples	1.7 to 2.2	5.0 to 7.2	2.4 to 3.6	0.02 to 0.35
Apricots	1.9	0.37	4.3	0
Bananas	5.8	3.8	6.6	3.0
Cherries	4.7 to 5.5	6.1 to 7.2	0	0
Cranberries	2.7	0.74	0.14	0
Currants	2.3 to 3.0	1.9 to 3.6	0.62	0
Dates	32.0	23.7	8.2	0
Grapes	8.2	7.2 to 8.0	0	0
Grape fruit	1.9	1.2	2.1	0
Lemon	1.4	1.4	0.4	0
Cantaloupe	1.2	0.8	3.3	0
Oranges	2.5	1.8	4.2	0
Peaches	1.4	0.93	6.6	0
Pears	2.2 to 3.5	6.0 to 7.0	1.0	0
Pineapple	2.3	1.4	7.9	0
Raspberry	2.3	2.4	1.0	0
Strawberry	2.6	2.3	1.3	0
Tomatoes	1.6	1.2	0	0.02

The structure of sucrose has not been definitely established, but, since it yields equal quantities of glucose and fructose by the addition of one molecule of water, it is considered an anhydride of these two sugars. Sucrose is dextrorotatory, $[\alpha]_D^{20} + 66.5°$, but when it is hydrolyzed with acid or the enzyme invertase to equal amounts of glucose and fructose the resulting mixture is levorotatory. For this reason the mixture resulting from such a hydrolysis has been termed "invert sugar." Sucrose is a nonreducing sugar, does not form a phenylhydrazone with phenylhydrazine, does not undergo direct alcoholic fermentation, and is, next to fructose, the sweetest of the common sugars.

2. *Maltose or Malt Sugar.*—Maltose is a reducing sugar, forms a characteristic osazone, is dextrorotatory, $[\alpha]_D^{20} + 137°$, and is broken down by hydrolysis into 2 molecules of glucose. It does not undergo alcoholic fermentation by yeast directly but must be broken down into glucose before such fermentation can occur. Maltose is widely distributed in plants, but generally it can be detected in only very small quantities. It is derived from starch by hydrolysis and should thus occur in plants wherever this process is taking place. It is formed in the greatest amount from this source during the germination of starchy seeds. In most cases, maltose is apparently hydrolyzed into glucose almost as rapidly as it is formed, so it is never detected in any considerable amount in the plant.

3. *Other Disaccharoses.*—Two of the less common disaccharoses of the plants that have been isolated are gentiobiose and melibiose. Gentiobiose is obtained by the partial hydrolysis of gentianose, a trisaccharose found in the roots of yellow gentian (*Gentiana lutea*). Gentiobiose is a reducing sugar and upon hydrolysis yields 2 molecules of glucose. Melibiose is obtained by the partial hydrolysis of the trisaccharose raffinose. It is a reducing sugar and when hydrolyzed breaks up into glucose and galactose.

c. The Trisaccharoses.—The trisaccharoses have the general formula $C_{18}H_{32}O_{16}$. When partially hydrolyzed they yield a monosaccharose and a disaccharose, but when completely hydrolyzed they yield three molecules of monosaccharoses. This indicates that the trisaccharoses are formed by the linking together of three monosaccharoses by the elimination of 2 molecules of water. There are five trisaccharoses known to occur in green plants, of which raffinose, melicitose, and gentianose are the most important. Raffinose occurs in cotton seeds, in the barley grain, and in the sugar beet. It is a nonreducing sugar and is strongly dextrorotatory, having a specific rotation of $[\alpha]_D^{20} + 104.5°$. According to Thatcher (1921), raffinose may break down by hydrolysis into three different compounds according to the catalyst used: (1) sucrose and galactose, (2) fructose and melibiose, or (3) fructose, glucose, and galactose.

Melicitose is a very sweet sugar that is known to occur in the sap of the European larch (*Larix europaea*), Douglas fir, and other conifers and frequently collects on the twigs in small white flakes that are called "manna." When this sugar is partially hydrolyzed it yields 1 molecule of glucose and 1 molecule of a disaccharose sugar called "turanose." When completely hydrolyzed it yields 2 molecules of glucose and 1 of fructose.

Gentianose occurs in the roots of the yellow gentian (*Gentiana lutea*). When partially hydrolyzed it yields fructose and gentiobiose and when completely hydrolyzed yields 1 molecule of fructose and 2 molecules of glucose.

B. The Nonsugars or Polysaccharoses

The polysaccharoses have the general formula $(C_6H_{10}O_5)_n$ or $(C_5H_8O_4)_n$ depending on whether they yield hexoses or pentoses on hydrolysis. They are on that account termed, respectively, "hexosans" or "pentosans." The hexosans may be further classified according to the type of hexose that they yield on hydrolysis into the dextrosans (glucosans), the levulosans (fructosans), the mannans, and the galactans. The polysaccharoses are substances with high molecular weights and are apparently composed of many molecules of a monosaccharose linked together through the elimination of water. The value of n has not been accurately determined for any of the polysaccharoses on account of their slight solubility in the solvents that are used for molecular-weight determinations. The value of n is estimated to be as low as 30 in some polysaccharoses and as high as 200 or more in others. The chief polysaccharoses that occur in the green plant are the celluloses, the amyloses or starches, the mannans, the galactans, and the two pentosans, araban and xylan.

1. The Celluloses.—Cellulose is the most abundant carbohydrate in the plant kingdom. It is one of the main components of the rigid cell wall that surrounds the protoplasm of practically every plant cell and, together with the various compounds that are united or closely associated with it, makes up in many cases the greater portion of the weight of the plant. The nature and properties of the celluloses are discussed fully under the subject of the constituents of the cell wall in Chap. I, so they will not be mentioned here.

2. The Amyloses or Starches.—The most important amyloses that occur in green plants are starch or amylum, dextrins, and inulin.

a. Starch or Amylum.—Next to cellulose, starch is the most abundant and widely distributed carbohydrate in the plant kingdom and is the most universal form of storage carbohydrates in plants. It may occur in the young cells near the growing points, in the medullary ray cells of the stems and roots, in the xylem and phloem parenchyma, in the mesophyll cells of the leaf, in the guard cells, in the cells of the cortex and pith, in the bundle sheaths, in seeds, fruits, tubers, and other places. There are few green plants in which starch does not appear in some of the tissues at one time or another in the life of the plant. Starch occurs in the greatest amount in certain seeds, roots, and tubers, which thus form one of the main sources of carbohydrates for the nourishment of the animal kingdom.

Starch is present in the seeds of about one-half of the families and genera of the monocotyledons and in the seeds of about one-sixth of the dicotyledons. When starch is present as a reserve product in seeds, other nonnitrogenous foods as fats and oils are usually absent or are present in only very small amounts. When fats and oils are the chief reserve foods, starch is generally absent. With but few exceptions, starch occurs in the plant in the insoluble form. In the soluble form it has been observed in the cell sap of the epidermal cells of *Saponaria officinalis* and *Arum italicum* and some other plants (Reichert, 1913).

1. *The Starch Grain.*—With the exception of the few cases of soluble starch that were mentioned above, starch always occurs in the green plant in the form of definite granules known as starch grains. These vary in size from macroscopic to almost ultramicroscopic dimensions (Fig. 23). Starch grains are exclusively a product of green plants and are always found within the plant cells. The number of grains that may occur in a single cell varies greatly. There may be as many as 100 or more of a small size and only a few or only a single grain of considerable size. As a general rule, the tissues above ground, with the exception of seeds, contain starch grains which are smaller and less fully developed than in the underground structures. The form or shape of starch grains varies in plants of different species, in the same plant in different parts, and even in the same part of a given plant. Lindet and Nottin (1923) observed in the case of the potato tuber that one-half the starch grains

measured from less than 1 to 10μ in diameter but that the starch grains of that size comprised only 1.5 per cent of the total weight of starch. Only 0.6 per cent of the grains measured from 60 to 80μ but made up about 20 per cent of the total weight. The maximum size observed was 100μ in diameter. The form of the grain may be affected by the age of the plant and by changes in the nutritive conditions, but the form is usually the same within certain limits for a given species. The general shape of the

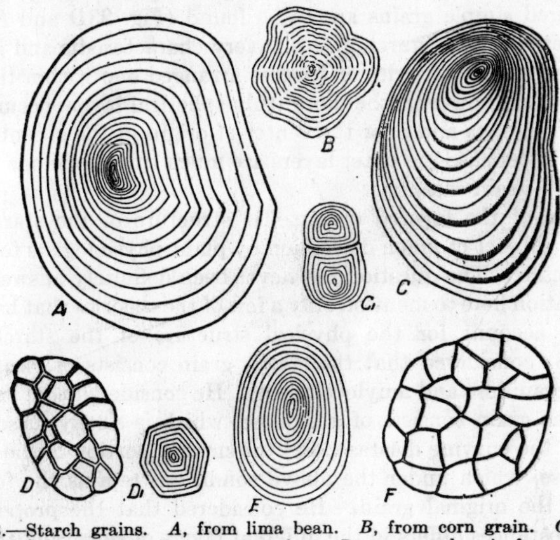

FIG. 23.—Starch grains. *A*, from lima bean. *B*, from corn grain. *C* from potato tuber. C_1, compound grain from potato tuber. *D*, compound grain from rice. D_1, one of the simple grains which compose the compound starch grain of rice. *E*, from wheat grain. *F*, compound grain from oats.

starch grains is so constant for a given species that the adulteration of flours and meals with starch flours from other sources can be detected and the starch used as an adulterant identified by a microscopic examination of the starch grains. The form of starch grains may be spherical, ellipsoidal, ovoid, lentiform, or, where closely packed or crowded together, polyhedral.

The structure of the starch grains is very characteristic in that each grain consists of numerous layers or lamellae which are laid down either concentrically or eccentrically around one or more morphological centers or points of origin. The point of origin in the starch grain has frequently been designated the hilum, nucleus, or locus of the grain. These first two terms, however, are now universally used in botanical literature in another sense, so that the "locus," "point," or "center of origin" are perhaps the best terms to use to designate the center around which the starch of the grain is deposited (Fig. 23). When the lamellae or layers of starch are deposited around a single center of origin the grain is termed a "simple" starch grain. When the deposition of starch is around two or more points of origin, the grain is said to be "compound." The number of centers around which starch may be deposited in a compound grain may vary from two to hundreds. When simple grains predominate there are usually a few scattered compound grains, *e.g.*, in the potato and wheat. In rice and oats the compound grains predominate, and only a few scattered simple grains are to be found (Fig. 23*D* and *F*). The layered structure of the starch grains is very characteristic and gives the general appearance of a series of spheres arranged one within the other. Strictly speaking, however, the more truly spherical layers occur only in the concentric grains and near the center of origin in the eccentric ones, since in the latter case the outer layers are much thicker on one side and thus make the grain eccentric.

The cause of the layered or lamellar structure of the starch grain has been the subject of much discussion by plant physiologists for almost a hundred years. The question has never been definitely answered, and it is the intention here to mention only a few of the theories that have been proposed to account for the physical structure of the starch grain. Nägeli (1858) considered that the starch grain consists of two distinct substances, granulose and amylocellulose. He considered that the larger portion of the grain consists of granulose, which is slowly dissolved by the action of the enzyme diastase; and the smaller portion of the grain of amylocellulose, which under the above conditions retains the form and structure of the original grain. He considered that the proportion of these two substances differs in the different layers of the grain, the dense layers containing relatively more amylocellulose than the soft or less dense layers, and the external parts of the grain more than the internal parts. The granulose part of the grain takes the blue color with iodine, while amylocellulose stains a dull or brownish red (Meyer, 1895). MacDougal (1895) considered that in the ordinary starch grain, amylose, consisting of two closely related forms α-amylose and β-amylose, and amylodextrin are present. He suggested that the dense layers of the grain are relatively rich in amylose and that the amylodextrins occur in larger quantities in the less dense porous layers. The amylose stains blue with iodine and the amylodextrin red. Kraemer (1902, 1905) suggested that the starch grain consists of colloidal and crystalloidal substances, these being arranged, for the most part, in distinct and separate lamellae. At the point of origin and in alternate lamellae the colloidal substance predominates but is associated with the crystalloid matter, while in the other layers the crystalloid substance occurs in the greater proportion. He held that differences in the starch grain show that starch instead of being a uniform substance is composed of several substances in varying proportions but more or less definitely arranged. Maquenne and Roux (1903, 1905) and Fernbach and Wolff (1904) considered that the starch granule consists of amylose and amylopectin. Amylose makes up the greater portion of the starch grain and is the substance that reacts with iodine. Amylopectin is not colored with iodine and is a mucilaginous substance that is thought to produce the gelatinization of starch in the form of starch paste.

Samec and Haerdtl (1920) in a study of the starches of potato, wheat, corn, rice, and horse-chestnut, among others, found that all contained an electrodialytically precipitable viscous portion that conducts electricity and a portion that is the opposite in all these respects. They considered the first-named portion to be the amylopectin described by Maquenne and the latter amylose. They found that the relative amount of these two substances differed in different starches. By special methods Walton (1929) separated from the starches of wheat and tapioca two types which were termed α- and β-amylose. The proportion of these two types was 24 to 76 for wheat and 17 to 83 for tapioca. Thurber (1933) found that the ratio of the two types of starches was approximately the same in the sweet potato and white potato. The viscosities of the two starches differed greatly, but Woodruff and Webber (1933) found no significant differences in the gels of the starches of hard and soft winter wheats.

Ling and Dinshaw (1923), Clayson and Schryver (1923), and Schryver and Thomas (1923) found in addition to amylose and amylopectin a substance resembling hemicellulose in many of the starches. This substance in wheat starch resists the action of taka-diastase and is soluble in hot water but separates from it in an amorphous form upon cooling. It is soluble in 0.1 N sodium hydroxide, from which solution it can be precipitated by acids.

Attempts have also been made to explain the lamellar structure of the starch grain upon the assumption that it is spherocrystalline in its composition. A spherocrystal is ordinarily defined as a more or less globular body composed of radially arranged crystals. Nägeli (1858) first suggested the crystalline structure of the starch grain and conceived it to be composed of minute crystalline structural units which he later termed "micellae." Schimper (1881) from studies with polarized light concluded that the grain is spherocrystalline in nature and consists of fibrous crystals arranged at right angles to the concentric layers. Meyer (1895) considered that the starch grain is composed of very thin, elongated needlelike or threadlike crystal units that are termed "trichites." These trichites are arranged in a radial manner at right angles to the main mass. The stratification of the grain he considered due to the varying thickness and number in successive layers of the more or less richly branched trichites. Sponsler (1922, 1923) studied the structure of the starch grain by means of X rays. He found that there is a regular and fairly uniform arrangement of atoms in the grain but that this regularity is destroyed when the grain is crushed, which shows that the regularity is not that of a crystalline structure. The evidence indicates that the starch grain is built up of concentric layers of units and that the structure is neither amorphous nor crystalline in the ordinary sense of the terms. Parts of the grain act as crystals in that for certain distances the layers or units are in planes, but taken as a whole the layers are curved. Van Sande-Bakhuyzen (1926) reported that the starch grains from seeds of plants which had been grown under constant conditions did not show lamellation. After heating these grains until they swelled, it was noted that they were formed of homogeneous radial needles. In the starch grains of the control seeds the needles were observed after heating, but they were in zones of different refractivity and solubility, which apparently cause the lamellation of the starch grains.

Schimper (1881) concluded from his observations on starch formation that starch grains never arise except in plastids. His observations were later confirmed by Meyer (1895) and this view of starch formation is now the commonly accepted one. The chloroplasts and leucoplasts are the plastids concerned in the formation of starch grains. The starch found in the chloroplasts may be termed "temporary," since it is stored there for only a very brief period until it can be translocated to other parts of the plant. Usually numerous grains are formed in a single chloroplast and sometimes project from the surface, giving the plastid an irregular appearance. These grains always remain small and are usually without a definite structure. According to Zirkle (1926), they are located within the central vacuole of the chloroplast.

According to Spoehr and Milner (1935) the yields of starch in percentage of dry weight of the leaf were 37.7 for *Nicotiana tabacum*, 13.4 for *Phaseolus coccineus*, 2.3 for *Linum usitatissimum*, 2.3 for the old leaves of *Hedera helix*, and 1.5 for the young leaves of this plant. Novello (1933) found that 52 of the 55 forms of palms examined by him elaborated starch in the chloroplasts. Three forms contained only lipides in their chloroplasts, and 23 forms contained both starch and lipides.

The most conspicuous and definite starch grains are those formed by the leucoplasts. These are the grains that make up the great bulk of the starch in the plant kingdom and compose thus the reserve starch in all parts of the plant. This type of starch is sometimes called "permanent starch," since it may remain intact for a considerable period of time. Apparently only a single starch grain originates in each leucoplast. The starch grain increases in size by the addition, accretion, or apposition of newly formed layers. It is not definitely known whether the grain in its development ruptures the leucoplast or whether the leucoplast stretches as the grain increases in size and thus remains intact and surrounds the exterior with a delicate film. Schimper (1881) showed that if the grain has its origin at the center of a spherical leucoplast, the strata of the grain will be laid down concentrically, because the conditions of growth are the same at every point of the surface. If the point of origin lies near the surface of the leucoplast, the stratification will be eccentric in character, since the deposition of starch will be more favored on one side. Lindet and Nottin (1923) noted in a study of the formation of potato starch that the sugar content of the cell sap during starch formation amounted to from 0.5 to 1.5 per cent. They considered that the leucoplasts contain during this process a mixture of sucrose, invert sugar, and maltose but could not detect any soluble starch.

2. *General Properties.*—The starch substance is not a unit body but exists in a number of stereoisomeric forms (Reichert, 1913, 1919). It not only differs in the grains of different plants and in the grains of the same plant, but differs in the starch substance of the outer layer and the enclosed part of the grain, in different lamellae, and in different parts of the same lamella. The lamellae vary in density and solubility, increasing in density and decreasing in solubility from within outward.

The outermost layer is the least soluble in both hot and cold water and is less digestible by weak acids and enzymes. While the starch grains are composed for the most part of amylose, they contain various polymers ranging in complexity from amylodextrin to amylocellulose (Mellanby, 1919). The grains of certain plants apparently do not contain ordinary starch but a modified form or mixture of ordinary starch and erythrodextrin, or erythrodextrin alone, since they stain a red violet or red with iodine. This reaction has been reported for the starch grains of the seeds of *Oryza sativa, Panicum miliaceum glutinosum,* and *Sorghum vulgare glutinosum.* The starch grains found in *Iris germanica, Chelidonium majus, Acer pseudoplatinus,* and *Gentiana lutea* among others also show this reaction (Meyer, 1886). From the preceding statements it would seem that it would be practically impossible to obtain a starch grain that could be considered typical in regard to its intimate structure (Kraemer, 1923).

Starch grains consist of from 80 to 85 per cent of starch substance, 15 to 20 per cent of water, and variable amounts of organic and inorganic substances including fats, protein, tannin, phosphates, and other matter. Samec and Haerdtl (1920) noted that all the starches examined by them contained phosphorus, the variation in amount being paralleled by the electric conductivity of the electrodialyzed solution. The major portion of the fatty material present in starch cannot be removed by solvents before hydrolysis, according to Taylor and Nelson (1920). When corn starch is hydrolyzed, fatty acids are liberated, palmitic acid being the principal one. The fat thus contained in starch is liberated when hydrolysis has reached the erythrodextrin stage. The table below adapted from Reichert (1913) shows the composition of some of the more common types of starch.

COMPOSITION OF STARCH

Kind of starch	Starch substance	Water	Ash	Fat
	Per cent			
Wheat	83.3	14	0.4	0.2
Corn	84.1	14	0.4	
Arrowroot	84.1	15.7	0.2	0.1
Tapioca	84.8	14.4	0.25	
Potato	79.6	19.2	0.3	0.04

It was concluded by Edwards and Ripperton (1933) that the electrolytes occurring naturally in starch are largely determined by the protoplasm of the cell rather than by a direct chemical equilibrium with the electrolytes of the cell sap. McNair (1932) identified the carbohydrates in 59 of the 295 families of gymnosperms and angiosperms. There is an indication that carbohydrates of a low molecular weight, with a low heat of combustion and a low potential energy, are more likely to be found in tropical families of plants than in those of temperate regions. Starch from temperate climates gelatinizes at a higher temperature than that from the tropics. Starch from plants of a temperate climate is less saturated toward iodine than that from tropical families.

Starch is insoluble in cold water but when it is boiled in water a colloidal suspension termed "starch paste" is obtained. The insolubility of uninjured raw starch grains in cold water seems to be due to some form of protective covering that is deposited by the leucoplast or by the cell sap. The idea, however, that the outer covering of the grain is a thin layer of cellulose or other nonstarch substance is no longer held. Reichert (1913), however, considered that some form of protective covering exists, since the rupture of the grain by grinding with sand or glass, the erosion by diastase, or the solution of the outer film by potassium hydroxide or other agents renders the grains soluble in cold water.

By boiling starch with dilute acids or by treating with acetone, a clear solution termed "soluble starch" is obtained. The formation of soluble starch with acetone was described by Fernbach (1912). His method as described by Haas and Hill (1913) consists in pouring a 1 to 2 per cent suspension of starch in a large excess of pure acetone and shaking vigorously. A flocculent precipitate is obtained which when filtered and ground up in a mortar with more acetone yields a light white powder that is completely soluble in cold water and gives the starch reactions. Raw starch, starch paste, and soluble starch give a blue color when treated with a solution of iodine in potassium iodide or a solution of iodine in alcohol. This color reaction is the most characteristic reaction of starch.

When starch is boiled for some time with dilute mineral acids it is converted into dextrins, maltose, and finally glucose as the end product. When starch paste is treated with a malt extract containing diastase, the starch is converted only to maltose as the end product (O'Sullivan, 1872). If, however, uninjured starch grains are subjected *in vitro* to the action of diastase under sterile conditions, absolutely no digestion occurs. If the grains, however, are broken or cracked or eroded, rapid erosion takes place similar to that observed when digestion takes place in the plant under natural conditions.

b. Dextrins.—The dextrins are transition products between starch and maltose. The carbohydrate called "soluble starch," which is found in the sap of the epidermal cells of *Arum italicum* and *Saponaria officinalis*, is perhaps a mixture of dextrins, while the starch grains that turn red with iodine, as has previously been described, are probably composed, in part at least, of dextrins. Weatherwax (1922) considered that the only carbohydrate in the endosperm of waxy maize is erythrodextrin. According to Parker (1935) the endosperm of sweet corn has a relatively high percentage of soluble polysaccharoses consisting of both dextrins and soluble starch. Although dextrins are probably being formed continuously in the hydrolysis of starch or in the formation of starch from sugar, they have not been observed to accumulate to any extent in the plant except in the few cases that have been mentioned.

The dextrins are readily soluble in water, from which they may be precipitated by alcohol. They are strongly dextrorotatory and are converted into glucose by hydrolysis with mineral acids. A large number of dextrins have been described, but only three fairly definite forms are recognized. These are (1) amylodextrin, which gives a blue color with iodine and is considered the chief constituent of soluble starch; (2) erythrodextrin, which gives a red color with iodine and has a neutral taste; and (3) achroodextrin, which has a sweetish taste and gives no color with iodine.

c. Inulin.—Inulin occurs as a reserve carbohydrate in the cell sap of numerous plants, especially the *Compositae*. It is found in the largest amounts in roots and tubers and occurs, if at all, in only very small amounts in the aerial parts. In the underground parts it may make up as much as 15 per cent of the dry weight (Shohl, 1923). Inulin is found in comparatively large amounts in the underground parts of *Inula helenium*, *Helianthus tuberosus*, *Dahlia variabilis*, *Lappa minor*, *Cichorium intybus*, *Solidago sp.*, and numerous others. Holm (1931) noted in the roots of numerous *Compositae* that inulin is never found in the epidermis, exodermis, phelloderm, sclerenchyma, or leptome. It is only occasionally present in the endodermis and pith. It is most abundant in the meristem near the primary hadrome and in the cortical parenchyma. In some of the monocotyledons it is found associated with starch, but as a general rule when inulin is present starch is absent. Some plants contain reserve carbohydrates of the same general type as inulin. Some of these are irisin in *Iris pseudacorus*, graminin in *Trisetum alpestre*, phleim in *Phleum pratense*, and triticin in *Triticum repens* (Dean, 1904).

Inulin is a white powder composed of finely divided granules. It is slightly soluble in cold water and very soluble in hot water, from which it may be precipitated by alcohol. An aqueous solution of inulin does not form a jelly or paste, is not colored by iodine, and is not fermentable. Inulin is slowly converted into fructose when boiled with water and converted very rapidly in the presence of an acid. It is also converted to fructose by the enzyme inulase. The methods for the extraction and preparation of inulin are described fully by Dean (1904), Willaman (1922), and Harding (1923).

3. Mannosans and Galactans.—The mannosans are present for the most part in the cell walls of plants and are generally classified as one of the groups of hemicelluloses. They are found especially in the cell walls of leaves, of wood in stems and roots, and in the cell walls of seeds and seed coats. The mannosans are strongly dextrorotatory, soluble in water with difficulty, and yield mannose upon hydrolysis. The galactans are polysaccharoses that yield galactose upon hydrolysis. They are slightly soluble in water and form gummy solutions. Like the mannosans, they are for the most part associated with the cell wall of various plant parts and are generally considered under the heading of "hemicelluloses."

4. Pentosans.—The pentosans have the general formula $(C_5H_8O_4)_n$ and occur, for the most part, in the cell walls of various plant parts. According to Thatcher (1921), they compose 22 to 25 per cent of the dry weight of wheat bran, 8 to 10 per cent of clover hay, 16 to 20 per cent of oats straw, 26 to 27 per cent of wheat straw, and as much as 60 to 92 per cent of various wood gums. The pentosan content of the leaves of corn amounted to 19.9, 17.6, 18.1, and 19.4 per cent, respectively, at the tasseling, silk forming, milk, and dent stages in analyses made by Ver Hulst, Peterson, and Fred (1923). The two chief pentosans are araban and xylan. Araban occurs in gum arabic and cherry gum. Xylan is found in the cell walls of the cells of straw, nut shells, seed coats, and corn cobs. The pentosans are soluble in cold water with difficulty but more soluble in hot water. They are very difficult to hydrolyze but finally yield the sugars arabinose and xylose.

III. PHOTOSYNTHESIS

A. Nature

It was mentioned at the beginning of this chapter that the first evident organic product that is synthesized by the green plant from the inorganic compounds that it absorbs is some form of carbohydrate. This carbohydrate is formed by the plant from carbon dioxide and water, and the term "carbon assimilation" or "photosynthesis" has been given to the process. Barnes (1893) first proposed the name "photosyntax," but later (1898) he changed to the term "photosynthesis," which is now universally used in America and to a considerable extent in England, but in Europe the term "carbon assimilation" is still in general use. Photosynthesis is commonly defined as the manufacture of some simple carbohydrate (probably sugar) from carbon dioxide and water by the chloroplasts in the presence of light. In this process, in addition to the formation of carbohydrate, oxygen always appears as a waste or end product. This liberation of oxygen by green plants was one of the earliest facts noted in plant physiology, and the conditions under which it is liberated were fairly well known long before the relationship of its appearance to the formation of carbohydrate was established.

The power of photosynthesis resides exclusively in the chloroplasts. These plastids thus have the power to transform the radiant energy of the sun into the potential energy of the carbohydrates. As will later be discussed, after the carbohydrates are once formed, the plant can apparently produce from them, regardless of light, most of the numerous complex compounds of which it is composed. The pigments of the chloroplasts are the agents in those plastids that absorb the radiant energy and aid at least in transforming it into the potential condition in the synthesized carbohydrates. A general knowledge of the nature of these pigments is therefore necessary for a proper understanding of the process of photosynthesis.

B. Pigments of the Chloroplasts

The pigments of the chloroplasts have received much consideration from the chemists and plant physiologists, and the literature concerning them is very voluminous. Due, however, to the lack of proper methods of extraction, purification, and analysis, the information in regard to these pigments was very confusing until the classical work of Willstätter and his workers from 1906 to 1926. In some of the most outstanding work of modern organic chemistry, they have succeeded in making the nature and chemistry of the leaf pigments as clear at least as that of many other plant substances. The composition and nature of the leaf pigments were found to be the same for all plants and constant for all conditions as is evidenced from the analysis of the pigments from various species of different families and from plants grown under a wide range of ecological conditions. The numerous works of Willstätter have been carefully translated and summarized by Schertz and Merz (1928), and a fine resumé is given by Jorgensen and Stiles (1917). The properties of chlorophyll, as well as methods for its determination, have also been clearly defined by Schertz (1928–1929) in numerous publications. Others who have more recently studied the properties and methods for the determination of the pigments of the chloroplasts are Sprague and Shive (1929), Guthrie (1929), Harriman (1930), Peterson (1930), Hilpert, Hofmeier, and Wolter (1931), Deleano and Dick (1934), Hicks and Panisset (1934), Zscheile (1934), and Kuhn (1935). According to Schertz (1929) the most important factors influencing the quantity of pigments are rainfall, soil moisture, nutrient elements in the soil, light, temperature, and humidity. Sprague and Shive (1929) showed in corn that the pigments in the chloroplasts did not increase proportionately with the growth rate. Thus chlorophyll content was more closely correlated with leaf area than with dry weight of leaves, while carotin and xanthophyll were more closely correlated in the opposite way.

According to the researches of Willstätter, the chloroplasts contain four pigments—two closely related chlorophyll pigments, chlorophyll component *a* and chlorophyll component *b*; and two yellow pigments, carotin and xanthophyll. A fifth pigment, fucoxanthin, is present in the brown algae. In the fresh green leaves the pigments occur in approximately the following proportions: chlorophyll *a*, 2 parts; chlorophyll *b*, three-fourths of 1 part; carotin, one-sixth of 1 part; and xanthophyll, one-third of 1 part per 1,000, respectively. The relative constant proportions of the various pigments of the leaf have been of much interest to investigators. Guthrie (1929) found that, on a dry basis, increasing the concentration of carbon dioxide decreased the total content of chlorophyll and carotinoids, but on the fresh weight basis a greater concentration effected little change. This treatment, however, did not change the ratios of the pigments. Increasing the length of day decreased the amount of all four pigments in the same proportion. Norris (1933) reported that in the development of chlorophyll and xanthophyll in etiolated plants there was a constant ratio of these pigments when the plants were exposed to light. The results indicated a close relationship between chlorophyll and xanthophyll, but not between these pigments and carotin. Oserkowsky (1932) found that chlorotic pear leaves were deficient in yellow pigments as well as in chlorophyll.

Various hypotheses have been advanced to explain the more or less constant ratio between the yellow and green pigments in leaves. Lubimenko (1927, 1928) suggested that these pigments are derived from a common substance. Because of the similarity between the constitution of the phytol of chlorophyll and of the phytol of the carotinoids, Smith (1930) concluded that this common substance either comes from the carotinoids or is produced from the same parent substance.

In the chloroplasts these pigments are mixed in a colloidal state with various colorless substances—fats, waxes, and salts of fatty acids among others. Thus in an alcoholic extract of dried leaves, the chlorophyll obtained is accompanied by six times its weight of other substances.

In the determination of chlorophyll, Harriman (1930) found that leaves which were dried at 78°C. lost approximately 70 per cent of their chlorophyll. At temperatures as low as 18° to 24°C., from 20 to 30 per cent of these pigments were destroyed. The leaves that were frozen with dry ice or desiccated at a reduced pressure over sulphuric acid at room temperatures lost little or no chlorophyll. Hilpert, Hofmeier, and Wolter (1931) believed that the chlorophyll in the leaf is chemically different from that which has been isolated. Zscheile (1934) considered that there is present in chlorophyll, a component "*c*" in addition to components *a* and *b*, which have commonly been reported.

1. The Chlorophyll Pigments. Chlorophyll Components *a* and *b*.—The green pigment of the chloroplasts is called "chlorophyll." This pigment is the most abundant one in these plastids and consists of two components—chlorophyll component *a* of the composition $C_{55}H_{72}O_5N_4Mg$, blue black in the solid state and greenish blue in solution; and chlorophyll component *b* of the composition $C_{55}H_{70}O_6N_4Mg$, green black in the solid state and in solution pure green. The term "chlorophyll" as it is now commonly used refers to these two green pigments taken collectively and freed from all the others that are associated with it in the chloroplasts. Chlorophyll always contains 2.7 per cent magnesium, which is the only metal in the ash.

Chlorophyll component *a* is very easily soluble in ether and absolute alcohol, only moderately so in cold methyl alcohol, and rather easily in warm methyl alcohol. It is easily soluble in 95 per cent and with difficulty in 80 per cent ethyl alcohol. It is dissolved with difficulty in 90 per cent methyl alcohol even when warm and is almost insoluble in 80 per cent methyl alcohol. It is easily soluble in acetone, chloroform, carbon disulphide, and benzol. It dissolves in petroleum ether with difficulty even when warm.

The solubility of chlorophyll component *b* is in general somewhat less than that of component *a* but the difference is very marked in petroleum ether. Chlorophyll *b* is wholly insoluble in petroleum ether at room temperatures, and the solvent becomes scarcely colored even at boiling.

a. The Chemistry of Chlorophyll.—In addition to the idea of Willstätter and his workers with regard to the structure of the chlorophyll components, Conant, Dietz, Bailey, and Kamerling (1931), Fischer and Grassl (1935) and others have submitted formulas for the chlorophyll components, which have been based on various observations and determinations of these pigments. The general formulas herein reported are taken from the works of Willstätter and are apparently correct in regard to the proportion and general arrangement of the elements that compose the two chlorophylls. The actual arrangement of the elements in the molecule, however, is known only theoretically. Chlorophyll is a combination of the tricarboxylic acid chlorophyllin $(C_{31}H_{29}N_4Mg)(COOH)_3$ with methyl alcohol (CH_3OH) and phytol or phytyl alcohol $(C_{20}H_{39}OH)$, which together compose about one-third of the chlorophyll molecule. It is thus an ester of the acid chlorophyllin.

The formulas for chlorophyll *a* and *b* are written:

Chlorophyll *a*: 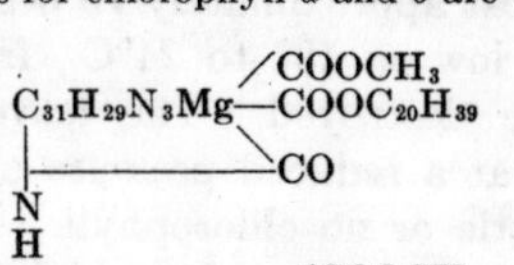

Chlorophyll *b*: 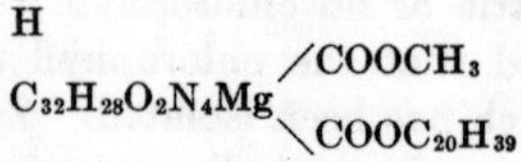

Although chlorophyllin is a tricarboxylic acid, only two of the acid (COOH) groups actually function in ester formation. The third acid group apparently does not exist as a free acid group. In chlorophyll *a* it is in what is known as the lactam ring

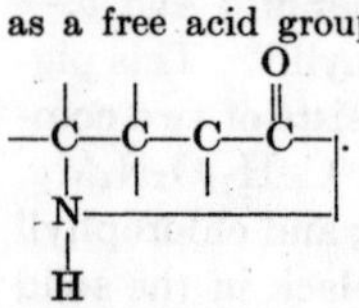

. In chlorophyll *b* it is considered by some to be in the lactone-arrangement,

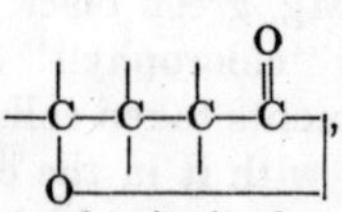

, group, the two bonds in each case being attached to different structural units in the molecule (Thatcher, 1921).

When chlorophyll is treated with dilute alkalies, the alcoholic groups of the esters are split off by hydrolysis, producing the tribasic acids—chlorophyllin *a* and chlorophyllin *b*. When these chlorophyllins are heated with alkali, the carboxyl groups are driven off successively, giving products which are termed "phyllins" but which contain magnesium. The chlorophyllins are easily decomposed but were isolated by Willstätter and were found on analysis to contain magnesium bound to nitrogen in a complex way. The magnesium cannot be electrolytically dissociated as a magnesium salt. The magnesium-containing group is very easily affected by acids but is stable in the presence of alkalies.

When chlorophyll is treated with dilute acids, the magnesium is removed and replaced with two hydrogen ions without otherwise changing the molecule. A series of decomposition products result which are called "phytins" and which correspond to the alkali decomposition products of chlorophyll, except that the magnesium is lacking.

It should be noted here that chlorophyll in nature is accompanied by the enzyme chlorophyllase. By precipitation with acetone, Mayer (1930) obtained an active chlorophyllase from an aqueous extract of macerated leaves. This enzyme is active in an alcoholic medium and replaces the phytol group of the chlorophyll with the ethyl group from the alcohol. When an alcoholic extract of this type is evaporated nearly to dryness, dark-green crystals—crystalline chlorophyll—are obtained. When chlorophyll is extracted by solvents other than alcohol, it is obtained in the amorphous form.

There is a striking chemical similarity between chlorophyll and hemoglobin, the characteristic, red coloring matter of the blood of higher animals. On that account, much work has been done in an attempt to establish a direct relationship between these two pigments. Much of this work is beyond the scope of this text, and consequently only a few statements will be made here. Roddis (1936) believed that hemoglobin might be derived from chlorophyll by the substitution of iron for magnesium. He mentioned that the same color methods that are used in estimating hemoglobin may be used for estimating the amount of chlorophyll. Raber (1931) grew corn plants in the dark for 5 to 10 days in nutrient solutions to which liver extract had been added. These plants were distinctly greener than the controls. He considered that the physiological effect of the liver extract in checking the etiolation of green plants has a striking resemblance to the effect of this extract in checking pernicious anaemia in animals. Noack and Kiessling (1929), and Inman and Rothemund (1932) studied the relationship between the decomposition products of chlorophyll in the digestive tract of animals and the decomposition products artificially derived from this pigment. They believed that some of these products have a close relationship to the hemoglobin of the blood.

b. Optical Properties.—Chlorophyll in alcoholic solution exhibits the phenomenon of "fluorescence," a property that is possessed by a considerable number of substances, in which they exhibit one color by transmitted and another by reflected light. This phenomenon was so called because it was first observed in fluorspar and appears to be due to an alteration in the wave lengths of radiant energy brought about by the action of the molecules of the substance. Generally the action is to increase the wave lengths, but in some few cases it is the reverse. Usually the yellow, green, and blue rays undergo the change. In the alcoholic solution of chlorophyll, the much shorter wave lengths of green and blue are emitted as the longer wave lengths of the red. Thus an alcoholic solution of chlorophyll *a* is blue-green by transmitted light and blood-red by reflected light. An alcoholic solution of chlorophyll *b* is yellow-green by transmitted light and brown-red by reflected light.

One of the striking properties of chlorophyll is its ability to absorb certain rays of light. This absorption is so complete that dark bands appear in the spectrum. Since the absorption spectrum of every colored solution changes with its concentration, the spectrum of chlorophyll must be determined either throughout a range of concentrations or by using layers that vary in thickness. The spectrum of chlorophyll shown in Fig. 24 is that of an acetone solution of chlorophyll made by dilution of an acetone leaf extract of 40 cc. of acetone containing 0.02 g. of chlorophyll to five times its volume with 85 per cent acetone. This spectrum was obtained from a layer of this solution 1 cm. in thickness in a glass vessel with parallel walls. Figure 24 shows the absorption spectra

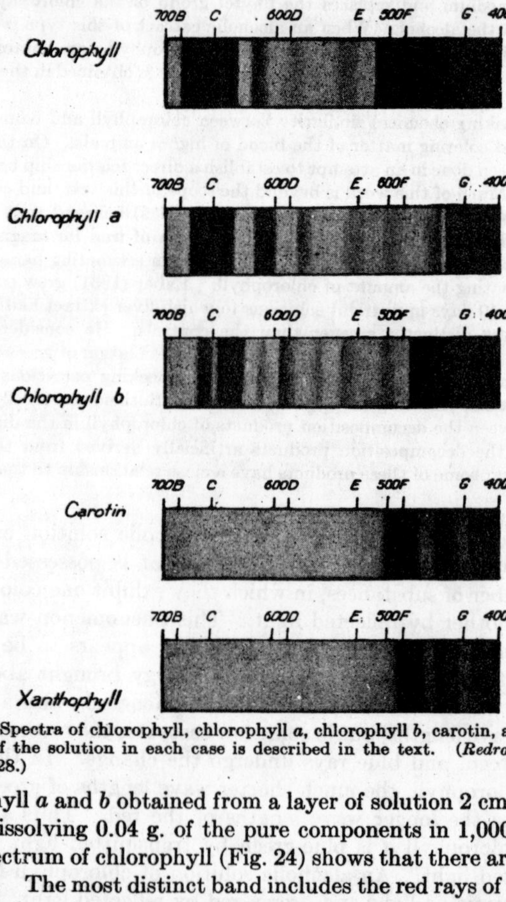

Fig. 24.—Spectra of chlorophyll, chlorophyll *a*, chlorophyll *b*, carotin, and xanthophyll. The nature of the solution in each case is described in the text. (*Redrawn from Schertz and Merz*, 1928.)

of chlorophyll *a* and *b* obtained from a layer of solution 2 cm. in thickness made by dissolving 0.04 g. of the pure components in 1,000 cc. of ether.

The spectrum of chlorophyll (Fig. 24) shows that there are five absorption bands. The most distinct band includes the red rays of 651 to 680mμ approximately on both sides of the Fraunhofer line *C*. This band appears in solutions of chlorophyll that are so dilute that none of the other absorption bands is evident. The next most distinct band and the greatest in width is one that includes most of the blue, indigo, and violet rays of 400 to 510mμ approximately. Three other bands of much less intensity are located between these two prominent ones. One of these is located in the light orange and includes approximately the rays 600 to 620mμ. The second is in the orange-yellow region and includes the rays 550 to 590mμ, while the third is in the yellowish-green portion and includes the rays 525 to 540mμ. These bands are rather indistinct and not intense, the intensity decreasing from the red toward the blue end of the spectrum. The etherial solution of chlorophyll *a* gives a spectrum in which the absorption band in the red is not so distinct or wide as in the chlorophyll solution. The band in the blue end of the spectrum is only one-half the width of that of chlorophyll and includes only the more distant portion of that region. The solution of chlorophyll *b* shows a distinct absorption band in the red ultra to the line *C* and only a narrow rather indistinct one on the infra side. The band in the blue end of the spectrum is distinct and is approximately three-fourths the width of that of chlorophyll.

c. The State of Chlorophyll in the Chloroplasts.—The location of chlorophyll in the chloroplasts has been mentioned in Chap. I, but the condition or state in which it occurs has not been discussed. According to the work of Willstätter and others, the evidence seems to indicate that chlorophyll is present in the chloroplasts in a colloidal mixture. This assumption is substantiated by the behavior of chlorophyll to its solvents and from the evidence derived from spectroscopic examination.

Willstätter found that solvents which dissolve the pure extracted substance do not extract the chlorophyll from the dried leaf. Thus the pure pigment is readily soluble in acetone, but if the dried powder of nettle leaves is placed therein, it can remain in the acetone for ½ hr. without coloring the liquid. If a little water is added, however, the color becomes intensely green. This behavior indicates that chlorophyll occurs in the leaf in a different state of matter from extracted chlorophyll. From the above statements it would seem that chlorophyll in the chloroplasts is in the colloidal condition, that water added to the pure organic solvents dissolves the mineral substances in the leaf, and that the salt solutions so formed alter the colloidal condition of the chlorophyll in the chloroplasts and make it easily soluble. The pure solvents can, however, extract chlorophyll from fresh leaves, since abundant water is present in them. Further support for the theory of the above reactions is furnished by the fact that colloidal solutions of chlorophyll in water made from a pure extracted pigment behave in a way similar to dried leaf powder. If a solution of this type is mixed with ether, the ether remains colorless, but if a little salt solution of calcium chloride or calcium nitrate is added, the etherial layer becomes colored green upon shaking. The salt solution has changed some of the chlorophyll from the colloidal condition, and as a result it is soluble in the ether.

It has been observed by many (Tsweet, 1910) that the absorption bands of the spectrum of the living leaf are displaced toward the red end of the spectrum as compared with the bands in the spectrum of extracted chlorophyll. It is also known that the condition of chlorophyll in fresh leaves is altered if the leaves are plunged into boiling water and that the chlorophyll is then more easily extracted by its solvents. A leaf that has thus been placed in water gives absorption bands that occupy practically the same position as those in the chlorophyll extract. It is assumed that the chlorophyll has been changed by this treatment from a colloidal solution to a true solution and is now dissolved in the waxy substances with which it is associated and which have become liquid as a result of the temperature change. It has also been shown by Herlitzka (1912) that the spectrum of living leaves agrees with that of a colloidal solution of chlorophyll, while both differ in the same way from the spectrum of true solutions of chlorophyll.

d. Formation.—The formation of chlorophyll is a physiological process that occurs only in living cells and under conditions favorable to life. The substance or substances from which chlorophyll arises have never been isolated, and their existence is only inferred. It is considered by some that a pigment called "chlorophyllogen" is formed independently of light in the chloroplasts and that it is rapidly transformed into chlorophyll under the influence of light (Palladin, 1922). The absorption spectrum of the pigments obtained from etiolated seedlings has an absorption band between 640mμ and 620mμ, which is due to a red fluorescing pigment that has been termed "protochlorophyll." According to Eyster (1928), this is a pigment that develops without the aid of light and changes photochemically into chlorophyll upon exposure to light.

Noack and Kiessling (1929) stated that acid splits off magnesium from protochlorophyll, the same as it does from chlorophyll, to form a pigment that they have designated as "protopheophytin." According to Rothemund (1935), most of the protochlorophyll disappears when the plant is placed in the light and is thus apparently transformed into chlorophyll. Protochlorophyll, along with chlorophyll, is probably present in all green leaves. It forms in the dark, but it is not known whether it arises from chlorophyll, from the precursor of chlorophyll, or from both. It has never been demonstrated that the living green plant can change protochlorophyll into chlorophyll. It has only been shown that, after irradiation of the plant, the absorption spectrum of protochlorophyll becomes weaker and the chlorophyll spectrum appears, becoming more intense with time. Protochlorophyll, however, has never been prepared artificially.

Light is one of the requisites for the formation of chlorophyll. The stem and leaves of most plants grown in darkness are always yellow. Such plants are said to be etiolated. They quickly turn green when exposed to light. Some plants or plant parts, however, as the seedlings of some conifers, the fronds of young ferns, the plumule of *Nelumbo*, and certain unicellular algae, are exceptions to this, since they become green in darkness. According to Palladin (1922), the conifer seedlings, however, form much less chlorophyll in darkness than in light. Skinner (1932) showed that even in total darkness certain algae, placed in soil partially sterilized by heat, are able to increase as much as 100-fold when incubated at room temperature for long periods of time. Light of medium intensity is the most favorable for chlorophyll formation. It is considered that in more intense light the formation and decomposition of chlorophyll occur simultaneously, so, as a net result, the greening is less pronounced than it is in diffuse light.

It was demonstrated by Wiesner (1874) that chlorophyll is formed in the red, orange, and yellow rays produced by a potassium dichromate solution and in the green, blue, and violet region produced by copper sulphate. He also showed that plants do not become green under the nonluminous heat rays. Sayre (1928) grew plants under colored glass plates and studied the effect of different wave lengths of radiant energy on the formation of chlorophyll in the seedlings of corn, wheat, oats, barley, sunflower, and radish. The wave lengths longer than 680mμ are not effective in the formation of chlorophyll, but all other regions of the remaining visible and ultraviolet spectrum to 300mμ are effective, provided the energy value is sufficient. For equal energy values, the red rays are more effective than the green, and the green more than the blue. The effectiveness of radiant energy in chlorophyll formation appears to increase with wave length to about 680mμ and then ends abruptly. Inman (1935) found that the absorption band of chlorophyll in the region of 666mμ could easily be detected after only 10 sec. of exposure to the light. After the exposure of etiolated leaves for 150 min., a typical chlorophyll absorption spectrum was obtained. Ulvin (1934) found that the leaves of radish grown in continuous light contained more chlorophyll than those grown in a 10-hr. daily light period. Meier (1934) studied the development of chlorophyll in 18 kinds of unicellular algae and found that 11 of them developed chlorophyll while growing for 30 days in continuous light, in the intermittent light of day and night, or in continuous darkness. Three showed only poor development of this pigment under all these conditions. One grew best in continuous light, and one grew best in continuous darkness. It was reported by Colla (1930) that radiation of 3300 to 3900 Å. from a mercury-vapor lamp deepened the green color of the plant. This change in color was due to the increase in the amount of chlorophyll.

After the exposure of barley roots to diffuse daylight or electric light for 6 to 10 days, Gautheret (1932) detected chlorophyll in 70 per cent of them, and by the Molisch test the chloroplasts gave the reaction for sugar.

The rate of production of chlorophyll depends upon temperature. Greening occurs most quickly in etiolated plants between 18 to 30°C. Wiesner (1877) found within that range of temperature that greening occurs in about 1.6 hr., while at 10°C. 3.5 hr. was required. Lubimenko and Hubbenet (1932) noted that the greening of etiolated wheat seedlings takes place within definite limits of temperature, beginning between 2 to 4°C., attains a maximum between 26 and 30°C., and ceases at or near 48°C.

A supply of iron is necessary for the formation of chlorophyll, and the probable function of that element in this regard is discussed in detail in Chap. VI. Many other elements also influence the development of chlorophyll. The effect of potassium, phosphorus, calcium, and magnesium on the color of plants is considered under the discussion in Chap. VI of the functions of these elements in the metabolism of the plant. Ville (1889) found in the case of hemp that the greatest decrease in chlorophyll and carotin was brought about by a deficiency in nitrates, while Schertz (1921) associated the mottling of *Coleus* plants with the same cause. Deuber (1926) in the soybean noted that the chloroplast pigments increased with the increasing concentrations of iron and sulphur in the cultural solution. The lack of iron or potassium in the nutrient solution resulted in a more marked depression of the chloroplast pigments than a lack of sulphur. When the sulphur content reached a concentration of 46 p.p.m., and potassium reached a concentration of 28 p.p.m., a marked decrease in the pigment content of the leaves occurred. Deuber, however, could not establish an exact proportional relation between the concentration or amount of any of the elements studied and the amount of pigment formed. Schertz (1929) noted that phosphorus, potassium and nitrogen may each be correlated with an effect on the formation of the chloroplast pigments. For the potato, high phosphorus produces more pigment than does potassium, but less than nitrogen. High yields of potatoes are correlated with heavy potassium fertilization, and this in turn with a low chlorophyll content of the leaves. Low yields are correlated with high nitrogen fertilization and a high chlorophyll content of the leaves. It was thought by Echevin (1934) that the parallelism in the disappearance of phospholipins and chlorophyll in the autumn indicated a relationship between these phosphorus compounds and the activity of the green pigment. In the leaves of pineapple, Tam and Magistad (1935) found indications that the amount of available nitrogen determines to a large degree the amount of chlorophyll formed, provided that all of the other necessary materials and conditions are not limiting factors. Ulvin (1934) reported that with sugar cane more chlorophyll was produced by plants receiving nitrogen in the form of nitrate than by those receiving this element in the form of ammonia.

Since magnesium and nitrogen enter into the molecular structure of chlorophyll, it is to be expected that a variation in the amount of these elements in the soil or in the cultural solution would influence the production of this pigment. However, the cause of chlorosis in plants that is due to variations of the calcium, sulphur, potassium, magnesium, phosphorus, or iron supply is not so easily explained, since these elements do not enter into the composition of chlorophyll. This question is generally answered by saying that the production of chlorophyll depends upon the general vigor and tone of the plant, which is known to vary with certain combinations and with certain concentrations of these elements.

Palladin (1891) has shown that carbohydrates in the leaves are essential to the formation of chlorophyll. Etiolated leaves that contain a considerable supply of carbohydrates green rapidly when placed in light, but those which contain little or no soluble carbohydrate remain yellow. The leaves that are deficient in carbohydrate, however, green rapidly when floated in the light upon a solution of cane or grape sugar. The presence of oxygen is also essential for the production of chlorophyll. Etiolated leaves in an atmosphere devoid of oxygen remain yellow in light. It has been assumed by some that oxygen, mineral nutrients, carbohydrates, and a favorable temperature are necessary for the formation of chlorophyllogen, which arises independently of light. The transformation of chlorophyllogen to chlorophyll in the living cells is considered to be dependent upon light.

Ruth (1922) noted that the chlorophyll content per unit area of the primordial leaves of the bean was increased slightly by spraying with Bordeaux mixture. Henrici (1926) found in South Africa that there was a pronounced difference between the amount of chlorophyll present in the morning and in the afternoon. Following a heavy rain there was an increase in the chlorophyll content, while drought caused a decrease.

e. Inheritance.—According to Demerec (1935) chlorophyll shows more peculiarities in its inheritance than any other known plant characteristic. In maize there are approximately 100 genetically different characters for chlorophyll. Some of these manifest themselves only in the seedling stage, others only in the mature plants, while still others appear in both the seedling and mature stages. Four types of plants are distinguished in regard to their chlorophyll content. They are: the albino, virescent, pale-green, and variegated forms. In the albino types, the chlorophyll is absent, and because of this the plants die at an early seedling stage. The virescent types are those which are albinos in the early stage but later develop chlorophyll. The pale greens are those plants in which the quantity of pigment is reduced at certain stages of development. The plants included in this type vary from plants that contain little chlorophyll to those having almost the normal amount. The variegated type includes those plants in which the content of chlorophyll varies in different regions of the leaf. These differences may show either by a mottling or by a striping of the leaf.

Miles (1915) believed that plastids are entirely absent from albino plants, but Randolph (1922) concluded that the failure of a plant to become green is not due to the absence of plastids or plastid primordia. The albino plants thus lack some physiological mechanism essential for the development of plastid color. This condition is brought about by the genetic constitution of the plant. A comparison of the size of plastids of various chlorophyll types of maize indicates that the size of the plastids is correlated with the amount of pigment present. Thus Trajkovich (1924) determined the chlorophyll content and measured the plastids of four chlorophyll types. He found a correlation between these two factors as shown in the following table:

Type	Relative amount of pigment		Average size of plastids, microns
	Green	Yellow	
Green	100	100	6.19
Xantha	19.7	100	4.62
Yellow	6.1	100	3.19
White	0	0	Primordial

At this point it is well to mention the effects of light rays on the coloring of apples, although this process is apparently in no manner concerned with the formation of chlorophyll. Arthur (1931) reported that the ideal light source for coloring apples is one that has little infrared but considerable ultraviolet extending to a wave length of 290mμ. Pearce and Streeter (1931) stated that the region in the solar spectrum from 3600 to 4500 Å. is the most influential in the coloring of McIntosh apples.

2. The Carotinoids.—Various yellowish pigments, which have been termed collectively the "carotinoids," are always associated with the chlorophylls in the chloroplasts. This group generally includes two types of pigments that are very similar in chemical composition. These are the carotins, or carotenes, and the xanthophylls. Fucoxanthin is a brownish-red pigment that is associated with the chlorophylls, carotins, and xanthophylls in the brown algae, and it imparts to them their characteristic color. The carotinoids may also occur in fruits, roots, and other plant parts where chlorophyll is absent. According to Howard (1925), the carotinoids of the fruits examined by her are granular or crystalline in form and are frequently contained in the chromoplasts. The amount of the carotinoids present in plant tissues apparently depends upon the environmental conditions and upon the type of plant. Thus Smith and Smith (1931) found that bagged Elberta peaches developed a higher content of carotinoids than the unbagged ones, while the reverse was true of nectarines and apricots. Whiteside, Edgar, and Goulden (1934) considered that although the carotinoid pigmentation of wheat is an inherent characteristic, the environmental conditions have an appreciable effect upon the amount present.

Mackinney (1935) observed that the content of chlorophyll and carotinoids fluctuated together, but that the ratio of the carotins to xanthophylls was markedly lower in the chlorotic leaves of the barley plant than in the normal leaves.

Murneek (1934) noted that the concentration of the carotinoids appeared to reach a maximum in the leaves of *Cosmos*, *Salvia*, and *Soja* at the time of flowering, after which they decreased. He stated there are strong indications that more yellow pigments are present in the female than in male plants of dioecious species. Roberts and Livingston (1935), however, could find no relationship between the content of carotinoids and the fruitfulness of the apple or tobacco. Schertz (1921 to 1929), Palmer (1934), Miller (1935), and Murneek (1936) discussed methods for the estimation of carotinoids and made suggestions for their nomenclature.

a. Carotins or Carotenes.—The pigments of this group are found not only in the chloroplasts but are widely distributed in both the amorphous and crystalline forms in seeds, fruits, and roots. According to Howard (1925) the carotins of carrot occur in both the crystalline and amorphous forms in the protoplasm. The carotins occur in great abundance in carrot roots, are in the grain of yellow corn and in ripe tomatoes, and are the pigments that give these parts their characteristic colors. Strain (1934) and Spoehr, Smith, Strain, and Milner (1935) stated that it is now definitely established that there are a large number of carotin pigments in the leaves and other plant parts. These are mostly mixtures of isomers of very similar structure and differ only slightly in most of their physical and chemical properties. Three of the more prevalent types of carotin are α-, β-, and γ-carotin; the second named generally occurs in the greatest amount. According to Mackinney (1935), dodder is one of the richest sources for γ-carotin. Mackinney and Milner (1933) found that the carotin which they isolated from carrot leaves contained approximately 10 per cent α-carotin, and traces of γ-carotin, thus closely resembling the nature of the pigments in the carrot root. Mackinney (1935) showed that both α- and β-carotins were present in the carrot root, and that there was no significant change in the ratio of the amounts of these two pigments with the development of the plant. The amount of carotin pigments varies widely in the roots of carrots. Thus Bills and McDonald (1932) found that some varieties of carrots had over eighty times as much carotin as did others. According to Matlack and Sando (1934) and Miller, Mackinney, and Zscheile (1935), the carotins from different localities and from different plant sources yield identical products. The carotins have the same general formula, $C_{40}H_{56}$. They are insoluble in water, but are very soluble in ether, chloroform, and carbon disulphide. They become bleached in air, and in dry air increase in weight 35 per cent by the addition of oxygen. The crystals are rhombohedra, and are orange-red by transmitted, and greenish-blue by reflected light. Smith (1932) reported that the carotins from the leaves of alfalfa, cauliflower, spinach, sunflower, chard, and sugar beet are like those of carrot in that they have 10 double bonds in the molecule. Lycopene or lycopersicin, an isomer of carotin, occurs in red tomatoes, and has 13 double bonds. β-Carotin has been termed "provitamin A." If a molecule of this pigment would separate in the middle and a molecule of water be added to each portion, the resulting product would be two molecules of vitamin A (Zechmeister, 1934). Deleano and Dick (1932, 1933), Strain (1934), and Russell, Taylor, and Chichester (1935) have reported methods for the preparation and determination of the carotins.

b. Xanthophylls.—These pigments have the general formula $C_{40}H_{56}O_2$. According to Spoehr, Smith, Strain, and Milner (1935), and Strain (1936) the leaves contain not less than 12, and probably more, xanthophylls. The heterogeneity of leaf xanthophylls and the variation of the properties of their constituents probably account for the divergent values which have been reported for the xanthophyll content of leaves.

The crystals of these pigments are pleochromatic, often with a steel luster. They are yellow in transmitted light, and are red only when two or more cross each other. The xanthophylls may absorb 36.5 per cent of their weight of oxygen. They are very easily soluble in chloroform and alcohol, soluble in carbon disulphide with difficulty, and insoluble in petroleum ether. The carotins and xanthophylls are very different in their color intensities, but there is no simple ratio of their color strengths, since this varies with the solvent and with the concentration. The carotins are stronger in color and are more red in carbon disulphide and ether, while the xanthophylls are rather greenish tinted in these solvents.

The carotins and xanthophylls show spectra that consist of two absorption bands in the blue and indigo blue in addition to the end absorption that starts at the beginning of the violet. In Fig. 24, the spectra of these two pigments were obtained by using a solution, 1 cm. thick, of 5 mg. of pigment per liter of ether. The absorption bands of xanthophyll are displaced slightly toward the violet, as compared to those of the carotin.

c. Fucoxanthin.—This brownish-red pigment is associated with carotin, xanthophyll, and chlorophyll in the brown algae. It has the formula $C_{40}H_{54}O_6$ and undergoes a 7 per cent increase in weight in air, owing to the absorption of oxygen. This pigment does not exhibit fluorescence.

3. Autumnal Coloration of Leaves.—A thorough discussion of the factors involved in the coloring of leaves in autumn presented by Stout (1936) and Roberts (1937). Only a few general facts will be mentioned.

The autumnal coloration of leaves is confined to the deciduous trees and shrubs, which shed their leaves at the approach of winter. According to Stout (1936) the areas of the globe in which this coloration is manifested are very limited. In the southern hemisphere there is only one small region, which is located in the southern portion of South America. In the northern hemisphere there are three relatively large but separated areas in which autumnal coloration appears. One is in eastern Asia, one is in southwestern Europe with extensions eastward and northward, and one in North America extending from the Gulf of St. Lawrence south to Florida and westward through the Mississippi Valley to the Great Plains area. The variety, intensity and brilliance of coloration vary greatly over this area in North America, depending primarily upon the kinds of plants native to a given region, upon the general climate, and upon the autumnal weather that prevails during a given season. The most gorgeous autumnal colorations that occur in the United States are in New England, New York, Pennsylvania, Michigan and northern Ohio. This is due primarily to the kind of trees and shrubs that are dominant in that general region and to the ideal weather conditions for this coloration that generally prevail prior to leaf fall.

A wide variation of colors is very prevalent and very lasting in many plant parts during their natural growth and development. Thus the bright colorings of apples, plums, peaches, cherries, and many berries are familiar to all. In roots there are the scarlet radish, the purple-topped turnip, the yellow carrot, and the red garden beet. The leaves of many plants are brilliantly colored during the entire season as shown in Coleus, Cockscomb, Joseph's Coat, striped grasses, and many others. The various colors are due to internal regulations in the plant which result from a combination of hereditary factors and environmental conditions. These colorations in plants are very similar to those seen in autumn but differ in that they are relatively permanent during the life of the plant, while the autumnal colors are of only relatively short duration.

The autumnal colorations may be roughly divided into the yellows and the reds. The former is due primarily to the carotinoids and the latter to anthocyanin. During the growing season, the yellow pigments in the chloroplasts are masked by the chlorophylls, which are the most abundant coloring matters in the leaves. When cell activity begins to cease as autumn approaches, the chlorophylls are not replaced as they break down, and the carotins and xanthophylls become evident. These pigments or their oxidation products are responsible for the yellow and brown autumnal coloration of leaves. The yellow colors are especially prominent in the leaves of willow, poplar and tulip trees.

The autumnal colors of red and purple as seen in the leaves of sumac, red oak, sweet gum, red maple and sugar maple are due primarily to the anthocyanin pigments of the cell sap. The particular type of pigment or pigments found in the leaves is to a great extent hereditary. The colors, however, vary in intensity according to the region in which the plants grow and according to the type of season that prevails previous to or during their formation.

C. Historical

In 1772 Priestley discovered that green plants confined in an atmosphere rich in fixed air (carbon dioxide) produced after a period of time a considerable amount of dephlogisticated air (oxygen). He, however, had no understanding of the factors concerned in the process. At the same time, Scheele working in Sweden reported just the opposite results, since the plants with which he worked produced fixed air (carbon dioxide). Upon learning of the results of Scheele, Priestley repeated his investigations, but his results were confusing, since sometimes the plants increased the oxygen in the air and sometimes they depleted it, and Priestley was unable to explain these variations. He, however, is given the credit for being the first to observe that oxygen is given off by green plants.

Jean Ingen-Housz, physician to the emperor of Austria, was interested in the effect of pure air upon the health of man and was led to investigate plants in this regard by the first report of Priestley. Ingen-Housz showed that plants were able to purify foul air in a few hours when placed in sunlight and that sunlight had no effect in increasing the amount of oxygen without the action of the plant. He also noted that the absorption of air and the exhaling of oxygen were more active the brighter the sunlight, and that at night, or under extremely shaded conditions, the plants acted upon the air just as animals. He observed that only the green parts of plants gave off oxygen and that roots, flowers, and fruits rendered the air impure. These results were published in 1774 but were not presented in the terms of modern chemistry until 17 years later.

In 1800 Jean Senebier, a minister of Geneva, published his researches on the influence of light upon vegetation. He considered that the oxygen given off came from the carbon dioxide absorbed by the plant, and by means of colored glass he was able to ascribe to the red rays of the spectrum the chief action of this process. In 1804, Nicolas de Saussure published his classical work, "Chemical Researches on Plants." Although a contemporary of the men just mentioned, his experiments were so well carried out and his data so well presented in the light of modern chemistry that Spoehr (1919) says that one might well believe that a century had elapsed between the time of De Saussure and that of his contemporaries. His experiments, which were entirely quantitative, showed that the elements of water were fixed in the plant at the same time as the carbon and that there was an increase in weight as a result of the process. He also noted that there was no normal nutrition of the plant without the absorption of nitrates and mineral substances.

The discovery of these four men, however, found no interest among the botanists of their time. They were absorbed in the description and classification of plants and had no time for the consideration of facts about plants discovered by men foreign to the field of botany—for Priestley, Ingen-Housz, Senebier, and De Saussure were chemists and physicists. The discoveries of these men were soon forgotten or misinterpreted and little more was accomplished in this line, with the exception of the proof by Boussingault that a plant may obtain all its carbon from the air, until Sachs took up the work in 1860 to 1865.

Sachs and his pupils established, for the most part, the foundation upon which our modern views of photosynthesis rest. He was the first to discover that the chlorophyll corpuscles (chloroplasts) are the organs concerned in the appropriation of carbon dioxide and the separation of oxygen. Sachs also showed that chlorophyll, except in a few cases, is formed only in the presence of light, and he further distinguished between the effect of light in this process and in the release of oxygen by the leaf. Starch grains in the chloroplasts had been observed by Von Mohl as early as 1837 and by several subsequent investigators, but the significance of these grains was in no way suspected. It remained for Sachs, however, to connect the appearance of starch with the fixation of carbon and water and the elimination of oxygen in the chloroplasts in the presence of light. He was thus the first to observe and prove that a carbohydrate as well as oxygen is a product of the fixation of carbon and water in the green plant. He also grasped the fact that the formation of carbohydrates by this process is the starting point for the production of all other organic compounds of the plant, as shown by his statement (1882): "In the nutrition of plants it is only necessary in the first place to decompose carbon dioxide under the influence of light in the cells containing chlorophyll, with the cooperation of certain mineral matter absorbed by the roots and to produce at the cost of its carbon an organic substance—starch—(carbohydrate) which then represents the starting point, so to speak, from which all the organic substances of the plant proceed by progressive chemical changes."

D. Products

Oxygen and carbohydrates are the two end products that are definitely known to be produced in the process of photosynthesis.

1. The Evolution of Oxygen.—It has already been stated that the evolution of oxygen by green plants in sunlight was the first fact observed in photosynthesis. This emission of oxygen is most easily observed in submerged aquatic plants, since in sunlight bubbles of gas escape from these plants and rise to the surface of the water. The gas which is thus emitted, however, is not pure oxygen but consists of a mixture of oxygen, nitrogen, and a small amount of carbon dioxide. The two latter gases are not emitted from the interior of the cells but are swept out of the intercellular spaces by the stream of oxygen gas. The oxygen content of the emitted gas varies from 25 to 85 per cent, increasing with the increased rate of bubble formation. Spoehr (1926) considered that when the rate of photosynthesis is high and the escaping gas stream correspondingly high, the oxygen sweeps out the nitrogen and carbon dioxide from the intercellular spaces faster than it can be replaced from the surrounding water. When the rate of photosynthesis is low, the escaping gas stream is slow due to slow oxygen formation, so that the nitrogen and carbon dioxide which are being swept out are replaced in the intercellular spaces from the surrounding water. Under these conditions the gas that escapes contains a higher percentage of nitrogen and carbon dioxide than when the photosynthetic rate is high. The emission of oxygen from aquatic plants may also be observed after the following manner: The water in which the plants are submerged is covered with a film of oil, and the container is placed in the dark until the plants have exhausted the oxygen supply in the water. A leuco compound of methylene blue or indigo carmine is then added, and shortly after the plants are placed in sunlight the liberation of oxygen is made manifest by the formation of the bright-colored dye close to the plant. Oxygen is the only gas that has definitely been proved to be emitted by the plant during photosynthesis. It was found by Rudolfs and Heukelekian (1931) that the dissolved oxygen, in waters containing large quantities of blue-green and green algae, could be decreased from supersaturation to 17 per cent by darkness, and could be increased to 282 per cent saturation by diffuse light.

The ratio of the volume of carbon dioxide absorbed to the volume of oxygen produced is termed the "photosynthetic" or "assimilation" quotient. It is now commonly written as CO_2/O_2 but in the earlier literature it was expressed as O/CO_2 or O_2/CO_2. It was observed by De Saussure (1804) and Boussingault (1864) that the photosynthetic ratio approximated unity. Their experiments, however, did not take into account the respiration of the plants. The determination of the photosynthetic ratio is difficult, because the process of respiration is proceeding at the same time and in the opposite direction in that oxygen is being absorbed and carbon dioxide given off.

Separation of these two reactions has been found very difficult. The first work on this problem was undertaken by Bonnier and Mangin (1886), who employed four methods for the separation of the gaseous exchanges due to photosynthesis and respiration, of which the following are the most important: (*a*) comparison of the gas exchange of the plant in the light and in the dark. The amount of carbon dioxide absorbed in the light includes not only that obtained from the surrounding air but also that which has been released by the cells in the process of respiration. The oxygen that is released by the plant in the process of photosynthesis includes not only that which escapes from the plant but also that used by the cells in the process of respiration. By placing the plants in the dark for a given period, the volume of carbon dioxide C' released and the volume of oxygen O' absorbed by the cells in respiration can be determined. By placing the plants in the light for the same period, the volume of oxygen O'' released into the air and the volume of carbon dioxide C'' absorbed from the air under these conditions is measured. The total volume of oxygen released in the photosynthetic process would thus be $O' + O'' = O$ and the total volume of carbon dioxide absorbed would be $C' + C'' = C$. The true photosynthetic quotient would thus be $\frac{C' + C''}{O' + O''} = \frac{C}{O} = \frac{CO^2}{O_2}$. This method is open to objection, since it is not definitely known that respiration proceeds at the same rate in the light as in the dark. (*b*) The second method used by Bonnier and Mangin is based on an observation of Bernard (1878) that the process of photosynthesis may be suppressed by an anesthetic without the suppression of respiration. Two similar quantities of leaves, one anesthetized, the other not, are placed in light and the gaseous exchange due to photosynthesis estimated according to the measure just mentioned. This method is not exact, since the amount of the anesthetic to apply in order to just suppress photosynthesis and not retard respiration is not known. (*c*) The third method for determining the gaseous exchange in photosynthesis consists in the removal by means of baryta water of all the carbon dioxide from the vessel containing one set of leaves. This also removes any escaping carbon dioxide evolved in respiration. The other set of leaves is placed under normal conditions of carbon dioxide supply. Thus, as in the second method, the difference between the oxygen content and the carbon dioxide content of the two vessels at the end of the experiment gives the true values of the oxygen and carbon dioxide evolved. Spoehr (1916) considered that this method is inexact, as the rate of carbon dioxide emission in the two vessels is not the same, since Spoehr and McGee (1924) showed that when the carbon dioxide content of the air surrounding a leaf is changed from a higher to a lower concentration the leaf showed a primary increased rate of carbon dioxide emission. When the carbon dioxide content of the air changed from a lower to a higher concentration, the leaf showed a reduced rate of carbon dioxide emission.

By the three methods, Bonnier and Mangin (1886) concluded that the volume of oxygen emitted in photosynthesis was somewhat greater than that of the carbon dioxide. Maquenne and Demoussy (1913) using the first-named method of Bonnier and Mangin investigated the gaseous exchange of some 30 different species of plants and concluded that the photosynthetic quotient is equal to unity. The same conclusion was also reached by Willstätter and Stoll (1918), who determined the photosynthetic quotient under conditions in which the photosynthetic activity was from twenty to thirty times higher than that of respiration. This was done since the chief errors in the determinations of the photosynthetic quotient are occasioned in determining the rate of respiration. If the rate of photosynthesis is high as compared to respiration, the errors occasioned in determining the respiration rate will have an insignificant effect on the determination of the photosynthetic quotient. It was found by Kostytschew (1921) that the photosynthetic quotient varies with time. When leaves were first exposed to sunlight the value of CO_2/O_2 was considerably greater than unity, about one-third of the carbon dioxide absorbed being fixed without oxygen evolution. After a short time, more oxygen is given off than carbon dioxide is absorbed (Spoehr, 1926). After a time, however, the CO_2/O_2 ratio will become practically unity.

The value of the photosynthetic quotient is of importance, since it yields some information in regard to the first products formed in photosynthesis, because in the determination of the nature of a reaction it is of the first importance to know the quantitative relation between the initial substances and the products of the reactions (Jorgensen and Stiles, 1917). When the photosynthetic quotient is exactly unity, it indicates that the carbon dioxide absorbed has been reduced to $C + O_2$, or in the hydrate form to a compound with the general formula $C_nH_{2n}O_n$. This, however, does not give any information as to the exact compound formed, since it might be formaldehyde or any other compound of that formula (page 93 of Spoehr, 1926). It is interesting to note the value of the calculated photosynthetic quotient for different compounds. For formic acid it would be 2.0; for oxalic acid, 4.0; for glyoxalic acid, 2.0; for glycollic acid, 1.3; for malic acid, 1.3; and for formaldehyde, 1.0.

Moldavan (1934) suggested that the carbon dioxide absorbed during the photosynthetic process and the oxygen absorbed during respiration differ isotopically from the oxygen eliminated in photosynthesis and the carbon dioxide that escapes during respiration.

2. The Production of Carbohydrates in the Leaf.—Before discussing the production of carbohydrates in the photosynthetic process, it would be best to enumerate those that have been found in the leaf. Exclusive of cellulose and the pectic substances that occur in the cell walls of the leaf cells, the carbohydrates that have been detected in the leaves or other photosynthetic organs of the plant are starch, sucrose, *d*-glucose, *d*-fructose, pentosans, dextrins, pentoses, and inulin. Some of the earlier workers (Brown and Morris, 1893) considered that maltose also is present, but later investigators (Davis, Daish, and Sawyer, 1916; and Dastur and Samant, 1933) were not able to detect it. Maltose is undoubtedly formed in the hydrolysis of the starch in the leaves, but it is evidently almost immediately transformed into other sugars, so that it is not detected by the ordinary chemical methods. Starch, sucrose, *d*-glucose, and *d*-fructose are the most abundant carbohydrates in leaves, the others mentioned above being found in only very small amounts.

Although carbohydrates are known to be the end products of photosynthesis, it is not definitely known which one is the first to be formed in the chloroplasts. The determination of the first carbohydrate formed in the leaf is attended with many difficulties. In the first place, it is impossible by any of the present methods of analysis to separate quantitatively the various groups of carbohydrates in the leaf, owing to the similarity of their properties and the relatively small amount of materials present. It would seem thus that to make any progress in this regard more exact methods for separation must be developed. The detection or isolation of the first carbohydrate formed in photosynthesis is also difficult, because as many as four functions involving carbohydrates may be proceeding simultaneously in the leaf. The first carbohydrate is being formed, and from it almost immediately other carbohydrates may be formed by condensation for temporary storage as starch and the more complex sugars. These temporary storage products are, in turn, being hydrolyzed for translocation. An appreciable amount of carbohydrates is also broken down in the process of respiration which is proceeding at all times in the cells of the leaf. It is thus impossible by present-day methods to separate the carbohydrates first formed in photosynthesis from those which are formed as intermediate products in the condensation of the temporary reserves and in the hydrolysis of these reverses for translocation. On this account, therefore, it is no wonder that so many divergent views are held as to the kind of carbohydrate first formed in the photosynthetic process.

a. Early Observations.—The basis of our knowledge of the carbohydrates of the leaves was laid by Sachs (1862, 1864, 1884) when he proved that the appearance of starch in the chloroplasts is a direct outcome of the fixation of carbon under the influence of light and chlorophyll. He stated that starch is the first visible product of photosynthesis and that it is translocated from the leaf in the form of sugar. He seems to have considered that all the carbohydrates synthesized in the leaf pass at one time of their history through the starch stage in the chloroplasts. Sachs, however, worked almost exclusively with the leaves of sunflower, squash, bean, and other plants that are abundant starch formers.

As early as 1856 Boehm observed that the chloroplasts of *Asphodelus luteus*, *Allium fistulosum*, and others do not normally form starch. Later (1883) he placed the ends of etiolated leaves of *Phaseolus vulgaris* in sugar solutions and noted that they formed starch, while leaves of galanthus, hyacinth, and iris laid in 10 per cent sugar also showed an abundance of starch. He reasoned from these results that the same sequence of events occurred in the photosynthetic process. Schimper (1885) not only held that starch is converted into sugar in the plant but, from his observations on the increase of starch in leaves which were artificially supplied with sugar solutions, he concluded that glucose precedes starch in the process of photosynthesis. He considered that starch is formed from the glucose when the concentration of the latter exceeds a certain maximum which differs in different plants. Finally, in 1885 to 1886, Meyer emphasized the fact that the formation of starch in plants was by no means universal, since he observed that many of the monocotyledonous plants and especially the *Liliaceae* form very little starch in their leaves and some none at all. A very important contribution to the knowledge of the carbohydrate content of the leaves was the observation of Kayser (1883) that both sucrose and reducing sugars occur in the leaves of grape, beet, potatoes, and onion. He was the first to isolate sucrose in the crystalline form from the leaves of the grape.

The work of Boehm, Meyer, and Schimper indicated that the formation of starch in the leaves is preceded by the formation of the more simple carbohydrates. The chloroplasts like the leucoplasts form starch only when the supply of formative carbohydrates is in excess of the metabolic needs and translocating power of the cell in which they are contained or when the solution of the formation product has reached a certain stage of concentration.

The work of Kraus (1869) is also frequently quoted in order to show that starch is probably not the first carbohydrate formed in photosynthesis. He observed that the formation of starch in the cells of *Spirogyra* did not occur until 5 min. after the commencement of illumination, while the evolution of oxygen commenced at once. It is now generally considered by botanists very unlikely that such a complex and insoluble compound as starch should be the first product formed in the process of photosynthesis. The general opinion is that the first carbohydrate produced in the process is some form of sugar. The evidence as to which sugar it is will be presented in the following topics:

b. Daily Variations of the Carbohydrates in the Leaves.—The first quantitative determinations of the sugars in the leaf were made by Girard (1883, 1884). He observed that the proportion of sucrose in the leaves of the sugar beet was frequently twice as great at the close of the day as the following morning, while the amount of hexose sugars remained about the same. In 1893 Brown and Morris published their classical work on the daily variation of the carbohydrates in the leaves of the nasturtium. The evidence they obtained was in accord with that of Meyer and Schimper that the starch in the chloroplasts is a secondary product and not the first one of photosynthesis. They also showed that the dissolution of the starch is brought about by the enzyme diastase. Brown and Morris noted that sucrose showed the greatest increase during the day of any of the carbohydrates of the leaf and that during the night it was the one most diminished.

Parkin (1912) found in the case of the leaves of snowdrop (*Galanthus nivalis*) that during any single day the percentage of hexoses remained fairly constant no matter in what hour of the 24 the leaves were examined. The sucrose content, however, fluctuated greatly, increasing during the day and diminishing during the night, as may be observed by the following example:

Content	Per cent, dry basis, leaves picked at	
	9 a.m.	4:30 p.m.
Sucrose	9.8	14.7
Hexoses	12.4	11.6
Total	22.2	26.3

Parkin found also that the proportion of sucrose to hexoses decreased as the season advanced. In the early season the quantity of cane sugar was more than double that of the reducing sugars, whereas seven weeks later the two types were present in approximately the same quantities.

Knowledge of the daily variations in the carbohydrates of the leaves was greatly increased by the work of Davis and Daish (1913, 1914), Davis and Sawyer (1916), Davis, Daish, and Sawyer (1916), Davis (1916), and Davis and Sawyer (1916), who developed new methods and perfected old ones for the determination of the carbohydrates of leaf material, and knowledge has been further increased by the more recent work of Langner (1927), Clements (1930), Barton-Wright and Pratt (1930), Kishi and Monobe (1931), Belval (1932), Cole (1932), Denny (1932), Puhr and Hume (1932), Heinicke (1933), Sampson and Samisch (1935), Hartt (1935), and Stanescu (1936). In the leaves of the mangold, Davis, Daish, and Sawyer observed the following facts: (1) During the earlier stages of growth when leaf formation is the principal function, sucrose was present in the leaf tissue in excess of the hexoses, but later in the season the latter sugars largely predominate. (2) All the sugars in the leaf increase in quantity from the first to the final stages of growth. (3) Of the total sugars, the hexoses form a progressively increasing proportion as the season advances. (4) In the first stages of growth practically all the hexoses and half the sucrose disappear during the night, but as the season proceeds a smaller proportion of the sugars disappear each night. (5) The pentosans form a larger and larger proportion of the matter insoluble in alcohol as the season advances.

In the leaves of the potato at the stage of growth when the tubers are beginning to develop, these investigators observed that the principal sugar present is sucrose, which increases in amount from sunrise to 2 P.M. and then falls off during the rest of the day and night. The hexoses, on the other hand, are present in the leaves in very small amounts, amounting to less than 1 per cent of the dry weight of the leaf. After the sucrose had reached its maximum at 2 P.M., the hexoses began to increase in the leaf, owing apparently to the hydrolysis of the sucrose. At the same time, soluble starch or dextrin is first detected in the leaf and its amount increased regularly up to 6 P.M., when the true starch reached its maximum for the day. After this time, both the soluble and the true starch decreased in amount, being converted, apparently, directly into hexoses. In none of the leaves of potato or other starch-bearing leaves were they able to detect maltose. The enzyme maltase evidently acts at once upon the maltose formed in the digestion of starch, so that there is no accumulation whatsoever of this sugar in the leaf.

Kishi and Monobe (1931) found in mulberry leaves that the total carbohydrates were least in amount at sunrise and greatest at sunset. Denny (1932) noted that herbaceous plants show marked changes in the content of carbohydrate from night until morning, while woody plants showed only slight changes during the same period. Puhr and Hume (1932) found that the total sugar in the leaves of corn increases during the day and decreases at night. The maximum amount of sugar occurred from 1 to 4 P.M., and the minimum amount from 1 to 4 A.M. The insoluble carbohydrates reached a maximum between 7 P.M. and 1 A.M., and a minimum between 4 and 7 A.M. Hartt (1935) reported that sucrose increased in the leaves of sugar cane during the day and decreased during the night. This sugar did not completely disappear from the leaves at any time during the day. It was found by Tschesnokov and Bazyrina (1930) that translocation in the potato did not begin until 4 to 6 P.M., reaching a maximum about 8 P.M. but continuing all night. In peas the maximum translocation occurred at the same time as maximum photosynthesis. They believed that this difference is due to the fact that the temporary storage product of potatoes is insoluble, while that of the peas is soluble. Heinicke (1934) believed that the foliage of apple leaves, which functions efficiently late in the season, increases the reserve carbohydrates in the stem tissues, and thus promotes a large leaf area the following spring. McCarty (1935) observed in the grasses, *Elymus ambiguus* and *Muhlenbergia gracilis*, that the trend of starch and sucrose during the season was from a low concentration early in the growth cycle to a high concentration at the close of the growing season. Sampson and Samisch (1935) found in the leaves of *Quercus gambelli* and *Q. kelloggii* in California that the carbohydrates increased very rapidly and remained constant after the initial rise in July. In the Utah species of oaks, however, the carbohydrates continued to accumulate until September. Stanescu (1936) noticed that toward the end of the vegetative period the accumulation of starch occurred later in the morning than during the summer.

In the leaves of *Tropaeolum majus*, *Cucurbita ficifolia*, *Vitis vinifera*, and others, Gast (1917) noted that sucrose was generally in excess of the other sugars, being less at night than during the daytime, and the proportion of sucrose to hexoses decreased during the night. Miller (1924) determined the changes of the carbohydrates in the leaves of corn and the sorghums at 2-hr. intervals during a 24-hr. period. The total sugars in the leaves of these plants began to increase between 4 and 6 A.M., reached a maximum that varied from 12 M. to 5 P.M., and decreased gradually from that time until daylight the following morning. The insoluble carbohydrates were estimated as starch, according to the official method of acid hydrolysis, and thus included besides starch the pentosans and other insoluble carbohydrates that are converted into reducing sugars by boiling with hydrochloric acid. The insoluble carbohydrates thus estimated generally reached a maximum later in the day than the sugars and, after they had reached a maximum, showed little decrease until about midnight, after which they decreased rapidly until daylight. The nonreducing sugars in the leaves of the plants studied were, in nine experiments out of ten, always in excess of the reducing sugars. The nonreducing sugars increased markedly during the day and decreased during the night, while the reducing sugars, as a rule, showed very little increase and the amount present at the different periods of the day was very irregular. The maximum increase in the reducing sugars in the leaves during the day amounted only to from one-tenth to one-third of the increase in the nonreducing sugars. An example of the daily variation of the carbohydrates in the leaves of corn is shown in the following table and Fig. 25. These data were collected from the uppermost fully developed leaves of plants 4 to 5 ft. in height.

Stanescu (1927) noted that in the leaves of *Acer negundo* and *Medicago sativa* the monosaccharoses remained practically constant during the day and were much smaller in amounts than the disaccharoses, which showed a marked increase during the day and a diminution at night. In the leaves of *Urtica dioica* and *Polyanthes tuberosa* the two sugars remained constant during the day, but the disaccharoses were always present in the greater amount. Kishi and Monobe (1931), Cole (1932), and Puhr and Hume (1932) observed that sucrose predominates in amount in the leaves and fluctuates during the day and night the most markedly of all the sugars.

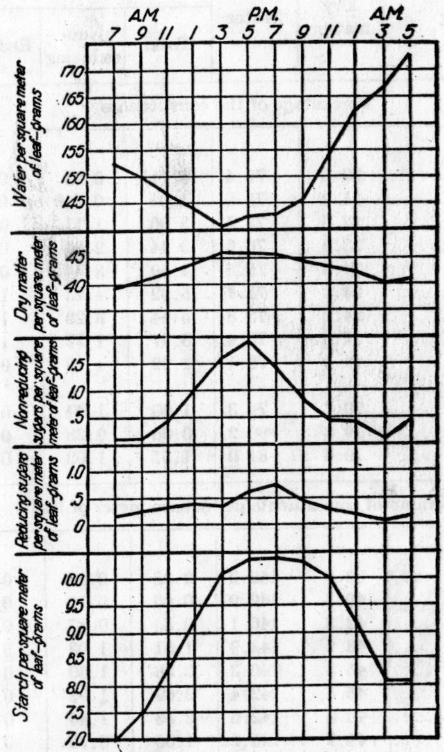

Fig. 25.—Graphs showing the variation in the water, dry matter, and carbohydrates of corn leaves during a 24-hr. period.

c. Variations in Different Portions of the Leaf.—It was noted by Parkin (1912) that the sugar content of the leaf of the snowdrop increased from above downward while the ratio of the sucrose to the hexose diminished. In the mangold leaf, Davis, Daish, and Sawyer (1916) found that the proportion of sugars and matter soluble in alcohol was always far greater in the petioles and midribs than in the blades of the leaves. In the midribs and petioles the hexoses always predominated greatly over the cane sugar. The proportion of hexoses to cane sugar was always very small in the blade of the leaf as compared with the value in the midrib. In passing from blades to midribs, from midribs to the tops of petioles,

Daily Variation of Water, Dry Matter, and Carbohydrates in the Leaves of Pride of Saline Corn, at Manhattan, Kans., July 3 and 4, 1919

Period ending	Dry matter	Water	Sugars			Starch[1]
			Total	Non-reducing	Reducing	
Percentage of the constituents						
July 3:						
7 a.m.	20.6	79.4	0.71	0.25	0.42	17.84
9 a.m.	21.2	78.8	1.01	0.31	0.65	18.72
11 a.m.	22.5	77.5	2.00	1.11	0.79	19.75
1 p.m.	23.4	76.6	3.44	2.34	0.90	21.12
3 p.m.	24.5	75.5	4.59	3.54	0.81	22.34
5 p.m.	24.3	75.7	5.92	4.23	1.41	22.85
7 p.m.	24.2	75.8	5.14	3.22	1.68	22.80
9 p.m.	23.6	76.4	3.47	1.77	1.05	23.13
11 p.m.	21.9	78.1	1.99	1.19	0.70	23.29
July 4:						
1 a.m.	20.7	79.3	1.60	1.04	0.48	21.61
3 a.m.	19.8	80.2	0.60	0.28	0.29	20.18
5 a.m.	19.0	81.0	1.51	1.02	0.40	19.88
Grams of constituents per square meter of leaf						
July 3:						
7 a.m.	39.3	152.2	0.28	0.09	0.16	7.01
9 a.m.	40.3	149.9	0.40	0.12	0.26	7.54
11 a.m.	42.3	146.1	0.85	0.47	0.33	8.35
1 p.m.	43.9	143.9	1.51	1.03	0.39	9.27
3 p.m.	45.3	140.3	2.08	1.60	0.37	10.12
5 p.m.	45.5	142.4	2.69	1.92	0.64	10.14
7 p.m.	45.3	142.6	2.33	1.46	0.76	10.33
9 p.m.	44.7	145.2	1.55	0.79	0.46	10.33
11 p.m.	43.0	153.8	0.85	0.51	0.30	10.01
July 4:						
1 a.m.	42.2	162.5	0.67	0.44	0.20	9.12
3 a.m.	40.0	166.0	0.24	0.11	0.12	8.07
5 a.m.	40.6	173.3	0.61	0.41	0.16	8.07

[1] The term "starch" as here used includes, besides the starch, the pentosans and other insoluble carbohydrates that undergo conversion into reducing sugars on boiling with hydrochloric acid according to the official method of acid hydrolysis for the estimation of starch.

and from the tops of petioles to the bottoms, the ratio of hexoses to cane sugar steadily and rapidly increased. Thus in the blade the ratio of hexoses to cane sugar was 0.307, at the top of petioles 1.42, and at the bottom of petioles 2.48. The excess of reducing sugars over nonreducing sugars in the leaf stems of the sugar beet and in the stalks of wheat has been noted by Colin (1914) and Colin and Belval (1922). Weevers (1923) determined the sucrose and hexose content of the green and yellow parts of variegated leaves. He examined the leaves of *Pelargonium zonale*, *Acer negundo*, and *Humulus lupulus* among others and found that both cane sugar and hexoses were in the green parts whereas, with few exceptions, sucrose was found only in the yellow parts.

Belval (1932) reported that the sugar in the blade of the leaf is sucrose and that it is progressively transformed into invert sugar in the veins and petioles.

d. The First Sugar Formed.—Owing to observations that (1) cane sugar is generally present in the leaves in considerable excess of the hexoses and shows a marked increase during the day and a decrease during the night while the hexoses remain practically constant and (2) the cane sugar of the leaves is changed into hexoses to be translocated from the leaf, as is evidenced by the excess of hexoses over cane sugar in the midribs and stems, Perrey (1882), Brown and Morris (1893), Davis, Daish, and Sawyer (1916), Parkin (1912, 1925), Gast (1917); and Colin (1916, 1917) considered that cane sugar is the first product of photosynthesis. They considered that the hexoses present in the leaf are more easily accounted for as the products of the hydrolysis of cane sugar than as its precursors. Parkin (1912, 1925) considered that the carbohydrates resulting from the photosynthetic process may be in no case truly up-grade products. The earliest sugar to appear in the free state may be split off from some complex molecule, and this sugar might easily be sucrose in the higher plants. The quantitative variations of cane sugar in the leaves during the day and night and its excess over the hexoses together with the relationship of these two sugars in the midribs and veins do not necessarily indicate that cane sugar is the first sugar formed in photosynthesis. It cannot be determined definitely from chemical analysis whether the marked increase in the amount of nonreducing sugars in the leaves during the day is due to the fact that they are the primary sugars of photosynthesis or to the fact that they are formed from the more simple sugars and accumulate in the leaves during the day as temporary storage products (Miller, 1924). It is just as reasonable to suppose that hexoses are formed and converted into cane sugar as a temporary storage product as it is to reason that cane sugar is the first one formed. Dixon and Mason (1916) by microchemical tests of the photosynthetic cells of several plants found that there was a considerable concentration of hexoses in the chloroplasts or in the protoplasm immediately surrounding them. Other experiments suggest that while sucrose is concentrated in the large vacuoles, invertase is held apart from it in the protoplasm. They considered that probably the hexoses are first formed and that, when the concentration reaches a certain limit, condensation to sucrose due to invertase or some saccharogenic enzyme takes place, and the sucrose thus formed is stored in the vacuole. Since the available space of the protoplasm is small, in sunlight the amount of sucrose will be greatly in excess of that in the protoplasm. On that account, the rise of sucrose on illumination shown by the analysis of leaves is not a cogent argument for regarding it as the primary sugar. The observations of Weevers (1923) also suggested that the hexoses are formed in the plants before the sucrose is formed. Thus the leaves of *Pelargonium zonale*, which were kept in the dark until they were depleted of sugar, produced when exposed to light first hexoses, then cane sugar, and finally starch. The fact that in the variegated leaves in most cases hexoses were found in the green portions while sucrose was confined to the yellow portion also indicated that the hexoses are the first sugars formed. Cane sugar frequently appears in considerable quantities in leaves that contain a large amount of starch. It is contended by those who consider sucrose to be the first products of photosynthesis that this sugar is not a transition product, since so far as any one knows cane sugar does not arise directly from starch. Priestley (1924) suggested that the hexoses could be the primary photosynthetic sugars and that the starch in the leaves could be formed from them. The starch or other carbohydrates could thus be used in the synthetic metabolism of the protoplasm, while cane sugar might arise as a secondary product of the metabolism of the cell and thus have no direct relationship with either the hexoses or the starch. In regard to the question concerning the first sugar formed in photosynthesis, an observation of Miller (1924) is worthy of note. He found that the total increase in the dry matter of the leaves during the day could not be accounted for by the increase in the sugars and insoluble carbohydrates during the same period. The increase in the total sugars and insoluble carbohydrates in the leaves during the day approximated only from 46 to 92 per cent of the total increase in the dry weight of the leaves for the same period. Since the cellulose content of the leaves did not increase during that period, it would appear that certain compounds were being formed which are not detected by the methods of carbohydrate determination as now used. Barton-Wright and Pratt (1930), working with the leaves of daffodil, narcissus, and pseudo narcissus, Clements (1930), with sunflower, soybean, and potato, and Virtanen and Nordlund (1934), with red clover and wheat, believed that sucrose is not the first product of photosynthesis. They considered that the hexoses are manufactured first, and that sucrose is later formed as a temporary storage product from these simple sugars.

From a chemist's viewpoint it would seem that the plant would first form the more simple carbohydrates from carbon dioxide and water and then by condensation form the more complex ones like starch and cane sugar. Before making this assumption, however, one should consider the words of Pfeffer: "It is a very confusing error to presume that an organism in its metabolic economy must follow a course which seems to man, under the influence of existing chemical and physical knowledge, to be the most plausible course" (Spoehr, 1926).

E. Chemistry

The chemical equation for photosynthesis is generally written as follows: $6CO_2 + 6H_2O \rightarrow C_6H_{12}O_6 + 6O_2$. This equation is based upon the fact that the volume of carbon dioxide absorbed is equal to the volume of oxygen emitted and that carbohydrates accumulate as products of the process. The equation thus represents the proportion of carbon dioxide and water used and the amount of oxygen released in the formation of hexose sugar. This equation is simple and shows little. It shows, so to speak, the materials that enter the hopper of the machine and the finished product that comes out at the spout but shows nothing concerning the intermediate stages in the process. Before considering the chemistry of photosynthesis, some statements should be made in regard to the general nature of the process, so that the difficulties involved in the experimental study of this subject may perhaps be better appreciated.

The outstanding fact of photosynthesis is the building up, from carbon dioxide and water, of compounds of higher energy content, the energy being supplied by the radiant energy of the light from the sun. The process of photosynthesis is thus an endothermal reaction, and there are no known analogous reactions in which there is a storing of energy approaching in amount that taking place in this process (Spoehr, 1926). It is through this process, as will be mentioned later, that the energy of the sun becomes available for use on the earth (see Peirce, 1934).

The conditions under which the synthesis of carbohydrates occurs are also baffling, since this process proceeds rapidly in the living plant under ordinary conditions of illumination and at ordinary temperatures. Outside the living plant, however, such synthesis can be brought about only very slowly and under conditions much different from those of the living plant. The photosynthetic process is thus closely associated with or dependent upon the life activities of the plant, but the relationship between this process and the protoplasm or living matter is in no manner definitely defined.

1. The Function of Chlorophyll.—Although it is known that chlorophyll and probably the other pigments of the chloroplasts are necessary for photosynthesis, the manner in which these pigments play a part is not definitely known. Chlorophyll has very characteristic chemical and physical properties and it is possible that it may play both a physical and chemical role in the photosynthetic process. Two of the physical properties of chlorophyll are the characteristic absorption spectrum and its power of fluorescence. It is now generally agreed that the chlorophyll absorbs the light energy necessary for photosynthesis, but the relation of the chlorophyll to the carbon dioxide that is ultimately reduced as a result of the absorbed energy is not known. Beyond the fact that chlorophyll absorbs certain rays of light which furnish the energy for photosynthesis, its functions are purely speculative. It is the intention here to mention only briefly some of the theories relative to photosynthesis. The student can readily discern from the discussion the almost total lack of experimental evidence on the subject, as is indicated by the wide diversity of views on the role that chlorophyll plays.

It has been considered by some that chlorophyll absorbs the energy of light and transmits it to another substance. Thus Usher and Priestley (1906, 1911) considered that the absorbed light energy is transferred to the carbon dioxide, which is thereupon reduced to formaldehyde. Tsweet (1911) was of the opinion that chlorophyll, since it exhibits fluorescence, functions in changing polychromatic light into monochromatic red light which is specifically absorbed by the carbon dioxide. As pointed out by Stiles (1925), however, carbon dioxide possesses no power for the absorption of light within the range of the visible spectrum. The carbon dioxide in the plant cell is present in an aqueous solution, and little is known concerning the absorption of the spectrum by the ions H^+ and $\overline{HCO_3}$ as they occur under this condition.

Baly, Heilbron, and Barker (1921) considered that light is absorbed by chlorophyll and radiated out again at infrared frequencies, which are utilized in the formation of formaldehyde and carbohydrates from carbon dioxide and water. Warburg and Negelein (1923), however, could observe no photosynthesis in *Chlorella* when exposed to infrared light of wave lengths of 800 to 900mμ and only a slight amount in wave lengths of 700 to 780mμ.

Kautsky, Hirsch, and Davidshöfer (1932) concluded that chlorophyll absorbs the light energy necessary for the process of photosynthesis, and passes it on to the system concerned in the assimilation of carbon dioxide. They stated that this energy transfer is associated with a reduction in the fluorescence of the chlorophyll. Dhar (1935) considered that chlorophyll and carotinoids act as photosensitizers and as reducing agents in the photoreduction of carbon dioxide.

Chlorophyll is considered by some to play a chemical part in photosynthesis as well as a physical role. It was suggested by Willstätter and Stoll (1918) that in the process of photosynthesis a compound is first formed between the chlorophyll and carbon dioxide and that light acts on this compound converting it into a substance of peroxide constitution which is then acted upon by an enzyme (Stiles, 1925). The presence of catalase in the photosynthetic regions has recently been determined. Von Euler, Hertzsch, Forssberg, and Hellström (1931) found in certain variegated plants that catalase activity is greater in the green than in the white or yellow portions of the leaves. Inman (1935) believed his observations indicated that whenever green plants are capable of evolving oxygen there is generally present within the cells active catalase that is available for acting on hydrogen peroxide. Emerson (1929) considered that the evidence indicates that photosynthesis involves an autocatalytic reaction, with chlorophyll playing some part in photosynthesis in addition to the absorption of light.

By some it is held that chlorophyll is acted upon by light to form a photochemical primary product that reacts with a derivative of carbon dioxide. Under this view it is considered that the actual reduction of the carbon dioxide or its derivatives is purely chemical, the light producing, by means of the chlorophyll, the reducing substance.

Dixon and Poole (1920) and Dixon and Ball (1922) performed experiments to determine whether the electrons were actually ejected from the chlorophyll by the incident radiation or were merely displaced within groups of atoms or from molecule to molecule of chlorophyll. They considered that photosynthesis is apparently caused by light the frequency of which is too low to effect the expulsion of the electrons from the chlorophyll molecule. The photosynthetic reactions must thus concern the chlorophyll molecule itself. The wave lengths that are effective in displacing the electrons of chlorophyll as indicated by its sensitizing action on the photographic plate are the same as those that are effective in photosynthesis. The theory that the chlorophyll molecule combines with carbon dioxide in the photosynthetic process has also been suggested by Gordon (1929), James (1934), and Baly (1935).

It would seem thus that the atomic groups of the leaf pigment enter into the reactions of photosynthesis and participate in the combinations and decompositions that ultimately lead to the formation of carbohydrates. From these observations, theories of photosynthesis which assume that the chlorophyll itself enters into the reactions are to be preferred to those suggestions which suppose that the reaction is accomplished externally to the chlorophyll by means of energy absorbed and transformed by it.

The role of the yellow pigments in the chloroplasts in photosynthesis is not known. The general indications are that they at least may act in a supplementary way in the process even if they may not be absolutely necessary (Ewart, 1918).

2. The Absorption of Carbon Dioxide by the Leaf.—The entrance of carbon dioxide into the leaf may rightly be considered the first stage in the photosynthetic process. It has been shown in Chap. VII that the capacity of the stomata for the diffusion of carbon dioxide into the leaf is far beyond that which is actually needed for the photosynthetic process provided that the partial pressure of this gas in the leaf is kept at approximately zero. The diffusion of carbonic acid in water, however, is a slow process, and this together with its low solubility in water and its low partial pressure in the atmosphere has long been recognized as conditions which to all appearances would be unfavorable to photosynthesis. According to Spoehr and McGee (1924), 1,000 cc. of water will dissolve 0.033 cc. of carbon dioxide at 25°C. from a concentration of 3 parts per 10,000 by volume. On the other hand, 1,000 g. of the leaves of sunflower with an area of 3.3 sq. m. and with a water content of 850 cc. would dissolve under normal conditions only 0.027 cc. of carbon dioxide if the water were considered as the absorption agency. This amount of leaf material, however, during the process of photosynthesis absorbs as much as 1,500 cc. of carbon dioxide per hour. The leaves of the nettle (*Urtica dioica*) have also been observed to have a high absorption capacity for carbon dioxide. Spoehr (1926), however, was unable to detect any absorption factor in the case of the leaves of spinach, turnip, lettuce, rhubarb, grass, and others, since the amount of gas that was absorbed was equivalent only to that which could be dissolved in the quantity of water present.

Since some leaves absorb a quantity of carbon dioxide greater than can be accounted for by the water present, it has been assumed that there is a substance in the leaf for absorbing this gas so that its absorption is accelerated and its concentration in the photosynthetic cells raised. Willstätter and Stoll (1918) considered that this substance is not related to the pigments of the chloroplasts but that it is an organic compound. Siegfried (1905) found that carbon dioxide combines with amino acids and concluded that the major portion of the carbon dioxide in the leaf forms definite compounds with the amino groups of the proteins and thus increases the concentration of carbon dioxide in the cells. He further considered that these compounds would dissociate to release the carbon dioxide as needed in the cells. Spoehr (1926), however, considered that the amount of nitrogen present is too small to account for all the carbon dioxide absorbed and believed that the indications are that the absorption of carbon dioxide is due to a carbonate-to-bicarbonate reaction. It is not known, however, whether the absorption capacity of a leaf for carbon dioxide has any relationship to the process of photosynthesis.

3. Theories Concerning Photosynthesis.—The great difference between the chemical constitution of a carbohydrate and the carbon dioxide and water out of which it is formed suggests that these compounds are not transformed into sugar at a single step but that a series of compounds increasing more and more in complexity are produced until sugar finally appears as the finished product. Numerous theories have been proposed as to the probable course of the reactions and in regard to the intermediate products that might be formed. It is interesting to note that most of the experimental work relative to the chemistry of photosynthesis has been done in an attempt to verify these theories.

a. Organic Acid Theory.—The first theory to explain the reactions that occur between the intake of carbon dioxide and water and the production of carbohydrates was made by Liebig (1843). He considered that the various organic acids as oxalic, tartaric, and malic were formed as intermediate products in photosynthesis. This theory was based on no experimental evidence and has found little or no support.

b. Formaldehyde Theory.—This theory in regard to the intermediate products in photosynthesis has received by far the most consideration of any that have been proposed. In fact, with but a few exceptions all the theories of photosynthesis that have been proposed assume that formaldehyde is the final stage of reduction in the process. The main differences of opinion in regard to the various theories of photosynthesis have centered largely around the question as to whether the reduction of carbon dioxide to formaldehyde is accomplished in one step or whether there are intermediate products (Spoehr, 1926). The formaldehyde theory was first proposed by Baeyer (1870), and, since this hypothesis has so greatly influenced the experimental work on photosynthesis, it seems desirable to review in considerable detail some of the facts regarding its origin. In 1861 Butlerow discovered that formaldehyde in aqueous alkaline solution condensed to an optically inactive syrup possessing some of the properties of hexose sugars. Baeyer (1870) in discussing Butlerow's results considered formaldehyde in solution to be $CH_2(OH)_2 \rightarrow H_2CO + H_2O$ and suggested that the results obtained by him might be due to the condensation of 6 molecules of $CH_2(OH)_2$ into a hexose sugar with the loss of 6 molecules of water. Baeyer also suggested that this might be the manner in which grape sugar is formed in the plant. He considered that the sunlight might split the carbon dioxide into carbon monoxide and oxygen, the oxygen escaping and the carbon monoxide being held by the chlorophyll. The monoxide is reduced to formaldehyde ($CO + H_2$) by the decomposition of water, and the formaldehyde is then condensed to sugar. Baeyer's hypothesis was formulated without any experimental evidence and was published only as a suggestion, yet it has directed the greater portion of the investigational work on photosynthesis and has become so commonplace in its mention that it is considered by many to be an established fact. Many modifications of Baeyer's theory have been proposed, but these differ but little from the original, and a detailed discussion of these theories is outside the province of this work. The experimental work that has been conducted in an attempt to prove the formaldehyde theory of photosynthesis may be summarized under four general headings as follows:

1. *The Reduction of Carbon Dioxide.*—From the chemical standpoint, the reduction of carbon dioxide is the most important as well as the most difficult process in photosynthesis, and many attempts with many methods have been tried to bring it about. Although these attempts have been made under varied conditions, many of which are not comparable to those of the plant, and have given very contradictory results, they at least show the behavior of carbon dioxide under different conditions and may thus give some little light either directly or indirectly upon the mode of reduction in the photosynthetic process.

Previous to 1907 all the attempts to reduce carbon dioxide had resulted in the production of formic acid. In that year Fenton by passing a stream of carbon dioxide for 18 to 20 hr. through pure water in contact with several rods of amalgamated magnesium obtained a solution that indicated the presence of formaldehyde as indicated by the color tests. Weak alkalies seemed to aid materially in this reaction. In 1906 Loeb by means of the silent electrode and by using something to take up the oxygen, *e.g.*, chlorophyll, obtained formaldehyde and formic acid with ease and in quantity from carbon dioxide and water. He also noted the formation of glycolaldehyde from hydrogen and carbon dioxide under these conditions. The synthesis of a hexose sugar from this compound is apparently a rather simple process. Gibson (1908) formulated a photoelectric theory of photosynthesis in which it was considered that formaldehyde is synthesized from carbon dioxide in the presence of water by feeble electric changes, which he considered occurred in the photosynthetic tissues when adequately illuminated, the light energy being transformed by the chlorophyll into electric energy. He considered that Loeb's experiment strengthened a part of this theory, and it has later (Dixon and Poole, 1920) been established that a slight photoelectric effect occurs in chlorophyll under illumination. Since the work of Loeb and Fenton, the experiments on the reduction of carbon dioxide have centered mainly around the influence of ultraviolet light. Work on the effect of ultraviolet light as obtained especially from the quartz mercury-vapor lamp has been reported by Berthelot and Gaudechon (1910), Usher and Priestley (1911), Stocklasa and Zdobnicky (1911, 1912), Spoehr (1916, 1923, 1926), and Baly, Heilbron, and Barker (1921, 1923). The results that have been reported are very contradictory. Some workers have obtained formaldehyde only in the presence of nascent hydrogen, while others have not noted the need of such. Some have obtained formaldehyde in the polymerized form, some both formaldehyde and sugar, while yet others could obtain no formaldehyde at all. Thus Baly, Heilbron, and Barker (1921) reported that an aqueous solution of carbon dioxide gives formaldehyde when exposed to light of wave length of 200mμ. Spoehr (1916, 1923) in numerous well-controlled experiments was, however, unable to obtain any definite evidence of the formation of formaldehyde from carbon dioxide and water under the action of ultraviolet light. Under the conditions of his experiments, however, he was able to obtain formic acid in small amounts. The reasons for such contradictory results are not known, but Spoehr (1923) suggested that where a direct reduction of carbon dioxide to formaldehyde by means of ultraviolet light has been reported there existed certain essential conditions or factors not known by the investigator, or there were some misinterpretations of the experimental observations.

It is doubtful if the conditions under which carbon dioxide was reduced in the various experiments just reported are comparable to the conditions that exist in the plant. Apparently the ultraviolet or any rays that lie outside the visible spectrum play little or no part in photosynthesis. Photosynthesis, for example, proceeds normally when ultraviolet rays are excluded from the plant, as in the case of their growing under ordinary glass. It would thus, in the words of Spoehr (1916), seem that we have no clear record of a reduction of carbon dioxide or its salts to formaldehyde which could be applied to the process going on in the leaf under the conditions that therein exist.

Considerable work has been done to determine the behavior of isolated chlorophyll and the other pigments in regard to the reduction of carbon dioxide and the formation of formaldehyde. It was reported by Usher and Priestley (1906, 1911) that films of extracted chlorophyll in the presence of carbon dioxide and moist air produced formaldehyde and hydrogen peroxide under the influence of light. The production of formaldehyde under similar conditions was observed by Schryver (1910), who considered that it was in combination with the chlorophyll.

Since then it has been observed by Wager (1914), Warner (1914), Jorgensen and Kidd (1917), Osterhout (1915, 1918), and Ewart (1920) that formaldehyde is formed when chlorophyll is exposed to the light but only in the presence of oxygen in a moist atmosphere. The formation of formaldehyde occurs regardless of the presence of carbon dioxide. When the extracted chlorophyll is thus exposed to the light, the first change observed is its yellowing and ultimate bleaching. In the first stage while bleaching is complete, the quantity of formaldehyde reaches a maximum and then diminishes. It is considered by most of the investigators just mentioned that the aldehyde which appears under these conditions is not produced by the reduction of carbon dioxide but rather by the oxidation or decomposition of chlorophyll under the influence of light and oxygen. It is on that account, therefore, suggested by Ewart (1907) and Wager (1914) and others that the production of sugar may be initiated by the photooxidation of chlorophyll and the subsequent polymerization of the aldehyde thus formed rather than by the direct photosynthesis of carbon dioxide and water. That chlorophyll or some component may decompose during photosynthesis was suggested by the work of Osterhout and Haas (1918). They found, in experiments with *Ulva*, *Potamogeton*, *Spirogyra*, and other plants that had been kept in the dark, that they began photosynthesis as soon as they were exposed to sunlight and steadily increased their rate until a constant speed was attained. Since no limiting factors as light and carbon dioxide were involved, these authors considered that the behavior indicated that sunlight decomposes a substance whose products either catalyze photosynthesis or enter directly into the reaction.

Osterhout (1918) and Burk (1927) employed aniline dyes to ascertain if aldehyde could be produced by them as in the case of chlorophyll. A considerable number gave positive results. Osterhout found methyl green and iodine green to be the most reliable. Burk used malachite green. Osterhout sprayed aqueous solutions of the dyes upon filter paper until the paper was a deep green color when dried. These were then exposed to sunlight under bell jars for several days until the color disappeared. A positive test for aldehyde was obtained in the majority of cases. Baly, Heilbron, and Barker (1921) found also that the photosynthesis of formaldehyde from carbon dioxide and water could be photocatalyzed by certain colored basic substances as colloidal uranium, colloidal ferric hydroxides, malachite green, and methyl orange. Under these conditions the formation of formaldehyde took place in visible light.

When carbon dioxide was exposed to ultraviolet light, Mezzadroli (1928) obtained the maximum yield of reducing substance with calcium bicarbonate in the presence of very finely powdered metallic magnesium. Rajvansi and Dhar (1932) obtained formaldehyde from carbon dioxide and water in the presence of sunlight and chromium oxide, cobalt carbonate, nickel carbonate, manganous chloride, copper carbonate, or nickel sulphate. Qureshi and Mohammad (1932) obtained formaldehyde when a colloidal solution of chlorophyll *a* and solutions of pure malachite green, methyl orange, and copper acetate were exposed to sunlight in sealed bulbs from which carbon dioxide was excluded.

2. *The Condensation of Formaldehyde to Sugar.*—Since it was assumed in Baeyer's hypothesis that formaldehyde is condensed to sugar in the presence of alkalies in the photosynthetic process, numerous experiments have been conducted in an attempt to bring this about in the laboratory. Positive results have been obtained but in many cases under conditions of high temperatures and in concentrations of alkalies that are in no way comparable to the conditions that prevail in the plant (Nef, 1913; Ewart, 1919). It has also been determined that a great complexity of reactions occurs when a solution of formaldehyde is treated with an alkali, so that not only some sugar but also a large number of other compounds are formed. The condensation of formaldehyde to sugar is thus not such a simple process as had formerly been supposed. The attempts to form sugar from formaldehyde under conditions comparable to those existing in the green plant have given conflicting results. Spoehr (1916) placed 3 per cent solutions of formaldehyde in tenth-normal solutions of weak alkalies in glass flasks and exposed them to sunlight for as long as 4 months. The solutions of formaldehyde in calcium carbonate, potassium bicarbonate, zinc carbonate, and basic magnesium carbonate showed no trace of sugar formation. The solutions of formaldehyde in lead hydroxide, calcium hydroxide, and potassium carbonate formed sugar in the dark as well as in the sunlight.

The formation of sugars on the exposure of aqueous solutions of formaldehyde to ultraviolet light was demonstrated by Moore and Webster (1918). In the same year it was reported by Baly, Heilbron, and Barker (1921), Baly (1922, 1924), and Heilbron (1923) that an aqueous solution of formaldehyde is polymerized to reducing sugars in light of wave length of 290mμ. In the presence of paraldehyde, sodium phenoxide, and certain metallic salts that absorb light of wave lengths 290mμ the yield of formaldehyde was materially increased, since these substances protected it from polymerization when it was formed.

In contrast to these investigators, Ewart (1920) concluded that the production of formaldehyde does not form a stage in the synthesis of sugar in the plant and that alkalies do not polymerize formaldehyde to sugar except to a very slight extent. Pronounced sugar formation occurs only when the alkali acts on a polymer such as *p*-formaldehyde, the polyhydrate, or *m*-formaldehyde, and in such cases the endothermal reaction may be very violent and not applicable to the conditions in the plant. Baly (1922) and Heilbron (1923) state that ordinary formaldehyde is not condensed to sugar under ordinary conditions, but they consider that the formaldehyde molecule produced in the process of photosynthesis is in a highly reactive state and has been designated by them as "activated formaldehyde." The formaldehyde of this type is quickly condensed to sugar and cannot be detected in the plant. The formaldehyde that is detected in the leaf they consider to be a secondary product from reactions other than photosynthesis. Baly (1928) by a suspension of pure aluminum hydroxide maintained by a stream of carbon dioxide exposed to ultraviolet light obtained a much greater yield of carbohydrates than if no suspensions were used. The best yield of carbohydrates, however, was obtained by passing a stream of carbon dioxide in water through a suspension of nickel carbonate or cobalt carbonate, exposed to the light from an ordinary tungsten-filament electric lamp. It was found that these particles used for the surfaces must be absolutely free from alkalies or the formation of carbohydrates will not occur. At times, even when freed from all alkali, the carbonates of nickel and cobalt were entirely ineffective in promoting photosynthesis. These suspensions could be activated, however, by heating to 120°C. or by exposure in thin layers to ultraviolet light. These experiments of Baly are important in that they indicate that surface phenomena are of primary importance in the reduction of carbon dioxide to carbohydrates and that sugar is formed directly from carbon dioxide by a process which is physically similar to that of the living plant. The amount of carbohydrate obtained, however, is very small, so it has not been possible to carry on a complete analysis of the different materials obtained in the process. It has, however, been fairly definitely determined that glucose and fructose are present. Emerson (1929), and Zscheile (1932), however, could not duplicate these results of Baly.

3. *The Detection of Intermediate Products in the Leaves.*—Most of the experiments for the determination of intermediate products of photosynthesis have been confined to attempts to identify formaldehyde in the green parts of plants. Many of the reports are of no value, since it has later been found that the methods used were at fault and were in many cases not specific for the substance being determined. The identification of formaldehyde in green leaves, however, has been reported by numerous and accurate investigators among whom are Grafe and Vieser (1906), Kimpflin (1907), Gibson (1908), Fincke (1913), Barton-Wright and Pratt (1930), Pollacci and Bergamaschi (1931), and Sommer, Bishop, and Otto (1933). There is thus little doubt but that formaldehyde occurs in the green parts of plants under certain conditions. It was noted by Von Euler and others (1931) that the green portion of certain etiolated leaves contained from two to five times more aldehyde than the yellow or white portions. There is no evidence, however, that it is a product of photosynthesis, since, as stated by Spoehr and others, there are a number of components of plants which may yield formaldehyde when exposed to light, or it may arise in the general metabolic reactions of the plant.

4. *Nutrition Experiments with Organic Compounds.*—It has been stated in Chap. VI that plants are capable of utilizing in their metabolism certain organic compounds if presented to their roots. This utilization is manifested by increased growth and by the formation of secondary or condensation products as evidenced, for example, by the appearance of starch in the tissue after the plant has been given sugar as a nutrient. Various organic compounds, principally formaldehyde, which are considered intermediate products of photosynthesis have been presented to plants to determine whether the plant could utilize them in the formation of carbohydrates. Formaldehyde has been presented to plants in nutrient solutions, by its introduction into the water in which aquatic plants are growing and in the form of vapor in the atmosphere bathing the aerial parts of the plant.

Bokorny (1891 to 1911) was the first to try the effect of formaldehyde vapor on plants, and his work has been followed by that of Grafe and Vieser (1909, 1911) and Baker (1913). These authors agree that formaldehyde can be used to some extent in the light for the synthesis of carbohydrates and that starch in some cases appears as a secondary product, although in some cases there were chances for errors in the experiments. They also noted that formaldehyde was not utilized in the dark and that the poisonous effects of formaldehyde were always more marked in the dark than in the light. Spoehr (1916) found that formaldehyde mixed with air quickly oxidized to formic acid in sunlight and suggests that formic acid might be the source of carbon in the formaldehyde experiments that have been mentioned. Jacoby (1919, 1922) placed abscised leaves of the nasturtium in the dark with the petioles immersed in water and with the laminae of the leaves surrounded by a humid, carbon dioxide-free air, containing the vapor of formaldehyde. The leaves subjected to the formaldehyde for 24.5 to 32 hr. increased in dry weight from 12 to 15 per cent as compared with an increase of 1.7 to 5.1 per cent in the controls. He considered that the formaldehyde under these experiments was fixed by the plant. Results similar to Jacoby's have been obtained by Sabalitschka and Riesenberg (1924) with *Phaseolus multiflorus* and *Pelargonium*.

The utilization of formaldehyde from nutrient solutions has been studied by Bokorny (1911), Nicholas and Nicolas (1922), and Sabalitschka and Weidling (1926). They found that plants can polymerize formaldehyde thus presented to carbohydrates equally well in the light or dark. The latter investigators found the optimum concentration of formaldehyde in the nutrient solution to be 0.024 per cent. Higher concentrations damaged the enzymes and retarded or inhibited the condensation. They considered that this offers strong confirmation of the hypothesis that formaldehyde is a stage in the production of starch under normal conditions.

It has generally been considered that if formaldehyde or other organic substances could be utilized in plant growth or in the formation of carbohydrates within the plants, this was evidence that they were intermediate products in photosynthesis. There seems, however, to be no grounds for such a conclusion. The organic compounds that plants may absorb and utilize in the formation of sugar and then starch are very numerous, and the experiments that have been performed, especially with formaldehyde, only make that fact the more evident but prove in no way that formaldehyde or any of the other substances so utilized are intermediate products in the process of photosynthesis.

c. Recent Theories.—A summary of the more recent ideas concerning the process of photosynthesis is presented here. James (1934) considered that a diffusion reaction, a photochemical reaction, and at least one thermal "dark" reaction are involved in the process. He proposed the following steps in photosynthesis, which are based largely on the statements of Willstätter and Stoll (1918), and Warburg (1919):

1. The carbon dioxide arriving at the surface of the chloroplasts reacts as carbonic acid, or some simple derivative, with the magnesium of the chlorophyll to form a dissociable addition compound.

2. Under the influence of light this compound undergoes internal rearrangement of the molecule giving an unstable compound, chlorophyll-formaldehyde-peroxide, in which the oxygen is only loosely held.

3. This compound in the presence of a peroxidase readily breaks down by two stages, each releasing ½ molecule of oxygen.

4. The gaseous oxygen escapes from the system, and the formaldehyde eventually polymerizes to sugar.

Baly (1935) suggested that in the process of photosynthesis a complex of chlorophyll *a* and hydrated carbon dioxide is converted by the action of light into chlorophyll *b* and activated formaldehyde, the latter being at once polymerized into hexoses. The chlorophyll *b* thus produced undergoes the dark reaction and is reduced to chlorophyll *a*. The findings of Burr (1936) that there is not a catalyst in the plant for carbon dioxide hydration throws doubts upon the view that carbon dioxide must become hydrated to carbonic acid before reacting with chlorophyll. The rate of the consumption of carbon dioxide in photosynthesis is far greater than the rate of uncatalyzed hydration of carbon dioxide.

Dhar (1935) submitted the following procedure in photosynthesis:

1. Partial activation of carbon dioxide and water, due to their adsorption by chlorophyll and other plant pigments.

2. Further activation of the adsorbed carbon dioxide and water by the absorption of part of the energy available from respiration and from the oxidation of carotin.

3. Absorption of light by chlorophyll, and other pigments, and the dissociation of activated water molecules into H and OH. The activated carbon dioxide molecules are then reduced to formaldehyde by the atomic-H produced from the sensitized photolysis of water.

4. The polymerization of formaldehyde to reducing sugar.

5. The formation of hydrogen peroxide from OH, and its rapid decomposition into water and hydrogen.

The student can easily judge from this discussion of the chemistry of photosynthesis that but little is known concerning the mechanism of the process. The facts that are known are that the process takes place under the influence of the visible portion of the spectrum, that chlorophyll, water, oxygen, and carbon dioxide are necessary, that carbohydrates are formed and oxygen eliminated, and that the process proceeds under the general conditions which are suitable to the activities of living organisms. These facts are not new and have been known in a general way for more than 70 years. The enormous amount of research upon the process of photosynthesis during the past half century has thrown little or no additional light upon the subject. The problem is evidently too complex for specialists in any one field of science to solve, and, in the words of Spoehr (1916): "The subject of photosynthesis requires for its investigation the masterly application of many branches of science—physics, chemistry, plant physiology and the frank cooperation of the most skilled workers in these various fields."

F. Factors That Affect Photosynthesis

The physiological processes that occur in plants are multiconditioned, so that in an investigation of the influence of one factor or condition, the interrelation of this factor with the others concerned in any process must be taken into consideration. It is, therefore, impossible to speak of a single condition as being the cause of an observed effect in a plant (Livingston, 1917), but one must consider that a given result depends upon numerous other external and internal conditions.

The conception of multiconditioned processes was first recognized by Liebig (1843) and was expressed in his law of the minimum in regard to the yield of field crops. This law as commonly stated says that "The yield of any crop always depends on that nutritive constituent which is present in minimum amount." This means, as stated by Hooker (1917), that if the available amounts of the essential plant nutrients are divided by their respective growth values, the smallest quantity obtained gives the maximum amount of growth possible. Liebig, however, apparently did not consider water supply, oxygen supply, temperature, and other factors which influence the yield of a crop as well as the supply of nutrients, so it is not nearly so easy to express the law of the minimum as might be inferred from its original rather simple presentation.

Thomas (1929) reviewed the work of Lagatu and Maume (1924, 1925) who showed that the absorption of nitrogen, phosphorus, and potassium by the grape is irreconcilable with Liebig's law. They found that:

1. The application of an incomplete fertilizer deficient in one of the elements, nitrogen, phosphorus, or potassium, results in an increased absorption of the other two.

2. The lack of balance in a fertilizer containing only two of the principal fertilizer constituents—nitrogen, phosphorus, and potassium—may be such that it will retard the absorption of the omitted one. Under such conditions the plant may take up less of the element in which the soil is deficient than if there had been no addition of the other two principal fertilizer constituents.

3. The lack of nutritional balance, resulting from the addition of an unbalanced fertilizer (except in a nitrogen deficiency), is indicated by decreased yields.

Bartholomew, Watts, and Janssen (1933) stated that Liebig's law of the minimum is not applicable to potassium salts, because the elimination of potassium from a nutrient solution results in an increased absorption of nitrogen and phosphorus by the plants.

Macy (1936) in discussing the limitations of nutrients on the development of plants proposed that the percentage of the limiting nutrient in the plant is directly proportional to the response of the plant to an increase in the supply of that nutrient.

The process of photosynthesis is one that is conditioned by numerous separate factors. It was realized by Pfeffer (1900) and Pantanelli (1904) that the optimum value in photosynthesis was not a fixed value in the case of any condition but might depend upon other conditions. It remained, however, for Blackman (1905) to enunciate this fact clearly and to crystallize the facts in regard to the interaction of factors not only in the process of photosynthesis but in regard to other physiological processes as well. In a consideration of the interaction of factors in the process of photosynthesis he stated his law of limiting factors: "When a process is conditioned as to its rapidity by a number of separate factors, the rate of the process is limited by the pace of the 'slowest' factor." The classical example used by Blackman was the interaction of carbon dioxide and light. Suppose that a leaf has enough light falling upon it to supply sufficient energy to decompose 5 cc. of carbon dioxide per hour. If the leaf is supplied, for example, with only 1 cc. of carbon dioxide per hour and then this amount is increased up to 5 cc. per hour, the rate of photosynthesis will increase from one- to fivefold. After the rate of carbon dioxide is increased beyond 5 cc. per hour, the rate of photosynthesis will remain the same as it was when the rate of carbon dioxide application was 5 cc. per hour. Light in this case is thus the limiting factor in the photosynthetic process. If the intensity of the light is increased until it is sufficient to decompose 10 cc. of carbon dioxide per hour, an increase in the pressure of the carbon dioxide will increase the rate of photosynthesis until the leaf is supplied with 10 cc. of carbon dioxide per hour. If a larger amount of carbon dioxide is supplied, the

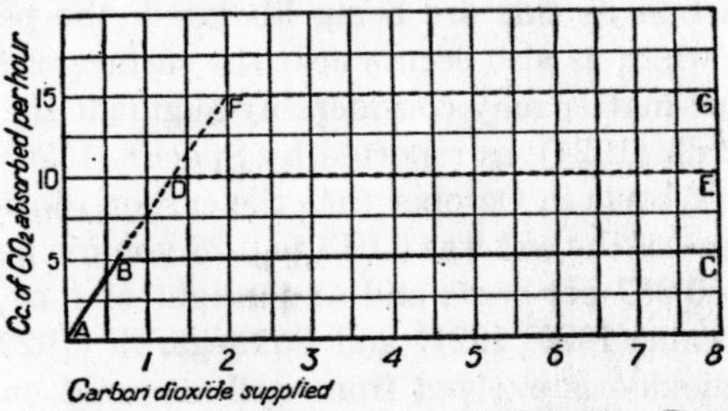

Fig. 26.—Diagram to illustrate the action of a limiting factor. Description in the text. (*After F. F. Blackman, "Annals of Botany,"* 1905.)

rate of photosynthesis will remain the same, since light will at that point again become the limiting factor (Fig. 26). Thus it is impossible to investigate the relation between carbon dioxide supplied and the rate of photosynthesis without considering the factor of light.

The law of limiting factors is an elaboration of the law of the minimum and is of general application where a process depends upon a number of factors. There is considerable difference of opinion regarding the general applicability of the law of limiting factors. Hooker (1917) considered that, although the individual processes obey the law, it does not apply to the questions of general development. Crocker (1918) considered that it is a question whether the law of limiting factors applies to plant activities as generally as or with anything like the rigidity assumed by some. He suggested that the question should not be so much what external factor is the limiting one as what internal condition or inhibitor must this factor act upon to initiate the reaction that is under consideration. Harder (1921), and Singh and Lal (1935) believed that, when the limiting factor comes into operation, the curve is smooth and regular with no sharp break as reported by Blackman.

The factors that influence the rate of photosynthesis may, in common with other factors that influence the general process of plants, be divided or grouped into external factors and internal factors, depending upon whether they are conditions that exist in the external medium or those that exist within the plant owing to its structure or composition. The external factors that influence photosynthesis are the carbon dioxide supply, light, temperature, water supply, and numerous other factors essential to the general growth and vigor of the plant. The known internal factors that play a part in the process are the chlorophyll content and the protoplasmic factors.

1. The Carbon Dioxide Supply. *a. Amount in the Air.*—The amount of carbon dioxide in the air is approximately 3 parts per 10,000 by volume, and this proportion is very constant whether the samples are taken over the sea or over the land. In industrial centers or in cities where large amounts of carbon dioxide are being liberated, the percentage may be increased somewhat, as also occurs near the surface of the soil where the decay of organic matter may considerably augment the average amount. Thus Lundegårdh (1924), as reported by Spoehr (1926), found in a well-fertilized field of beets in October that the carbon dioxide content of the air at the surface of the soil was 0.053 to 0.28 volume per cent; above the leaves, 0.04 to 0.067 per cent; and at a height of 1 m., 0.03 to 0.07 per cent. Bornemann (1920, 1921) and Lundegårdh (1922) considered that more carbon dioxide is evolved from well-manured and well-cultivated land than from that which is not manured or cultivated and considered that one of the advantages of good cultivation is the release of large amounts of carbon dioxide at the soil surface. Keuhl (1926) believed that mineral fertilizers are beneficial to a certain extent in that they cause a greater production of carbon dioxide by hastening bacterial action in the soil. Reinau (1927) believed that the carbon dioxide arising from the soil is of more significance to plants than that in the atmosphere above the plants. He considered that there should be sufficient organic material in the soil to provide for a sufficient flow of this gas around the plant. Appleman (1927) found that the volumetric concentration of carbon dioxide, in the soils of Maryland, was as high as 5 per cent in some cases. Gerlach (1921), however, could obtain no positive evidence that stable or green manures could act as producers of carbon dioxide in amounts that might be beneficial to crops. The fact that the concentration of carbon dioxide is considerably higher near the soil surface than in the upper atmosphere may be of great importance in the growth of plants, since, as will be shown later, carbon dioxide can be used by plants to advantage in much stronger concentration than that which prevails in the general atmosphere.

The carbon dioxide content of the soil atmosphere is always higher than that of the atmosphere above ground. Lundegårdh (1924) stated that it varies from 0.12 to 2.5 per cent by volume, while Banal (1926) stated that the amount is from 5 to 10 per cent higher than that of the general atmosphere.

The carbon dioxide of the air that is combined by the plant is replaced by the decay of organic matter, by the respiration of animals and plants, by the combustion of wood, coal, gasoline, and other products, by the disintegration of rocks, especially limestone, and by the gases escaping from volcanoes. Owing to these replacements the carbon dioxide content of the air remains practically constant. The carbon dioxide content of water should also be noted here. Water can absorb from the air, at 760 mm., 0.04 per cent of its own volume of carbon dioxide at 10°C., 0.03 per cent at 15°C., and 0.02 per cent at 20°C. Sea water contains in both the free and combined state about fifty times as much carbon dioxide as does the atmosphere, but the greater portion of it is not available to the plant.

b. Amount Used by the Plant.—The relatively small amount of carbon dioxide in the air was for a long time a stumbling block in the determination of the source of the plant's carbon supply. It was difficult to conceive that an element which constitutes from 40 to 45 per cent of the dry weight of the plant kingdom could be obtained from the small quantity that exists in the atmosphere. An enormous volume of air must be depleted of carbon dioxide to supply the carbon for a crop, as may be illustrated in the case of corn by the following example:

In 10,000 l. of air there are approximately 3.1 l. of carbon dioxide. Since 1 l. of carbon dioxide weighs approximately 2.0 g. and since carbon constitutes three-elevenths of the weight of carbon dioxide, 3 l. of carbon dioxide contain approximately 1.7 g. of carbon. Thus in 10,000 l. of air there is present in the form of carbon dioxide 1.7 g. of carbon. A single mature corn plant including stem, leaves, grain, cob, and roots contains 364 g. of carbon (Latshaw and Miller, 1924). Thus a single corn plant must deplete $364 \times 10,000 \div 1.7$ or 2,141,176 l. of air of its carbon dioxide to obtain the carbon that it has combined. Since 1 l. of air weighs approximately 1.3 g., the weight of the air that would be depleted by such a plant would be $2,141,176 \times 1.3$ or 2,783,528 g., which is equivalent to 2,783.5 kilos or 3.1 tons. A single corn plant thus to obtain its supply of carbon must deplete 3.1 tons of air of its carbon. Considering 6,000 corn plants to the acre, an acre of such plants would thus deplete 18,600 tons of air of its carbon dioxide in order to obtain the total amount of carbon that these plants contain.

Heinicke and Hoffman (1932) found that the amount of carbon dioxide in 100 l. of normal air varied from 38 to 70 mg. in a warm, unventilated greenhouse. In some cases as much as 25 per cent of the carbon dioxide was removed by passing the ordinary atmosphere over a leaf, but as a rule the removal was less than 10 per cent. The amount of carbon dioxide absorbed during a 1-hr. period per 100 sq. cm. of leaf surface varied from less than 1 to as much as 25 mg.

The evidence in regard to the ability of the plant to use carbon monoxide is confusing. Under some conditions it apparently can be used by the plant to advantage, while under others it has a toxic effect. Thus Bottomley and Jackson (1903) found that young plants of nasturtium grown in sterilized sand and in air in which the carbon dioxide had been replaced by an equal quantity of carbon monoxide did not grow, but that when the amount of carbon monoxide was increased to twenty times the carbon dioxide, the plants grew well and were normal and healthy, provided that oxygen was added in amount sufficient to keep its pressure the same as air. Plants placed in air free from carbon dioxide but containing 10 per cent of carbon monoxide produced abundant starch when placed in the sunlight. They noted also that when carbon monoxide was so used, only one-half the normal amount of oxygen was given off. On the other hand, however, Richards and MacDougal (1904) found that carbon monoxide was very toxic to seedlings of corn, sunflower, wheat, and rice that were grown in an atmosphere in which the nitrogen had been replaced with carbon monoxide but with a normal oxygen pressure.

It has long been known that a plant can obtain all the carbon from the air that it needs for its growth and development, but since the soil atmosphere contains such a relatively high concentration of carbon dioxide the question has frequently arisen whether the plant is able to draw on this supply through the roots and utilize it in photosynthesis. Two early investigators, Godlewski (1873) and Moll (1878), were unable to obtain any starch in the leaves of plants that were grown in air free of carbon dioxide but with the roots growing in soil rich in organic matter. Later investigators, Cailletet (1911), Moillard (1912), Maquenne (1911), Pollacci (1917, 1920), Breazeale (1923), Banal (1926), Stocklasa (1929), Bergamaschi (1932), and Livingston and Beall (1934), however, have obtained evidence that plants may absorb carbon dioxide from the soil to advantage in the process of photosynthesis. Thus, for example, Pollacci (1920) grew plants in an air free from carbon dioxide but with the roots in soil rich in humus or in nutrient solutions containing carbon dioxide and observed that plants of *Zea mays*, *Acer pseudoplatanus*, *Quercus aesculus*, and others lived under such conditions and stored starch. Livingston and Beall (1934) believed that as much as 5 per cent or more of the carbon dioxide used by the plant comes from the soil. They thought that the most probable means of transport of this gas is the transpiration stream. Zijlstra (1909) and Moll (1909) considered that carbon dioxide was only translocated for short distances in plants, and on that account the amount of this gas absorbed by the roots would be of little significance in the process of photosynthesis. There thus appears to be evidence that a green plant may absorb some carbon dioxide from the soil and thus supplement its supply from the air.

c. Concentration and the Rate of Photosynthesis.—The experimental evidence in regard to the increase in the photosynthetic rate due to increasing the normal carbon dioxide supply of the atmosphere is rather confusing. This is due to the fact that many workers did not consider other factors that are known to play a part and to the fact that the interaction of numerous factors in this regard is not understood by the investigators today. A rather detailed discussion of the experimental work in regard to the effect of the concentration of carbon dioxide on the photosynthetic rate will be given, since this subject is of interest not only from a purely scientific standpoint but from the practical viewpoint as well. In 1873, Godlewski reported that the optimum value of the carbon dioxide content for photosynthesis for clear days was between 5 and 10 per cent for the plants with which he worked, while Kreusler (1885 to 1890) noted that the photosynthetic rate increased with the increase of carbon dioxide concentration and reached its maximum when the carbon dioxide content was thirty-five times that of the normal, or approximately 1 per cent of the atmosphere. Under more exact control methods Brown and Escombe (1902) found with concentrations of carbon dioxide lying between 0.6 part and 6 parts per 10,000 of air, when the air was passed over leaves attached to the plant and exposed to various intensities of sunlight, that the rate of absorption of carbon dioxide was strictly proportional to its partial pressure. Thus for example, in the case of the leaves of the sunflower where the mean concentrations of carbon dioxide over the leaf were 2.22 parts per 10,000 and 14.82 parts per 10,000, respectively, the ratio of the partial pressures was as 1:6.6, while the carbon dioxide absorbed by the leaves under these conditions was, respectively, 248.2 cc. and 1,802.8 cc. or in the ratio of 1:7.2. In another case, the ratio of the partial pressures of the carbon dioxide was 1:4.4 and the ratio of the carbon dioxide absorbed by the leaves, 1:5.3. Blackman and Smith (1911) studied the effect of different concentrations of carbon dioxide upon the rate of photosynthesis of *Elodea* and *Fontinalis*, submerged water plants, under like conditions of temperature and light, the carbon dioxide supply being varied through a range of 0.0025 to 0.054 g. per 100 cc. of water. It was found that in the weaker solutions of carbon dioxide the rate of photosynthesis increased directly with the carbon dioxide supply, provided light was not a limiting factor, but that with higher concentrations the rate of photosynthesis became depressed. Boysen-Jensen (1918) and Lundegårdh (1921) working with leaves of land plants found results similar to those obtained by Blackman and Smith. Warburg (1919) and Harder (1921) working on water plants failed to find a direct proportionality between carbon dioxide concentration and the rate of photosynthesis. Thus Warburg (1919) in working with *Chlorella* found that photosynthesis is proportional to the carbon dioxide concentration between 0.05 and 10 where the unit concentration is that of carbon dioxide in water in equilibrium with the atmosphere. Above this limit further increases in carbon dioxide concentration resulted in increased photosynthesis until the process became constant.

The effects of the concentration of carbon dioxide on the photosynthetic rate have been studied more recently by Christopher (1933), Heinicke and Hoffman (1933), Miller and Burr (1935), and Burgess (1935). It was shown by Heinicke and Hoffman (1933), and Christopher (1933) that the rate of photosynthesis falls off rapidly if the air supply to the leaves is less than 2 l. per hour per square centimeter. Miller and Burr (1935) found that many types of potted plants reduce the content of carbon dioxide to 0.01 per cent by volume, and that they maintain this concentration in light of about 2,000 foot-candles intensity. Deneke (1931) stated that the absorption of carbon dioxide by *Ficus elastica* and *Tradescantia pendula*, among others, reached a maximum at a wind velocity of 100 m. per minute, and that it could not be increased appreciably by higher velocities. In this connection, too, it was observed by Blackman and Smith (1911) that plants vary in their ability to assimilate carbon dioxide from the same concentration. Thus under a given set of conditions *Fontinalis* assimilated only one-half as much carbon dioxide as did *Elodea*. They suggested that this difference in utilization might be due to the difference in the absorption ability of the two plants. The behavior of plants toward different concentrations of carbon dioxide and light intensity in relation to photosynthesis has been recently again investigated by Maskell (1928) and James (1928) in regard to both land plants and submerged plants with the thought of accounting for some of the differences recorded by various workers on this problem. In experiments of this type it should be remembered that only the concentration of carbon dioxide in the external medium is open to the direct control of the experimenter, and that the internal rates of diffusion are due to many and varied factors which in many cases are beyond his control. The rate of diffusion from the external surface of the plant to the surface of the chloroplasts is apparently the important determining factor. Thus Maskell (1928) considered that the rate of apparent photosynthesis when carbon dioxide is a limiting factor may be regarded as being determined by a potential, the external carbon dioxide concentration, and a series of resistances, namely the stomatal resistance to diffusion, that in the intercellular space system, the liquid diffusion path up to the surface of the chloroplast, and, furthermore, "resistances" in the photochemical and chemical phases of photosynthesis. The form of the relation between the carbon dioxide supply and photosynthesis may be greatly modified by the alteration in the relative magnitude of the resistance in the diffusion phase, which may be altered by numerous and varied conditions. When the relation of the carbon dioxide concentration to the rate of photosynthesis is considered in this light it is seen why inconsistent results have been obtained. The whole curve expressing the relation between the rate of photosynthesis and the concentration of carbon dioxide when external factors are kept constant may be regarded as consisting of three parts (Stiles, 1925). The first ascending part of the curve, corresponding to the condition where, with increasing carbon dioxide concentration, photosynthesis increases proportionately, is approximately a straight line. This merges with or without a break into a part parallel or approximately so to the axis of the carbon dioxide concentration where light, stomata, protoplasm, rate of diffusion, etc., are limiting the process. This region of the curve then passes over into a descending part, where with increasing carbon dioxide concentration, the rate of photosynthesis is lowered on account of toxic action due to the high concentration of the gas.

The discovery that green plants can increase their photosynthetic rate with an increase of the carbon dioxide content of the atmosphere has stimulated investigations in regard to the utilization of this principle in agricultural practice. Such experiments have been confined mostly to plants growing in the greenhouse, although considerable work has been done under field conditions.

d. Application in Agricultural Practice.—Brown and Escombe (1902) and Demoussy (1903 to 1904) did the first work in applying increased amounts of carbon dioxide to plants upon a relatively large scale. Demoussy obtained increases in dry weight of 158 per cent for those plants growing under conditions of carbon dioxide fertilization. Brown and Escombe, on the other hand, obtained only negative results. They grew the plants in closed roomy compartments in which the carbon dioxide supply varied from three to one hundred times that of normal. They supplied the plants for 12 hr. with this concentration, after which they were exposed to normal conditions for the next 12 hr. They found that a concentration of carbon dioxide as high as 0.1 per cent was decidedly injurious to plants under these conditions and their control plants were always the more vigorous. The treated plants developed abnormally in that their leaf area was reduced; the internodes developed more slowly, while the flower buds did not open, and no fruit was produced. Negative results were also obtained by Cummings and Jones (1918) when plants were grown in closed containers with an increase of the normal carbon dioxide concentration.

It has thus developed, if any reliable results are to be obtained by carbon dioxide fertilization, that the plants must be grown in open compartments under as nearly normal conditions as possible with the exception of the concentration of the carbon dioxide (Bolas and Henderson, 1928). The increased humidity of the air in a closed container is apparently one of the detrimental factors when experiments are conducted in that manner. The purity of the carbon dioxide is a very important factor in this type of experiment (Owen and Williams, 1923; Cerighelli, 1921). The distribution of the carbon dioxide must also be considered. Cummings and Jones (1918, 1920) allowed the gas to diffuse slowly but continuously around the plants during the application period, the only precautions being that the escaping gas did not come in direct contact with the leaves but was liberated a few inches from the plant. In most cases, however, the amounts of carbon dioxide that have been used have not been definitely measured. The gas has simply been liberated alongside or among the plants growing in open containers or in the field. Under such conditions it has been found that there is little or no danger of increasing the carbon dioxide content to toxic amounts. Cummings and Jones, using open boxes 26 in. high, 26 in. long, and 18 in. wide, added during an 8-hr. period as much as 348 l. of gas, the dry weight of the plants increasing with the increased quantities added up to that amount.

In practically all cases where the carbon dioxide supply to field and greenhouse crops has been increased, beneficial results have been obtained as measured by increased yield of grain, fruit, or amount of dry matter produced. In Europe, H. Fischer (1912 to 1927) has been one of the leading investigators in using carbon dioxide as an aerial fertilizer. In some cases he has purified the carbon dioxide from the gases that emanate from smelter furnaces and has conveyed it in pipes to greenhouses and field plots. By this means increased yield and more vigorous growth were obtained with potatoes, beets, tomatoes, and bush beans. Favorable results from the application of carbon dioxide have also been obtained by Riedel (1919, 1921), Cummings and Jones (1918, 1920), Jess (1921), Bornemann (1920), Owen, Small, and Williams (1926), and Gradenwitz (1920). Thus Riedel (1919, 1921) reported that the yields from tomato plants in a greenhouse into which carbon dioxide was introduced through perforated pipes was 175 per cent of the weight of the yield in a greenhouse with ordinary air. Cucumbers under like conditions increased 235 per cent over controls, while spinach, potatoes, and barley increased 150, 190, and 100 per cent, respectively, over the controls. Field plots gave yields varying from one and one-half to three times those of the ungassed plots. Jess (1921) in outdoor experiments with Irish potatoes increased the average weight of the tubers from 140 to 330 g. by the application of carbon dioxide. In the greenhouse the yield of tomatoes was increased from 29.5 kilos for an untreated house to 81.3 kilos for the treated one, while the yield of cucumbers was increased from 138 to 235 kilos. In America the most extensive work on the fertilization of plants with carbon dioxide has been reported by Cummings and Jones (1918, 1920). These experiments were all under greenhouse conditions and the plants were grown in large open containers in the manner that has previously been described. The plants used in these experiments included peas, beans, radishes, potatoes, lettuce, endive, Swiss chard, nasturtium, and strawberries. In the case of beans, the dry weight of the seeds produced by the treated plants was from 32 to 204 per cent higher than the checks, while the dry weight of the pods was from 75 to 143 per cent higher than the controls. The percentage of proteins was practically the same for both treated and untreated plants, while the carbohydrates showed an increase. In this connection it is worthy of note that Kostytschew observed that under conditions of increased carbon dioxide content the rate of photosynthesis is decidedly higher in legumes than in nonleguminous plants. Cummings and Jones (1918) found also, in the case of peas, that the total dry matter of the plant was from 18 to 117 per cent greater than the checks, while the dry weight of the seed increased from 167 to 291 per cent over the control. The results for the potatoes showed that the total number of tubers was 338 for the treated and 231 for the untreated, while the gain in weight of the tubers ranged from 7 to 325 per cent of the controls. Endive, lettuce, and Swiss chard all showed a marked response to treatment with carbon dioxide. In the case of lettuce and Swiss chard, the number of leaves was increased approximately 10 per cent. The leaves of lettuce, however, were darker green and tougher in the treated than in the untreated. The average gain for strawberries in weight was 80 per cent, while the increase in the number of plants was 55 per cent.

Nasturtium plants showed marked and definite response to treatment with carbon dioxide. The gross weight was greater, more flowers bloomed, and blooming began earlier than with the untreated ones. Small and White (1930), and White (1930) tried different methods for supplying carbon dioxide to greenhouse plants. The application of this gas in excess of the amount contained in ordinary air increased the yield of tomatoes but was not profitable. Some of the effects on tomato plants were: a shortening of the period of time between flower opening and the ripening of the fruit, a high percentage of the bloom developing into fruit, and a lower percentage of fruit retarded in ripening. Reid (1930) found that for squash a content of carbon dioxide of 1 per cent, as compared to 0.02 per cent, increased both the fresh and dry weight of the plant. A much greater root system was produced, and a much greater amount of strengthening tissue was developed. A smaller leaf area was formed, and there was a larger amount of starch and reducing substances in the leaves. More of the total nitrogen was found in the roots and stems, and less in the leaves of those plants which were grown in the higher concentration of carbon dioxide. Wilson, Fred, and Salmon (1933) found for clover that as the carbon dioxide in the atmosphere was augmented from 0.03 to 0.1 per cent, the leaf area, excess of carbohydrates, and the number of nodules were increased. Further increments in the amount of carbon dioxide, however, did not induce correspondingly greater development. Georgi, Orcutt, and Wilson (1933) noted that if red-clover plants were supplied with the same quantity of carbon dioxide, but at different partial pressures, the higher the partial pressure of the gas the greater the increase in dry weight, in the amount of nitrogen fixed, and in the number of nodules. They considered that the most important factor is the pressure at which the gas is applied and not the total quantity available. Johnston (1935) found that wheat growing in air enriched with carbon dioxide showed an increase in the number of tillers, weight of straw, number of heads, and number of grains. Bolas and Melville (1935) found that when fertilized with carbon dioxide the tomato plants growing in a small greenhouse increased their yield of fruit 23.9 per cent for the first half of the season, and 13.9 per cent for the whole season.

Lemmerman (1920, 1926), Gerlach (1919, 1926), and Spirgartis (1923) are the only investigators who do not report an increase in plant production from application of carbon dioxide. A general review of the experiments in regard to the application of increased amounts of carbon dioxide to plants is given by Kuiper (1920). While the application of carbon dioxide apparently has possibilities for increasing crop production, the experimental evidence cannot yet be welded into a scientific system or into a working basis (Rippel, 1926). Johnston (1935) stated that the practicability of carbon dioxide fertilization in field experiments is yet an unsolved problem. The mere escape of the gas is in itself not sufficient, but a circulating system must be provided in order to secure a more uniform distribution. The methods of distribution thus far devised, however, are very unsatisfactory. The results obtained will no doubt be varied due to the interrelations of carbon dioxide with light, temperature, moisture conditions, time and duration of treatments, and the specific effect on different plants.

2. Supply of Light. *a. Intensity.*—According to Withrow (1936) the intensity of sunlight at midday in summer in the temperate zone is approximately 10,000 to 12,000 foot-candles. According to experiments in the greenhouse, this is greatly in excess of what plants actually need for their optimum development. Experimental work indicates that an intensity of 2,000 to 3,000 foot-candles is sufficient for an optimum growth, although plants vary widely in that regard. Most plants will grow fairly well and produce seed in an intensity of light approximating 500 foot-candles. They may produce seed in a light intensity as low as 250 foot-candles, although they may be dwarfed in vegetative growth. Artificial light is as yet so costly that it is practical for greenhouse culture only in cases where it might aid in the maturing of a crop that would otherwise be totally lost. As will be mentioned in Chap. XIV, increasing the length of day by the use of artificial light is very practical because light intensities of one-third to 10 foot-candles are sufficient for that purpose. Arthur and Porter (1935) constructed an insulated greenhouse that allowed the rays of the sun to penetrate only through the roof. The energy of the sun was supplemented by artificial light which, together with the rays of the sun, heated the house in addition to furnishing the energy necessary for photosynthesis. In the region of New York City the best growth was obtained during the winter months by supplementing the daylight with artificial light for 5 to 6 hours per day.

The intensity of light at which photosynthesis will occur in various water plants has been given considerable attention. Gail (1922) and Shelford and Gail (1922) found that photosynthesis in the red algae begins at depths at which the red and orange light is reduced to approximately 1 per cent, and it continues to a depth at which the intensity of light is approximately only 0.0032 per cent of the incident rays. Schomer (1934) found in the lakes of Wisconsin that the depth for optimum photosynthesis varied with the plant and with the weather conditions. On bright days the depth for optimum photosynthesis was at 5 m. for *Ceratophyllum* and *Elodea*, while on dark, cloudy days it was at the surface. The maximum rate of photosynthesis of algae occurred at a depth of 7 m. on bright days, while on cloudy days it was at 0.5 m. Tschudy (1934) found that most of the photosynthesis in red and brown algae occurs at a depth of less than 10 m. The red algae can utilize the light that penetrates to a depth of 25 m., while the brown algae seem unable to synthesize carbohydrates below 15 m. of water.

The experimental work on the influence of the intensity of light upon the rate of photosynthesis previous to 1905 is of doubtful value, since the factors other than the intensity of light were not given due consideration. For a review of the early literature on this topic the student is referred to Stiles (1925) and to Brown and Heise (1917). The latter reviewers concluded that this early experimental work does not indicate that carbon dioxide assimilation in plants is proportional to the light intensity. They considered that these experiments indicate a progressively smaller increase of the rate of photosynthesis for each increase in light intensity, and that this progressive decrease in the rate of augmentation continues until a point is reached at which further increase in light produces no measurable increase in assimilation.

In 1905 Blackman and Matthaei, however, investigated the influence of light intensity upon the photosynthetic rate with a full realization of the importance of other factors and under well-controlled conditions. They concluded that if the temperature and carbon dioxide are in excess, the rate of photosynthesis is proportional to the intensity of the incident light. For every temperature there is a maximum light intensity which will produce a maximum rate of photosynthesis at that temperature. It has been observed by Osterhout and Haas (1918), Warburg (1919), and Spoehr and McGee (1923) that when plants have been kept in darkness for a period and then exposed to sunlight, the rate of photosynthesis is low at first and then steadily increases until a maximum is reached. The term "photochemical induction" has been given by Stiles (1925) to this phenomenon. Harder (1930) noted in *Frontenalis* and *Cladophora* that carbon assimilation under constant conditions of light, temperature, water, and carbon dioxide reached a maximum slowly in plants that had been darkened for several hours. Li (1929) noted that when certain plants are changed from light of high available energy for photosynthesis to light of low available energy there is an inhibition of this process, and vice versa.

The intermittent application of light has been observed to have a marked influence on the photosynthetic rate. Thus Warburg (1919), as reported by Stiles (1925) and Spoehr (1926), found in the case of *Chlorella* that with alternations of 8,000 per minute the rate of photosynthesis was 100 per cent above that in continuous illumination. With an alternation of four light and four dark periods per minute, the rate of photosynthesis was only 10 per cent above that of continuous illumination. Emerson and Arnold (1932) made measurements of photosynthesis in continuous and flashing light of high intensity. For each flash of light, there were present about 4,800 molecules of chlorophyll for each molecule of carbon dioxide reduced. The length of time required for one unit in the photosynthetic mechanism to complete the cycle of the photochemical and "Blackman" reactions was found to be about 0.02 sec. at 25°C. Spoehr (1926) considered that this behavior might be explained by assuming that during the dark period carbon dioxide is synthesized by the chloroplasts and moved away so that when they are again exposed to light there are available higher concentrations of the necessary material for photosynthesis, which would tend to increase its rate. This phenomenon occurs only under conditions of high light intensity and is not noticeable under conditions of low illumination.

In the process of photosynthesis, carbon dioxide and water are used and oxygen is given off as a by-product, while in the process of respiration, which is proceeding at the same time, oxygen is utilized and carbon dioxide and water are given off as waste products. Since the rate of photosynthesis increases with the intensity of light, while the process of respiration is independent of this factor, there will be a light intensity for every plant at every temperature at which the building-up process of photosynthesis will just equal the tearing-down process of respiration. Under such conditions carbon dioxide and oxygen will be neither absorbed nor set free. This point in the intensity of the incident light has been called the "compensation point" (Plaetzer, 1917). The value of the compensation point varies widely for different species and for different temperatures.

It was observed by Blackman and Matthaei (1905) that if light is a limiting factor, equal areas of leaves of different plants equally illuminated give equal photosynthetic rates. They also observed that plants differ in their photosynthetic rates. Thus at 29.5°C. cherry laurel leaves reached their maximum rate of photosynthesis at 0.36 of full sunlight, while *Helianthus tuberosus* required 0.69 of full sunshine to reach its maximum photosynthetic rate. Dastur and Asana (1932) found with *Allium cepa* and *Helianthus annuus* that the amount of carbohydrate formed in leaves in polarized light was not statistically different from that formed in ordinary light. Later Dastur and Gunjikar (1934) noted that the carbohydrate content of leaves exposed to elliptically polarized light was less than that of leaves exposed to ordinary light.

b. Wave Lengths of Light.—There are numerous factors entering into a solution of this problem which are difficult of estimation and control but which greatly influence any results that may be obtained. Many of these factors were not considered by the early investigators, while the more recent investigators, who realize these difficulties, have not been able satisfactorily to measure or control them. Some of the difficulties that enter into a solution of this problem are: (1) the measurement of the energy in the different portions of the spectrum, (2) the methods of obtaining the different wave lengths used, (3) methods for measuring the rate of photosynthesis, (4) the relative absorption of the different wave lengths by different plants, (5) and variation in the light supply.

The relative distribution of energy in various spectra varies widely, so, unless the sources of energy used are the same, widely different results will be obtained. Sunlight also varies in intensity and composition at the surface of the earth, from time to time, so different portions of the spectrum may vary independently of each other. It should also be noted that, if equal intensities of different lights are presented to the plant, the plant exhibits selective absorption so the greatest rate of photosynthesis will be brought about by the rays that are most absorbed regardless of what would occur if the plant absorbed them equally. On account of the difficulties that have just been enumerated, the investigations in regard to photosynthesis and wave length have been productive of but few data that are conclusive.

The range of wave lengths of light in which photosynthesis may occur was investigated by Timiriazeff (1890, 1904) and Ursprung (1917) by means of the iodine-starch method. By this method the spectrum is thrown upon the leaf for a period, after which the chlorophyll is removed and the leaf is tested for starch with iodine after the usual manner, the depth of color being taken as an index to the rate of starch formation in the various regions of the spectrum. In *Phaseolus multiflorus* (Ursprung, 1917) exposed to various sources of light, starch formation was found to occur throughout the whole visible spectrum if sufficient time were allowed. Starch formation was thus found to occur between the wave lengths 330 and 760mμ. The maximum activity apparently was in the region 687 to 656mμ. In the normal solar spectrum, starch formation in the blue requires a longer time than in the red. Urspiung (1918) reported that he was able to observe slight starch formation in the infrared portion of the spectrum in *Phaseolus vulgaris* which had been exposed for 40 hr. The starch-iodine method for determining the rate of photosynthesis for an experiment of this type is, however, open to serious objections. The formation of starch is, without doubt, secondary to photosynthesis and can occur in the dark as well as in the light, provided a supply of sugars is present. The formation of starch might be influenced by light in an entirely different manner from that influencing the process of photosynthesis. The role of the ultraviolet rays in photosynthesis apparently is of little or no consequence, as has been mentioned in the discussion of the theories of photosynthesis. Plants can carry on normal photosynthesis under conditions that exclude ultraviolet rays, while the experimental attempts to produce photosynthesis in plants in ultraviolet light are not convincing.

The relative value of the different rays of light in the process of photosynthesis was studied by Kniep and Minder (1909) for *Elodea canadensis*. They measured the energy value of red, blue, and green rays incident upon the plant and determined the rate of photosynthesis by the oxygen-bubble method. Their observations indicated that the red and the blue lights of the same intensity gave the same rate of photosynthesis, but they could observe no photosynthesis in green light. This work, however, although a great step in the direction of properly controlled experiments of this type, gave results that were unreliable, since the screens used allowed rays other than those desired to pass, unless successive screens were used, which diminished the intensity of the light to a point where the intensity became a limiting factor. Lubimenko (1923) in experiments with 8 species of plants used monochromatic light with red rays from 760 to 600mμ and blue rays from 480 to 400mμ and assumed the intensity of the blue rays to be 85 per cent of the red. The experiments carried on at 20°C. for 6 hr. in a clear sky with a carbon dioxide content ranging from 9 to 11 per cent showed that the rate of photosynthesis was greater in red than in blue light, being double in the former as compared with the latter. The rate of photosynthesis was retarded with time in both red and blue light. In species adapted to diffuse light of low intensity, as *Hedera helix* and *Aspidistra elatior*, the activity of the blue rays equalled or exceeded that of the red rays. Wurmser (1925) in experiments with *Ulva* and other sea algae reported that the liberation of oxygen in green light of 490 to 590mμ was higher than that in the red rays of 590 to 700mμ, the rate of green to red being as 1.15:1.00.

Stiles (1925) considered that the experimental evidence that has been presented indicates that, with equal intensity of incident light, photosynthesis is influenced by wave lengths, being greatest in the red between the B and C lines and least in the blue violet. Warburg and Negelein (1923) agreed with this in that they consider that the rate of photosynthesis decreases with decreasing wave length. They further considered that there is no apparent relation between the efficiency of photosynthesis and the absorption bands of chlorophyll. Thus the yield of photosynthesis in the red, a region of high absorption, is greater than in the green, a region of low absorption, and the yield in the green is higher than that in the blue, the region of highest absorption (Spoehr, 1926). Since there are different degrees of absorption of the different wave lengths by the leaf cells due to specific differences of the cells themselves or to the thickness of the leaves, it would appear to be impossible to find values for the relative rates of photosynthesis, in light of different wave lengths, which will hold in general for all plants and all conditions.

Dangeard (1927) noted in *Chlorella vulgaris* and *Scenedesmus acutus* that the amount of growth in the various regions of the spectrum was closely correlated with the intensity of absorption by the chlorophyll. Tottingham and Moore (1931) found that the most consistent compositional response of plants grown under Vitaglass was an increased percentage of the lipides in the dry matter. Meier (1932) reported that the rays of ultraviolet light from 2536 to 3022 Å. killed cultures of some of the green algae. The wave lengths longer than 3022 Å. had no appreciable lethal effect. The ozone in the upper atmosphere serves as a filter for the injurious rays of the sun and thus protects organisms against them. Arnold (1934) reported that an unidentified unit in the mechanism of the photosynthesis of *Chlorella pyrenoidosa* is rendered inactive by the absorption of 1 quantum of ultraviolet light of a wave length of 2537 Å. Burns (1933, 1934) found that the infrared rays longer than 1,100mμ are detrimental to photosynthesis, and that white pine and Norway spruce were able to utilize all the visible spectrum except a portion of the blue and violet. It was reported by Dastur and Samant (1933) that the production of starch, total carbohydrates, and total sugars is much greater in diffuse daylight than in artificial light. He did not attribute these differences to any variations in the intensity of the light but to the difference in its quality. Dastur and Mehta (1935) concluded from the use of artificial light that photosynthetic activity is highest in white light, intermediate in red light, and very feeble in the blue-violet region of the spectrum. Thus the rate of photosynthesis does not depend alone on the total energy content delivered to the plant, but also on the distribution of radiation of different wave lengths. Arthur (1929) found that plants do not develop normally unless exposed to both the red and blue rays of the spectrum. The ultraviolet region of sunlight, which is not transmitted by greenhouse glass, is of no definite benefit to growing plants, and the ultraviolet region beyond a wave length of 290mμ is very injurious to green plants.

3. Temperature. *a. Coefficient.*—The temperature coefficient, as has been stated in Chap. II, is denoted by Q_{10} and is the ratio of the rate of a reaction or process at a given temperature to the rate of the process at a temperature 10° lower. The temperature coefficient for purely physical processes is relatively low, being from 1.2 to 1.4 at the temperatures that ordinarily prevail in the plant. The temperature coefficient for chemical reactions are, on the other hand, relatively high, ranging from 2 to 3, while relatively low temperature coefficients ranging from 1 to 1.4 are characteristic of photochemical reactions.

It was observed by Blackman and Matthaei (1905) that between 5 and 25°C. the temperature coefficient of photosynthesis in cherry laurel was 2.1 and for artichoke 2.5, which suggests that it may be different for different species. Osterhout and Haas (1918) noted that the temperature coefficient of photosynthesis in the case of *Ulva rigida* between 17 and 27° was 1.81. Since light reactions ordinarily have low temperature coefficients, they assumed that the process of photosynthesis involves a light reaction with a low coefficient followed by an ordinary chemical reaction with a high temperature coefficient, so that as a result the temperature coefficient of the process as a whole is low. This is in line with the idea that photosynthesis is a complex of reactions falling under a diffusion phase, a photochemical or light phase, and a chemical or dark phase (James, 1928). In a critical review of the literature in regard to the influence of temperature on the rate of photosynthesis, Brown and Heise (1917) considered that the work, for the most part, indicates temperature coefficients which are of the same order of magnitude as photochemical coefficients. The temperature coefficient of photosynthesis is apparently influenced by the chlorophyll content of the leaves. Thus Willstätter and Stoll (1918) found that the leaves of *Ulmus* with low chlorophyll content showed a temperature coefficient of 1.34 as compared to 1.5 between 15 to 25°C. for leaves with a high content of the pigment.

When neither light nor the concentration of carbon dioxide is a limiting factor, the rate of photosynthesis is increased by an increase in temperature just as are many chemical reactions. However, when the light intensity is low, temperature has little effect—a characteristic of photochemical reactions. It is thus considered that when the light intensity is low a photochemical reaction determines the rate of photosynthesis, whereas when the light intensity and the supply of carbon dioxide are both high, a "dark," chemical reaction, the rate of which is determined by temperature, limits the whole process. The existence of the "dark" reaction was first established by workers in the laboratory of F. F. Blackman, and it is now frequently termed the "Blackman" reaction (Gordon, 1929; and Kohn, 1935).

Time, successive periods, hours	Rate of photosynthesis, grams of CO_2 combined per 50 cm.² of leaf per hour, at	
	8.8°C.	37.5°C.
2	0.0039	0.0574
2	0.0039	0.0352
2	0.0038	0.0278
2	0.00385	0.0218

The temperature coefficient of photosynthesis has been investigated with the idea that it might throw some light on the nature of the reactions involved; however, the temperature coefficient in photosynthesis is not so indicative of the nature of the process as it is in a simple reaction. The process of photosynthesis consists of a series of reactions that are influenced by numerous factors, any one of which, other than temperature, might be the limiting one.

b. Range.—The threshold temperature of photosynthesis varies greatly for different plants. Matthaei (1905) found that photosynthesis took place in the leaves of cherry laurel at −6°C. Henrici observed photosynthesis in lichens at −20°C. and in alpine plants at −16°C. Ewart (1896) stated that the evolution of oxygen ceases between 0 and 2°C. in the case of warm, temperate, and subtropical plants and between 4 and 8°C. for tropical plants. Provided that no other factor is a limiting one, the rate of photosynthesis increases with an increase in temperature until about 25°C., as observed by Matthaei (1905) and Blackman and Matthaei for cherry laurel. Above a temperature of 25°C., however, complications arise. Below 25°C. the rate of photosynthesis remains constant at a given temperature hour after hour, but above 25°C. it decreases with time so that the initial rate is not maintained. The falling off of the initial rate is irregular; it is more rapid the higher the temperature; and at any temperature above 25°C., it is greater at first and subsequently becomes less rapid. The data in the table on page 594, taken from Matthaei (1905), illustrate the behavior of photosynthesis in the leaf of cherry laurel at a relatively low and a relatively high temperature.

Owing to this falling off in the rate of photosynthesis at the higher temperatures, the previous history of the leaf as regards temperature would determine the value of the photosynthetic rate. Thus the temperature at which the highest rate is observed will depend upon the time that has elapsed between the commencement of the experiment and the measurement of the photosynthetic rate. On this account, some regard the optimum temperature as the highest temperature that can be maintained continuously without a resulting depression of the process under consideration.

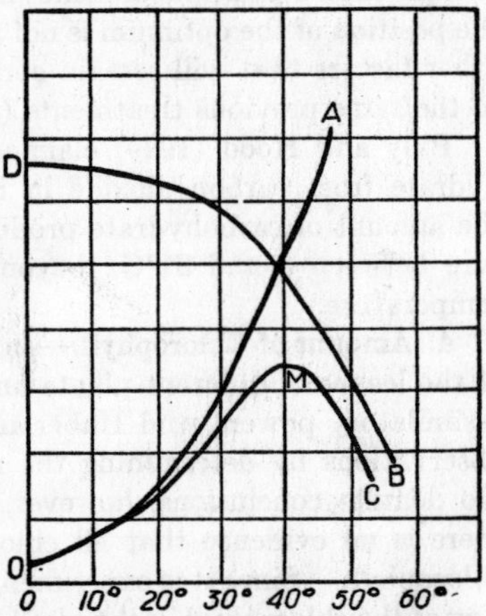

FIG. 27.—Graphs showing the relation between temperature and enzyme action. (*Redrawn from Jorgensen and Stiles*, 1917, *after Duclaux*, 1899.) The graph *OA* shows the relation between temperature and enzyme action if the enzyme activity remains unimpaired. The graph *DB* represents the relation between temperature and quantity of enzyme. The graph *OMC* represents the actual graph between temperature and enzyme action.

The behavior of photosynthesis at higher temperatures appears similar to that of hydrolytic enzymes (Blackman, 1905). Thus Kjeldahl (1879) noted that malt diastase hydrolyzed increasing quantities of starch up to 63°C., after which the reaction falls off rapidly, becoming nothing at 86°C. This decrease in the reaction is apparently due to the destruction of the enzyme by heat. This characteristic behavior of enzymes was further investigated by Tammann (1892, 1895) and by Duclaux (1899) and has been termed "Tammann's principle." This principle is shown by the following curves (Fig. 27): The curve *OA* shows the relation between temperature and the enzyme action, provided the reaction is in no way hindered by the temperature. The curve *DB* represents the relation between the temperature and the quantity of enzymes, since it is being destroyed by heat. The curve *OMC* represents the actual curve between temperature and the enzyme action. The apparent production of an optimum is thus due to two opposed processes, the increased hydrolytic action of the enzyme and the destruction of the enzyme due to heat. Evidence was obtained by Molisch (1925) which indicated that an enzyme might be concerned in the photosynthetic process. He observed that green leaves from a wide range of plants dried at 30 to 40°C. and pulverized liberated oxygen when illuminated. Leaf material, however, that was heated to 96°C. did not thus behave, while material prepared from leaves that were killed by freezing could liberate oxygen in illumination. If Tammann's principle or some similar one is involved in photosynthesis, the position of the optimum is not a definite fixed point but depends upon other factors that will remain constant only if the plants are subjected to the same previous treatments (Jorgensen and Stiles, 1917).

Baly and Hood (1929) claimed in the artificial formation of carbohydrate from carbon dioxide in the presence of nickel carbonate that the amount of carbohydrate produced was a linear function of temperature between 5 and 31°C., beyond which the yield fell off with rising temperature.

4. Amount of Chlorophyll.—In 1879 Weber observed that equal areas of the leaves of different plants under the same conditions had different assimilatory powers, and Haberlandt (1882) attempted to explain these observations by determining the number of chloroplasts per unit area. No definite conclusions, however, can be drawn by this method, since there is no evidence that all chloroplasts contain the same amount of chlorophyll. Since it is experimentally impossible to vary the concentration of the chlorophyll in the plant, the relation of the chlorophyll content to rate of photosynthesis has been studied by using plants from different habitats, young and old leaves, green and yellow leaves of different varieties, and etiolated plants.

a. Plants of Different Habitats and of Different Varieties.—It was observed by Lubimenko (1905, 1908) that shade plants could accomplish the same amount of photosynthesis with a lower illumination than the sun plants and that the chlorophyll content of the former was higher than that of the latter. The sun plants with the low chlorophyll content showed the maximum rate of photosynthesis at the highest light intensities, while the shade plants showed a decreased rate at the same intensities. He considered that leaves with a high chlorophyll content have a high absorption coefficient and that the optimum temperature and light intensity for photosynthesis decrease with chlorophyll content. Henrici (1918) made observations somewhat in accord with those of Lubimenko, since she noted that lowland plants may have as much as 2.3 times more chlorophyll than the alpine plants of the same species, and in strong light the rate of photosynthesis in the alpine plants was higher than in the lowland plants. She stated further that alpine plants assimilate more rapidly than lowland plants when red rays predominate around sunset but less rapidly than lowland plants when blue rays predominate.

Willstätter and Stoll (1918) in their discussion of the relation of the chlorophyll content to photosynthesis introduced the term "assimilation number" or "photosynthetic number." The photosynthetic number may be defined as the number of units of carbon dioxide absorbed per hour per unit of chlorophyll. It is the ratio of the number of grams of carbon dioxide absorbed per hour by a unit of leaf to the number of grams of chlorophyll contained in that unit. If the rate of photosynthesis depends only on the chlorophyll content, then the photosynthetic number should be constant, but if other factors than chlorophyll content influence the rate, the photosynthetic numbers will show variations. These authors determined the photosynthetic number for a large number of plants at a temperature of 25°C., with a 5 per cent carbon dioxide supply and a supply of light equal to 48,000 lux. The following examples taken at random show the variation of the photosynthetic number for different plants: *Cucurbita pepo*, 12.1; *Helianthus annuus*, 10.9; *Hydrangea opuloides*, 6.5; and *Acer pseudoplatanus*, 5.2. In experiments with light-green or yellow and normal green varieties of plants, Plester (1912), Willstätter and Stoll (1918), and Fleischer (1935), observed that the rate of photosynthesis increased with the chlorophyll content, but they were not able to establish any relation between these two factors.

Briggs (1935) stated that when illumination is weak the assimilation of young leaves increases with age even when the chlorophyll carbon content is maintained at a constant value. He suggested that chlorophyll combines with carbon dioxide, is then activated by light energy, and subsequently is broken down into free chlorophyll and other products. Apparently when the concentration of carbon dioxide and the intensity of illumination are very great, all the chlorophyll will be in the form of the activated compound, so that the rate of reaction will be proportionate to the amount of chlorophyll present.

Ireland and Yeats (1933) found a positive correlation between the content of chlorophyll and the yield of kafir. Sprague and Curtis (1933) believed that the mean values for chlorophyll concentration and total chlorophyll for selfed lines of corn are reasonably reliable indexes of the total yield that will be produced by their hybrids. Ulvin (1934) reported that the percentage of the dry matter of corn leaves increased in direct proportion to the chlorophyll content.

b. Etiolated Plants.—In experiments with etiolated plants of barley, *Vicia faba*, and *Phaseolus*, Irving (1910) and Briggs (1920) concluded that etiolated leaves do not possess any appreciable power of photosynthesis. They observed further that the development of photosynthetic activity in the young leaves lagged behind greening and did not appear until after the leaves had attained a full green color, when it developed very rapidly. They considered that photosynthetic activity is dependent upon some other factor than chlorophyll and is not developed so quickly as the pigment that remains idle until the other factor becomes active. Willstätter and Stoll (1918) were not able to duplicate the results of Irving (1910), but according to Briggs (1920) the difference in the results is due to the difference in the age of the material used. In the case of seedlings of plants such as *Helianthus annuus*, *Acer*, and *Cucurbita*, where the first photosynthetic organ is one that also serves as a storage organ, Briggs (1922) observed that the photosynthetic activity is fully developed at germination. With this type, photosynthesis under natural conditions of growth in the field showed no lag behind greening. In such plants as *Phaseolus, Ricinus*, and *Zea* where the seedling develops a specialized photosynthetic organ different from the storage organ, the photosynthetic activity was not developed until some time after germination, and photosynthesis under natural conditions shows a corresponding lag. Inman (1935) noted that, after etiolated plants of corn, wheat, and oats were transferred from the dark to the light, the evolution of oxygen began about the time that the eye could detect the appearance of a green color in the leaves.

At the present time it is definitely known that only those cells which contain chlorophyll are capable of photosynthesis, but the quantitative role of the pigment in this process has not been established.

5. Water Supply.—Water plays both a direct and an indirect role in the process of photosynthesis. It plays a direct role in that it enters into chemical combination with carbon dioxide to form carbohydrates in the process. It plays an indirect role in that it maintains the turgidity of the leaf cells and thus keeps the stomata open and allows an unobstructed intake of carbon dioxide. Since the amount of water used in chemical combination is relatively small, the greatest hindrance to photosynthesis due to a limited water supply comes from the secondary effect of the closure of the stomata. Thoday (1910) found that the turgid leaves of *Helianthus annuus* carried on photosynthesis approximately ten times more rapidly than did leaves that were wilted to drooping during the experiment. In withering leaves of *Tropaeolum majus*, Schroeder and Horn (1922) and Horn (1923) noted that starch was broken down into sugar and that the cane sugar steadily increased with the decreasing water content. Iljin (1923) found that when the water content of the leaves of *Bidens tripartita* was reduced 43 to 44 per cent, a reduction of 53 to 78 per cent of photosynthesis occurred. In *Phlomis pungens* a water loss of 34 per cent caused a reduction of 13 per cent in photosynthesis. In these experiments the full activity of photosynthesis was not regained at once upon the recovery of normal turgidity and in some cases showed a reduction of 29 per cent 16 hr. after complete recovery of turgor. Iljin (1915) considered that plants that are adapted to a dry habitat lose less water per amount of carbon dioxide decomposed than do mesophytes. Owing to water loss the stomata of the mesophytes close, and as a result the intake of carbon dioxide is reduced and photosynthesis is checked, while in the xerophytic plants it is going on at the normal rate. It was observed by Brilliant (1924) that, with a loss of 41 to 63 per cent of the water content of the leaves of *Hedera helix* and *Impatiens parviflora*, photosynthesis was almost stopped. The process was at its maximum when the water content was reduced only 5 to 15 per cent. Young plants are not so much affected by the loss of water as are more mature ones. Dastur (1924, 1925) also found that there is a direct correlation between the decrease in the rate of transpiration and the fall in the water content, per unit of leaf area. Those plant tissues, placed most unfavorably in regard to their water supply, are the first to lose their power of photosynthesis, this inhibition appearing first in the marginal and intravascular regions and then gradually proceeding inwardly toward the central and main fibrovascular bundles. Yuncker (1916), however, found that the greater amount of dry matter per unit of leaf area was produced in those corn plants that showed the lower amount of transpiration and that grew in the drier soil. He considered that this was due to the more active respiration and growth in the leaves with the higher water content. The leaves with the lower water content were carrying on respiration less rapidly, and as a consequence dry matter accumulated. Skvortzov (1931), Dastur and Desai (1933), Smyth (1934), Childers and Cowart (1935), and Heinicke and Childers (1935) have shown that the water content of the leaf is closely allied with the process of photosynthesis. Any fluctuation in the water content is almost immediately followed by a similar fluctuation in the rate of photosynthesis. Iljin (1929) found more sugar in leaves in dry than in wet habitats. The leaves of *Rumex crispus* and *R. conglomeratus* contained almost twice as much sugar when withered as when turgid. The lack of translocation may have been a factor in this case. Molisch (1921) noted that wilting hastens the disappearance of starch from starch-filled leaves, and Schroeder and Herrman (1931) found in wilted nasturtium leaves that the sucrose content increased at the expense of starch. Hartt (1934) found evidence that a greater synthesis of sucrose occurred in the leaves of the sugar cane when the plant was supplied with water than in those from which it was withheld, although some photosynthesis occurred at the wilting point. McKay (1935) found that photosynthesis began in 6 to 10 min. after water was added to drought-treated plants of the xerophytic moss, *Grimmia montana*. Bernbeck (1924) showed that a deficiency of water retards the rate of photosynthesis independently of the closing of the stomata.

6. Other External Factors.—It has been shown by Hoffman (1932, 1933) and Christopher (1935) that lime-sulphur, flotation, and oil sprays decrease the rate of photosynthesis, the decreases ranging from 17 to 40 per cent.

Fisher (1934) found in various apple varieties that the size of the fruit was positively correlated with the leaf extent per apple. He considered that this relationship is due to the greater amount of food synthesized per fruit. The weight of fruit produced per unit of leaf surface was least in the McIntosh variety and greatest in Rome Beauty. He suggested that these results may be due to differences in the photosynthetic efficiency of the leaves of these two varieties. Gustafson and Stoldt (1936) found with the tomato that the efficiency of the plant in setting fruit is highest when the leaf area per fruit is small. After setting, however, the size of the fruit is increased by a larger leaf area.

It was found by Eidelman and Bankul (1933) that the removal of some of the leaf blades of wheat and barley intensified the photosynthetic rate in the remaining ones. Lubimenko and Stscheglova (1932) removed 20 to 30 per cent of the leaf surface of barley, bean, oats, and buckwheat by perforating the leaves. The amount of carbon dioxide absorbed was diminished for the first 2 days after this treatment. A considerable increase in the absorption of carbon dioxide then occurred, and the process reached a maximum in 6 to 8 days. In some cases the perforated leaves were absorbing more carbon dioxide than the controls after a period of 18 days. By perforating the leaves of wheat and barley to a degree not to exceed 10 per cent of the surface, Shcheglova and Chernysheva (1933) obtained increases in the rate of photosynthesis that persisted for several days. Eldredge (1935) found with corn in Iowa that total leaf removal, by stripping at weekly intervals from the four-leaf stage to the tasseling stage, caused reductions in yield in almost direct proportion to the percentage of leaves that were unrolled when the injury was inflicted. Thus the reduction in yield varied from 9 per cent in early June to 100 per cent on July 20, at the pre-tasseling stage. The severe shredding that removed about 50 per cent of the open leaves caused losses in yield ranging from 2 per cent, when this mutilation occurred in early June, to 50 per cent when it was performed at the pre-tasseling stage.

Curry and Trelease (1935) showed that with 99.9 per cent of deuterium oxide the rate of photosynthesis in *Chlorella* was only about 0.4 per cent of that with ordinary water. Wallace (1932) noted that sublethal doses of ether increased the rate of photosynthesis. This was due possibly to the increase in the opening of the stomata.

7. Internal Factors.—The chlorophyll and the protoplasmic structure of the chloroplast are mutually dependent upon one another. Chlorophyll cannot carry on photosynthesis when separated from the plastid, and the plastid devoid of chlorophyll is totally unable to carry on this process. The nature of the mutual dependence of the chloroplast upon the general cytoplasm of the cell, however, is not definitely known. It is considered by some (Ewart, 1898) that chloroplasts isolated from the general cytoplasm can still function in photosynthesis, while others (Kny, 1897, 1898) believed that they are unable to do so under such conditions. In general, however, it may be stated that the process of photosynthesis is intimately associated with the vital activities of the plant, so any factors that affect the protoplasm will have their effect upon photosynthesis.

Pickett (1933) determined the average cross-sectional area of the intercellular spaces of various varieties of apples. In a portion of leaf magnified 900 times the areas of these intercellular spaces were as follows:

Variety	Average area, sq. in.	Variety	Average area, sq. in.
Delicious	8.8	York	12.7
Jonathan	9.5	Wealthy	12.7
Gano	10.4	Liveland	17.7
Winesap	12.4		

Pickett (1934) found that the leaves of Liveland apples have a greater area of intercellular spaces than those of the Delicious variety. The rate of photosynthesis is the higher in the former variety, and he believed that the more extensive intercellular spaces are conducive to greater photosynthetic activity.

The data in regard to the effect of the oxygen supply upon photosynthesis are conflicting. Harvey (1928) found that 14 species of marine algae including greens, reds, and browns are able to produce oxygen from carbon dioxide when illuminated in the complete absence of oxygen. The oxygen appeared in the external medium within a second after illumination. Willstätter and Stoll (1918) found that plants exhibit marked differences in regard to the amount of oxygen necessary for photosynthesis. Thus *Pelargonium* is quite sensitive, while *Cyclamen* is very tolerant to the lack of this gas. The influence of the lack of oxygen on photosynthesis is apparently thus largely one of degree, some plants being easily inhibited in photosynthesis, while others withstand the absence of oxygen for longer periods without any change in the photosynthetic rate. Willstätter and Stoll considered that some oxygen, however, is absolutely essential for photosynthesis. It seems doubtful in any of the experiments that have been reported whether the oxygen supply was completely exhausted, since it is very difficult to free the plant entirely of the gas. An amount sufficient for the plant under consideration might have been available. Singh and Lal (1935) studied the rate of photosynthesis of the young, mature, and old leaves of wheat, flax, and sugar cane. Their data showed a low value for the young leaves, the highest value when the maximum vegetative growth occurred, and a slowing down with age until photosynthesis ceased at senescence.

Work by Ewart (1897, 1898), Pantanelli (1903), Ursprung (1917), and Yap (1920) indicates that the rate of photosynthesis may be checked by continuous exposure to light or by exposure to intense light. This inactivation might be due to the destruction of the chlorophyll or to injury of the protoplasm of the chloroplast or to both these factors, as suggested by Pantanelli (1903). It was noted by Yap (1920) that the rate of photosynthesis of the sugar cane decreased from 10 A.M. to 4 P.M., the process being the most active from 8 to 10 A.M. He considered in this case that the intensity of light decreased the rate of photosynthesis. Ursprung (1917) found that the inactivation of photosynthesis by continuous exposure to light in the case of *Phaseolus* began first in the orange-red portion of the spectrum where the highest photosynthetic rate was proceeding and then spread as the light intensity was increased to the region of shorter wave lengths. The term "solarization" was given by Ursprung to this effect of light upon the photosynthetic activity.

Holman (1930) stated that the term "solarization," as used in reference to plants, refers to a decrease or complete disappearance of starch following the long exposure of leaves to light of an intensity that initially was favorable to abundant starch formation. It is assumed that the effect of solarization is upon the process of photosynthesis, and it is only noticeable through the disappearance of the starch. Solarization apparently has no permanent effects upon the activities of the leaf, since after a period of darkness it again regains its original photosynthetic power. Stanescu (1924) observed that solarization is, in general, more pronounced in leaves with a medium rate of starch production. He was not able to find a definite relation between the appearance of solarization and the intensity of light, although those leaves which grew with their surface turned toward the south were solarized more frequently and more clearly. Emerson (1935) found in *Chlorella* that a light intensity fourteen times greater than that to which the cells are accustomed causes no injurious effects provided that the carbon dioxide supply remains adequate. If the supply of carbon dioxide is lowered, however, injury to the carbon-assimilatory mechanism results, but it is not accompanied by any injury to the chlorophyll. He believed that solarization can be greatly delayed or prevented by increasing the concentration of carbon dioxide.

The rate of photosynthesis is decreased by the accumulation of the products of the process. This behavior has been observed particularly with leaves that have been removed from the plant, since no means of translocation exists under these conditions. In many plants, the sugar which is formed in excess of that which can be translocated at once is converted into temporary starch in the chloroplasts. In these cases it is considered that this accumulation of starch in the chloroplasts impairs their activity by interfering with the photosynthetic process, which is considered by some to occur at the surface of these plastids. The retardation of photosynthesis by the accumulation of sugar in those leaves which do not form starch is apparently associated with the osmotic relations of the cells, and when a certain concentration of the cell sap is reached photosynthesis ceases.

The effect of the carbohydrate content of the leaf upon the rate of photosynthesis was studied by Saposchinkoff (1890, 1893). In the case of the detached leaves of *Vitis labrusca* and *Vitis vinifera* it was found that photosynthesis ceased when the carbohydrate content reached 17 to 25 per cent of the dry weight in the former and 23 to 29 per cent in the latter. These observations were confirmed by Ewart (1896), who also observed that leaves cease photosynthesis after they have been fed sugar for a time. Certain plants store up sugar, which has been produced in excess of that which is translocated from the leaf, as temporary starch in the chloroplasts. This starch appears after from 6 min. to 2 hr. or more, depending upon the plant and the conditions prevailing (Andrews, 1925). Plants that thus form starch have been termed "starch" plants, while those which form little or no starch are termed "sugar" plants. It has been stated by Müller (1904) that starch leaves exceed the sugar leaves in the total production of carbohydrates during the day, the limit of accumulation being higher in the starch leaves. He found that the maximum rate of photosynthesis remained almost stationary during the remainder of the day. Winkler (1898) showed that in ordinary starch-forming leaves 0.2 to 0.5 per cent of sugar is the critical concentration at which they will form starch. For sugar leaves the concentration attains a concentration of sugar as high as 18 per cent in the case of the sugar cane before starch will appear. The onion was the only plant in his experiments that resisted all feeding attempts to form starch. Leaves not detached from the stems but emptied of their starch by a sufficient period in darkness carry on photosynthesis and accumulate starch at a rate very much greater than normal leaves when they are exposed anew to the light.

Lubimenko (1927) noted in leaves low in starch that its accumulation occurs only in cells surrounding the vascular bundles. After starch plants are depleted of this carbohydrate and again exposed to favorable conditions for its production the first grains appear nearest the vascular bundles. According to Langner (1927), the amount of starch present in the leaves at any given time is not necessarily a direct result of photosynthesis. The mode of accumulation of starch is not the same for all leaves or even for those of the same species. It is a process primarily dependent upon internal factors that are not yet known (Stanescu, Aronescu, and Mihăilescu, 1929). Chapman and Camp (1932) found in the variegated leaves of *Pelargonium hortorium* that starch does not occur in the nongreen portion unless the leaf is placed in a solution of glucose, the optimal concentration of which is approximately 0.5 molecular. It was noted by Heinicke (1932) that the ringing of apple twigs reduced the photosynthetic activity of the leaves above the girdle as much as 33 to 50 per cent. This reduction might be due either to the harmful influence of accumulated products or to a lack of water and nutrients.

Suit and Hibbert (1934) introduced bacterial cultures of *Bacillus subtilis* containing the levan enzyme into young potato plants at stated intervals during the growing season. From four of the 30 plants so treated, they claim to have obtained tubers that were free from starch except in a peripheral ring of tissue a fraction of an inch in width. They believed this indicated that the type of carbohydrate formed in plants is influenced by internal conditions. It was observed by Gruzit and Hibbard (1916) that the dry weight per unit area of leaves of seedlings grown in a complete culture was less than that of leaves of seedlings grown in a solution lacking an element as potassium, calcium, or phosphorus. The explanation for this lies in a reduced translocation of the carbohydrate that accumulates in the leaf and results in a retarded photosynthesis, since the actual amount of material formed is greater in those plants growing in a complete nutrient solution.

In experiments with *Phaseolus vulgaris* grown in cultural solutions devoid of potassium, magnesium, iron, or phosphorus, Briggs (1922) found that the photosynthetic activity was lowered. This result may be attributed to two causes. The lack of certain elements might cause an accumulation of carbohydrates, since the growing parts of the plant in their absence cannot utilize the carbohydrates as rapidly as the leaves can synthesize them. On the other hand, the deficiency of salts may act directly upon the photosynthetic mechanism by reducing the actual leaf surface or by decreasing the rate per unit of leaf. Briggs considered that the chief factor involved in the latter case is a decrease in the "reactive surface" of the chloroplast. This is not necessarily the same as the actual visible chloroplast surface. The internal surface of the plastid is just as important as the visible surface in the process and may be greatly influenced by nutritive conditions. In conclusion, it should be stated in regard to protoplasmic factors that any factor or set of factors that affects the protoplasm in general will influence, to some extent at least, the photosynthetic process. In this connection the influence of fungi upon the photosynthetic activity should be mentioned. Long (1919) observed that rusts and mildews interfered with photosynthesis in all cases that she observed. Thus in *Avena* affected by *Puccinia coronata*, when it was well developed but not eruptive, the photosynthetic activity was reduced to 72 per cent and in the erupted stage to 48 per cent. *Puccinia graminis* on wheat reduced the rate of photosynthesis to 50 per cent in the stage before the pustules became brown and in the eruptive stage to 39 per cent.

Trelease and Trelease (1929) found that the leaves of wheat, with an abundant store of carbohydrates supplied by photosynthesis or artificially, were much more susceptible to mildew than those which were low in carbohydrates.

G. The Energy Relations of Photosynthesis

The process of photosynthesis is one in which the radiant energy of the sun is transformed into potential energy in the form of the organic compounds that are synthesized. In order to study the energy relations in the process it is necessary to know the amount of the compounds synthesized and the amount of energy available to the plant, so it is those topics that will now be considered.

1. Methods of Determining the Rate of Photosynthesis.—Three general methods have been used to measure the photosynthetic activity of the leaves and stems. These methods are based on (*a*) the liberation of oxygen, (*b*) the intake of carbon dioxide, and (*c*) the amount of organic substance or dry matter produced. It should be mentioned at the beginning that none of the methods that have been devised for the measurement of photosynthesis is satisfactory, since none takes into consideration all the factors concerned and since frequently the three methods do not yield the same results. The conflicting results obtained by the different methods are no doubt due to the fact that, although photosynthesis is a series or chain of reactions more or less dependent upon each other, each of the three methods is based upon a different chemical reaction in the process. Thus the intake of carbon dioxide occurs at the beginning of photosynthesis, and the increase in dry matter is the last stage in the process, and it is not known at which step in the reaction oxygen is liberated.

In the measurement of photosynthesis, the process of respiration is a difficulty regardless of the method used. Respiration goes on simultaneously in the same cells with photosynthesis, so there is a reduction and an oxidation process occurring at the same time. In photosynthesis, carbon dioxide is absorbed and carbohydrates are formed with the release of oxygen; while, in respiration, oxygen is absorbed, carbohydrates are broken down, and carbon dioxide released. The process of photosynthesis generally proceeds at a more rapid rate than does respiration. The quantity of carbon dioxide, therefore, absorbed from the exterior will be less than that actually used in the process of photosynthesis by an amount equal to the carbon dioxide evolved in respiration and utilized in photosynthesis before it can leave the cells. If the evolution of oxygen is used to measure photosynthesis, the amount of this gas that escapes is not all that has been liberated in the process, since some is utilized in respiration before it can escape from the cell. If photosynthesis is measured by the increase in dry weight, the loss in weight due to respiration must also be considered. The method usually used to correct for respiration is to determine its rate in the same plant parts or upon checks in the dark and then correct for this factor. The principal objection to this method of procedure is the uncertainty as to whether respiration goes on at the same rate in the light as in the dark. The value obtained for the rate of photosynthesis without correcting for the process of respiration is termed the "apparent rate of photosynthesis" as compared to the "true rate of photosynthesis," which has been corrected for the process of respiration. Hicks (1934) in *Lemna minor* found that the rate of photosynthesis was six times that of the respiratory rate under certain conditions.

a. Liberation of Oxygen.—The methods that have been devised to demonstrate the liberation of oxygen in the process of photosynthesis may be classified under the following headings: (1) The use of bacteria, (2) the use of oxygen-absorbing compounds, (3) the bubble-counting method, and (4) gas-analytical methods.

1. *The Use of Bacteria.*—Two types of bacteria have been used to demonstrate the liberation of oxygen: (*a*) luminous bacteria, which emit light only in the presence of oxygen, and (*b*) motile bacteria, which are active only in the presence of this gas. The plant material, however, that may be used in experiments of this type is limited to a size that can be observed under a relatively high power of the microscope.

2. *The Use of Oxygen-absorbing Compounds.*—Certain dyestuffs that are reduced to colorless substances react with oxygen, reforming the original colored compound. These reduced compounds are termed "leucobases" and are used to demonstrate the liberation of oxygen by plants. One of the most frequently used dyes for this purpose is indigo or indigo carmine. When an aqueous solution of this dye is reduced by sodium hyposulphite ($NaHSO_2$), the blue color disappears. When a water plant is illuminated in a solution of this reduced dye, the blue color reappears in the vicinity of the leaves due to the oxidation brought about by the oxygen evolved in photosynthesis.

If a leaf is immersed in defibrated venous blood and exposed to the light, the evolution of oxygen produces the red color of oxyhemoglobin in the vicinity of the leaf. The methods that have so far been mentioned are purely qualitative and have no value for quantitative work.

3. *Bubble Counting.*—When cut parts of an aquatic plant are placed in water with a supply of carbon dioxide and illuminated, bubbles of gas escape from the cut ends or surfaces. The major portion of this gas is oxygen, and it was shown by Sachs (1864) that the rate at which these bubbles are liberated may be taken as a relative measure of the rate of photosynthesis. This method is a comparatively simple one and has been used extensively in botanical laboratories, for both qualitative and quantitative work. A piece of water plant is securely submerged in water in which carbon dioxide is dissolved, and the gas as it escapes is collected in an inverted funnel, or test tube if it is so desired. The rate of photosynthesis is estimated by the number of bubbles that escape in a unit of time. For accurate quantitative work, however, this method is open to criticism. In the first place, the bubbles are not pure oxygen. Some of the oxygen that they contain passes out into the water, and some nitrogen from the water enters the bubbles. The bubbles are not always of the same size, being smaller when photosynthesis is rapid than when it is slow. Lastly, in some cases oxygen does not always escape from the plant in the form of bubbles at the same rate as it is formed.

Wilmot (1921) devised a "glass bubbler" that when fitted to the cut stem of a submerged water plant caused the liberated bubbles to be of a definite and constant size. This apparatus also delivered the bubbles directly into a cup so that they did not come into direct contact with the solutions that were being used.

4. *Gas-analytical Methods.*—These methods involve the analysis of the air in which a plant has been confined or the analysis of samples of air that has passed over the plant. The latter procedure is the more simple and satisfactory. The analysis of the air in experiments of this type is similar in procedure to ordinary gas analysis with the exception of certain modifications in apparatus that are necessary to expose the leaf or leaves to the air and to collect the air after it has been in contact with them. A discussion of the methods of gas analysis, however, is beyond the scope of this work. A concise discussion of the forms of apparatus and of absorbents that have been used is given by Spoehr (1926).

b. Absorption of Carbon Dioxide.—The determination of the amount of carbon dioxide used is the best known method for the measurement of photosynthesis in land plants. One of the objections to the method is that generally only a single leaf can be used and the behavior of detached leaves in photosynthetic activity is known to differ greatly from leaves that are attached to the plant. The carbon dioxide content of the air is first determined, and then the content of this gas in the air is determined after it has been pulled in a stream over the leaf in the dark. By this means the rate of respiration of the leaf is determined. The apparatus is then placed in the light and the carbon dioxide content of the air that has passed over the leaf is determined as before. The correction is made for respiration and the amount of carbon dioxide used in photosynthesis is calculated. This method was first used by Kreusler (1885) and has been used and modified since that time by numerous workers including Matthaei (1905), Blackman and Matthaei (1905), Brown and Escombe (1905), Willstätter and Stoll (1918), and Spoehr and McGee (1923, 1924). This method, although relatively simple in its procedure, involves many details that must be very carefully manipulated or the results will be of no value. Among these details are: (1) the regulation of the air stream, (2) the constant temperature of this stream, (3) the carbon dioxide content, (4) the regularity of illumination, and (5) the construction of forms of apparatus suitable for the collection of the gas and at the same time placing the plant under favorable conditions for photosynthesis.

The amount of carbon dioxide used in photosynthesis may be demonstrated in a rather simple manner by the eudiometric method first employed by Pfeffer (1871) and modified by Ganong (1908). The leaf or plant part is placed in a closed vessel of known volume to which is attached a graduated burette. A known amount of carbon dioxide is introduced into the apparatus, and after a period of time the amount remaining in the vessel is determined by using a concentrated solution of alkali as an absorbent, the carbon dioxide content being determined by the height to which the liquid rises in the graduated burette. Similar methods for the demonstration and measurement of photosynthesis have also been described by Osterhout (1918, 1919), by Osterhout and Haas (1918), and by Heinicke and Hoffman (1933).

c. Increase in Organic Matter. 1. *Qualitative Methods.*—The increase of the carbohydrates in photosynthesis is easily demonstrated in a qualitative way in those leaves that form starch. The presence of starch or its increase in amount may be easily demonstrated by the iodine method, which was first reported by Sachs (1884) and which has become the most used qualitative method for demonstrating starch in plant tissue. The plant is placed in the dark for a period before exposure to light, or portions of the leaf are shaded from light while others are exposed. When determinations are to be made, the leaf is detached, dipped in hot water, and rendered colorless by the extraction of the chlorophyll with ethyl alcohol. After this the leaves are placed in a solution of iodine in potassium iodide in water. The leaves or portions thereof that have been kept in the dark or shielded from the light will remain unstained, while the portions that have been exposed to light are colored from violet to black according to the amount of starch present. This method, however, is applicable only to those leaves which form starch.

The increase in carbohydrates by photosynthesis in sugar leaves can be demonstrated in a qualitative way by noting the increased reducing power of the cell sap with Fehling's solution or a similar one. This increase in reducing power may be determined in a microchemical way or by working directly with the expressed sap of the leaves.

2. *Quantitative Methods.* (a) *Weighing.*—This method was first used by Sachs in 1884 and is sometimes called the "half-leaf method." As originally devised, it consisted in removing one-half of an attached leaf at the beginning of the experiment by cutting along the midrib and then determining the dry weight of this severed portion. After exposure to light for a given period, the other half of the leaf was removed after the same manner and its dry weight determined. The method was later modified by Sachs and others in that only small portions of the leaf were removed from each side, thus enabling more uniform samples to be taken and eliminating errors due to irregular veins and the lack of symmetry in the two halves of the leaf.

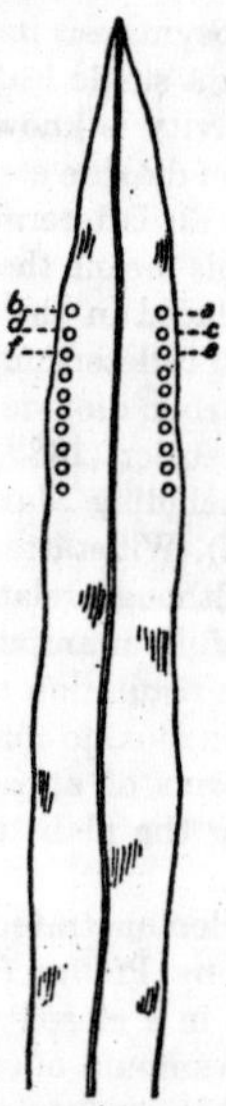

FIG. 28.—Diagram to illustrate the "leaf-punch" method for determining the variations in dry matter, water, carbohydrates, or nitrogen during a 24-hr. period. Description in the text.

Ganong (1908) devised a leaf punch that removes a disk of leaf with an area of 1 sq. cm. by means of which, if proper precautions are used, samples of very uniform weight and structure may be obtained. By beginning toward the tips of the leaves with this instrument, a series of samples may be taken at different periods of the day without seriously disturbing the conducting system of the leaf. Miller (1917) in determining the changes in the dry matter in the leaves of corn and the sorghums during the day and night obtained samples with a Ganong leaf punch after the following manner:

Thirty representative plants were selected and a leaf chosen on each plant for furnishing all the samples for an experiment extending over the desired length of time. Figure 28 shows the manner in which the leaf samples were obtained. The figure shows the appearance of a leaf at the end of a 40-hr. experiment. At 7 A.M. a single sample was taken from each of the 30 selected leaves at *a* toward the tip of the leaf. At 9 A.M. a sample was taken from each of the 30 leaves at *b* directly opposite *a*. At 11 A.M. the samples were collected from the leaves at *c* directly below *a*, and then at the next 2-hr. period at *d*, and so on. The samples for a 40-hr. experiment were thus obtained from a portion of the leaves representing less than 6 in. of their respective lengths. The samples were collected in weighed vials which were then quickly stoppered, weighed, placed in an oven at 100 to 108°C., and dried to constant weight.

The increase in dry weight that is obtained for a given area of leaf in an experiment of this kind does not represent the total weight of the product formed by photosynthesis during that period. Translocation of products from the leaf takes place during the period of photosynthesis, while a certain amount of the product of photosynthesis is utilized in respiration, which is proceeding simultaneously with photosynthesis. The increase in dry weight thus obtained represents the difference between the total weight of the products formed and the weight of the material that has been moved from the leaf or utilized in respiration. Sachs attempted to correct for the translocation by placing a detached leaf in water as a control, since translocation from the leaf does not occur under such conditions. Brown and Escombe (1905), however, showed that a detached leaf does not utilize carbon dioxide in the same proportion as an attached leaf, so such a correction is unreliable.

Sachs also considered that the total weight of photosynthate made during the day in a given area of leaf could be determined by adding to the gain during the day the loss in weight of the same area during the night. This should give the total increase in weight due to photosynthesis, provided that respiration and translocation proceed at the same rate during the daylight hours as they do during the night—which, however, is not definitely known to be a fact. The following data taken from the work of Miller (1917) show how the dry matter varies during the day and night in the leaves of Dwarf Yellow milo.

VARIATION IN DRY MATTER IN THE LEAVES OF DWARF YELLOW MILO DURING A 24-HR. PERIOD AT GARDEN CITY, KANS.

Time	Dry matter per square meter of leaf, grams	Increase or decrease in dry matter per square meter of leaf, grams
5 a.m.	50.3	
7 a.m.	50.8	+0.5
9 a.m.	53.4	+2.6
11 a.m.	55.7	+2.3
1 p.m.	58.3	+2.6
3 p.m.	61.0	+2.7
5 p.m.	61.5	+0.5
7 p.m.	60.2	−1.3
9 p.m.	58.0	−2.2
11 p.m.	57.8	−0.2
1 a.m.	55.6	−2.2
3 a.m.	54.9	−0.7
5 a.m.	52.1	−2.8

These data show that during the 24-hr. period there was manufactured in the leaf from 5 A.M. to 5 P.M. 11.2 g. of dry matter per square meter of leaf in excess of that which was translocated and used in respiration. From 5 P.M. to 5 A.M., 9.4 g. of dry matter disappeared per square meter of leaf. If the rate of translocation and respiration was the same during the day as during the night, the total amount of photosynthate during the day from 5 A.M. to 5 P.M. was 20.6 g. per square meter of leaf.

As pointed out by Thoday (1910), there are numerous objections to the dry-weight method of determining the rate of photosynthesis other than those above mentioned. The dry weight obtained includes the increase not only of carbohydrates but of proteins and oils as well. Changes in dry weight may consist in part of ash to as much as 5 per cent. The changes in ash content should be determined and a deduction made for the same. Apparent increases in dry weight would result from any shrinking in area of the leaf due to water loss during the day. Thoday (1910) considered that the dry-weight method gives useful results for rates of increase greater than 2 mg. per square decimeter per hour.

(b) *The Twin-leaf Method.*—Denny (1930) believed that the twin-leaf method, or opposite-leaf method, can be used to advantage in many cases. This method is applicable only for those plants that have opposite leaves. Although two opposite leaves may vary more than two half leaves, they are under more nearly normal conditions than two half leaves. The percentage difference in the fresh weight of opposite leaves may be as much as 4.2 or as little as 0.3 per cent.

(c). *Saccharification*.—This method consists of hydrolyzing the entire carbohydrate content of the leaf to hexoses and estimating the products thus formed as glucose. The method is essentially the same as that recommended by the Association of Official Agricultural Chemists but must be modified to meet the conditions that are peculiar to the material under consideration. In this method a correction must also be made for respiration and translocation, if the actual amount of photosynthate is to be determined.

Pickett (1935) determined the rate of photosynthesis in apple leaves by the punch method of Sachs, by the carbon dioxide-absorption method of Heinicke and Hoffman, and by the saccharification method. He reported that all these methods have disadvantages, it being necessary for one to choose the method that is best suited for the conditions under which one has to work.

2. The Rate of Photosynthesis.—It is of interest to know the rate at which carbohydrates are manufactured by the plant in the process of photosynthesis. The average rate of photosynthesis was determined by Miller (1917) for corn, kafir, and milo under the conditions that prevail in the field in Kansas during the growing season. The data for a large number of experiments for three growing seasons are averaged in the table below. These data have been corrected for translocation and respiration and thus approximate the actual amount of photosynthate manufactured by the leaves during the periods mentioned.

AVERAGE RATE OF PHOTOSYNTHESIS FOR EACH SQUARE METER OF LEAF FOR CORN, KAFIR, AND MILO DURING EACH 2-HR. PERIOD OF THE DAY

Plant	a.m.		p.m.		
	7 to 9	9 to 11	11 to 1	1 to 3	3 to 5
Corn	3.8	1.9	1.4	1.2	1.4
Kafir	3.0	2.1	1.2	2.1	1.2
Milo	2.3	2.7	3.8	3.5	1.4

The high rate of photosynthesis in corn and kafir from 7 to 9 A.M. as compared with other periods of the day may be due to water relations. During the growing season in the Great Plains, the water content of the leaves, due to a high rate of transpiration, is apparently below the optimum for some of the physiological processes for the majority of plants.

It also has been observed by Miller that the average rate of photosynthesis during a 10-hr. period for pumpkin, cowpeas, and soybeans was respectively 1.8, 0.85, and 0.8 g. per square meter per hour under field conditions. It is of interest to note that the rate for pumpkin is approximately that reported by Sachs (1884) for *Helianthus annuus*. The rates of photosynthesis just mentioned are much lower than those obtained by workers who have determined the rate by the amount of carbon dioxide taken up. They, however, used concentrations of carbon dioxide that were many times higher than normal. Thus Blackman and Matthaei (1905) using 6.3 per cent concentration of carbon dioxide obtained a rate of 3.9 g. per square meter per hour for *Helianthus annuus* at 30°C. in strong sunlight. Willstätter and Stoll (1918) in a 5 per cent concentration of carbon dioxide at 25°C. with a light intensity of 48,000 lux obtained a rate of 5.5 g. per square meter per hour with *Helianthus annuus* and under the same conditions, but with an atmosphere of 4 per cent carbon dioxide a rate of 4.3 g. per square meter per hour for *Cucurbita pepo*. In the ordinary atmosphere, McLean (1920) obtained a maximum absorption of carbon dioxide by the leaves of sugar cane that was equivalent to only 0.35 g. per square meter per hour of carbohydrate. Heinicke (1932) found that the highest rate of carbon assimilation in apple leaves was 35 mg. of carbon dioxide per hour per square centimeter, the most common rate being 5 to 10 mg. Under identical external conditions, the same plants may vary as much as 500 per cent in their photosynthetic rate.

3. The Total Incident Radiation.—In order to understand the energy relations of the green plant, a general idea must be had of the total incident radiation of the sun. The thermopile, pyroheliometer, radiometer, radiomicrometer, and bolometer are some of the instruments that have been used to determine the intensity of solar radiation, but a description of these instruments does not belong here. Shirley (1931) discussed the available sources of light, and the characteristics of the instruments that are available for light measurements.

The intensity of solar radiation has been measured by means of the heat produced when the radiation is absorbed on a black surface at right angles to the rays. The data thus obtained are generally converted into calories per square centimeter per minute (Spoehr, 1926). The intensity of solar radiation is not a constant but will depend upon the height above sea level, the condition of the atmosphere, and the position of the sun. The maximum intensities of solar radiation that have been reported vary from 1.15 to 1.75 cal. per square centimeter per minute depending upon the position and general condition when the observations were made. Spoehr (1926) considered that 1.35 cal. per square centimeter per minute is a conservative estimate of the energy that reaches the earth's surface during the 6 hr. of the most intense solar radiation of the day. Thus there would be received 1.35 by 60 by 6 or 486 cal. per square centimeter during that period. Taking 90 days as a growing season, the total radiation falling upon that surface during that time would be

43,740 cal. Since there are approximately 41,000,000 sq. cm. per acre, the total energy received in 90 days by that surface would be 1,793,340,-000,000 cal. According to Spoehr (1926), the heat of combustion of 1 kg. of anthracite coal is equal to 8,000 kg. cal., so that the total incident radiation on an acre during a 90-day period during the growing season would be equivalent to the energy derived from the combustion of 224,167 kg. or 246 tons of anthracite coal.

This represents sufficient energy to heat a seven-room house for 50 years during the months heat is required in the North Temperate Zone. Another way of expressing this is that if only 1 per cent of all the energy falling for 6 months on the land surface of the globe was fixed, it would equal the energy contained in the world's consumption of coal for 200 years—assuming that 1,000,000 tons were used annually. The energy falling annually on the total surface of the United States is equivalent to 7,000 trillion horsepower, which is approximately fourteen times all the energy used in industry in this country from all known sources including that furnished by man and beasts (Egloff, 1936). Thus, the amount of energy reaching the surface of the earth from the sun is enormous.

4. The Coefficient of Absorption of Radiant Energy for Leaves.—As stated by Brown and Escombe (1905), the coefficient of absorption of radiant energy by a leaf is the difference between the solar radiant energy falling upon the leaf in full sunshine and the amount transmitted through it. These investigators measured the total radiant energy by means of a radiometer. The leaf was then interposed so that the light passed through it before falling upon the radiometer. The amount of energy absorbed by the leaf was thus determined, but no account was taken of the reflection or radiation from the leaf surface. This error would tend to increase unduly the estimate of the coefficient of absorption. Brown and Escombe found that the coefficient of absorption was fairly constant for mature and healthy leaves of the same species of plant, but there was considerable variation in the leaves of different species. Thus the coefficient of absorption of the leaves of *Helianthus annuus* was 0.686; for *Polygonum Weyrichii*, 0.647; for *Verbascum olympicum*, 0.758; and for *Archium majus*, 0.728. They observed in most cases no significant differences in the absorption coefficient of young and old leaves. Brown and Escombe measured the absorption and transmission of the radiant energy by the white and green portions of the leaf of *Acer negundo*. They found that the coefficient of absorption of the green portion of the leaf was 0.787, while that of the white portion was 0.745. If the transmission through the albino leaf is taken as 100, that of the green leaf would be 83.5, a difference of 16 per cent, which may be regarded as expressing the increase in the absorptive power due to the coloring matter of the leaf. In this regard, Timiriazeff (1904) noted that the chlorophyll of a certain area of leaf absorbed only 27, 29, and 23.5 per cent of the radiant energy in the case of maple, lime, and oak, respectively. Puriewitsch (1914) by means of the bolometer found that the leaves of different plants absorbed only 18 to 27 per cent of the incident solar radiation. Long (1919) by means of a photometer noted the total incident light absorbed by the leaves to be 27.3, 43.4, and 29.2 per cent of the total incident light for dandelion, bean, and sunflower, respectively. These values reported by Puriewitsch and Long are much lower than those reported by Brown and Escombe.

Shull (1929) found that the amount of reflection from leaves varies with the wave length, the maximum reflection being of rays in the region of 540 to 560mμ. The reflection in this region of the spectrum varies from 6 to 8 per cent in the darkest green leaves to 20 to 25 per cent in the lightest green ones. The amount of reflection is not dependent upon hairiness or the smoothness of the cuticle. Thus the leaves of *Verbascum thapsus* and *Arbutilon theophrasti* show but little more reflection than the leaves of nonhairy plants. The amount of reflection decreases with the age of the leaf, which apparently is due to the greater amount of chlorophyll. The presence of fungi, however, on the surface increases reflection. The presence of anthocyanin shifts the position of maximal reflection. Thus in the autumn-colored leaves of *Psedera* the maximal reflection occurred at 640mμ instead of 540 to 560mμ—the usual region for maximal reflection in green leaves.

Briggs (1929) stated that photosynthetic efficiency is the ratio of the energy fixed in the leaf to the energy absorbed by it. Neither factor can be measured directly. In a leaf the system involved in the reflection of light is very complicated. Light undergoes some reflection every time it strikes an interface. The fraction of light reflected depends upon the refractive indexes, which themselves depend upon the wave length of the light and upon the angle of incidence. In land plants, reflection will occur at the upper surface of the leaves, on the inside where the cell walls abut on the intercellular spaces, at the interfaces of the cell sap, cytoplasm, and cell wall. For those leaves of *Liriodendron* which had become yellow, the reflection was as high as 50 per cent. Shull (1930) criticized the data on energy relations obtained by Brown and Escombe (1905) and stated that there should be thorough reinvestigations of the energy exchange between the leaf and its environment, and of the internal transformation of energy in the process of photosynthesis with reference to the variability of the reflection and absorption of energy in all regions of the spectrum.

Kalitin (1931) using an Angstrom pyranometer found the following reaction of various leaves to incident light.

Plant	Percentage of incident light		
	Reflected	Absorbed	Transmitted
Acer	29	39	32
Populus	42	24	34
Tilia	33	27	40
Ulmus	35	16	49
Cornus	35	25	40

Schanderl and Kaempfert (1933) with an improved actinometer found that ferns allowed 37 per cent of the incident radiation to be transmitted. Desert plants were found to be the most efficient absorbers of light in that only 15 to 30 per cent of the direct rays was transmitted, while in diffuse light the absorption was complete.

Dastur and Gunjikar (1934) studied the coefficient of absorption of the leaves of 12 plants to ordinary light rays and to light that was 89 per cent polarized. The average absorption coefficient for the normal light was 0.895, and for the polarized light, 0.917.

The cause for these differences in the absorption coefficients is difficult to determine and only emphasizes the fact that our knowledge concerning even the absorption of energy by the leaves is very limited.

In considering the absorption coefficient of the leaves, the quality of the rays transmitted or absorbed must be taken into consideration. The green leaf is selective in its absorption of the various wave lengths of solar radiation incident upon it, a behavior that would be suspected, to a degree at least, owing to the selective property of chlorophyll. This selective power of the leaf is shown by the quantity of light which is transmitted when leaves are superimposed upon each other. If the leaf possessed no power of selection, it would be expected that the transmitted portion of the radiant energy would diminish in geometric proportion as the number of leaves was increased in arithmetic proportion (Brown and Escombe, 1905). Thus, for example, if the leaf of *Helianthus annuus* having a transmission coefficient of 0.313 is superimposed upon another, the coefficient of transmission should be $(0.313)^2 = 0.098$, with three such leaves $(0.313)^3 = 0.030$, and so on, if the leaf had no power of selective absorption. This, however, is not the case, since Brown and Escombe found that the coefficient of transmission through two leaves of sunflower was 0.174 and through three leaves 0.116, while the radiation that should have been transmitted in the absence of selective absorption would have been 0.098 and 0.030, respectively. A similar observation was made by Timiriazeff with a solution of chlorophyll. He found, for example, that although the chlorophyll which had been dissolved out of a given area of maple leaf arrested 27 per cent of the energy of direct sunlight, this absorption was increased to only 31 per cent by a triple concentration of the solution.

5. The Utilization of Solar Energy in the Leaves.—A portion of the energy that is absorbed by the leaf is utilized in photosynthesis and in transpiration, and a certain portion is lost by thermal emission into the surrounding air, provided the temperature of the surrounding medium is lower than that of the leaf. The question naturally arises as to what proportions of the absorbed energy are used in photosynthesis and transpiration. Knowledge in this regard is, however, very limited and fragmentary, because experimental evidence on this subject is difficult to obtain. This difficulty is due to the fact that so many factors must be controlled and measured by methods that in many cases are doubtful in their reliability and accuracy. Some of the factors that must be controlled, measured, or taken into account are the total radiation, the coefficient of absorption, the amount of carbon dioxide used, the amount of water vapor given off, the intensity of respiration, the effect of the accumulation of products on photosynthesis, and the influence of the general factors upon the action of the stomata and the interchange of gases.

Briggs (1929) stated in this regard "that the amount of energy fixed in the immediate products of photosynthesis is obscured partly by the fact that the molecular mechanism of the reaction is not established and partly by the complex setting of the reactions in the living cells."

a. Determination of the Energy Used in Photosynthesis.—The energy used in photosynthesis has been estimated from the amount of carbon dioxide absorbed, from the amount of oxygen given off, and from the increase in dry weight. In all cases the determinations are reduced to the actual carbohydrate formed, correction always being made for respiration. In calculating the energy utilized by these methods, however, the difficulty that the proportions of the various carbohydrates are unknown is encountered, and, since each differs in its energy value, the energy utilized in producing the total carbohydrate products can be only approximated. Brown and Escombe (1905) determined the weight of carbon dioxide absorbed and multiplied this by the factor 0.640 to determine the weight of the carbohydrate produced, the factor being based on the carbohydrate content of the leaf as determined by previous investigators. Puriewitsch (1914) measured the increase in dry weight per unit area by the half-leaf method and the heat of combustion per unit area and thus determined the heat of combustion of the products of assimilation. The values obtained by him were higher than the value for glucose, starch, sucrose, or cellulose and suggest the production of fat or protein in the leaf during the period of photosynthesis.

b. The Energy Used in Photosynthesis.—The most extensive work that has been done to determine the energy relations of the leaf is that of Brown and Escombe (1905).

The work of Brown and Escombe shows that as little as 0.5 per cent of the total incident radiation in full sunshine may be utilized in the process of photosynthesis, but that as much as 4.5 per cent may be utilized when the sunshine approximates only 13 per cent of full intensity. Puriewitsch (1914) by measuring the incident energy with the bolometer and determining the energy used in photosynthesis by the increase in the heat of combustion per unit of leaf area found the following utilization of the total incident energy: *Acer platanoides*, 0.6 to 2.7 per cent; *Polygonum sacchalinese*, 1.1 to 7.7 per cent; *Helianthus annuus*, 4.5 per cent; and *Saxifraga cordifolia*, 5.0 per cent. Some of these percentages are considerably higher than those of Brown and Escombe. This may be due to the fact that the products of photosynthesis had not yet accumulated and thus did not exert a hindering influence on the rate in certain experiments. The figures of both Brown and Escombe and Puriewitsch make it evident that with a high light intensity only a small part of the incident radiation is utilized in photosynthesis. As the light intensity decreases, however, the proportion of the total incident radiation used in photosynthesis increases. This is what would be expected if light were present in excess and not a limiting factor.

The energy relations of photosynthesis in crop plants growing in the field may be approximated and are of some interest. In the case of the pumpkin plant the rate of photosynthesis is approximately 1.8 g. per square meter per hour. If this increase in photosynthate is considered as starch and its heat of combustion taken as 4,200 g.-cal., the energy used in photosynthesis would be somewhat less than 1 per cent of the total incident radiation if such radiation were considered as 1.35 cal. per square centimeter per minute. In the case of cowpeas and soybeans where the rate of photosynthesis is only about 0.8 g. per square meter per hour the energy used in photosynthesis would be only about 0.4 per cent of the total incident radiation.

Miller (1928) observed that the maximum daily increase in the dry weight of corn plants that had reached their full leaf development was 18.3 g. under field conditions in Kansas. Assuming this total increase in weight as starch and its heat of combustion as 4,200 g.-cal. and considering 6,000 corn plants per acre, the total energy fixed during the day would be 451,000,000 cal. The total incident radiation on an acre for a 6-hr. day would amount to 19,926,000,000 cal. considering 41,000,000 sq. cm. to the acre. The energy utilized in photosynthesis would thus be 451 ÷ 19,926 or 2.2 per cent of the total incident radiation on the acre of surface. Transeau (1926) estimated that the corn plant utilized in photosynthesis only about 1.6 per cent of the total energy available to it. This, however, does not take into consideration the material utilized in respiration. Pütter, as quoted by Spoehr (1926), estimated that the utilization of the total incident solar energy by the crop plants in the production of organic matter was as follows, allowance being made for the material used in respiration: summer wheat, 3.26 per cent; summer rye, 2.60 per cent; oats, 3.31 per cent; potatoes, 3.02 per cent; and beets, 2.12 per cent.

6. The Economic Importance of Photosynthesis.—The immediate source of the energy supply that is needed continuously by all living organisms, both plant and animal, is food. This food is manufactured from simple inorganic substances by the green plant with the aid of energy derived from the sun. Food thus represents a supply of energy that has been stored by the plant from the rays of the sun. All life on the earth thus depends upon the energy that comes from the sun through the intermediary of the green plant. The green plant is thus the sole agent that has the power to transform the kinetic energy of the sun into the potential form. This is accomplished through the process of photosynthesis; and sugar, starch, cellulose, lignocellulose, fats and oils, proteins, and the multitude of plant organic compounds are stores of potential energy that has thus been transformed. This storage of the energy of the sun has been going on for millions of years and has always been in excess of that needed for the maintenance of plant and animal life. This fact is evidenced at the present time by the forests that until comparatively recently furnished man with fuel for his bodily warmth and for industrial power. The energy stored up in plant materials in the past ages became "fossil energy" and is now stored in the form of coal and oil.

The present industrial civilization is a machine-using age dependent upon a continuous and abundant supply of stored energy that may be readily released to the kinetic form for the operation of these machines. At present, coal and oil are the two main sources of this stored energy which, as before stated, has been made possible through the process of photosynthesis through millions of years.

The question that is now of considerable concern, to those who are looking to the future, is, what sources can be drawn upon for a supply of energy when the supply of stored energy, oil especially, is greatly depleted? Alcohol derived from grains, cellulose, and other plant products has been the source that is most commonly suggested. Such a substitution, however, is much more involved and difficult than is commonly supposed. The production of alcohol from plant products as a source of power for industry has serious objections. The question of disturbing the equilibrium of the present food supply is not one of the least of these objections.

Thus Spoehr (1922) stated that the total average annual yield of corn in the United States (2,740,000,000 bu.) if converted into alcohol would produce only 7,500,000,000 gal. of alcohol, which would be equivalent to 5,000,000,000 gal. of gasoline. This is about one-fourth of the present yearly consumption. Thus the present production of grain from all sources in this country would scarcely more than supply the present needs for this fuel, without leaving any for a food supply. The industrial age has been made possible because an enormous supply of stored energy is close at hand or immediately available, and climatic changes, diseases, insect pests, and numerous other factors have no influence upon the supply. Such a certain and undisturbed source of energy would not thus be available if the supply of energy were furnished by the crop of the current year.

Although the green plant is the sole converter of solar energy through the process of photosynthesis, it is, as has previously been mentioned, a very inefficient machine, utilizing only from 0.5 to 3 per cent of the total energy falling upon it. It would appear that the solution of the future fuel supply lies in the discovery of the physics and chemistry of photosynthesis and by their application artificially transforming the kinetic energy of the sun rather than by depending upon this transformation by the slow-acting plant. If man can solve the problem of this transformation of energy by the plant and improve it, he will have at hand an almost unlimited and inexhaustible source of energy.

Bibliography

ANDREWS, F. M., 1925: Starch formation, *Proc. Ind. Acad. Sci.*, **35**: 182–184.

APPLEMAN, C. O., 1927: Percentage of carbon dioxide in soil air, *Soil Sci.*, **24**: 241–245.

ARCHBOLD, H. K. and A. M. BARTER, 1935: A fructose anhydride from the leaves of the barley plant, *Biochem. J.*, **29**: 2689–2693.

ARNOLD, W., 1934: The effect of ultra-violet light on photosynthesis, *J. Gen. Physiol.*, **17**: 135–143.

———, 1933: The order of the Blackman reaction in photosynthesis, *J. Gen. Physiol.*, **17**: 145–149.

——— and H. I. KOHN, 1934: The chlorophyll unit in photosynthesis, *J. Gen. Physiol.*, **18**: 109–112.

ARTHUR, J. M., 1929: Some effects of radiant energy on plants, *J. Optic Soc. Am. and Rev. Sci. Inst.*, **18**: 253–263.

———, 1931: Color development in apples after picking, *Am. J. Bot.*, **18**: 896–897.

——— and L. C. PORTER, 1935: A new type of insulated greenhouse heated and lighted by Mazda lamps, *Contr. Boyce Thompson Inst.*, **7**: 131–146.

BAEYER, A., 1870: Ueber die Wasserentziehung und ihre Bedeutung für das Pflanzenleben und die Gährung, *Ber. chem. Ges.*, **3**: 63–78.

BAKER, S. M., 1913: Quantitative experiments on the effects of formaldehyde on living plants, *Ann. Bot.*, **27**: 411–443.

BALY, E. C. C., and J. B. DAVIS, 1927: Photosynthesis of naturally occurring compounds. III, Photosynthesis in vivo and in vitro, *Proc. Roy. Soc.*, A, **116**: 219–226

——— and N. R. Hood, 1929: The photosynthesis of naturally occurring compounds. IV, The temperature coefficient of the photosynthesis of carbohydrates from carbonic acid, *Proc. Roy. Soc.*, A, **122**: 393–398.

———, I. M. Heilbron, and W. F. Barker, 1921: Photocatalysis. I, The synthesis of formaldehyde and carbohydrates from carbon dioxide and water, *J. Chem. Soc. Trans.*, **119**: 1025–1035.

———, 1922: Photosynthesis, *Nature*, **109**: 344–346.

———, I. M. Heilbron, and W. F. Barker, 1923: Photochemical production of formaldehyde, *Nature*, **112**: 323.

———, 1924: Photosynthesis, *Ind. and Eng. Chem.*, **16**: 1016–1018.

———, 1928: Photosynthesis, *Sci.*, **68**: 364–367.

———, 1935: The kinetics of photosynthesis, *Proc. Roy. Soc.*, B, **117**: 218–239.

Banal, R., 1926: Un fertilizzante fondamentale: l'anidride carbonica. Problemi ed esperienze sull' assimilazione del carbonio, *L'Italia agricola*, **63**: 118–121.

Barnes, C. R., 1893: On the food of green plants, *Bot. Gaz.*, **18**: 403–411.

———, 1898: So-called "assimilation," *Bot. Cent.*, **76**: 255–259.

Bartholomew, R. P., V. M. Watts, and G. Janssen, 1933: The effect of variations in the nutrient media upon the nitrogen, phosphorus, and potassium content in plants with special reference to the tomato, *Ark. Sta. Bull.* 288.

Barton-Wright, E. C., and M. C. Pratt, 1930: Studies in photosynthesis. I, The formaldehyde hypothesis, *Biochem. J.*, **24**: 1210–1216.

——— and ———, 1930: Studies of photosynthesis. II, The first sugar of carbon assimilation and the nature of the carbohydrates in the narcissus leaf, *Biochem. J.*, **24**: 1217–1234.

Bazyrina, K. N., and V. Tschesnokov, 1930: Der Einfluss der Luftdüngung auf die Pflanzen, *Planta*, **11**: 463–472; *Biol. Abst.*, **8**: 873.

Belval, H., 1932: Transformations of sugars in the banana, the formation and disappearance of starch, *Rev. Gén. Bot.*, **44**: 513–525.

Bergamaschi, M., 1932: Sull' assorbimento del biossido di carbonio per opera delle radici e sulla sua utilizzazione nella fotosintesi clorofilliana, *Biol. Abst.*, **6**: 1891.

Bernard, C., 1878: "Leçons sur les phénomènes de la vie commune aux animaux et aux végétaux," Paris.

Bernbeck, O., 1924: Wind und Pflanze, *Flora*, **117**: 293–300.

Berthelot, D., and H. Gaudechon, 1910: Synthèse photochimique des hydrates de carbone aux dépens des éléments de l'anhydride carbonique et de la vapeur d'eau, en l'absence de chlorophyll, *C. R. Acad. Sci. Paris*, **150**: 1690–1693.

Bills, C. E., and F. G. McDonald, 1932: The carotene content of ten varieties of carrots, *Sci.*, **76**: 108.

Blackman, F. F., and G. L. C. Matthaei, 1905: Experimental researches in vegetable assimilation and respiration. IV, A quantitative study of carbon-dioxide assimilation and leaf-temperature in natural illumination, *Proc. Roy. Soc.*, B, **76**: 402–460.

———, 1905: Optima and limiting factors, *Ann. Bot.*, **19**: 281–295.

———, 1910: Experimental researches on vegetable assimilation and respiration. VIII, A new method for estimating the gaseous exchanges of submerged plants, *Proc. Roy. Soc.*, B, **83**: 374–388.

——— and A. M. Smith, 1911: Experimental researches on vegetable assimilation and respiration. IX, On assimilation in submerged water plants and its relation to the concentration of carbon dioxide and other factors, *Proc. Roy. Soc.*, B, **83**: 389–412.

Boehm, J. A., 1856: Beiträge zur näheren Kenntniss des Chlorophylls, *Sitzungsber. Akad. Wiss. Wien*, **22**: 479.

———, 1883: Ueber Stärkebildung aus Zucker, *Bot. Ztg.*, **41**: 33–38, 49–54.

Bokorny, T., 1891: Ueber Stärkebildung aus Formaldehyd, *Ber. bot. Ges.*, **9**: 103–106.

———, 1892: Ernährung von grünen Pflanzenzellen mit Formaldehyd, *Landw. Jahrb.*, **21**: 445–465.

———, 1897: Ueber die organische Ernährung von grünen Pflanzen und ihre Bedeutung in der Natur, *Biol. Cent.*, **17**: 1–20, 33–48.

———, 1908: Ueber die Assimilation des Formaldehyds und die Versuche dieses Zwischenproduct bei Kohlensäure-Assimilation nachzuweisen. Assimilation von Glycerin und Zucker, *Arch. ges. Physiol.*, **125**: 467–490.

———, 1909: Weitere Mitteilung über CO_2-Assimilation und Ernährung von Pflanzen mit Formaldehyd, *Arch. ges. Physiol.*, **128**: 565–586.

———, 1910: Die bisherigen Versuche das Formaldehyd direkt in Blättern nachzuweisen, *Chem. Z.*, **33**: 1141–1143, 1150–1151.

———, 1911: Ernährung von grünen Pflanzen mit Formaldehyd und formaldehydabspaltenden Substanzen, *Biochem. Z.*, **36**: 83–97.

Bolas, B. D., and F. Y. Henderson, 1928: The effect of increased atmospheric carbon dioxide on the growth of plants. I, *Ann. Bot.*, **42**: 509–523.

——— and R. Melville, 1935: The effect on the tomato plant of carbon dioxide produced by combustion, *Ann. App. Biol.*, **22**: 1–15.

Bonnier, G., and L. Mangin, 1886: Recherches sur l'action chlorophyllienne séparée de la respiration, *Ann. Sci. Nat. Bot.*, 7e, **3**: 1–44.

Bornemann, O., 1920: Kohlensäure und Pflanzenwachstum, *Mitteil. landw. Ges.*, **35**: 693–695; *Bot. Abst.*, **8**: 2.

———, G. Lemmerman, and F. Riedel, 1921: Zur Kohlenstoffernährung der Kulturpflanzen, *Mitteil. landw. Ges.*, **36**: 481–485, 496–498.

Bose, J. C., 1924: "Physiology of Photosynthesis," 286 pp., Longmans, Green and Company, New York.

Bottomley, W. B., and H. Jackson, 1903: Some preliminary observations on the assimilation of carbon monoxide by green plants, *Proc. Roy. Soc.*, **72**: 130–131.

Boussingault, J. B., 1864: De la végétation dans l'obscurité, *Ann. Sci. Nat. Bot.*, 5e, **1**: 314–324.

Boysen-Jensen, P., 1918: Studies on the production of matter in light and shadow plants, *Bot. Tidssk.*, **36**: 219–262.

Breazeale, J. F., 1923: The absorption of carbon by the roots of plants, *J. Agr. Res.*, **26**: 303–313.

Briggs, G. E., 1920: Experimental researches on vegetable assimilation and respiration. XIII, The development of photosynthetic activity during germination, *Proc. Roy. Soc.*, B, **91**: 249–268.

———, 1922: Experimental researches on vegetable assimilation and respiration. XV, The development of photosynthetic activity during germination of different types of seeds, *Proc. Roy. Soc.*, B, **94**: 12–19.

———, 1922: Experimental researches on vegetable assimilation and respiration. XVI, The characteristics of subnormal photosynthetic activity resulting from deficiency of nutrient salts, *Proc. Roy. Soc.*, B, **94**: 20–35.

———, 1929: Experimental researches on vegetable assimilation and respiration. XX, The energetic efficiency of photosynthesis in green plants. Some new data and a discussion of the problems, *Proc. Roy Soc.*, B, **105**: 1–35.

———, 1933: Experimental researches on vegetable assimilation and respiration. XXI, Induction phases in photosynthesis and their bearing on the mechanism of the process, *Proc. Roy. Soc.*, B, **113**: 1–42.

———, 1935: Photosynthesis in intermittent light in relation to current formulations of the photosynthetic mechanism, *Biol. Rev.*, **10**: 460–482.

Brilliant, B., 1924: Le teneur en eau dans les feuilles et l'énergie assimilatrice, *C. R. Acad. Sci. Paris*, **178**: 2122–2125.

Brown, H. T., and G. H. Morris, 1893: A contribution to the chemistry and physiology of foliage leaves, *J. Chem. Soc.*, **63**: 604–677.

——— and F. Escombe, 1902: The influence of varying amounts of carbon dioxide in the air on the photosynthetic process of leaves and on the mode of growth of plants, *Proc. Roy. Soc.*, **70**: 397–413.

——— and ———, 1905: Researches on some of the physiological processes of green leaves, with special reference to the interchange of energy between the leaf and its surroundings, *Proc. Roy. Soc.*, B, **76**: 29–112.

——— and W. E. Wilson, 1905: On the thermal emissivity of a green leaf in still and moving air, *Proc. Roy. Soc.*, B, **76**: 122–137.

Brown, W. H., and G. W. Heise, 1917: The application of photochemical temperature coefficients to the velocity of carbon dioxide assimilation, *Philippine J. Sci.*, C, **12**: 1–24.

Buchanan, J. H., and G. G. Naudain, 1923: Influence of starch on strength of wheat flour, *Ind. and Eng. Chem.*, **15**: 1050–1051.

Burgess, A. H., 1935: The effect of the rate of flow of air upon assimilation and of fluids upon other natural processes, *Ann. Bot.*, **49**: 567–578.

Burk, D., 1927: Photosynthesis with malachite green, *J. Am. Chem. Soc.*, **49**: 1819–1825.

——— and H. Lineweaver, 1935: The kinetic mechanism of photosynthesis, *Symposia Quant. Biol.*, **3**: 165–183.

Burns, G. R., 1933: Photosynthesis in various portions of the spectrum, *Plant Physiol.*, **8**: 247–262.

———, 1934: Long and short wave-length limits of photosynthesis, *Plant Physiol.*, **9**: 645–652.

Burr, G. O., 1936: Carbonic anhydrase and photosynthesis, *Proc. Roy. Soc.*, B., **120**: 42–46.

Butlerow, A., 1861: Bildung einer zuckerartigen Substanz durch Synthese, *Ann. Chem. Pharm.*, **120**: 295–298.

Cailletet, M. L., 1911: Sur l'origine du carbone assimilé par les plantes, *C. R. Acad. Sci. Paris*, **152**: 1215–1217.

Cerighelli, R., 1921: Influence de l'anhydride carbonique sur le développement des plantes—emploi de CO_2 comme en grais atmosphérique, *Ann. Sci. Agron.*, **38**: 68–75.

Chapman, A. G., and W. H. Camp, 1932: Starch synthesis in the variegated leaves of *Pelargonium*, *Ohio J. Sci.*, **32**: 197–217.

Childers, N. F., and F. F. Cowart, 1935: The photosynthesis, transpiration and stomata of apple leaves as affected by certain nutrient deficiencies, *Proc. Am. Soc. Hort. Sci.*, **33**: 160–163.

Chouchak, D., 1929: L'assimilation chlorophyllienne de l'acide carbonique par les feuilles vertes dans un champ électrique, *Rev. Gén. Bot.*, **41**: 465–468.

Christopher, E. P., 1933: Influence of the amount of air supplied to apple leaves upon their CO_2 assimilation, *Proc. Am. Soc. Hort. Sci.*, **30**: 435–439.

———, 1934: The intensity of light striking leaves of apple trees at different times of day, *Proc. Am. Soc. Hort. Sci.*, **32**: 86–92.

———, 1935: The effect of flotation sulphur spray on the CO_2 assimilation of apple leaves, *Proc. Am. Soc. Hort. Sci.*, **33**: 149–151.

CLAYSON, D. H. F., and S. B. SCHRYVER, 1923: The hemicelluloses. I, The hemicellulose of wheat flour, *Biochem. J.*, **17**: 493–496.

CLEMENTS, H. F., 1930: Hourly variations in carbohydrate content of leaves and petioles, *Bot. Gaz.*, **89**: 241–272.

———, 1932: Mannose and the first sugar of photosynthesis, *Plant Physiol.*, **7**: 547–550.

COLE, R. C., 1932: The diurnal and seasonal changes in the sugar content of the sap and tissue of potato plants as affected by soil fertilization, *Soil Sci.*, **33**: 347–362.

COLIN, M. H., 1914: Sur la saccharogénie dans la betterave, *C. R. Acad. Sci. Paris*, **159**: 687–689.

———, 1916–1917: Le saccharose dans le betterave. Formation et disparition, *Rev. Gén. Bot.*, **28**: 289–299, 321–328, 368–380; **29**: 21–32, 56–64, 89–96, 113–127. Quoted by Stiles, 1925.

———, 1918: The origin of inulin in plants, *C. R. Acad. Sci. Paris*, **166**: 224–227; *Exp. Sta. Rec.*, **39**: 524.

——— and H. BELVAL, 1922: La genèse des hydrates de carbone dans le blé. Présence de lèvulosanes dans la tige, *C. R. Acad. Sci. Paris*, **175**: 1441–1443.

COLLA, S., 1930: Formation of chlorophyll in plants exposed to ultra-violet rays, *Ann. Bot. (Rome)*, **18**: 329–349; *Exp. Sta. Rec.*, **67**: 20.

COMBES, R., 1928: Étude critique de la méthode de Sachs appliquée à la mesure des migrations des substances, *C. R. Acad. Sci. Paris.*, **187**: 666–668.

———, 1928: Influence des traumatisme sur les migrations des substances chez les végétaux, *C. R. Acad. Sci. Paris*, **187**: 993–995.

CONANT, J. B., E. M. DIETZ, C. F. BAILEY, and S. E. KAMERLING, 1931: Studies in the chlorophyll series. V, The structure of chlorophyll A, *J. Am. Chem. Soc.*, **53**: 2382–2393.

———, ———, and S. E. KAMERLING, 1931: The dehydrogenation of chlorophyll and the mechanism of photosynthesis, *Sci.*, **73**: 268.

COWART, F. F., 1935: Apple leaf structure as related to position of the leaf upon the shoot and to type of growth, *Proc. Am. Soc. Hort. Sci.*, **33**: 145–148.

CROCKER, W., 1918: Law of the minimum—a review of Hooker's work, *Bot. Gaz.*, **65**: 287–288.

CUMMINGS, M. B., and C. H. JONES, 1918: The aerial fertilization of plants with carbon dioxide, *Vt. Sta. Bull.* 211.

——— and ———, 1920: The aerial fertilization of plants with carbon dioxide, *J. Chem. Soc.*, **118**: 267.

CURRY, J., and S. F. TRELEASE, 1935: Influence of deuterium oxide on the rate of photosynthesis, Sci., 82: 18.

DANGEARD, P. A., 1927: Recherches sur l'assimilation chlorophyllienne et les questions qui s'y rattachent, *Botaniste*, **19**: 1–397; *Biol. Abst.*, **3**: 474.

DASTUR, R. H., 1924: Water content, a factor in photosynthesis, *Ann. Bot.*, **38**: 779–788.

———, 1925: The relation between water content and photosynthesis, *Ann. Bot.*, **39**: 769–786.

——— and R. D. ASANA, 1932: Effect of plane-polarized light on the formation of carbohydrates in leaves, *Ann. Bot.*, **46**: 879–891.

——— and J. J. CHINOY, 1932: Carbon dioxide assimilation of the leaves of the rice plant, *Oryza sativa, Indian J. Agr. Sci.*, **2**: 431–454.

——— and B. L. DESAI, 1933: The relation between water-content, chlorophyll content, and the rate of photosynthesis in some tropical plants at different temperatures, *Ann. Bot.*, **47**: 69–88.

——— and K. M. Samant, 1933: A study of the products of photosynthesis in leaves in artificial and in natural light, *Ann. Bot.*, **47**: 295–304.

——— and ———, 1933: A method for the determination of carbohydrates in leaves, *Indian J. Agr. Sci.*, **3**: 460–477; *Exp. Sta. Rec.*, **70**: 580.

——— and L. K. Gunjikar, 1934: Effect of elliptically polarized light on the formation of carbohydrates in leaves, *Ann. Bot.*, **48**: 1003–1012.

——— and ———, 1935: Energy absorption by leaves in normal and plane polarized light, *Ann. Bot.*, **49**: 273–281.

——— and R. J. Mehta, 1935: The study of the effect of blue-violet rays on photosynthesis, *Ann. Bot.*, **49**: 809–821.

Davidson, G. F., and W. A. Richardson, 1936: The molecular structure of cellulose and starch, *Sci. Prog.*, **31**: 68–77.

Davis, W. A., and A. J. Daish, 1913: A study of the methods of estimation of carbohydrates, especially in plant extracts. A new method for the estimation of maltose in presence of other sugars, *J. Agr. Sci.*, **5**: 437–468.

——— and ———, 1914: Methods of estimating carbohydrates. II, The estimation of starch in plant material. The use of taka-diastase, *J. Agr. Sci.*, **6**: 152–168.

——— and G. C. Sawyer, 1914: The estimation of carbohydrates. IV, The presence of free pentoses in plant extracts and the influence of other sugars on their estimation, *J. Agr. Sci.*, **6**: 406–412.

———, 1916: Studies of the formation and translocation of carbohydrates in plants. II, The Dextrose-laevulose ratio in the mangold, *J. Agr. Sci.*, **7**: 327–351.

———, A. J. Daish, and G. C. Sawyer, 1916: Studies of the formation and translocation of carbohydrates in plants. I, The carbohydrates of the mangold leaf, *J. Agr. Sci.*, **7**: 255–326.

——— and G. C. Sawyer, 1916: Studies of the formation and translocation of carbohydrates in plants. III, The carbohydrates of the leaf and leaf stalks of the potato. The mechanism of the degradation of starch in the leaf, *J. Agr. Sci.*, **7**: 352–384.

Dean, A. L., 1904: On inulin, *Am. Chem. J.*, **32**: 69–84.

Deleano, N. T., and J. Dick, 1932: Beiträge zur Kenntnis des Carotins. Neue Methoden zur Darstellung, Nachweis und Bestimmung, *Bull. Soc. Chem. Roumania*, **14**: 117–170.

——— and ———, 1933: Beiträge zur Kenntnis des Carotins. I, *Biochem. Z.*, **259**: 110–133.

——— and ———, 1934: Détermination de la chlorophylle dans les feuilles de *Salix fragilis* et de *Populus alba*, *Bull. Soc. Chem. Biol.*, **16**: 749–756.

Demerec, M., 1935: Behavior of chlorophyll in inheritance, *Symposia Quant. Biol.*, **3**: 80–86.

Demoussy, E., 1903–1904: Sur la végétation dans des atmosphères riches en acide carbonique. *C. R. Acad. Sci. Paris*, **136**: 325–328; **138**: 291–293 (1904); **139**: 883–885 (1904).

Deneke, H., 1931: Über den Einfluss bewegter Luft auf die Kohlensäureassimilation, *Jahr. wiss. Bot.*, **74**: 1. Quoted by Burgess, 1935.

Denny, F. E., 1930: The twin leaf method of studying changes in leaves, *Am. J. Bot.*, **17**: 818–842.

———, 1932: Changes in leaves during the night, *Contr. Boyce Thompson Inst.*, **4**: 65–83.

———, 1933: Bases for calculations in measuring changes in leaves during the night, *Contr. Boyce Thompson Inst.*, **5**: 181–194.

———, 1934: Starch determination methods involving solubility in acids, *Contr. Boyce Thompson Inst.*, **6**: 381–394.

De Saussure, N. T., 1804: "Recherches chimiques sur la végétation," Paris.

Deuber, C. G., 1926: Influence of mineral elements upon the development of chloroplast pigments of soybeans, *Bot. Gaz.*, **82**: 132–152.

Dhar, N. R., 1935: Chemistry of photosynthesis, *Symposia Quant. Biol.*, **3**: 151–164.

Dixon, H. H., and T. G. Mason, 1916: The primary sugar of photosynthesis, *Nature*, **97**: 160.

——— and H. H. Poole, 1920: Photosynthesis and the electronic theory, *Sci. Proc. Roy. Dublin Soc.*, **16**: 63–77.

——— and ———, 1920: Photosynthesis and the electronic theory, *Notes Bot. School Trinity Col. Dublin*, **3**: 90–104.

——— and N. G. Ball, 1922: Photosynthesis and the electronic theory, *Notes Bot. School Trinity Col. Dublin*, **3**: 199–205.

Duclaux, E., 1899: "Traité de microbiologie." 2, "Diastases, Toxines et Venins," Masson et Cie, Paris, 768 pp.

Dunlap, A. A., 1931: Carbohydrate variations accompanying the mosaic disease of tobacco, *Am. J. Bot.*, **18**: 328–336.

Echevin, R., 1934: L'évolution des phospholipides des feuilles au cours du jaunissement automnal, *C. R. Acad. Sci. Paris*, **198**: 1254–1256.

Edwards, D. W., and J. C. Ripperton, 1933: Some factors affecting the electrolytes of the starch granules, *J. Agr. Res.*, **47**: 179–191.

Egloff, G., 1936: Modern energy supplies, *Sci. Month.*, **42**: 291–300.

Eidelman, Z. M., and E. A. Bankul, 1933: Effect of the mechanical reduction of the leaf surface and different nutritive conditions on the accumulation of dry matter in cereals, *Lenin. Acad. Agr. Sci., U.S.S.R., Inst. Plant Protect.*, **1933**: 113–130; *Exp. Sta. Rec.*, **70**: 596.

Eldredge, J. C., 1935: The effect of injury in imitation of hail damage on the development of the corn plant, *Iowa Res. Bull.* 185.

Emerson, R., 1929: The relation between maximum rate of photosynthesis and concentration of chlorophyll, *J. Gen. Physiol.*, **12**: 609–622.

———, 1929: Photosynthesis as a function of light intensity and of temperature with different concentrations of chlorophyll, *J. Gen. Physiol.*, **12**: 623–639.

———, 1929: On the behavior of nickel carbonate in relation to photosynthesis, *J. Gen. Physiol.*, **13**: 163–169.

——— and W. Arnold, 1932: The photochemical reaction in photosynthesis, *J. Gen. Physiol.*, **16**: 191–205.

——— and L. Green, 1934: Kinetics of photosynthesis, *Nature*, **134**: 289–290.

———, 1935: The effect of intense light on the assimilatory mechanism of green plants, and its bearing on the carbon dioxide factor, *Symposia Quant. Biol.*, **3**: 128–137.

Ewart, A. J., 1896: On assimilatory inhibition in plants, *J. Linn. Soc. Bot.*, **31**: 364–461.

———, 1897: The effect of tropical insolation, *Ann. Bot.*, **11**: 439–480.

———, 1898: The action of cold and of sunlight upon aquatic plants, *Ann. Bot.*, **12**: 363–397.

———, 1898: Can isolated chloroplastids continue to assimilate? *Bot. Cent.*, **75**: 33–36.

———, 1907: On the supposed extracellular photosynthesis of carbon dioxide by chlorophyll, *Proc. Roy. Soc.*, B, **80**: 30–36.

———, 1918: On chlorophyll, carotin, and xanthophyll and on the production of sugar from formaldehyde, *Proc. Roy. Soc. Victoria*, **30**: 178–209.

———, 1919: On the synthesis of sugars from formaldehyde, *Proc. Roy. Soc. Victoria*, **31**: 378–387.

———, 1920: On the synthesis of sugar from formaldehyde and its polymers, its quantitative relations and its exothermic character, *Proc. Roy. Soc. Victoria*, **32**: 168–188.

Eyster, W. H., 1928: Photochlorophyll, *Sci.*, **68**: 569–570.

Fenton, H. J. H., 1907: The reduction of carbon dioxide to formaldehyde in aqueous solution, *J. Chem. Soc. Trans.*, **91**: 687–694.

Fernbach, A., and J. Wolff, 1904: Nouvelles observations sur la formation diastasique de l'amyloicellulose, *C. R. Acad. Sci. Paris*, **138**: 819–821.

———, 1912: Sur une nouvelle forme d'amidon soluble, *C. R. Acad. Sci. Paris*, **155**: 617–618.

Fincke, H., 1913: Über den Nachweis von Formaldehyd in Pflanzen, *Biochem. Z.*, **52**: 214–225.

Fischer, H., 1912: Carbonic-acid gas as a plant nutrient, *Gartenflora*, **61**: 298–307; *Exp. Sta. Rec.*, **28**: 837.

———, 1913: The effect of an increased amount of carbonic acid in the air on green plants, *Jahresber. Angew. Bot.*, **11**: 1–8; *Exp. Sta. Rec.*, **31**: 140.

———, 1919: The carbon nutrition of cultivated plants, *Gartenflora*, **68**: 165–168; *Exp. Sta. Rec.*, **42**: 137.

———, 1920: Plant growth and carbon dioxide, *Naturwiss.*, **8**: 413–417; *Exp. Sta. Rec.*, **45**: 218.

———, 1921: Carbon dioxide manuring, *Angew. Bot.*, **3**: 129–144; *Exp. Sta. Rec.*, **49**: 522.

———, 1927: Die Kohlensäure-Ernährung der Pflanzen, *Ber. bot. Ges.*, **45**: 331–339.

——— and J. Grassl, 1935: Weiterer Beitrag zur Feinstruktur von Chlorophyll *b*, *Liebigs Ann.*, **517**: 1–21.

Fisher, D. V., 1934: Leaf area in relation to fruit size and tree growth, *Sci. Agr.*, **14**: 512–518.

Fleischer, W. E., 1935: The relation between chlorophyll content and rate of photosynthesis, *J. Gen. Physiol.*, **18**: 573–597.

Gail, F. W., 1922: Photosynthesis in some of the red and brown algae as related to depth and light, *Pub. Puget Sound Biol. Sta.*, **3**: 141–176.

Galwialo, M. J., 1925: Zur Frage nach der Photosynthese der Kohlenhydrate, *Biochem. Z.*, **158**: 65–75.

Ganong, W. F., 1906: Normal apparatus, *Bot. Gaz.*, **41**: 209–213.

———, 1908: "Plant Physiology," Henry Holt & Company, pp. 107–109.

Gast, W., 1917: Quantitative Untersuchungen über den Kohlenhydratstoffwechsel im Laubblatt, *Z. physiol. Chem.*, **99**: 1–54.

Gautheret, R. J., 1932: The production of chlorophyll in roots exposed to light, particularly the root of barley, *C. R. Acad. Sci. Paris*, **194**: 1510–1513.

Georgi, C. E., F. S. Orcutt, and P. W. Wilson, 1933: Further studies on the relation between the carbon assimilation and nitrogen fixation in leguminous plants, *Soil Sci.*, **36**: 375–382.

Gerlach, P., 1919: Kohlensäuredüngung, *Mitt. deut. landw. Ges.*, **34**: 77–82.

———, 1921: Carbon dioxide nutrition of plants and stable manure, *Mitt. deut. landw. Ges.*, **36**: 147–150; *Exp. Sta. Rec.*, **46**: 424.

———, 1926: Ueber Kohlensäuredüngung, *Z. Pflanzenernähr. und Düng.*, **5**: 65–69.

Gibson, R. J. H., 1908: A photoelectric theory of photosynthesis, *Ann. Bot.*, **22**: 117–120.

Girard, A., 1883: Recherches sur la saccharogénie dans la betterave, *C. R. Acad. Sci. Paris*, **97**: 1305–1308.

———, 1884: Recherches sur la saccharogénie dans la betterave, *C. R. Acad. Sci. Paris*, **99**: 808–811.

Giroud, A., R. Ratsimamanga, and C. P. Leblond, 1934: Parallelism between the occurrence of vitamin C and chlorophyll, *C. R. Soc. Biol.*, **117**: 612–614; *Chem. Abst.*, **29**: 1131.

———, ———, and ———, 1935: Relation between vitamin C and the carotenoids. Ripening of fruits, *C. R. Soc. Biol.*, **118**: 874–876; *Chem. Abst.*, **29**: 3702.

Godlewski, E., 1873: Abhängigkeit der Sauerstoffausscheidung der Blätter von dem Kohlensäuregehalt der Luft, *Arb. bot. Inst. Würzburg*, **1**: 343–370.

Gordon, R. B., 1929: Suggested equations for the photosynthetic reaction, *Ohio J. Sci.*, **29**: 131–132.

Gradenwitz, A., 1920: Carbonic acid gas to fertilize the air, *Sci. Am.*, **123**: 549.

Grafe, V., and E. Vieser, 1909–1911: Untersuchungen über das Verhalten grüner Pflanzen zum gasförmigen Formaldehyd. I, II, *Ber. bot. Ges.*, **27**: 431–446; **29**: 19–26 (1911).

Griffin, A., 1935: The effect of interrupted translocation upon loss of chlorophyll in leaves during autumn coloration, *Butler Univ. Bot. Studies*, **3**: 129–137.

Gruzit, O. M., and R. P. Hibbard, 1916: The influence of an incomplete culture solution on photosynthesis, *Rept. Mich. Acad. Sci.*, **18**: 50–52.

Gustafson, F. G., and E. Stoldt, 1936: Some relations between leaf area and fruit size in tomatoes, *Plant Physiol.*, **11**: 445–451.

Guthrie, J. D., 1929: Effect of environmental conditions on the chloroplast pigments, *Am. J. Bot.*, **16**: 716–747.

Haas, P., and T. G. Hill, 1913: "The Chemistry of Plant Products," Longmans, Green and Company, 400 pp.

Haberlandt, G., 1882: Vergleichende Anatomie des assimilatorischen Gewebesystems der Pflanzen, *Jahrb. wiss. Bot.*, **13**: 74–188.

Hanes, C. S., 1936: The determination of starch in plant tissue with particular reference to the apple fruit, *Biochem. J.*, **30**: 168–175.

Harder, R., 1921: Kritische Versuche zu Blackmans Theorie der "begrenzenden Factoren" bei der Kohlensäureassimilation, *Jahrb. wiss. Bot.*, **60**: 531–571.

———, 1930: Über die Assimilation der Kohlensäure bei konstanten Aussenbedingungen. I, *Planta*, **11**: 263–293.

Harding, T. S., 1923: History of inulin, its discovery and methods of preparation, *Sugar*, **25**: 636–638; *Exp. Sta. Rec.*, **51**: 409.

Harriman, P. A., 1930: Effect of various methods of storage on the chlorophyll content of leaves, *Plant Physiol.*, **5**: 599–606.

Hartt, C. E., 1934: Water and cane ripening, *Hawaiian Planters' Rec.*, **38**: 193–206.

———, 1935: The fluctuations of sugars in the leaf blades of the cane sugar plant during the day and night, *Hawaiian Planters' Rec.*, **39**: 298–326.

Harvey, E. N., 1928: Photosynthesis in absence of oxygen, *Plant Physiol.*, **3**: 85–89.

Haworth, W. N., and E. L. Hirst, 1936: The chemistry of the carbohydrates and glucosides, *Am. Rev. Biochem.*, **5**: 81–100.

Heilbron, I. M., 1923: The photosynthesis of plant products, *Nature*, **111**: 502–504; *Bot. Abst.*, **12**: 981.

Heinicke, A. J., 1932: Assimilation of carbon dioxide by apple leaves under natural conditions, abst., *Am. J. Bot.*, **19**: 845.

———, 1932: The assimilation of carbon dioxide by apple leaves as affected by ringing the stem, *Proc. Am. Soc. Hort. Sci.*, **29**: 225–229.

——— and M. B. Hoffman, 1932: An apparatus for determining the absorption of carbon dioxide by leaves under natural conditions, *Sci.*, **77**: 55–58.

——— and ———, 1933: The rate of photosynthesis of apple leaves under natural conditions. I, *N. Y. Sta. (Cornell) Bull.* 577.

——— and N. F. Childers, 1935: The influence of water deficiency in photosynthesis and transpiration of apple leaves, *Proc. Am. Soc. Hort. Sci.*, **33**: 155–159.

Henrici, M., 1918: Chlorophyllgehalt und Kohlensäureassimilation bei Alpen- und Ebenenpflanzen, *Verhand. Naturforsch. Ges. Basel*, **30**: 43–136.

———, 1926: The chlorophyll content of grasses in Bechuanaland, *Union So. Africa Dept. Agr. Vet. Ed. and Res.*, **12**: 259–270.

Herlitzka, A., 1912: Über den Zustand des Chlorophylls in der Pflanze und über kolloidales Chlorophyll, *Biochem. Z.*, **38**: 321–330.

Hibbert, H., 1933: The plant synthesis of carbohydrates and polysaccharides, *Can. J. Res.*, **8**: 103–104.

Hicks, P. A., 1934: Interaction of factors in the growth of *Lemna*. V, Some preliminary observations upon the interaction of temperature and light on the growth of *Lemna*, *Ann. Bot.*, **48**: 515–523.

——— and T. E. Panisset, 1934: The quantitative determination of minute amounts of chlorophyll, *New Phytol.*, **33**: 199–210.

Hilpert, S., H. Hofmeier, and A. Wolter, 1931: Über den Zustand des Chlorophylls in der Pflanze, *Ber. chem. Ges.*, **64**: 2570–2577.

Hoffman, M. B., 1932: The effect of certain spray materials on the carbon dioxide assimilation by McIntosh apple leaves, *Proc. Am. Soc. Hort. Sci.*, **29**: 389–393.

———, 1933: Carbon dioxide assimilation by apple leaves as affected by lime sulfur sprays. II, Field experiments, *Proc. Am. Soc. Hort. Sci.*, **30**: 169–175.

Holm, T., 1931: The apparent influence of inulin on the meristem in roots of *Compositae*, *Beih. bot. Cent.*, **47**: 359–377; *Exp. Sta. Rec.*, **66**: 520.

Holman, R., 1930: On solarization of leaves, *Univ. Calif. Pub. (Bot.)*, **16**: 139–151.

Hooker, H. D., 1917: Liebig's law of the minimum in relation to general biological problems, *Sci.*, **46**: 197–204.

Hoover, W. H., E. S. Johnston, and F. S. Brackett, 1933: Carbon dioxide assimilation in a higher plant, *Smithsonian Misc. Coll.*, **87**: No. 16: 1–19.

Horn, T., 1923: Das gegenseitige Mengenverhältnis der Kohlenhydrate im Laubblatt in seiner Abhängigkeit von Wassergehalt, *Bot. Archiv.*, **3**: 137–172; *Bot. Abst.*, **13**: 1019.

Howard, G., 1925: Pigment studies with special reference to carotinoids in fruits, *Ann. Mo. Bot. Gard.*, **12**: 145–212.

Iljin, W. S., 1915: Transpiration and assimilation in steppe plants, *Bull. Acad. Imp. Sci. Petrograd.*, 6 ser., **9**: 346–367; *Exp. Sta. Rec.*, **36**: 734.

———, 1923: Der Einfluss des Wassermangels auf die Kohlenstoffassimilation durch die Pflanzen, *Flora*, **116**: 360–378.

———, 1929: Standortsfeuchtigkeit und der Zuckergehalt in den Pflanzen, *Planta*, **7**: 59–71.

Ingen-Housz, J., 1779: "Experiment upon Vegetables, Discovering Their Great Power of Purifying Common Air in the Sunshine and of Injuring in the Shade and Night," London.

Inman, O. L., and P. Rothemund, 1932: The decomposition of chlorophyll by the animal body, abst., *Am. J. Bot.*, **19**: 839.

———, 1935: Formation of chlorophyll and the beginning of photosynthesis, *Plant Physiol.*, **10**: 401–403.

———, 1935: The evolution of oxygen in the process of photosynthesis, *Symposia Quant. Biol.*, **3**: 184–190.

Ireland, J. C., and P. A. Yeats, 1933: Chlorophyll content of grain sorghums, *Bot. Gaz.*, **95**: 300–315.

Irving, A. A., 1910: The beginning of photosynthesis and the development of chlorophyll. *Ann. Bot.*, **24**: 805–818.

JACOBY, M., 1919, 1922: Über das Formaldehyd als Übergangsstufe zwischen der eigentlichen Assimilation und der Kohlenhydratbildung in der Pflanze. I, II, *Biochem. Z.*, **101**: 1–6; **128**: 119–121.

JAMES, W. O., 1928: Experimental researches on vegetable assimilation and respiration. XIX, The effect of variations of carbon dioxide supply upon the rate of assimilation of submerged water plants, *Proc. Roy. Soc.*, B, **103**: 1–42.

———, 1934: The dynamics of photosynthesis, *New Phytol.*, **33**: 8–40.

———, 1935: The rate of photosynthesis, *Nature*, **136**: 220–221.

JESS, M., 1921: Carbonic acid gas as a fertilizer, *J. Agr. Prat.*, **35**: 250–252; *Exp. Sta. Rec.*, **45**: 344.

JOHNSTON, E. S., 1935: Aerial fertilization of wheat plants with carbon-dioxide gas, *Smithsonian Misc. Coll.*, **94**: No. 15: 1–9.

JORGENSEN, I., and F. KIDD, 1917: Some photochemical experiments with pure chlorophyll and their bearing on theories of carbon assimilation, *Proc. Roy. Soc.*, B, **89**: 342–361.

——— and W. STILES, 1917: Carbon assimilation. A review of recent work on the pigments of the green leaf and the processes connected with them, *New Phytol.*, repr., **10**: 1–180.

KALITIN, N. N., 1931: Determination of reflection and absorption of the solar radiation by the plant leaves, *J. Soc. Bot. Russ.*, **16**: 101–110.

KAUTSKY, H., A. HIRSCH, and F. DAVIDSHÖFER, 1932: Energy transfers at surfaces. VI, Carbon dioxide assimilation. I, *Ber. chem. Ges.*, **65**B: 1762–1770.

KAYSER, R., 1883: Ueber das Vorkommen von Rohrzucker und einigen seiner Unwandlungsproducte im Organismus der Pflanzen, *Landw. Versuchs-Stat.*, **29**: 461–473.

KEUHL, H. J., 1926: The concentration of carbon dioxide in the air above cultivated areas, *Z. Pflanzenernähr. u. Düng.*, **6**: 318–378.

KIMPFLIN, G., 1907: Sur la présence du menthanal dans les végétaux vertes, *C. R. Acad. Sci. Paris*, **144**: 148–150.

KISHI, Y., and S. MONOBE, 1931: On the quantitative changes of the chemical constituents of mulberry leaves during 24 hours, (In Japanese), *Bull. Kjusu. Imp. Univ. Fukuoka*, **4**: 531–599; *Biol. Abst.*, **8**: 335.

KJELDAHL, J., 1879: Recherches sur le ferment production du sucre, *C. R. trav. lab. Carlsberg.*

KLEIN, G., and O. WERNER, 1926: Formaldehyd als Zwischenprodukt bei der Kohlensäureassimilation, *Biochem. Z.*, **168**: 361–386.

KNIEP, H., and F. MINDER, 1909: Ueber den Einfluss verschiedenfarbigen Lichtes auf die Kohlensäureassimilation, *Z. Bot.*, **1**: 619–650.

KNY, L., 1897: Die Abhängigkeit der Chlorophyllfunction von den Chromatophoren und von Cytoplasma, *Ber. bot. Ges.*, **15**: 388–403.

———, 1898: Vermögen isolirter Chlorophyllkörper im Lichte Sauerstoff auszuscheiden? *Bot. Cent.*, **73**: 426–439.

KOHN, H. I., 1935: Inhibition of photosynthesis in *Chlorella pyrenoidosa* by the iodoacetyl radical, *J. Gen. Physiol.*, **19**: 23–34.

KOSTYTSCHEW, S., 1921: Studien über Photosynthese. I, Das Verhältnis CO_2/O_2 bei der Kohlensäureassimilation, *Ber. bot. Ges.*, **39**: 319–328; *Bot. Abst.*, **12**: 744.

———, 1922: Studien über Photosynthese. IV, Die CO_2 Assimilation der Leguminosen, *Ber. bot. Ges.*, **40**: 112–119.

KRAEMER, H., 1902: The structure of the starch grain, *Bot. Gaz.*, **34**: 341–355.

———, 1905: Further observations on the structure of the starch grain, *Bot. Gaz.*, **40**: 305–310.

———, 1923: The starch grains, *Sci.*, **57**: 175.

Kraus, G., 1869: Einige Beobachtungen über den Einfluss des Lichts und der Wärme auf die Stärkeerzeugung im Chlorophyll, *Jahrb. wiss. Bot.*, **7**: 511–531.

Kreusler, U., 1885: Ueber eine Methode zur Beobachtung der Assimilation und Athmung der Pflanzen und über einige diese Vorgänge beeinflussenden Momente, *Landw. Jahrb.*, **14**: 913–965.

———, 1887: Beobachtungen über die Kohlensäure-Aufnahme und -Ausgabe (Assimilation und Athmung) der Pflanzen. II, Mittheilung. Abhängigkeit von Entwicklungszustand—Einfluss der Temperatur, *Landw. Jahrb.*, **16**: 711–755.

———, 1888: Beobachtung über die Kohlensäure-Aufnahme und -Ausgabe (Assimilation und Athmung) der Pflanzen. III, Mittheilung. Einfluss der Temperatur, *Landw. Jahrb.*, **17**: 161–175.

———, 1890: Beobachtungen über Assimilation und Athmung der Kohlensäureausscheidung seitens getödteter Exempläre; Kohlensäureverbrauch, wenn Ober- und Unterseite der Blätter dem Licht zugewendet, *Landw. Jahrb.*, **19**: 649–668.

Kuhn, R., 1935: Plant pigments, *Ann. Rev. Biochem.*, **4**: 479–496.

Kuiper, K. J., 1920: Koolsuurbemesting nachtverlichting en andere groeibevorderende factoren in de plantenteelt. (Effects of CO_2 manuring, night illumination and other growth-stimulating factors upon plant culture), *Cultura*, **32**: 332–344, 355–368; *Bot. Abst.*, **8**: 96.

Kursanov, A. L., 1934: The photosynthesis of green fruits and its dependence on the normal activity of the leaves, *Planta*, **22**: 240–250; *Chem. Abst.*, **28**: 5498–5499.

Kylin, H., 1918: Zur Kenntnis der wasserlöslichen Kohlenhydrate der Laubblätter, *Z. physiol. Chem.*, **150**: 77–88.

Lagatu, H., and L. Maume, 1924: Évolution remarquablement regulière de certains rapports physiologiques (chaux, magnésie, potasse) dans les feuilles de la vigne bien alimentée, *C. R. Acad. Sci. Paris*, **179**: 782–785.

——— and ———, 1924: Étude, par l'analyse périodique des feuilles, de l'influence des engrais de chaux, de magnésie et de potasse sur la vigne, *C. R. Acad. Sci. Paris*, **179**: 932–935.

——— and ———, 1925: Relation linéaire entre les quantités successives d'acide phosphorique et d'azote dans la feuille de la vigne bien alimentée, *C. R. Acad. Sci. Paris*, **180**: 1179–1181.

Langner, W., 1927: Über die Verteilung der Stärke in Laubblättern zu verschiedenen Tageszeiten, *Jahrb. wiss. Bot.*, **67**: 291–333.

Lemmerman, O., 1920: Ueber die Kohlensäureernährung der Pflanzen, *Mitteil. landw. Ges.*, **35**: 696–699; *Bot. Abst.*, **8**: 5.

———, 1926: Untersuchungen über die Bedeutung der Bodenkohlensäure für die Ernährung der Pflanzen und über die Wirkung einiger Humus-bezw. Kohlensäuredünger, *Z. Pflanzenernähr. u. Düng.*, **5**: 70–85.

Li, T., 1929: The immediate effect of change of light on the rate of photosynthesis, *Ann. Bot.*, **43**: 587–601.

Liebig, J., 1843: "Chemistry in Its Application to Agriculture and Physiology," 3d ed., Peterson, Philadelphia.

———, 1843: Die Wechselwirthschaft, *Ann. Chem. Pharm.*, **46**: 58–97.

Lindet, L., and P. Nottin, 1923: Évolution des grains de fécule dans le tubercule de la pomme de terre, *C. R. Acad. Sci. Paris.*, **176**: 149–155.

Ling, A. R., and R. N. Dinshaw, 1923: Studies on starch. I, The nature of polymerized amylose and amylopectin, *J. Chem. Soc.*, **123**: 2666–2688.

Livingston, B. E., 1917: A quarter-century of growth in plant physiology, *Plant World*, **20**: 1–15.

——— and R. Beall, 1934: The soil as direct source of carbon dioxide for ordinary plants, *Plant Physiol.*, **9**: 237–259.

Loeb, W., 1905–1906: Zur Kenntnis der Assimilation der Kohlensäure, *Z. Elektrochem.*, **11**: 745–752; **12**: 282–312.

Long, F. L., 1919: The quantitative determination of photosynthetic activity in plants, *Physiol. Res.*, **2**: 277–300.

Loomis, W. E., and K. H. Burnett, 1931: Photosynthesis in corn, *Proc. Iowa Acad. Sci.*, **38**: 150.

Lubimenko, W., 1905: Sur la sensibilité de l'appareil chlorophyllien des plantes ombrophiles et ombrophobes, *Rev. Gén. Bot.*, **17**: 381–415.

———, 1908: La concentration du pigment vert et l'assimilation chlorophyllienne, *Rev. Gén. Bot.*, **20**: 162–177, 217–238, 253–267, 285–297.

———, 1923: Action spécifique des rayons lumineux de diverses couleurs dans la photosynthése, *C. R. Acad. Sci. Paris*, **177**: 606–608; *Bot. Abst.*, **13**: 568.

———, 1927, 1928: Les pigments de plastes et leur transformation dans les tissus vivants de la plante, *Rev. Gén. Bot.*, **39**: 547–559, 619–637, 698–710 (1927); **40**: 23–29, 88–94, 146–155, 226–243, 303–318, 372–381.

——— and E. P. Gubbenet, 1930: Effect of temperature on rate of accumulation of chlorophyll in etiolated germinated plants, *Bull. Inst. Sci. Lesshaft.* (*Russian*), **16**: 165–188; *Biol. Abst.*, **6**: 1892.

——— and E. R. Hubbenet, 1932: The influence of temperature on the rate of accumulation of chlorophyll in etiolated seedlings, *New Phytol.*, **31**: 26–57.

——— and O. A. Stscheglova, 1932: Effect of protoplasmic irritation on photosynthesis, *Planta*, **18**: 383–404; *Chem. Abst.*, **27**: 4830–4831.

Lundegårdh, H., 1921: Ecological studies in the assimilation of certain forest plants and short plants, *Svensk. Bot. Tidssk.*, **15**: 46–95.

———, 1922: Theoretical and practical basis for carbon dioxid fertilization, *Angew. Bot.*, **4**: 120–151; *Exp. Sta. Rec.*, **49**: 421.

———, 1924: "Der Kreislauf der Kohlensäure in der Natur," Gustav Fischer, Jena, 308 pp., 47 figures.

MacDougal, D. T., 1895: Nature and life history of starch grains, *Bot. Gaz.*, **20**: 458–459.

MacKinney, G., and H. W. Milner, 1933: Carrot leaf carotene, *J. Am. Chem. Soc.*, **55**: 4728–4729.

———, 1935: Development of the chlorophyll and carotenoid pigments in barley seedlings, *Plant Physiol.*, **10**: 365–373.

———, 1935: Properties of carotenes from certain roots and leaves at various stages of development, *J. Biol. Chem.*, **108**: 45–49.

———, 1935: On the plastid pigments of marsh dodder, *J. Biol. Chem.*, **112**: 421–424.

Macy, P., 1936: The quantitative mineral nutrient requirements of plants, *Plant Physiol.*, **11**: 749–764.

Magistad, O. C., 1935: Carotene and xanthophyll in pineapples, *Plant Physiol.*, **10**: 187–191.

Maquenne, L., 1903: Sur la rétrogradation de l'empois d'amidon, *C. R. Acad. Sci. Paris*, **137**: 88–90.

——— and E. Roux, 1905: Sur la constitution la saccharification et la rétrogradation des empois de fécule, *C. R. Acad. Sci. Paris*, **140**: 1303–1308.

———, 1911: À propos d'une communication récente de M. L. Cailletet, *C. R. Acad. Sci. Paris*, **152**: 1818–1819.

——— and E. Demoussy, 1913: Sur la valeur des coefficients chlorophylliens et leurs rapports avec les quotients respiratoires réels, *C. R. Acad. Sci. Paris*, **156**: 506–512.

MARTIN, E. V., 1934: Effect of solar radiation on transpiration of *Helianthus annuus*, *Plant Physiol.*, **10**: 341–354.

MARTIN, W. E., 1936: Distribution of certain sugars in Bosc pears, *Plant Physiol.*, **11**: 139–147.

MARX, D., 1929: The effect of small electric currents on the assimilation of *Elodea canadensis*, *Ann. Bot.*, **43**: 163–172.

MASKELL, E. J., 1927: Field observations on starch production in the leaves of the potato, *Ann. Bot.*, **41**: 327–344.

———, 1928: Experimental researches on vegetable assimilation and respiration. XVII, The diurnal rhythm of assimilation in leaves of cherry laurel as limiting concentrations of carbon dioxide, *Proc. Roy. Soc.*, B, **102**: 467–488.

———, 1928: Experimental researches on vegetable assimilation and respiration. XVIII, The relation between stomatal opening and assimilation—a critical study of assimilation rates and porometer rates in leaves of cherry laurel, *Proc. Roy. Soc.*, B, **102**: 488–533.

MATLACK, M. B., and C. E. SANDO, 1934: A contribution to the chemistry of tomato pigments. The coloring matter in American red and purple tomatoes (*Lycopersicum esculentum*), *J. Biol. Chem.*, **104**: 407–414.

MATTHAEI, G. L. C., 1902: The effect of temperature on carbon dioxide assimilation, *Ann. Bot.*, **16**: 591–593.

———, 1905: Experimental researches on vegetable assimilation and respiration. III, On the effect of temperature on carbon-dioxide assimilation, *Phil. Trans. Roy. Soc.*, **197**: 47–105.

MAYER, H., 1930: Untersuchungen über die Chlorophyllase, *Planta*, **11**: 294–330.

MCCARTY, E. C., 1935: Seasonal march of carbohydrates in *Elymus ambiguus* and *Muhlenbergia gracilis* and their reaction under moderate grazing use, *Plant Physiol.*, **10**: 727–738.

MCKAY, E., 1935: Photosynthesis in *Grimmia montana*, *Plant Physiol.*, **10**: 803–809.

MCLEAN, F. T., 1920: Field studies of the carbon dioxide absorption of coconut leaves, *Ann. Bot.*, **34**: 367–389.

MCNAIR, J. B., 1932: Some properties of plant substances in relation to climate of habitat—volatile oils, saponins, cyanogenetic glucosides, and carbohydrates, *Am. J. Bot.*, **19**: 168–192.

MEIER, F. E., 1932: Lethal action of ultra-violet light on a unicellular green alga, *Smithsonian Misc. Coll.*, **87**: No. 10: 1–11.

———, 1934: Colonial formation of unicellular green algae under various light conditions, *Smithsonian Misc. Coll.*, **92**: No. 5: 1–14.

———, 1934: Effects of intensities and wave lengths of light on unicellular green algae, *Smithsonian Misc. Coll.*, **92**: No. 6: 1–27.

———, 1936: Growth of a green alga in isolated wave-length regions, *Smithsonian Misc. Coll.*, **94**: No. 17: 1–12.

MELLANBY, J., 1919: The composition of starch. I, Precipitation by colloidal iron. II, Precipitation by iodine and electrolytes, *Biochem. J.*, **13**: 28–36.

MEYER, A., 1881: Ueber die Structur der Stärkekörner, *Bot. Ztg.*, **39**: 841–852, 856–864.

———, 1885: Ueber die Assimilationsproducte der Laubblätter angiospermer Pflanzen, *Bot. Ztg.*, **43**: 417–423, 433–440, 449–458, 465–472, 481–491, 497–507.

———, 1886: Bildung der Stärkekörner in den Laubblättern aux Zuckerarten, Mannit und Glycerin, *Bot. Ztg.*, **44**: 81–88, 105–113, 129–137, 145–151.

———, 1886: Ueber Stärkekörner, welche sich mit Jod roth färben, *Ber. bot. Ges.*, **4**: 337–362.

———, 1895: "Untersuchungen über die Stärkekörnerwesen und Lebensgeschichte der Stärkekörner der hoheren Pflanzen," Gustav Fischer, Jena, 318 pp.

Meyer, B. S., and D. S. Rader, 1936: Simple apparatus for the quantitative determination of photosynthetic and respiratory ratios, *Plant Physiol.*, **11**: 437–443.

Mezzadroli, G., 1928: Action of ultra-violet rays on the formation of sugars and aldehydes by breaking down solutions of bicarbonates and CO_2 in the presence of colloidal, reducing catalysts, *Rev. Indus. y. Agr. Tucumán* (*Italian*), 1928; *Biol. Abst.*, **6**: 703.

Miles, F. C., 1915: A genetic and cytological study of certain types of albinism in maize, *J. Genetics*, **4**: 193–214.

Miller, E. C., 1917: Daily variation of water and dry matter in the leaves of corn and the sorghums, *J. Agr. Res.*, **10**: 11–47.

———, 1924: Daily variation of the carbohydrates in the leaves of corn and the sorghums, *J. Agr. Res.*, **27**: 785–808.

———, 1928: Unpub. data, *Kans. Sta.*

Miller, E. S., 1935: Improved methods for the purification of the common carotenoids and the quantitative measurement of their absorption spectra, *Bot. Gaz.*, **96**: 447–467.

——— and G. O. Burr, 1935: Carbon dioxide balance at high light intensities, *Plant Physiol.*, **10**: 93–114.

———, G. Mackinney, and F. P. Zscheile, Jr., 1935: Absorption spectra of alpha and beta carotenes and lycopene, *Plant Physiol.*, **10**: 375–381.

Moillard, M., 1912: L'humus est-il une source directe de carbone pour les plantes vertes supérieures? *C. R. Acad. Sci. Paris*, **154**: 291–294.

Moldavan, A., 1934: Isotopic CO_2 and O_2 in plants, *Sci.*, **79**: 455.

Molisch, H., 1921: Über den Einfluss der Transpiration auf das Verschwinden der Stärke in den Blättern, *Ber. bot. Ges.*, **39**: 339–344.

———, 1925: Carbon dioxide assimilation in dead leaves, *Z. Bot.*, **17**: 577–593; *Exp. Sta. Rec.*, **57**: 118.

Moll, J. W., 1878: Ueber die Herkunft des Kohlenstoffs der Pflanzen, *Arb. bot. Inst. Würzburg*, **2**: 105–113.

———, 1909: Communication on presenting the dissertation of Mr. K. Zijlstra entitled "Kohlensäuretransport in Blättern," *Proc. Akad. Amsterdam*, **2**: 649–668. Quoted by Livingston and Beall, 1934.

Moore, B., and T. A. Webster, 1918: Action of light rays on organic compounds and the photosynthesis of organic from inorganic compounds in presence of inorganic colloids, *Proc. Roy. Soc.*, B, **90**: 168–186.

Müller, A., 1904: Die Assimilationsgrösse bei Zucker und Stärkeblättern, *Jahrb. wiss. Bot.*, **40**: 443–498.

Murneek, A. E., 1934: Relation of carotinoid pigments to sexual reproduction in plants, *Sci.*, **79**: 528.

———, 1936: Determination of the chloroplast pigments of plants, *Sci.*, **83**: 327.

Nägeli, C., 1858: "Die Stärkekörner. Morphologische, physiologische, chemisch-physikalische und systematisch-botanische," Monographie, Zurich, 625 pp.

Nef, J. U., 1913: Dissociationsvorgänge in der Zuckergruppe, *Ann. Chem.*, **403**: 204–383.

Nelson, J. M., and M. Auchincloss, 1933: The effects of glucose and fructose on the sucrose content in potato slices, *J. Am. Chem. Soc.*, **55**: 3769–3772.

Nicholas, E., and G., Nicolas, 1922: Influence du formol sur les végétaux supérieurs, *C. R. Acad. Sci. Paris*, **175**: 1437–1439.

Noack, K., and W. Kiessling, 1929: Formation of chlorophyll and its relation to the blood pigment, *Z. physiol. Chem.*, **182**: 13–49.

———, 1929: Formation of chlorophyll and its relation to the blood pigment, *Naturwiss.*, **17**: 104.

NORRIS, R. J., 1933: Observations on the development of chlorophyll and carotinoid pigments in etiolated plants, *Bull. Basic Sci. Res. Univ. Sci.*, **5**: 23–32; *Biol. Abst.*, **9**: 1481.

NOVELLO, R., 1933: Alcune osservazioni sui cloroplasti delle palme, *Atti R. Accad. Naz. Lincei Rend.*, **18**: 245–248; *Biol. Abst.*, **10**: 33.

OSERKOWSKY, J., 1932: Relation between the green and the yellow pigments in chlorotic leaves, *Plant Physiol.*, **7**: 711–716.

OSTERHOUT, W. J. V., 1915: Artificial photosynthesis by means of chlorophyll, *Sci.*, **42**: 68.

———, 1918: A demonstration of photosynthesis, *Am. J. Bot.*, **5**: 105–111.

———, 1918: A simple method of demonstrating the production of aldehyde by chlorophyll and by aniline dyes in the presence of sunlight, *Am. J. Bot.*, **5**: 511–513.

——— and A. R. C. HAAS, 1918: On the dynamics of photosynthesis, *J. Gen. Physiol.*, **1**: 1–16.

——— and ———, 1918: Dynamical aspects of photosynthesis, *Proc. Nat. Acad. Sci.*, **4**: 85–91.

——— and ———, 1918: A simple method of measuring photosynthesis, *Sci.*, **47**: 420–422.

———, 1919: Apparatus for the study of photosynthesis and respiration, *Bot. Gaz.*, **68**: 60–62.

O'SULLIVAN, C., 1872: On the transformation-products of starch, *J. Chem. Soc.*, **25**: 579–588.

OWEN, O., 1923: Carbon dioxide in relation to glasshouse crops, *Ann. App. Biol.*, **10**: 312–317.

——— and P. H. WILLIAMS, 1923: The preparation of an atmosphere rich in carbon dioxide, *Ann. App. Biol.*, **10**: 318–325.

———, T. SMALL, and P. H. WILLIAMS, 1926: Carbon dioxide in relation to glasshouse crops. III, The effect of enriched atmospheres on tomatoes and cucumbers, *Ann. App. Biol.*, **13**: 560–577.

PALLADIN, V. I., 1922: "Plant Physiology." English translation by B. E. Livingston. P. Blakiston's Son & Company, Philadelphia.

PALLADIN, W., 1891: Ergrünen und Wachsthum der etiolirten Blätter, *Ber. bot. Ges.*, **9**: 229–232.

PALMER, L. S., 1934: The biological and chemical nomenclature for the carotenoids, *Sci.*, **79**: 488–490.

PANTANELLI, E., 1904: Abhängigkeit der Sauerstoffausscheidung belichteter Pflanzen von äusseren Bedingungen, *Jahrb. wiss. Bot.*, **39**: 167–228.

PARKER, M. W., 1935: Physical and chemical properties of the soluble polysaccharides in sweet corn, *Plant Physiol.*, **10**: 713–725.

PARKIN, J., 1912: The carbohydrates of the foliage leaf of the snowdrop (*Galanthus nivalis*) and their bearing on the first sugar of photosynthesis, *Biochem. J.*, **6**: 1–47.

———, 1925: The first sugar of photosynthesis and the role of cane sugar in the plant—a reply to Professor J. H. Priestley, *New Phytol.*, **24**: 57–64.

PEARCE, G. W., and L. R. STREETER, 1931: A report on the effect of light on pigment formation in apples, *J. Biol. Chem.*, **92**: 743–749.

PEIRCE, G. J., 1934: The greatest factory in the world, *Sci. Month.*, **39**: 464–467.

PERREY, A., 1882: Sur l'origin des matières sucrées dans la plante, *C. R. Acad. Sci. Paris*, **94**: 1124–1125.

PETERSON, P. D., 1930: Methods for the quantitative extraction and separation of the plastid pigments of tobacco, *Plant Physiol.*, **5**: 257–261.

PFEFFER, W., 1871: Die Wirkung farbigen Lichtes auf die Zersetzung der Kohlensäure in Pflanzen, *Arb. bot. Inst. Würzburg,* **1**: 1–76.

———, 1900: "The Physiology of Plants." English translation, Vol. I, Clarendon Press.

PICKETT, W. F., 1933: A comparative study of the intercellular spaces of apple leaves, *Proc. Am. Soc. Hort. Sci.,* **30**: 156–161.

———, 1934: Photosynthetic activity and internal structure of apple leaves are correlated, *Proc. Am. Soc. Hort. Sci.,* **32**: 81–85.

———, 1935: A comparison of three methods of measuring photosynthetic activity of apple leaves, *Proc. Am. Soc. Hort. Sci.,* **33**: 152–154.

PLAETZER, H., 1917: Untersuchungen über die Assimilation und Atmung von Wasserpflanzen, *Verhandl. Phys. med. Ges: Würzburg,* **45**: 31–102.

PLESTER, W., 1912: Kohlensäureassimilation und Atmung bei varietäten derselben Art, die sich durch ihre Blattfärbung unterscheiden, *Beitr. Biol. Pflanzen,* **11**: 249–304.

POLLACCI, G., 1917: Carbon assimilation in green plants, *Atti Ist. Bot. Univ. Pavia,* Ser. II, **17**: 29–51.

———, 1920: Sul carbonio delle piante verdi (the carbon of green plants), *Atti Ist. Bot. Univ. Pavia,* Ser. II, **17**: 29–51; *Bot. Abst.,* **13**: 1212.

——— and M. BERGAMASCHI, 1931: Sulla formazione di aldeide formica in piante vive durante la fotosintesi clorofilliana, *Atti Ist. Bot. Univ. Pavia,* **2**: 1–64; *Biol. Abst.,* **8**: 874.

POROWSKI, G. I., 1925: Über die Lichtabsorption von Blättern einiger Bäume, *Biochem. Z.,* **165**: 420–426.

PRESLEY, J. T., 1936: Rubber content of golden-rod leaves affected by light, *Sci.,* **83**: 436.

PRIESTLEY, J., 1774: "Experiments and Observations on Different Kinds of Air," 342 pp.

PRIESTLEY, J. H., 1924: The first sugar of photosynthesis and the role of cane sugar in the plant, *New Phytol.,* **23**: 255–264.

PUHR, L. F., and A. N. HUME, 1932: Variations in amounts of carbohydrates in the leaves of corn, *S. Dak. Sta. Bull.* 270.

PURIEWITSCH, K., 1914: Untersuchungen über Photosynthese, *Jahrb. wiss. Bot.,* **53**: 210–254.

QURESHI, M., and S. S. MOHAMMAD, 1932: Photochemical reduction of carbon dioxide in aqueous solution, *J. Phys. Chem.,* **36**: 2205–2216; *Biol. Abst.,* **8**: 1914.

RABER, O., 1931: A possible relationship between hemoglobin and chlorophyll as shown by the use of liver extract, *Sci.,* **73**: 457–458.

RAJVANSI, A. R., and N. R. DHAR, 1932: Photosynthesis in tropical sunlight. III, Synthesis of formaldehyde, *J. Phys. Chem.,* **36**: 568–574.

REICHERT, E. T., 1913: The differentiation and specificity of starches in relation to genera, species, etc., *Carnegie Inst. Wash. Pub.* 173.

———, 1919: A biochemic basis for the study of problems of taxonomy, heredity, evolution, etc., with special reference to the starches and tissues of parent-stocks and hybrid-stocks and the starches and hemoglobins of varieties, species and genera, *Carnegie Inst. Wash. Pub.* 270.

REID, M. E., 1930: Growth and nitrogen metabolism of squash seedlings. III, With respect to high and low carbohydrate synthesis, *Am. J. Bot.,* **17**: 579–601.

REINAU, E. H., 1927: Forschungsergebnisse zur Kohlensäurefrage, *Angew. Bot.,* **9**: 12–20.

RICHARDS, H. M., and D. T. MACDOUGAL, 1904: The influence of carbon monoxide and other gases upon plants, *Bull. Torrey Bot. Club,* **31**: 57–66.

RIEDEL, F., 1919: Die Ausnützung der Hochofenabgase zur Kohlensäuredüngung, *Stahl u. Eisen*, **39**: 1497–1506.

———, 1921: Importance of carbon dioxide as a fertilizer for vegetables, *Gartenwelt*, **25**: 302–304; **34**: 336–338 (1921); *Exp. Sta. Rec.*, **45**: 834.

RIPPEL, A., 1926: Kohlensäure und Pflanzenerzeugung, *Z. Pflanzennähr. u. Düng.*, **5**: 49–64.

ROBERTS, H. F., 1937: The causes of autumn coloration, *Sci. Mo.*, **45**: 427–435.

ROBERTS, R. H., and N. LIVINGSTON, 1935: Plant pigments and reproduction, *Sci.*, **82**: 596.

RODDIS, L. H., 1936: Chlorophyllometry, *Plant Physiol.*, **11**: 211–212.

ROSECRANS, C. Z., 1934: The determination of CO_2 in the atmosphere of a closed system, *Sci.*, **80**: 483–484.

ROSEN, H. R., and W. M. ROBERDS, 1933: A device for measuring intensity of illumination, *Sci.*, **73**: 241–242.

ROTHEMUND, P., 1935: Protochlorophyll, *Symposia Quant. Biol.*, **3**: 71–79.

RUDOLFS, W., and H. HEUKELEKIAN, 1931: Effect of sunlight and green organisms on reaeration of streams, *Ind. and Eng. Chem.*, **23**: 75–78.

RUSSELL, W. C., M. W. TAYLOR, and D. F. CHICHESTER, 1935: Colorimetric determination of carotene in plant tissue, *Plant Physiol.*, **10**: 325–340.

RUTH, W. A., 1922: The effect of Bordeaux mixture on the chlorophyll content of bean leaves, *Am. J. Bot.*, **9**: 535–551.

SABALITSCHKA, T., and H. RIESENBERG, 1924: Über die Ernährung von Pflanzen mit Aldehyden. II, III, IV, *Biochem. Z.*, **144**: 545–550, 551–555; **145**: 373–378.

——— and H. WEIDLING, 1926: Polymerisation des Formaldehyds durch *Elodea canadensis* zu höheren Kohlenhydraten, *Biochem. Z.*, **172**: 45–57.

SACHS, J., 1862: Über den Einfluss des Lichtes auf die Bildung des Amylums in den Chlorophyllkörnern, *Bot. Ztg.*, **20**: 365–373.

———, 1864: Über die Auflösung und Wiederbildung des Amylums in den Chlorophyllkörnern bei wechselnder Beleuchtung, *Bot. Ztg.*, **22**: 289–294.

———, 1884: Ein Beitrag zur Kenntniss der Ernährungsthätigkeit der Blätter, *Arbeiten bot. Inst. Würzburg*, **3**: 1–33.

SAMEC, M., and H. HAERDTL, 1920: Studien über Pflanzenkolloide. IX, Zur Kenntniss verschiedener Stärkearten, *Beih. Kolloid Chem.*, **12**: 281–300.

SAMPSON, A. W., and R. SAMISCH, 1935: Growth and seasonal changes in composition of oak leaves, *Plant Physiol.*, **10**: 739–751.

SAPOSCHINKOFF, W., 1890: Bildung und Wanderung der Kohlenhydrate in den Laubblättern, *Ber. bot. Ges.*, **8**: 233–242.

———, 1891: Ueber die Grenzen der Anhäufung der Kohlenhydrate in den Blättern der Weinrebe und anderer Pflanzen, *Ber. bot. Ges.*, **9**: 293–300.

———, 1893: Beitrag zur Kenntniss der Grenzen der Anhäufung von Kohlenhydraten in den Blättern, *Ber. bot. Ges.*, **11**: 391–393.

SAUER, M. E., 1936: The chlorolytic action of serum, *Plant Physiol.*, **11**: 159–166.

SAYRE, J. D., 1928: The development of chlorophyll in seedlings in different ranges of wave lengths of light, *Plant Physiol.*, **3**: 71–77.

SAYWELL, L. G., and D. P. ROBERTSON, 1932: Carbohydrate content of tomato fruit, *Plant Physiol.*, **7**: 705–710.

SCHANDERL, H., and W. KAEMPFERT, 1933: Über die Strahlungsdurchlässigkeit von Blättern und Blattgeweben, *Planta*, **18**: 700–750.

SCHERTZ, F. M., 1921: A chemical and physiological study of mottling of leaves, *Bot. Gaz.*, **71**: 81–130.

———, 1925: Some physical and chemical properties of carotin and the preparation of the pure pigment, *J. Agr. Res.*, **30**: 469–475.

———, 1925: Some physical and chemical properties of xanthophyll and the preparation of the pure pigment, *J. Agr. Res.*, **30**: 575–587.

———, 1928: The extraction and separation of chlorophyll (a and b), carotin and xanthophyll in fresh green leaves, preliminary to their quantitative determination, *Plant Physiol.*, **3**: 211–216.

———, 1928: The quantitative determination of chlorophyll, *Plant Physiol.*, **3**: 323–334.

———, 1928: The preparation of chlorophyll, *Plant Physiol.*, **3**: 487–499.

———, 1928: The chloroplast pigments, their functions and the probable relation of chlorophyll to the vitamines, *Quart. Rev. Biol.*, **3**: 459–485.

———, 1929: Seasonal variation of the chloroplast pigments in several plants on the mall at Washington, D. C., *Plant Physiol.*, **4**: 133–139.

———, 1929: The effect of potassium, nitrogen and phosphorus fertilizing upon the chloroplast pigments, upon the mineral content of the leaves and upon production in crop plants, *Plant Physiol.*, **4**: 269–278.

———, 1929: The pure pigments, carotin and xanthophyll and the Tsweet adsorption method, *Plant Physiol.*, **4**: 337–348.

Schimper, A. F. W., 1880: Untersuchungen über die Entstehung der Stärkekörner, *Bot. Ztg.*, **38**: 881–902.

———, 1881: Untersuchungen über das Wachsthum der Stärkekörner, *Bot. Ztg.*, **39**: 185–194, 201–211, 217–227.

———, 1885: Über die Bildung und Wanderung der Kohlenhydrate in den Laubblättern, *Bot. Ztg.*, **43**: 737–743, 753–763, 769–787.

Schomer, H. A., 1934: Photosynthesis of water plants at various depths in the lakes of northeastern Wisconsin, *Ecology*, **15**: 217–218.

Schroeder, H., and T. Horn, 1922: Das gegenseitige Mengenverhältnis der Kohlenhydrate im Laubblatt im seiner Abhängigkeit vom Wassergehalt, *Biochem. Z.*, **130**: 165–198.

——— and F. Herrman, 1931: Über die Kohlenhydrate und den Kohlenhydratstoffwechsel der Laubblätter. I, Die Zunahme des Saccharosegehaltes beim Welken, *Biochem. Z.*, **235**: 407–425.

Schroeder, R. A., 1935: The effect of some summer oil sprays upon the carbon dioxide absorption of apple leaves, *Proc. Am. Soc. Hort. Sci.*, **33**: 170–172.

Schryver, L. B., 1910: The photochemical formation of formaldehyde in green plants, *Proc. Roy. Soc.*, B, **82**: 226–232.

Schryver, S. B., and E. M. Thomas, 1923: The hemicelluloses. II, The hemicellulose content of starches, *Biochem. J.*, **17**: 497–500.

Sen, P. K., and V. H. Blackman, 1933: On conditions leading to the injection of leaves submerged in water, *Ann. Bot.*, **47**: 663–671.

Senebier, J., 1800: "Physiologie végétale," Geneve.

Shcheglova, O. A., and E. V. Chernysheva, 1933: The influence of mechanical reduction of the leaf surface on the development, accumulation of dry matter and yield of spring wheat and barley, *Bull. Plant Protection*, III, ser., **3**: 73–111; *Biol. Abst.*, **9**: 748.

Shelford, V. E., and F. W. Gail, 1922: A study of the light penetration into sea water made with the Kunz photoelectric cell with particular reference to the distribution of plants, *Pub. Puget Sound Biol. Sta.*, **3**: 141–176.

Shirley, H. L., 1931: Light sources and light measurements, *Plant Physiol.*, **6**: 447–466.

Shohl, A. T., 1923: Analysis of the Jerusalem artichoke, *J. Am. Chem. Soc.*, **45**: 2754–2756.

SHULL, C. A., 1929: A spectrophotometric study of reflection of light from leaf surfaces, *Bot. Gaz.*, **87**: 583–607.

———, 1930: The mass factor in the energy relations of leaves, *Plant Physiol.*, **5**: 279–282.

SIEGFRIED, M., 1905: Über die Bindung von Kohlensäure durch amphotere Amidokörper, *Z. physiol. Chem.*, **44**: 85–96.

SINGH, B. N., and K. N. LAL, 1935: Limitations of Blackman's law of limiting factors and Harder's concept of relative minimum as applied to photosynthesis, *Plant Physiol.*, **10**: 245–268.

——— and ———, 1935: Investigations of the effect of age on assimilation of leaves, *Ann. Bot.*, **49**: 291–307.

SJOSTROM, O. A., 1936: Microscopy of starches and their modifications, *Ind. and Eng. Chem.*, **28**: 63–74.

SKINNER, C. E., 1932: The soil as a habitat for growth of green algae, *Soil Sci.*, **34**: 25–29.

SKVORTZOV, S. S., 1931: Influence of desiccating winds on photosynthesis, *Bull. App. Bot., Genetics, and Plant Breeding (Leningrad)*, **25**: 45–66; *Chem. Abst.*, **26**: 5605.

SMALL, T., and H. L. WHITE, 1930: Carbon dioxide in relation to greenhouse crops. IV, The effect on tomatoes of an enriched atmosphere maintained by means of a stove, *Ann. App. Biol.*, **17**: 81–90.

SMITH, A. M., 1919: The temperature coefficient of photosynthesis—a reply to a criticism, *Ann. Bot.*, **33**: 517–536.

SMITH, J., 1932: Carotene. IV, The hydrogenation of carotenes obtained from different sources of dihydrocarotene and of lycopin, *J. Biol. Chem.*, **96**: 35–51.

SMITH, L. E. W., and O. SMITH, 1931: Light and carotinoid content of certain fruits and vegetables, *Plant Physiol.*, **6**: 265–275.

SMITH, S. H. C., 1930: The yellow pigments of green leaves: Their chemical constitution and possible function in photosynthesis, *Contr. Marine Biol., Stanford Univ. Press*, 145–160.

SMYTH, E. M., 1934: The determination of CO_2 content of an atmosphere in a closed system, *Sci.*, **80**: 294.

SOMMER, A. L., E. R. BISHOP, and I. G. OTTO, 1933: Detection and estimation of formaldehyde within the cell of a green plant by the Allison apparatus, *Plant Physiol.*, **8**: 564–567.

SPIRGATIS, P., 1923: The growth factor carbon dioxide, *Bot. Arch.*, **4**: 381–403; *Exp. Sta. Rec.*, **52**: 424.

SPOEHR, H. A., 1913: Photochemische Vorgänge bei der diurnalen Entsäurung der Succulenten, *Biochem. Z.*, **57**: 95–111.

———, 1916: Theories of photosynthesis in the light of some new facts, *Plant World*, **19**: 1–16.

———, 1917: The pentose sugars in plant metabolism, *Plant World*, **20**: 365–379.

———, 1919: The carbohydrate economy of cacti, *Carnegie Inst. Wash. Pub.* 287.

———, 1919: The development of conceptions of photosynthesis since Ingen-Housz, *Sci. Mo.*, **9**: 32–47.

———, 1922: Photosynthesis and the possible use of solar energy, *J. Ind. Eng. Chem.*, **14**: 1142–1145.

———, 1923: The reduction of carbon dioxide by ultraviolet light, *J. Am. Chem. Soc.*, **45**: 1184–1187.

——— and J. M. McGEE, 1923: Studies in plant respiration and photosynthesis, *Carnegie Inst. Wash. Pub.* 325.

——— and J. M. McGee, 1924: Investigations in photosynthesis. An electrometric method of determining CO_2, *Ind. and Eng. Chem.*, **16**: 128–130.

——— and ———, 1924: The effect of fluctuations in the CO_2 content of the atmosphere and the rate of respiration of leaves, *Am. J. Bot.*, **11**: 493–502.

——— and ———, 1924: Absorption of carbon dioxide the first step in photosynthesis, *Sci.*, 59: 513–514.

———, 1926: "Photosynthesis," Chemical Catalog Company, Inc., New York, 393 pp.

——— and H. W. Milner, 1935: Leaf starch: its isolation and some of its properties, *J. Biol. Chem.*, **111**: 679–687.

———, J. H. C. Smith, H. H. Strain, and H. W. Milner, 1935: Photosynthesis—plant pigments, *Carnegie Inst. Year Book*, **34**: 192–198.

Sponsler, O. L., 1922: The structure of the starch grain, *Am. J. Bot.*, **9**: 471–492.

———, 1923: Structural units of starch determined by X-ray crystal structure method, *J. Gen. Physiol.*, **5**: 757–777.

Sprague, H. B., and J. W. Shive, 1929: A study of the relations between chloroplast pigments and dry weights of tops in dent corn, *Plant Physiol.*, **4**: 165–192.

——— and N. Curtis, 1933: Chlorophyll content as an index of the productive capacity of self lines of corn and their hybrids, *J. Am. Soc. Agron.*, **25**: 709–723.

Stanescu, P. P., 1924: Les variations quantitatives de l'amidon dans les feuilles des plantes vertes pendant une journée (24 heures), *C. R. Acad. Sci. Paris*, **178**: 117–119.

———, 1927: Contributions à l'étude de la photosynthèse, *Ann. Scien. de l'Université de Jassy*, **15**: 161–212.

———, 1927: "Les variations quantitatives des products de la photosynthèse dans les feuilles des plantes vertes pendant un jour (24 heures)," thèse, Bucarest.

———, A. Aronescu, and I. G. Mihăilescu, 1929: Sur un mode particulier d'accumulation transitoire de l'amidon dans les feuilles des amylophiles, *Bull. Acad. Sci. Roumaine*, **12**, No. 6: 1–3.

———, 1929: Ueber das Welken und Austrocknen der Pflanzen, *Bull. Acad. Sci. Roumaine*, **12**: 171–175.

———, ———, and ———, 1932: Observations sur l'évolution diurne de l'accumulation transitoire de l'amidon dans les feuilles des plantes vertes, *Bull. Acad. Sci. Roumaine*, **15**: 80–83.

———, 1936: Daily variations in products of photosynthesis, water content, and acidity of leaves toward the end of the vegetative period, *Am. J. Bot.*, **23**: 374–379.

Stiles, W., 1925: "Photosynthesis—The Assimilation of Carbon by Green Plants," Longmans, Green & Company, New York, 268 pp.

Stocklasa, J., and W. Zdobnicky, 1911: Ueber photochemische Synthese der Kohlenhydrate aus CO_2 und H_2 in Anwesenheit von KOH und in Abwesenheit von Chlorophyll, *Monatsh. Chem.*, **32**: 53–75.

——— and ———, 1912: Ueber die photochemische Synthese der Kohlenhydrate unter Einwirkung der Ultravioletten Strahlen, *Biochem. Z.*, **41**: 333–372.

———, 1929: Dynamik und Energetik der Kohlensäure-assimilation. Die Ernährung der Pflanze, *Deutsch. Kalisyndikat, Berlin*, **25**: 97–105. Quoted by Livingston and Beall, 1934.

Stout, A. B., 1936: Autumn coloration, *J. N. Y. Bot. Gard.*, **37**: 7–11.

Strain, H. H., 1934: The separation of carotenes by adsorption on magnesium oxide, *Sci.*, **79**: 325–326.

———, 1934: Carotene. VIII, Separation of carotenes by absorption, *J. Biol. Chem.*, **105**: 523–535.

———, 1936: Leaf xanthophylls, Sci., **83**: 241–242.

Suit, R. F., and H. Hibbert, 1934: A starchless potato induced by the introduction of foreign enzymes, *Sci.*, **79**: 78–79.

Tageeva, S. V., 1931: Study of photosynthesis in connection with photoperiodism, *Bull. App. Bot., Genetics, and Plant Breeding (Leningrad)*, **27**: 197–245; *Chem. Abst.*, **26**: 5605.

Tam, R. K., and O. C. Magistad, 1935: Relationship between nitrogen fertilization and chlorophyll content in pineapple plants, *Plant Physiol.*, **10**: 159–168.

Tammann, G., 1892: Die Reactionen der ungeformten Fermente, *Z. physiol. Chem.*, **16**: 271–328.

———, 1895: Zur Wirkung ungeformter Fermente, *Z. physikal. Chem.*, **18**: 426–442.

Taylor, T. C., and J. M. Nelson, 1920: Fat associated with starch, *J. Am. Chem. Soc.*, **42**: 1726–1738.

Thatcher, R. W., 1921: "The Chemistry of Plant Life," McGraw-Hill Book Company, Inc., New York, 268 pp.

Thoday, D., 1909: Experimental researches on vegetable assimilation and respiration. V, A critical examination of Sachs-method for using increase of dry weight as a measure of carbon dioxide assimilation in leaves, *Proc. Roy. Soc.*, B, **82**: 1–56.

———, 1910: Experimental researches on vegetable assimilation and respiration. VI, Some experiments on assimilation in the open air, *Proc. Roy. Soc.*, B, **82**: 421–450.

Thomas, A. W., 1915: The chemical constitution of starch—a review, *Biochem. Bull.*, **4**: 379–397.

Thomas, W., 1929: Balanced fertilizers and Liebig's law of the minimum, *Sci.*, **70**: 383–384.

Thurber, F. H., 1933: Chemical and physical properties of sweet potato starch, *Ind. and Eng. Chem.*, **25**: 565–568.

Timiriazeff, C., 1890: Enregistrement photographique de la function chlorophyllienne par la plante vivante, *C. R. Acad. Sci. Paris*, **110**: 1346–1347.

———, 1904: The cosmical function of the green plant, *Proc. Roy. Soc.*, **72**: 424–461.

Tottingham, W. E., and J. G. Moore, 1931: Some phases of plant development under vita glass, *J. Agr. Res.*, **43**: 133–163.

Trajkovich, H., 1924: Inheritance of xantha seedlings in maize, *N. Y. Sta. (Cornell) Mem.*, **82**: 1–13.

Transeau, E. N., 1926: The accumulation of energy by plants, *Ohio J. Sci.*, **26**: 1–11.

Trelease, S. F., and H. M. Trelease, 1929: Susceptibility of wheat to mildew as influenced by carbohydrate supply, *Bull. Torrey Bot. Club*, **56**: 65–92.

Tschesnokov, V., and K. Bazyrina, 1930: Die Ableitung der Assimilate aus dem Blatt, *Planta*, **11**: 473–484.

Tschudy, R. H., 1934: Depth studies on photosynthesis of the red algae, *Am. J. Bot.*, **21**: 546–556.

Tsweet, M. S., 1910: "Chromophylls in the Plant and Animal Worlds" (Russian), Warsaw, 379 pp.; *Exp. Sta. Rec.*, **26**: 710.

———, 1911: Eine Hypothese über den Mechanismus der photosynthetischen Energie-übertragung, *Z. physiol. Chem.*, **76**: 413–419.

Ulvin, G. B., 1934: Chlorophyll production under various environmental conditions, *Plant Physiol.*, **9**: 59–81.

Ursprung, A., 1917: Über die Stärkebildung im Spektrum, *Ber. bot. Ges.*, **35**: 44–69.

———, 1918: Über die Absorptionskurve des grünen Farbstoffes lebender Blätter, *Ber. bot. Ges.*, **36**: 73–85.

———, 1918: Ueber die Bedeutung der Wellenlänge für die Stärkebildung, *Ber. bot. Ges.*, **36**: 86–100.

USHER, F. L., and J. H. PRIESTLEY, 1906: The mechanism of carbon assimilation in green plants: the photolytic decomposition of carbon dioxide *in vitro*, *Proc. Roy. Soc.*, B, 78: 318–327.

——— and ———, 1906: A study of the mechanism of carbon assimilation in green plants, *Proc. Roy. Soc.*, B, **77**: 369–376.

——— and ———, 1911: The mechanism of carbon assimilation. III, *Proc. Roy. Soc.*, B, **84**: 101–112.

VAN DER PLANK, J. E., 1936: The estimation of sugars in the leaf of the mangold (*Beta vulgaris*), *Biochem. J.*, **30**: 457–462.

VAN DE SANDE-BAKHUYZEN, H. L., 1926: The structure of starch grains from wheat grown under constant conditions, *Proc. Soc. Exp. Biol. and Med.*, **23**: 302–305.

VAN PAAUW, F., 1932: The indirect action of external factors on photosynthesis, *Rec. trav. bot. Néerl.*, **29**: 497–620.

VER HULST, J. H., W. H. PETERSON, and E. B. FRED, 1923: Distribution of pentosans in the corn plant at different stages of growth, *J. Agr. Res.*, **23**: 655–665.

VILLE, G., 1889: Recherches sur les relations qui existent entre la couleur des plantes et la richesse des terres en agents de fertilité, *C. R. Acad. Sci. Paris*, **109**: 397–400.

VINES, S. H., 1886: "Lectures on the Physiology of Plants," University Press (John Wilson & Son, Inc.), Cambridge, Mass., x + 710 pp.

VIRTANEN, A. I., and M. NORDLUND, 1934: Synthesis of sucrose in plant tissue, *Biochem. J.*, **28**: 1729–1732.

VON EULER, H., and H. HELLSTRÖM, 1929: Über die Bildung von Xanthophyll, Carotin und Chlorophyll in belichteten und unbelichteten Gerstenkeimlingen, *Z. physiol. Chem.*, **183**: 177–183.

———, W. HERTZSCH, A. FORSSBERG, and H. HELLSTRÖM, 1931: Vergleichende Versuche über verschiedene Arten von Chlorophylldefekten, *Z. Indukt. Abstamm. u. Vererb.*, **60**: 1–16; *Biol. Abst.*, **8**: 602.

WAGER, H., 1914: The action of light on chlorophyll, *Proc. Roy. Soc.*, B, **87**: 386–407.

WALLACE, R. H., 1932: The effect of ether and chloroform upon the rate of photosynthesis in detached leaves of *Acer negundo*, abst., *Am. J. Bot.*, **19**: 847.

WALTER, H., 1926: Die Verdunstung von Wasser in bewegter Luft und ihre Abhängigkeit von der Grösse der Oberfläche, *Z. Bot.*, **18**: 1–47.

WALTON, R. P., 1929: Separation and characterization of starch amyloses, diss., *Columbia Univ.*, New York, 12 pp.

WARBURG, O., 1919: Über die Geschwindigkeit der photochemischen Kohlensäurezersetzung in lebenden Zellen. I, *Biochem. Z.*, **100**: 230–270.

——— and E. NEGELEIN, 1923: Über den Einfluss der Wellenlänge auf den Energieumsatz bei der Kohlensäureassimilation, *Z. physiol. Chem.*, **106**: 191–218.

———, 1925: Versuche über die Assimilation der Kohlensäure, *Biochem. Z.*, **166**: 386–406.

WARNER, C. H., 1914: Formaldehyde as an oxidation product of chlorophyll extracts, *Proc. Roy. Soc.*, B, **87**: 378–386.

WATSON, D. J., 1936: The effect of potassium chloride on the diurnal changes of the carbohydrates of the potato leaf, *Ann. Bot.*, **50**: 59–83.

WEATHERWAX, P., 1922: A rare carbohydrate in waxy maize, *Genetics*, **7**: 568–572.

WEBER, C., 1879: Ueber specifische Assimilationsenergie, *Arb. bot. Inst. Würzburg*, **2**: 346–352.

WEEVERS, T., 1923: The first carbohydrates that originate during the assimilatory process—a physiological study with variegated leaves. *Koninklijke Akad. von Wetensch.*, 6, *Amsterdam Proc.*, **27**: 1–11, Eng. summary.

WEIER, T. E., 1933: Plastid structure and its possible effect on photosynthesis, abst., *Am. J. Bot.*, **20**: 677.

WHITE, H. L., 1930: Carbon dioxide in relation to glasshouse crops. V, An analysis of the response of the tomato crop to an atmosphere enriched with carbon dioxide, *Ann. App. Biol.*, **17**: 755–766.

WHITESIDE, A. G. O., J. EDGAR, and C. H. GOULDEN, 1934: The influence of environment on the carotenoid content of hard red spring wheat, *Cereal Chem.*, **11**: 615–625.

WIDDOWSON, E. M., and R. A. MCCANCE, 1935: The available carbohydrate of fruits, *Biochem. J.*, **29**: 151–156.

WIESNER, J., 1874: Untersuchungen über die Beziehungen des Lichtes zum Chlorophyll, *Sitzungsber. Akad. Wiss. Wien*, **69**: 327–385.

———, 1877: "Die Entstehung des Chlorophylls in der Pflanze," Wien.

WILLAMAN, J. J., 1922: The preparation of inulin, with special reference to artichoke tubers as a source, *J. Biol. Chem.*, **51**: 275–285.

WILLSTÄTTER, R., and A. STOLL, 1918: "Untersuchungen über die Assimilation der Kohlensäure," Julius Springer, Berlin.

——— and ———, 1928: "Investigations on Chlorophyll. Methods and Results," English translation by F. M. Schertz and A. R. Merz. Science Press, Lancaster, Pa., 380 pp.

WILMOT, A. J., 1921: Experimental researches on vegetable assimilation and respiration. XIV, Assimilation by submerged plants in dilute solutions of bicarbonates and of acids: an improved bubble-counting technique, *Proc. Roy. Soc.*, B, **92**: 304–327.

WILSON, P. W., E. B. FRED, and M. R. SALMON, 1933: Relation between carbon dioxide and elemental nitrogen assimilation in leguminous plants, *Soil Sci.*, **35**: 145–166.

WINKLER, H., 1898: Über die Stärkebildung in den verschiedenartigen Chromatophoren, *Jahrb. wiss. Bot.*, **32**: 525.

WITHROW, R., 1936: Private communication.

WOODRUFF, S., and L. R. WEBBER, 1933: A photomicrographic study of gelatinized wheat starch, *J. Agr. Res.*, **46**: 1099–1108.

WURMSER, R., 1925: Sur l'activité des diverses radiations dans la photosynthèses, *C. R. Acad. Sci. Paris*, **181**: 374–376.

YANOVSKY, E., and R. M. KINGSBURY, 1931: New sources of inulin, *J. Am. Chem. Soc.*, **53**: 1597–1601.

YAP, G. G., 1920: A study of the photosynthesis of sugar cane, *Philippine J. Agr.*, **8**: 269–276.

YUNCKER, T. G., 1916: A study of the relation of soil moisture to transpiration and photosynthesis in the corn plant, *Plant World*, **19**: 151–161.

ZECHMEISTER, L., 1934: "Carotenoide," 8 vol., Julius Springer XII + 338 pp., 85 Figs., Berlin; Review, *Bot. Gaz.*, **96**: 378–380.

ZIJLSTRA, K., 1909: Kohlensäuretransport in Blättern, *Rec. trav. bot. Néerl.*, **6**: 99–210. Quoted by Livingston and Beall, 1934.

ZIRKLE, C., 1926: The structure of the chloroplast in certain higher plants. I, II, *Am. J. Bot.*, **13**: 301–341.

ZSCHEILE, F. P., 1932: Attempted photosynthesis of carbohydrates *in vitro* with visible light, *J. Am. Chem. Soc.*, **54**: 973–976.

———, 1934: An improved method for the purification of chlorophylls a and b; Quantitative measurement of their absorption spectra. Evidence for the existence of a third component of chlorophyll, *Bot. Gaz.*, **95**: 529–562.

CHAPTER IX

THE NITROGEN METABOLISM OF THE GREEN PLANT

I. GENERAL RELATION OF NITROGEN TO THE PLANT

Nitrogen enters into the structure of chlorophyll, the amino acids, amides, alkaloids, protein, and the protoplasm of the plant. It occurs for the most part in organic combination, and, as will be noted in a subsequent heading, ammonia, nitrates, and nitrites are found, as a rule, only in traces if at all. The percentage of nitrogen in the various plant parts will vary with the age, type of tissue, and the kind of plant as well as with the period of the day when the examination is made. In the corn plant at the period of the late milk stage when the grain was glazed and dented (Latshaw and Miller, 1924), the leaves contained 25 per cent of the total nitrogen in the plant, the stem 14 per cent, the grain 46 per cent, the cobs 9 per cent, and the roots 6 per cent. The nitrogen content of the dry weight of the leaves varied from 1.2 to 1.4 per cent, that of the stem from 0.5 to 1.0 per cent, and that of the grain from 2 to 2.2 per cent. Miller (1929) observed the nitrogen content of various leaves when the plants were in a vigorous vegetative condition previous to blooming. The average nitrogen content for different periods of the day was for soybeans 5.8 per cent, for cowpeas 5.6 per cent, for garden beans 4.5 per cent, for pumpkin 4.5 per cent, for feterita 3.6 to 4.1 per cent, for kafir 3.6 to 4.2 per cent, and for corn 3.2 to 3.8 per cent of the dry weight of these leaves.

Armstrong and Albert (1931) found in cotton that shortly before bud formation 80 to 90 per cent of the nitrogen in the plant was in the leaves, while at the end of fruit setting 40 to 60 per cent of the total nitrogen of the plant was in the bolls. In some seasons, from 40 to 50 per cent of the nitrogen of the crop was absorbed in about 2 weeks. Cameron and Appleman (1933) noted that the average crop of oranges removes about 35 lb. of nitrogen per acre. At no time do the roots of the orange tree contain more than 21 per cent of the total nitrogen of the tree. Excluding the leaves, the aerial portions of the plant contain more nitrogen than the roots. In Connecticut, it was observed by Morgan and Street (1935) that the leaves of tobacco attained a maximum nitrogen content approximately 40 days after setting, and these leaves lost nitrogen after the plants were topped. By the time of cutting, the tobacco plants had extracted 114 lb. of nitrogen per acre from the soil. Of this amount 39.3 per cent was in the crop leaves, 21 per cent in the sucker leaves, 26 per cent in the stalks, and 13.2 per cent in the roots.

A large amount of nitrogen in the soil produces a rank growth of foliage, giving an inordinate growth of stem and leaves. Thus Gračinin (1932) found an inverse relation between the growth in length of the roots of corn, barley, wheat and rye and the amount of nitrogen in the nutrient medium, and the curve of growth for the aerial organs rose with this increase in nitrogen. The roots were more sensitive to a change in the supply of nitrogen than the tops. According to Verner (1933), an increased leaf area is the most striking result obtained by fertilizing apple trees with nitrates. Crowther (1935) stated that one of the main functions of nitrogen is the initiation of meristematic activity. He noted in cotton that the total growth of the plant depends primarily on the rate of development of the leaf surface. Variations in the growth rate of leaves are determined for the most part by variations in the supply of available nitrogen. The size of the plant is thus largely a measure of the rate of nitrogen metabolism. The rate of uptake of nitrogen is determined primarily by the concentration of nitrogen in the soil solution, while the speed of development of the plant is proportional to the inflow of nitrogen. In the tomato, Fisher (1935) observed that an excess of nitrogen stimulated vegetative growth at the expense of flowers and fruit development. It was found by Das (1936) in Hawaii that increasing the application of nitrogen to sugar cane increased the leaf area, rate of leaf and joint formation, rate of stem elongation, lodging, and tillering, and decreased the concentration of sucrose in the expressed sap.

If plants can be grown to maturity, the excess foliage resulting from an abundant supply of nitrogen has no apparent effect on the yield. Frequently, however, under such conditions ripening occurs prematurely, due to various causes, so that considerable amounts of food materials are not transferred from the vegetative parts to the seed or grain, and as a result the grain is shriveled.

It was observed by Thatcher (1921) for cabbage and lettuce, by Pearsall and Ewing (1929) for radish, turnip, and dandelion, by Gourley (1930) for the fruit of the apple, by Armstrong and Albert (1931) in the leaves, stalk, and fruit of cotton, and by Garner and others (1934) for tobacco leaves that an abundant supply of nitrogen increases the water content of the tissues of these various plants. Pearsall and Ewing (1929) considered that this increased succulence results from a lower rate of transpiration of the plants with an abundant supply of nitrogen as compared to those with a limited supply. This reduction in transpiration may be due to an accumulation of amino acids, which in some manner lower the hydrogen-ion concentration and thus allow a greater swelling of the protoplasmic colloids that would retard the loss of water by transpiration.

The amount of nitrogen in the plant is determined in general by the concentration of this element in the soil. Thus Gainey and Sewell (1932) in a study of the so-called "nitrogen spots," commonly observed in the wheat fields of Kansas and other midwestern States, reported that these spots are characterized by a higher nitrogen content than that of the adjoining soil. The plants growing in these spots have a higher nitrogen content than those growing in the surrounding soil. Richardson and Gurney (1933, 1935) found in Australia that nitrate accumulated in fallow soil, and this was a major factor in accounting for the heavy increase in crop yield from fallow as compared to stubble land. Nicol (1934) stated that in agricultural soils the nitrogen as nitrates may amount to as much as 300 p.p.m. of moist soil.

Hamner (1936) reported that there is a marked increase in the respiration rate upon the application of nitrate to the plant provided there is an initial reserve of carbohydrate.

In the absence of a sufficient supply of available nitrogen, the leaves are stunted, and a yellowing occurs. Thus Fisher (1935) noted that tomato plants grown in a cultural solution deficient in nitrogen showed a yellowing of the entire plant in 6 to 8 days. The lower leaves dried slowly and were dropped. A decreased amount of protoplasm was formed, and there was a general reduction in the growth of leaves and stem. According to Valleau and Johnson (1927), and Haas (1929) the frenching of the leaves of tobacco and other plants occurs when there is a deficiency of nitrates but disappears upon the application of sufficient available nitrogen to the soil. Under greenhouse conditions, Shear (1933) could control this disease by the application of nitrogenous fertilizers, but that method failed in the field.

Jones (1936) applied an acidulated (H_2SO_4) solution of diphenylamine to plant tissues to determine the need for nitrogen. When deposited on a section of tissue, a drop of this solution imparts a blue to blue-black coloration, depending upon whether there is a trace or a relatively large amount of nitrate present. A lack of blue color indicates an absence of nitrates, signifying a deficiency of nitrogen in the plant and its root environment. These tests should be made upon older tissues, because the younger portions may show a low amount of nitrates due to their usage in the synthesis of organic nitrogenous compounds.

II. SOURCES OF NITROGEN SUPPLY OF PLANT

The possible sources of the nitrogen supply of the plant are the various nitrogenous compounds in the soil and the combined and elemental nitrogen of the atmosphere. The absorption of the nitrogenous compounds of the soil will first be considered.

A. Absorption from the Soil

The combined nitrogen in the soil exists in the form of inorganic and organic compounds. The former are principally the nitrates, nitrites, and ammonium salts, while the latter include a long list of the decomposition products of the proteins, protoplasm, and other complex nitrogenous substances of plants and animals. A partial list of the various organic nitrogenous compounds that have been found in the soil is given in Chap. III.

1. Inorganic Nitrogen.—Early in the history of plant nutrition it became generally accepted that plants, in general, absorb the combined inorganic nitrogen preferably in the form of nitrates. In some cases, however, plants apparently did equally well when nitrogen was applied to the soil in the form of ammonium salts or as nitrates. Since these experiments were not made under sterile conditions, it is not definitely known whether these salts were absorbed as such or not. Since 1889, however, a considerable amount of work has been done, apparently under sterile conditions, to determine the relative value of nitrates, nitrites and ammonium salts in plant nutrition.

a. Nitrates and Ammonium Salts.—The investigations from 1889 until about 1930 established the fact that some plants grow equally well with either nitrates or ammonium salts as a source of nitrogen, and that others, although assimilating ammonium salts in the absence of nitrates, seem to grow better when nitrates are applied. From 1930 until the present time, the factors that influence the relative value of nitrates and ammonium salts in the nutrition of plants have been studied.

1. *Relative Value.*—Müntz (1889), Pitsch (1887 to 1896), Griffiths (1891), and Gerlach and Vogel (1905) worked with soils under apparently sterile conditions and showed that beans, barley, hemp, and corn were able to grow in the absence of nitrates, but they did not prove conclusively that ammonium salts were the sole source of the nitrogen obtained by the plants. According to Treboux (1904), *Lemna minor*, mosses, diatoms, and certain green algae used by him utilized effectively ammonium

nitrogen. Krüger (1905) concluded that ammonium salts and nitrates are equally suitable for mustard, oats, and barley, and that, if anything, ammonium salts are better than nitrates for potatoes, while for beets nitrates are superior to ammonium salts. It has been shown by Mazé (1898, 1900) and Prianischnikow (1908, 1923) that corn can utilize ammonium salts as readily as nitrates, while Brigham (1917) concluded that ammonium sulphate is a much better source of nitrogen than sodium nitrate. In the case of sugar cane, McGeorge (1923) concluded that this plant will not grow without some nitrate nitrogen. The cane in an ammoniacal nutrient solution sent out strong, vigorous shoots, but practically no root development took place, while an excellent growth of both roots and tops occurred in a solution containing nitrates. Stewart (1925) and others found that the pineapple plant is capable of assimilating all its nitrogen in the form of ammonium salts, although the best growth of plants was made by those growing in solutions in which the nitrogen was present in the form of nitrates. The indications were that both nitrates and ammoniacal nitrogen can be utilized by these plants. The relative value of ammonium salts and nitrates in the nutrition of wheat and peas was observed by Hutchinson and Miller (1909), who grew these plants in sand and water cultures and found that ammonium sulphate was assimilated by them directly and that in the case of peas there was no difference between the plants supplied with ammonium and those that had sodium nitrate. Wheat plants showed a decided preference for nitrogen in the form of nitrates.

The nitrogen nutrition of rice has been studied by numerous investigators, and they all report that, under some conditions at least, the ammonium salts are superior to the nitrates in the growth of this plant. Kellner (1884) noted that swamp rice, in pots, during its early development grew better with ammonium salts than with nitrates but that during later growth nitrates proved the more effective. He also showed that the formation of nitrates in paddy soils took place slowly, while ammonia was formed in large quantities. Kelley (1911) applied ammonium sulphate to some rice plants and sodium nitrate to others. The application of the former was followed by an increase in the yield of straw and grain, but sodium nitrate was ineffective. In sand cultures unhealthy and stunted plants resulted if nitrates were used as the only source of combined nitrogen, while the use of ammonium salts resulted in vigorous apparently normal plants. The same beneficial returns from ammonium salts in contrast to nitrates have also been obtained by Nagaoka (1904), Daikuhara (1905), Espino (1920), and Trelease and Paulino (1920).

Zahnley and Duley (1934) found that ammonium sulphate, sodium nitrate, and urea were equally effective for growth when applied to Kentucky bluegrass, Washington bent grass, and other grasses.

The relative value of nitrates and ammonium salts in the nutrition of plants depends upon numerous factors. Among these are: reaction of the medium in which the roots are growing; age of the plants; kind of plant; concentration of the medium; light; and the presence of other ions (Beaumont and Moore, 1933). The two most important factors are the following:

(a) *Reaction of the Medium.*—The pH value of the medium in which the roots are growing has a marked influence upon the rate of absorption and utilization of nitrates and ammonium salts. Pirschle (1929) was one of the first to show that in a pronounced acid medium, plants cannot obtain sufficient nitrogen from ammonium salts. Later (1931) he noted that plants tolerate a much wider pH range for the utilization of nitrates than for ammonium salts, and that with neither compound is there a single pH value at which all plants make their optimum growth. Tiedjens and Robbins (1931) found that tomato plants grew well when nitrogen was supplied as ammonium sulphate in a medium with a pH of 8.0, and that the best growth with calcium nitrate occurred at a pH 5.0 to 6.0, while with ammonium nitrate the best growth was obtained at a pH of 4.0 to 5.0. They observed that, although seedling trees of peach and apple could absorb and assimilate ammonium salts over a wide pH range, they did not assimilate a sufficient amount of nitrogen for maximum growth unless the culture solution had a pH value of 7.0 to 8.0. Naftel (1931) noticed that the absorption of NH_4 by the cotton plant increased as the acidity of the culture solution decreased, while the absorption of NO_3 was only slightly affected by the reaction of the medium. The highest absorption of total nitrogen usually occurred at pH 6.0 and was greatest when both forms of nitrogen were present. Arrington and Shive (1935) found with tomato plants that the rate of absorption of cation nitrogen from a medium with a pH of 7.0 was more than three times as high as the rate at pH 4.0. For anion nitrogen, the rate of absorption was somewhat greater at pH 4.0 than at pH 7.0.

The observation that plants absorb nitrogen in the form of ammonium salts more rapidly from the nutrient medium at a relatively high pH, while the nitrogen in the form of nitrates is absorbed more rapidly at a lower pH value has been reported also by Addoms and Mounce (1932) for young cranberry plants, by Tiedjens and Blake (1932) for apple trees, by Clark (1933) for strawberry plants, by Davidson and Shive (1934) for peach trees, and by Tiedjens (1934) for tomato, cotton, and the seedling plants of several varieties of apple.

Clark and Shive (1934) grew tomato plants in solutions containing approximately equal portions of nitrogen in the NH_4 and NO_3 forms. Their observations relative to the influence of the reaction of the medium on the rate of absorption agree with those of other investigators. They observed further, however, in 41-day-old plants that the maximum rate of absorption of nitrogen as NH_4 was higher than that of nitrogen as NO_3. The rate of absorption of NO_3 by the older plants was not so greatly influenced by the pH value of the solution as it was in the younger plants.

Conrad (1934) considered that a plant absorbs the NO_3 ion more rapidly from a more acid medium because it can secure more easily therefrom the requisite hydrogen-ions to accompany the NO_3 ions into the plant. The same reasoning is applied for the absorption of the NH_4 ions from the more alkaline solutions. When both ions are present in approximately equal concentrations in neutral solutions, more NH_4 ions will be absorbed because less energy is required to incorporate the nitrogen of the NH_4 ions into protein than in the case of the NO_3 ions.

(*b*) *The Age and Kind of Plant.*—It was reported by Pardo (1930) that young rice plants cannot use nitrates but thrive on ammonium sulphate, while the older plants do well on either form. Young sugar cane uses nitrates to better advantage than it does ammonium salts. Holley and others (1931) noted that young cotton plants grew more rapidly during the first 2 or 3 weeks in a nitrate solution than in one containing ammonium salts. Although the production of dry matter was always favored more when the plants were in nitrate solutions, it was favored least at the age of 5 to 6 weeks. Pirschle and Mengdehl (1931) observed that young plants used equal amounts of nitrogen, as the anion and cation of ammonium nitrate, but that older plants absorbed the NH_4 ion to a greater extent than the NO_3 ion. According to Thelin and Beaumont (1934) young plants of rice and wheat accumulated nitrogen better from ammonium sulphate than from nitrates. In a perennial rye grass, Lewis (1936) noted that except at an early stage the percentage of nitrogen in the herbage was higher when nitrates were applied to the soil than when ammonium nitrogen was applied.

Stahl and Shive (1933), and Sessions and Shive (1933) found with oats that the absorption of nitrogen as NH_4 is highest during the earliest periods, then gradually declines, and reaches its minimum about maturity. The absorption of nitrogen as NO_3 is at a minimum at the earlier period, rapidly increases to reach a maximum at or about blooming, and then declines toward maturity. The total nitrogen in the plants varied with the total nitrogen of the solution in which they were growing although not in a direct proportion. In buckwheat the absorption of nitrogen as NH_4 is at the maximum at the beginning of the blooming period, declines rapidly after blooming, and is low during the later stage of growth. The quantity of nitrogen absorbed as NO_3 is very low at the beginning of the blooming period, increases rapidly during blooming and then declines rapidly. The maximum absorption of nitrogen occurs at the time of maximum absorption of nitrogen as NH_4, which is at the beginning of the flowering period. The maximum rate of absorption of NH_4 is approximately six times the maximum for NO_3. During the greater part of the life of buckwheat the absorption of NH_4 is the predominating factor in determining the rate of nitrogen assimilation.

Dastur and Malkani (1933) found that rice seedlings in contact with different concentrations of ammonium salts for varying periods of time gave the following order for the quantity of ammonium ions absorbed: $SO_4 < PO_4 < NO_3 < Cl$ for early stages, and $SO_4 < NO_3 < PO_4 < Cl$ for the later stage. The order of the quantity of NO_3 ion absorbed was: $NH_4 < Mg < Ca < K < Na$ for the early stage, and $NH_4 < K < Mg < Ca < Na$ for the later stage. The absorption of NH_4 was greater in the early stage of growth, but in later growth the absorption of NO_3 predominated.

2. *Availability.*—It was observed by Prianischnikow (1908, 1923) and Shulov (1912) that plants which take up nitrogen exclusively as ammonium salts generally contain very distinctly higher percentages of nitrogen than other plants supplied with nitrates. These observations have been substantiated by Pardo (1930, 1933) for sugar cane, by Loo (1931) for corn, and by Tiedjens and Robbins (1931) for tomato.

Kinoshita (1897) with seedlings of various kinds, and Pantanelli and Severini (1910, 1911) for wheat, rice, flax, and corn found that the nitrogen in ammonium compounds is in a form that can be utilized more readily by the plant in the formation of organic nitrogenous compounds than the nitrogen of the nitrates. Klein (1930) for numerous plants; Addoms and Mounce (1931) for cranberries; Tiedjens and Robbins (1931) for tomato, peach, and apple seedlings; Tiedjens and Blake (1932) for apple trees; and Tiedjens (1934) for cotton, tomato, and seedling apple trees reported that in all cases the nitrogen in the form of ammonium salts was utilized directly by these plants in the synthesis of nitrogenous compounds. Lewis (1936) for perennial rye grass, and Clark (1936) for tomato observed that more nitrogen accumulated in the tissues when nitrates were used than when ammonium salts were applied. They considered that this indicated that the nitrogen in the form of ammonium salts was quickly utilized and thus did not accumulate. It has been noticed by several investigators that many plants require a much lower concentration of ammonium than nitrate nitrogen in the nutrient solution to produce an equal volume of growth. This also is believed to indicate that the nitrogen in the form of ammonium is much more readily utilized than when it is in the form of nitrates. Nightingale (1934, 1936) and others have observed that the intake of nitrogen in the form of NH_4 is followed by a more rapid synthesis of amides, amino acids, and other soluble organic compounds than when nitrates are supplied to the plants.

Under certain conditions, however, some of the above-mentioned plants may grow better and produce more dry matter with nitrates than with ammonium. This was observed by Beaumont and others (1931) for tobacco; by Holley, Pickett, and Dulin (1931) for cotton; by Pardo (1933) for sugar cane; and by Arrington and Shive (1935) and Clark (1936) for the tomato plant. Beaumont, Eisenmenger, and Moore (1933) grew plants of timothy, bluegrass, and other grasses, and alsike, red, and white clovers in nutrient solutions containing sodium nitrate, ammonium sulphate, and urea. As judged by the appearance of plants, by the weight of dry matter produced, and by the chemical composition, the order of assimilation of nitrogen by the grasses was sodium nitrate, urea, and ammonium sulphate; by the clovers: urea, sodium nitrate, and ammonium sulphate.

3. *General Effects*.—Frear (1931) observed a negative correlation between the nitrate nitrogen in the sap of the leaves of the beet and the weight of the leaves. It was found by Hopkins, Wilson, and Peterson (1932) that the addition of nitrogen in the form of nitrates to clover plants growing in agar, generally resulted in a decrease in the number of nodules when the concentration was 2 to 3 parts per 100,000. The amount of nitrogen fixed by the nodules was also reduced, and if the concentration of nitrate was sufficiently increased, fixation ceased. Harrison (1934) noted in bluegrass supplied with calcium nitrate that the leaf blades were shorter and more upright and that the rhizomes were more numerous, stockier, and more branched than when supplied with ammonium sulphate. Lewis (1936) found that the per-

centage of phosphorus pentoxide in perennial rye grass was higher when the nitrogen was applied in the form of ammonium than when it was applied as nitrates.

4. *Toxicity.*—Numerous explanations have been proposed to explain the fact that many plants respond better to nitrates than to ammonium salts. By some it is considered that the basic ions combined with the nitrates may exert a stimulating effect while the acid ion of the ammonium salt may be injurious to certain plants. It is also considered that nitrates may be more available than the ammonium salts, since the former are very soluble and not fixed, while the latter salts are fixed and held more firmly and do not circulate so freely in the soil. On that account the ammonium salts do not come in contact with the root hair to the same extent that the nitrates do and hence are not so readily absorbed by the plant. It has been suggested by Willis and Carrero (1923) that the observation that nitrates are less suitable than ammonium salts for the fertilization of young rice plants may be based on the influence on the plants of the residues of the fertilizer used rather than on the inferiority of nitric nitrogen as a nutrient. They consider that under the conditions under which they worked in Puerto Rico the injury noted, which has generally been ascribed to the toxic effects of the nitrites derived from nitrates by reduction, was a manifestation of chlorosis caused by the action of the basic residues of the nitrate salts used as nutrients. Furthermore, the nitrogen of calcium nitrate may be equally suitable with that of ammonium sulphate in the physiological processes of the rice plant when it is used under cultural conditions in which the reaction of the unassimilated residue of the nitrate does not interfere with the absorption and utilization of iron.

It was stated by Willis and Rankin (1932) that ammonium hydroxide as a fertilizer is toxic to plants except under well-prescribed conditions, and Tidmore (1933) reported that the concentration of acid phosphate as a buffer must be very high in order to prevent injury by ammonium hydroxide. However, if the ammonium was supplied in small amounts under such conditions, excellent response in plant growth was obtained. Beaumont and Moore (1933), and Blackman (1934) believed that the toxicity from NH_4 salts of strong acids is due primarily to the accumulation of the ammonium ions and to increased acidity. Thelin and Beaumont (1934) found that the toxicity of ammonium sulphate was more pronounced with wheat than with rice, and that toxicity increased with the age of the plants.

b. Nitrites.—It was observed by Schultz (1903) that, in dilute solutions, nitrites seemed to be more reasily absorbed by plants than the nitrates. In some cases (Stutzer, 1906) a dilute solution of nitrites seems to be beneficial to some plants and injurious to others. Fairly concentrated solutions of nitrites are always more toxic to plants than the same concentration of nitrates. It was observed by Perciabosco and Rosso (1909) that plants which are supplied with nitrites contain distinctly higher percentages of nitrogen than when given nitrates. According to Nightingale (1936), nitrites generally do not accumulate in plants, and thus can be detected in appreciable amounts only after the application of nitrates to plants deficient in nitrogen.

Mevius and Dikussar (1930) and Dikussar (1935) reported that sweet corn can utilize nitrogen of nitrites in either neutral or alkaline solutions. The optimum concentration is approximately 50 mg. of nitrite nitrogen per liter, but at a pH of 7.0 as much as 200 mg. per liter is not injurious.

With nitrates, an increase of two- to three-fold in the exterior medium causes only a slight increase in the amount of nitrogen in a plant. An increase in the amount of nitrite in a medium, however, is followed by a rapid increase in assimilation and in the total amount of nitrogen in the plant.

Eggleton (1935) reported that nitrites occur naturally in the spring growth of grass, and that the amount is increased when the grass is fertilized with ammonium sulphate or sodium nitrate. He suggested that nitrites play a significant part in the grass "tetany" of cattle, which is usually associated with herbage of high inorganic content. Both nitrites and amino compounds increase upon the application of ammonium salts. It appears that the leaves can transform ammonium salts to nitrites.

2. Organic Nitrogen.—The effect of organic nitrogen on the growth of plants has been studied in two general ways. The first is concerned with the direct assimilation of organic nitrogen by the plant, and the second has to do with the stimulating effects of minute quantities of organic nitrogenous matter upon the rate of growth.

a. Assimilation.—Previous to 1911 considerable experimental work had been done with the nutrition of plants with organic nitrogenous compounds, but the value of much of the data presented is uncertain, since in many cases the plants were not grown under conditions that would prevent bacterial action. More or less satisfactory evidence of the assimilation of organic nitrogenous compounds by green plants had been obtained for the following compounds: methyl, amyl and allyl amines, acetamide, leucine, urea, aspartic acid, asparagine, glutamine, uric acid, hippuric acid, and tyrosine. The gains of nitrogen, however, were very small, and in many cases negative results were obtained by other investigators. The reader is referred to Hutchinson and Miller (1911) for a thorough and detailed review of the literature on the subject previous to this date. They grew wheat and peas in cultural solutions under sterile conditions. The ordinary nutrient solutions were used with organic substances as a source of nitrogen. They found that these plants could assimilate acetamide, urea, barbituric acid, alloxan, formamide, glycine, amino propionic acid, oxamide, sodium aspartate, and peptone.

Under sterile conditions where no reduction of nitrogenous compounds to nitrites or nitrates took place, Schreiner and Skinner (1912) reported that the following compounds entered the plant and reacted with the protoplasm in building up plant protein: nucleic acid, hypoxanthine, xanthine, guanine, creatinine, creatine, histidine, arginine, alloxan, asparagine, leucine, glycocoll, and others. Brigham (1917) found that corn could directly assimilate and use some of the nitrogen in asparagine, casein, cottonseed meal, hemoglobin, linseed meal, uric acid, peptone, guanine, alanine, urea, creatine, malt, and glycocoll. Eight of the substances that were directly available to the plant produced better growth when acted upon by *Bacillus subtilis*, probably because of ammonification. These were peptone, guanine, alanine, linseed meal, cottonseed meal, casein, hemoglobin, and urea. Ciamician and Ravenna (1919 to 1920) have reported the effect of a large number of the more uncommon organic nitrogenous compounds on plants. Crowther (1925) found that wheat and white mustard could obtain nitrogen from various organic compounds among which were dried blood, peptone, amino acetic acid, oxamide, and pyridine. Coville (1926) in preliminary experiments noted that buttermilk applied to young blueberry plants increased their height 32 to 37 per cent besides increasing the general appearance of their vigor. Skimmed milk when applied to the soil gave better results than buttermilk, owing perhaps to the fact that the sweet milk penetrated the soil more thoroughly. Azaleas also responded to treatment in much the same manner as the blueberry plants. The indications are that casein is the most active fertilizer of any of the derivatives of the buttermilk and skimmed milk used in the experiments.

Pirschle (1929), and Yamaguchi (1930) believed that plants can utilize urea directly. Klein (1930) reported that amino acids may be absorbed directly but are not equally utilizable, aspartic and glutamic acids being superior to glycine and alanine. Macht (1934) considered that the levo varieties of the amino acids exhibit a greater physiological activity than the dextro varieties. Addoms and Mounce (1932) found that glycine itself was absorbed by cranberry plants. Other investigators have reported that certain organic substances are not used by the plant directly. Thus Willis and Rankin (1930), and Beaumont and others (1931) found that the nitrogenous material in cottonseed meal is changed to nitrate and ammonium before being absorbed and utilized by the plant. Knudson (1933) obtained negative results in the use of glycine, lucine, and aspartic acid as nutrients in the culture of orchids.

The studies of the effect of organic nitrogenous compounds on the nutrition of green plants seem to indicate that they can commonly supplement but in only a few cases replace the inorganic nitrogenous salts. The experimental work would seem to show at least that green plants growing in a heavily manured soil in the field or in a rich compost as frequently used in greenhouses can absorb directly and utilize in their metabolism larger or smaller amounts of complex organic nitrogenous compounds.

b. Stimulation.—It has been observed in numerous cases that small amounts of certain organic nitrogenous matter exert a stimulating effect upon the rate of growth and the reproduction of certain plants. These organic substances have been termed "auximones."

1. *Auximones.*—Such substances may be similar to or identical with the growth substance discussed in Chap. XIV. It should be remembered that, however essential vitamins may be for animal growth, they may be waste products in plants. The vitamins needed by the animal may not be identical with the accessory substances required for plant growth. The terms "phytamins" and "nutrilites" have been suggested for accessory plant-growth substances.

(*a*) *Effects.*—It was observed by Bottomley (1917 to 1920) that the growth of the water plants *Lemna minor*, *Salvinia natans*, *Azolla filiculoides*, and *Limnobium stoloniferum* in Detmer's solution was greatly accelerated by the addition of various amounts of extract from partially decayed peat and other vegetable matter. In one case where the addition of this organic material amounted to 368 p.p.m. after 6 weeks, the treated plants of *Lemna minor* showed a multiplication to twenty times and an increase in weight to sixty-two times that of the plants growing in the water containing mineral salts only. An examination of the pond water in which the plants grew vigorously showed 1,577 p.p.m. of dissolved solids, of which 488 p.p.m. were organic material. The inference was that in their natural habitat these plants utilize a certain portion of these organic nitrogenous compounds in their metabolism. The extracts from the partially decayed peat were proved to be derivatives of nucleic acid. Bottomley found that the nitrogen-fixing bacteria have the power of elaborating products from carbohydrate and elementary nitrogen, which also greatly increase the growth of *Lemna* plants.

Mockeridge (1917, 1924) investigated the effect of varying quantities of nucleic acid derivatives on the growth of plants of *Lemna minor* and found that, although the effect obtained was approximately proportional to the quantity of material supplied, it was not directly proportional to it. The growth of these plants was also accelerated by the addition of sterilized cultures of *Azotobacter* to the medium in which they were growing. Since yeast was found to have plant-growth promoting power on *Lemna minor* and since it contains nucleic acid radicals, the *Azotobacter* were examined for traces of these constituents. Purine and pyrimidine bases, phosphoric acid, and a carbohydrate were all shown to be present, and since all the necessary radicals for the formation of nucleic acid were thus isolated, it was concluded that the beneficial action on the growth of *Lemna minor* by sterilized cultures of *Azotobacter* was due to these organic substances. Ashby (1929) found that small quantities of organic matter added to inorganic solutions greatly increased the rate of growth of *Lemna minor*. Hartley and Greenwood (1933) and Tyagny-Ryadno (1933) reported that barnyard manure in small amounts has a greater effect on farm crops than can be explained by its contents of total nitrogen, phosphorus, and gross organic matter. Popoff (1933) found that extracts of the roots, stems, and growing tips of seedlings of maize greatly stimulated the growth of *Euglena gracilis*.

Clark and Roller (1924) and Clark (1924), however, concluded that the growth of *Lemna minor* in mineral solutions depends upon the suitable concentration of salts and that small amounts of organic matter are not essential for growth and reproduction and cannot be classed with vitamins, which are necessary for animal growth.

Clark (1930) and Clark and Roller (1931) found that the rate of reproduction of *Lemna minor* and *Lemna major* was greatly increased by the addition of sterile organic extracts to a nonsterile medium, but that these extracts had no influence when they were added to a sterile medium. Saeger (1925) and Wolfe (1926) in experiments with plants closely related to those used by Bottomley reported that such plants will grow and reproduce in both Detmer's and Knop's solutions which are properly diluted or balanced. In some cases the addition of organic compounds slightly accelerated the growth and in others depressed it. They considered that the necessity of organic accessories (auximones) in the nutrition of green plants can thus not be accepted as an established fact.

(b) *Origin.*—According to Nicol (1934) the origin of accessory substances, whether required for the proper growth of plants or for that of the animals which ingest them, may be as follows:

(1) Derived from inorganic compounds of nitrogen.
 a. Directly built up within the plant.
 b. Synthesized by microorganisms in the soil.

(2) Derived from organic compounds of nitrogen.
 a. Synthesized by nodule bacteria.
  1. Used wholly within the host plant.
  2. Excreted and then absorbed by associated plants.
 b. Organic manures of plant or animal origin.

2. *Legumes upon Nonlegumes.*—According to Nicol (1934) it has been observed by Lyon and Bizzell (1911), Evans (1916), and Stallings (1926) that timothy and redtop grown with clover and alfalfa, oats grown with peas, and wheat grown with soybeans showed either an increased content of nitrogen or a better growth than when grown alone.

Lipman (1910, 1912) found that oats could secure an adequate supply of nitrogen in a soil devoid of nitrogen if its roots were separated by only a porous membrane from the roots of field peas growing in the adjoining soil. There was little or no growth of the oats when a glazed impermeable membrane separated the roots of the two plants. These effects occurred before there was any disintegration of the roots of the pea so that no compounds beneficial to the oats could originate after that manner. Lipman believed that compounds of nitrogen pass from the roots of some legumes and may be available to the roots of nonleguminous plants growing in the adjoining medium. Virtanen and Von Hausen (1930) noted that red clover growing in sand excreted nitrogenous substances therein. Virtanen, von Hausen, and Karström (1933) found that the roots of inoculated peas excreted various forms of nitrogenous organic compounds into the surrounding medium in the following proportions.

Type of Nitrogen	Percentage of Total Nitrogen
Amino	77.4
Amide	3.3
Volatile basic	2.7

Nicol (1934) stated that, "It can be considered an established fact that the production of nitrogenous compounds produced by one plant is available to another plant, although the mode of excretion is obscure."

B. Absorption from the Air

About 80 per cent of the atmosphere is composed of nitrogen in the elemental form. There are also present small quantities of nitrogen in the form of ammonia, nitrates, and nitrites. Rainfall and snow thus contain nitrogen in this form taken up in their passage through the atmosphere. Russell and Richards (1919) over a period of 28 years at Rothamsted found that with an average rainfall of 28.82 in. the ammoniacal content amounted annually to 2.64 lb. per acre, while the nitric nitrogen was about one-half as much, or 1.33 lb. per acre. It was observed by

Wilson (1921) at Ithaca, N. Y., that with an average yearly rainfall of 29.31 in. from May, 1915, to May, 1920, 12.51 lb. of nitrogen per acre were brought down annually. Of this amount 11.5 lb. were in the form of ammoniacal nitrogen, while 1.01 lb. were in the form of nitrate nitrogen. There is, however, considerable doubt as to what extent the green plant can absorb this free and combined nitrogen of the atmosphere. A historical résumé of the early work in this field is essential in order to appreciate the general opinion of the subject that prevails at this time.

1. Historical.—De Saussure (1804) considered that the plants with which he worked did not take up appreciable quantities of the nitrogen supplied to them in the free and gaseous form. He believed that the source of the nitrogen of plants is more probably the nitrogenous compounds of the soil and the small amount of ammonia that he demonstrated to exist in the atmosphere. In 1837 Boussingault took up the question of the source of the nitrogen of plants where De Saussure had left it more than 30 years before and for 20 years carried on experiments with a large variety of plants to determine if any of these absorbed free nitrogen. His conclusions were that neither leguminous nor nonleguminous plants were able, either when their supplies of combined nitrogen were limited to that contained in the seed sown or when their vigor of growth was stimulated by artificial supplies of combined nitrogen, to assimilate the free or uncombined nitrogen of the atmosphere. Ville, a French contemporary of Boussingault, however, in his works published from 1849 to 1857, reported results that are exactly the opposite of those obtained by the latter. He found that the plants in his experiments showed a very considerable gain of nitrogen during growth whether they were subjected to a current of unwashed air or to one of ammonia-free air and also when the plants were grown in free air and their activity of development increased by the use of nitrates or other nitrogenous matters as manure. This gain of nitrogen he considered to be due to the assimilation of free or uncombined nitrogen of the air.

Lawes, Gilbert, and Pugh in 1860 published the results of their experiments at Rothamsted (1857 to 1859) in which they grew grain plants both with and without a supply of combined nitrogen other than that contained in the seed sown. From these experiments, which were conducted over a wide range of conditions, character, and amount of growth and in the amount of combined nitrogen involved, they concluded that in no case was there any evidence of the assimilation of uncombined nitrogen. Their results of similar experiments with leguminous plants indicated that no assimilation of free nitrogen by the plants occurred. They concluded, however, that, since in practice leguminous plants assimilate from some source so much more nitrogen than grain plants under equal circumstances of combined nitrogen, it would be desirable if the evidence of further experiments with these plants under conditions of more healthy growth could be obtained. Their inference in this regard was correct, since it was shown later that they had sacrificed in their attempt for accuracy the conditions that are necessary for the symbiotic relationship of bacteria and the roots of the legumes. Finally, in 1888 Hellriegel and Wilfarth published the results of their classical work on the nitrogenous nutrition of legumes. They observed that legumes differ fundamentally from the grains in their nutrition with respect to nitrogen. The latter can satisfy their nitrogen need only by means of assimilable combinations existing in the soil, while the former in addition to the nitrogen of the soil have at their service a second source upon which they draw for nitrogen and this source is the elementary nitrogen of the atmosphere. They stated further that the legumes do not possess by themselves the faculty of assimilating the free nitrogen from the air but that it is necessary for certain microorganisms of the soil to enter into a symbiotic relationship with the plants in order to secure this result. Beyerinck (1888) and Prazmowski (1890) were able to secure pure cultures of the tubercle bacterium and gave to it the name of *Bacillus radicicola.* Thus by the work of these four investigators the relationship of the legumes in regard to their nitrogen supply was placed upon a basis that is now universally accepted.

2. Nonleguminous Plants.—Although it is commonly considered that the nonleguminous plants cannot utilize the free nitrogen of the atmosphere, considerable work has recently been done to investigate the validity of this assumption. Recently Lipman and Taylor (1922, 1924) have called attention to the fact that the assumption that nonleguminous plants cannot assimilate free nitrogen is based almost exclusively upon the work of Boussingault (1854 to 1855) in which he claimed that neither the leguminous nor nonleguminous plants could assimilate free nitrogen. They further pointed out that the work of Ville (1853 to 1857), which indicated that all plants could utilize free nitrogen, has been entirely overlooked.

a. The Algae.—Since numerous blue-green and green algae inhabit the soil and since some of these resemble the bacteria in their morphology or are closely related to the fungi in their structure, it has been thought that they might fix free nitrogen and thus be an important factor in the nitrogen relations of the soil and the higher plants. Accordingly a considerable amount of experimental work has been done to determine whether these plants possess the power to fix free nitrogen.

Frank (1888 to 1889) obtained positive results for the blue-green algae *Nostoc* and *Gloeocapsa,* but his experiments were not performed under sterile conditions. Kossowitch (1894) was the first to use pure cultures of algae in this type of work. He used *Cystococcus* and showed clearly that under sterile conditions this alga could not fix free nitrogen either in the absence or in the presence of glucose. Schramm (1914) worked with seven species of the green algae and found that in the absence of combined nitrogen no growth took place, so he concluded that these algae could not under these conditions assimilate free nitrogen. Similar results were also obtained by Muenscher (1923) for *Chlorella*. Wann (1920 to 1921) obtained experimental results that led him to conclude that seven species of the green algae (*Chlorophyceae*) exhibited the ability to fix free nitrogen when grown in pure cultures on mineral nutrient agar media containing either ammonium nitrate or calcium nitrate as a source of nitrogen and glucose. The work of Wann was repeated by Bristol and Page (1923), who showed that his data were not correct owing to the faults of the methods of nitrogen determination that he used.

Moore and others (1919 to 1921) concluded from their observations that in the absence of all other sources of nitrogen save the elemental nitrogen of the atmosphere, but with an abundance of carbon dioxide, fresh-water unicellular algae can fix nitrogen, grow, and form proteins. The rate of growth is greatly accelerated, however, if nitrates or oxides of nitrogen are available. They considered that the green seaweed (*Enteromorpha compressus*) can fix elemental nitrogen from sea water in the presence of sunlight but not in darkness, and thus indirectly from the air. Their results are open to criticism, since they did not work with sterile cultures and depended only on the turbidity of the water as an indicator of the presence of bacteria. The results of all the experimental work thus indicate that the algae examined cannot fix free nitrogen, and we must conclude, in the words of Bristol and Page (1923): "It is conceivable that green algae might assimilate atmospheric nitrogen under certain conditions, as yet unknown, but at present there is no trustworthy evidence that they can do so."

However, Drewes (1928) and Allison and Morris (1930) found convincing evidence that the blue-green algae, *Anabaena variabilis* and *Phormidium molle*, are important nonsymbiotic nitrogen-fixing organisms. In 75 days, in the absence of sugar, they fixed on the average 5 mg. of nitrogen per 100 cc. of culture medium. When 1 g. of sucrose was added, 8.5 mg. of nitrogen was fixed. The fixation occurred only in sunlight and was negligible in darkness. Copeland (1932) found that the fixation of nitrogen by the blue-green algae was shown only by certain strains, and he considered that this power is a physiological specialization that occurs only under conditions of nitrogen deficiency.

b. The Higher Nonleguminous Plants.—The ability of the higher green nonleguminous plants to fix atmospheric nitrogen has been investigated recently by several investigators.

Mameli de Calvino and Pollacci (1911 to 1923) worked with a wide range of plants in relation to their source of nitrogen. The plants used included lichens, mosses, and aquatic and terrestrial phanerogams and were grown under the best known conditions to overcome incomplete sterilization of culture, error due to presence of nitrogen compounds in the air, and incomplete development of the plants. Their data showed that all the plants tested had taken up nitrogen in greater or lesser quantities from the air in which respiration and assimilation took place and that more free nitrogen was taken from the air when the culture medium was supplied with small quantities of nitrogen compounds. Some of the species of the higher plants which they claim can assimilate some free nitrogen directly from the air without the aid of symbiotic microorganisms are *Raphanus sativus, Acer negundo, Cucurbita pepo*, and *Polygonum fagopyrum.*

Lipman and Taylor (1922, 1924) claimed to have secured conclusive evidence from experiments carried on with wheat and barley in culture solutions with and without nitrate nitrogen that the cultures gained nitrogen at the expense of the elementary nitrogen of the atmosphere. They reported that in wheat plants there was a gain of nitrogen from the air which varied from 13 to 21 per cent of the total amount of nitrogen found in the plant. The cultures used by these investigators were not sterile, but they concluded that the small number of bacteria present and the low amount of organic matter in the cultures available for them could not account for the gains in nitrogen observed. Lipman and Taylor believed that the fixation of nitrogen occurs in the leaves of the plants. With the dwarf variety of *Pisum sativum*, however, under as nearly sterile conditions as could be obtained in nutrient solutions, Burk (1927) was unable to observe any fixation of nitrogen.

The results reported by Lipman and Taylor have been skeptically received. It would seem that if any nitrogen is fixed by the nonleguminous green plants it is very small in amount and is inconsequential when compared with that absorbed by the roots in the combined form.

Brown (1933) believed from his experiments that plants of *Lolium* met some of their nitrogen requirements by the use of atmospheric nitrogen, but Ludwig (1934) in experiments with willow cuttings found that no significant nitrogen fixation occurred under the conditions involved. It has not been proved to the satisfaction of all that the fixation of nitrogen by the nonleguminous green plants so far reported has not been due to the action of bacteria, and according to Fisher (1917) it should be considered that where claims for nitrogen fixation are made a need exists for the proof that the technique was not in error.

The absorption by the aerial parts of the plant of the combined nitrogen in the air is considered by some (Moore, 1921) to be significant in the metabolism of the plant. He considered that nitrites may be absorbed in considerable quantities from rain and dew, since his experiments indicated that nitrite was present in these waters in amounts of 1 part per 10,000,000 to 2 p.p.m. These concentrations seem at first glance to be so extremely low that the nitrite would be of no nutritional value to the plant, but Moore points out that the demand of a plant for nitrogen is relatively small and that a concentration of nitrites or nitrates in the atmosphere or cell-sap equivalent to 1 part nitrogen to 120,000,000 parts water could supply a sufficient quantity for assimilative purposes.

III. THE PROTEINS OF THE GREEN PLANT

The proteins are complex organic substances composed of carbon, hydrogen, oxygen, and nitrogen, usually sulphur, and sometimes phosphorus and are compounds which, for the most part, yield α-amino acids upon hydrolysis. The proteins occur in some form or another in every living plant or animal cell and are essential to all life processes, since they are the main constituents of the protoplasm. The proteins occur in plants in the dissolved state in the cell sap, in a semidissolved state in the protoplasm, and are stored in the insoluble form as reserves in the cells of seeds, tubers, bulbs, buds, roots, and other plant parts. The reserve proteins make up the major portion of the proteins found in plants and occur in the cells with nonnitrogenous reserves of carbohydrates and oils. The undissolved protein in plant cells may be in the form of crystals, in the form of aleurone grains, and in the form of aleurone. Crystalline proteins are found in the seeds of flax, squash, cotton, sunflower, rape, mustard, peanuts, and in the potato tuber. The term "aleurone grain" is used in a broad sense to denote all noncrystalline protein bodies of a more or less definite shape, and Osborne (1924) stated that the aleurone grain may be irregular, semicrystalline with faces and angles on a part of the surface or distorted spheres. The aleurone grains may be rather complicated in their structure, as in the case of those in the castor bean. These grains consist of an amorphous protein matrix in which are embedded a protein crystalloid and a globoid consisting of a double phosphate of calcium and magnesium. The matrix and its inclusions are surrounded by an outer layer of protein that is not so readily soluble as the matrix (Fig. 29). The protein that occurs in

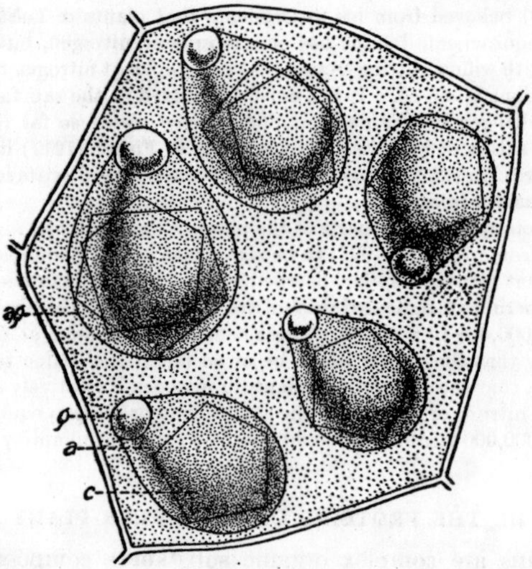

FIG. 29.—Section of a cell from the endosperm of the castor bean (*Ricinus communis*) showing the aleurone grains. *ag*, aleurone grain. *c*, crystal of protein. *a*, amorphous protein. *g*, globoid.

plant cells in an amorphous, finely granular form is generally designated as "aleurone."

In the seeds of the grains and grasses the outermost layer of cells of the endosperm is termed the "aleurone layer." This layer is composed of short, prismatic, rather thin-walled cells and receives its name from the fact that these cells contain, for the most part, protein either as aleurone grains or in the amorphous form regardless of storage materials in the rest of the endosperm (Fig. 33).

The amount of protein in a plant or plant part may vary greatly with the strain of plant used and the conditions under which the plant is grown. Thus Alway and Nesom (1930) found that the protein content of various strains of Canary grass (*Phalaris arundinaceae*) varied from

6.6 to 25.2 per cent. It ranged from 2.8 to 11.9 per cent in the culms, from 8.5 to 23.5 per cent in the leaves, and from 9.4 to 30.5 per cent in the panicles. Enlow and Coleman (1929) noted that the grasses of Florida which were mowed frequently averaged much higher in protein than those which were cut at the end of the season. The protein content of most plants could be maintained at a higher level by frequent light applications of a nitrogenous fertilizer.

A. Physical Properties

The proteins have no definite melting points or boiling points but carbonize on heating and give off gases. They are colloidal in character and thus when in solution do not pass through parchment, collodion, or other membranes. All of the solutions of plant proteins are optically active, rotating the plane of polarized light to the left. The proteins differ widely as to their solubility in water and in salt solutions, and these differences in solubility are used as a basis for their classification. The proteins are insoluble in strong salt solutions and are precipitated out of their solutions without change in their composition by saturating the solution with various neutral salts as sodium chloride, ammonium sulphate, and magnesium sulphate. Dilution of such saturated solutions will cause the precipitated protein to redissolve. All the natural proteins when in a colloidal solution may be coagulated by heat, alcohol, or enzymes, forming a semisolid gel, which cannot again be rendered soluble except by decomposition.

B. Chemical Properties

The average percentage of the elements that compose plant proteins is approximately as follows: carbon, 52 per cent; oxygen, 22 per cent; hydrogen, 7 per cent; nitrogen, 17 per cent; and sulphur, about 0.6 per cent. Phosphorus is also present in certain proteins in small amounts. The percentages of carbon, hydrogen, and oxygen vary within comparatively narrow limits, but the sulphur content varies to a greater extent in the different proteins than any other of their constituent elements. Thus in legumin it amounts to only 0.385 per cent of the dry weight of the protein. Since it has been shown that many plant proteins yield cystine on hydrolysis, it is considered that in proteins much of the sulphur is in that form. By the present methods of determining cystine sulphur, however, the amount of sulphur in the proteins that cannot be accounted for by the cystine determinations ranges from 24 to 80 per cent.

The amount of nitrogen is very similar in many proteins. Thus from Osborne (1924) it is noted that the globulin from squash seed contains 18.5 per cent nitrogen, edestin from the hemp seed 18.7, excelsin from the Brazil nut 18.3, globulin from the cottonseed 18.6, and legumin from peas 18.0 per cent. Of the more than 20 plant proteins mentioned by Osborne (1924) the nitrogen content ranges from 15.9 per cent for the legumin of the horse bean to 19.0 per cent for corylin of the hazelnut. In general, it may be stated that the proteins from plants contain from 2 to 3 per cent more nitrogen than the animal proteins.

The molecule of even the most simple protein is very large. The molecular weights of some of the proteins have been estimated by various methods, but exact data are still lacking in this regard. The complexity of the protein molecule is shown by the calculated formula of zein and gliadin as given by Thatcher (1921):

Zein from corn $C_{736}H_{1,161}N_{184}O_{208}S_3$

Gliadin from wheat $C_{685}H_{1,068}N_{196}O_{211}S_5$

1. The Amino Acids.—The proteins are apparently compounds formed by the union of amino acids, since their products of hydrolysis are all acids of this type. Since these acids are the units out of which the protein molecule is built and since the characteristics of the proteins are due in part to the characteristics of the amino acids, a few general statements in regard to their nature should be made. An amino acid may be regarded as an organic acid, in which one or more hydrogens of the noncarboxyl group is replaced by the amino group NH_2, or, viewed from another standpoint, an amino acid may be considered as a substituted ammonia, one hydrogen of ammonia being replaced by an organic acid. Thus amino-acetic acid or glycine, $\begin{array}{c} NH_2 \\ | \\ H-C-COOH \\ | \\ H \end{array}$, is derived from acetic acid, $\begin{array}{c} H \\ | \\ H-C-COOH \\ | \\ H \end{array}$. From propionic acid, $\begin{array}{c} H\ \ H \\ |\ \ \ | \\ H-C-C-COOH \\ |\ \ \ | \\ H\ \ H \end{array}$, two amino acids may be derived: α-amino propionic acid or alanine, $\begin{array}{c} H\ \ NH_2 \\ |\ \ \ | \\ H-C-C-COOH \\ |\ \ \ | \\ H\ \ H \end{array}$, or β-amino propionic acid, $\begin{array}{c} NH_2\ \ H \\ |\ \ \ \ | \\ H-C-C-COOH \\ |\ \ \ \ | \\ H\ \ \ H \end{array}$. The amino acids that result from the hydrolysis of protein and out of which proteins are supposed to be built are all α-amino acids, which means that the NH_2 group, or one of the NH_2 groups, is attached to the carbon atom nearest to the COOH group. Since the amino acids contain both the basic NH_2 group and the acid COOH group, they easily unite together to form larger molecules, the linkage taking place between the NH_2 group of one amino acid and the COOH group of the other with the elimination of water. A compound thus formed will contain a free NH_2 group and a free COOH group, so that another amino acid may be attached, further to increase the size and complexity of the molecule, and so on. In the laboratory as many as 18 of these acids have been caused to unite in this manner, forming compounds that exhibit some of the characteristics of the natural proteins (Fischer, 1899 to 1906, quoted by Thatcher, 1921). The following amino acids have been obtained by the hydrolysis of plant proteins or have been found in the free form in different plant tissues especially in germinating seeds and in growing buds:

Amino acids	Derivative name	Formula
Glycine	α-aminoacetic acid	$CH_2.NH_2COOH$
Alanine	α-aminopropionic acid	CH_3CHNH_2COOH
Valine	α-aminoisovaleric acid	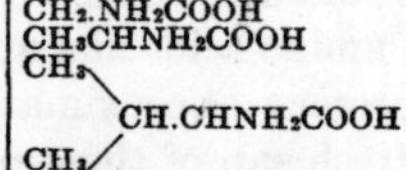
Leucine	α-aminoisocaproic acid	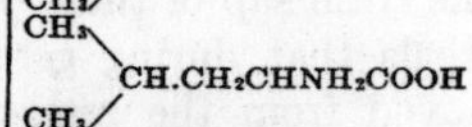
Serine	α-amino β-hydroxypropionic acid	$CH_2OHCHNH_2COOH$
Aspartic acid	α-aminosuccinic acid	$COOH.CH_2.CHNH_2COOH$
Glutamic acid	α-aminoglutaric acid	$COOH.CH_2.CH_2.CHNH_2COOH$
Arginine	α-amino δ-guanidine valeric acid	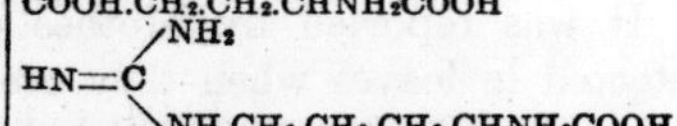
Lysine	α-ε-di-amino caproic acid	$NH_2.CH_2.CH_2.CH_2.CH.NH_2COOH$
Cystine	di-(α-amino β-thio propionic acid)	$HOOC.CHNH_2.CH_2SSH_2C.CHNH_2COOH$
Phenyl alanine	α-amino β-phenyl propionic acid	$C_6H_5.CH_2CHNH_2COOH$
Tyrosine	α-amino β-parahydroxy phenyl propionic acid	$OH.C_6H_4CH_2CHNH_2COOH$
Proline	α-pyrrolidine carboxylic acid	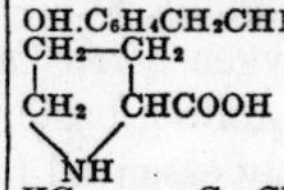
Histidine	α-amino β-imidazol propionic acid	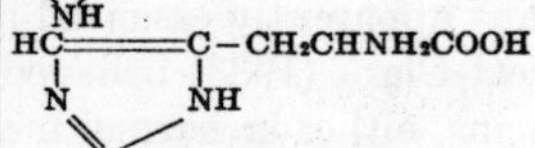
Tryptophane	α-amino β-indole propionic acid	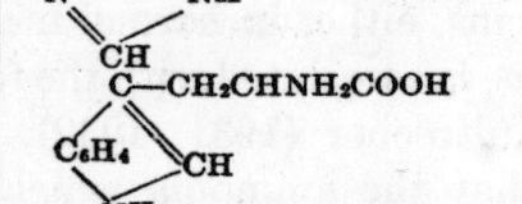

Pollard and Chibnall (1934) found that the proteins from grass contain cystine in amounts varying from 0.3 to 0.95 per cent, while the proteins of alfalfa contain as much as 1.2 per cent of this amino acid. Csonka and Jones (1934) noted that the amount of cystine, tryptophane, and tyrosine of the soybean varied with the variety. The percentage of these amino acids on a dry basis of the oil-free meal was 0.35 to 0.48 for cystine, 0.93 to 1.2 for tryptophane, and 2.3 to 2.6 for tyrosine. According to Maranon (1932) the old leaves of camphor showing signs of chlorophyll degradation have a larger amount of nitrogen in the form of amino acids than either the young or the full-grown leaves. Dhar and

Mukherjee (1934) synthesized amino acids by exposing solutions of glycerol and nitrates, or glucose and nitrates to sunlight in the presence of titanium oxide as a catalyst.

2. The Amides.—An amide is a compound resulting from the replacement of 1 or more atoms of hydrogen in ammonia by a univalent acid radical. Thus 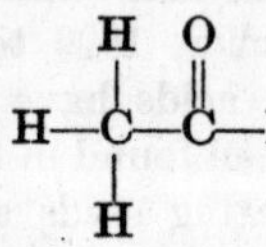 is acetamide.

The amides are highly reactive substances, and, according to Vickery, Pucher and Clark (1936), the amount present in plants at any time is largely dependent on the circumstances under which the plants have been grown. It was noted by Barbera (1933) that the apical parts of alfalfa are very rich in amino acids and amides. These two types of compounds collectively represent approximately 50 per cent of the nitrogen substances in the fresh sap of these parts. McCalla (1934) found with the seeds of cereals that during germination the amide groups are more readily removed from the reserve protein than are any other of its structural units.

It was reported by Mothes (1926, 1931) that no amides can be detected in leaves when they are exposed to the light or are supplied with glucose in the dark. Schulze (1911) assumed that the amides are used in the synthesis of protein. When the carbohydrates of the leaves are reduced to a low point, amides are produced and ammonia appears. In the absence of oxygen *neither* amides *nor* ammonia appear, but there is an increase of the amino, basic, and other nitrogen fractions. Oxidation is thus apparently essential for the production of amides.

Bennett-Clark (1933) believed that the disappearance of amino acids and proteins, either in normal metabolism or under special experimental conditions, is associated with the formation of either amides or ammonium salts. Kultzscher (1931, 1932), and Vickery and Pucher (1931) considered that the ammonia which accumulates in the plant as the end product of physiological changes may become toxic unless it is rendered inactive by transformation into amides or ammonium salts. They believed that the formation of amides is a defensive mechanism for the detoxication of ammonia, the latter resulting from metabolic processes or from an excessive reduction of nitrates.

a. Asparagine.—This amide is the most abundant one in plants and has been more thoroughly studied than any other. It is the amide of aspartic acid and has the formula $CONH_2CH_2CHNH_2COOH$. It was first noted in asparagus and is named after that plant. It occurs in asparagus, onion bulbs, and in the seedlings of beets, peas, beans, and numerous others. It is especially abundant in seedlings when they are supplied with an abundance of nitrates (Zaleski, 1898; Nightingale and Schermerhorn, 1928; Rahn, 1932). The abundance of asparagine in the seedlings of legumes is shown by the following data of Schulze as presented by Murneek (1935):

Age of seedlings, days	Protein nitrogen, per cent	Asparagine nitrogen, per cent	Other nitrogen, mostly amino acids, per cent
6	5.5	1.2	1.7
12	1.7	4.0	2.4
24	1.8	5.1	1.4

Prianischnikow (1924) advanced the hypothesis that asparagine is synthesized in the plant in response to an accumulation of ammonia. This amide can then be translocated and stored for subsequent synthesis in which nitrogen is required. Chibnall (1922, 1924) showed that asparagine disappears at night from the leaves of the bean and that it comes largely from the hydrolysis of protein. According to Wassilieff (1908), Schulze and Winterstein (1910), and Schulze (1911) nitrogen may be translocated in the form of asparagine to the developing seeds and pods of legumes, and it then remains in the mature seed or fruit.

It was observed by Mothes (1926, 1931) that in the presence of some carbohydrates any excess of ammonia is stored in asparagine. If sufficient carbohydrates are available the asparagine is used in the synthesis of proteins. When ammonium salts are fed to leaves high in carbohydrates, proteins are formed quickly. If carbohydrates are present in limited quantities, asparagine will be formed, but when carbohydrates are absent, ammonia will accumulate in the cells until poisoning of the leaves occurs. Thus asparagine apparently has a dual function in the removal of excess ammonia and in the storage of nitrogen. McKie and Barnett (1936) considered that asparagine is formed from amino acids. A union of aspartic acid with ammonia forms ammonium aspartate, from which, by dehydration, asparagine is produced. According to the work of Smirnow (1923), malic and succinic acids seem to be the two acids that in the presence of ammonia are concerned in the synthesis of asparagine.

b. Glutamine.—This amide is apparently widely distributed in plants. Most seeds that contain oil as a reserve food produce glutamine instead of asparagine upon germination. Glutamine, the amide of glutamic acid, has the formula

$$CONH_2CH_2CH_2CHNH_2COOH.$$

Vickery, Pucher, and Clark (1934) grew tomato plants in sand cultures at a pH of 6.7 using calcium nitrate and ammonium sulphate as sources of nitrogen. It was found that the glutamine nitrogen composed over 15 per cent of the total nitrogen in the stems when ammonium sulphate was used as s source of nitrogen, and less than 2 per cent when the plants were grown in nitrate. Greenhill and Chibnall (1934) noticed under certain conditions that perennial rye grass, when supplied with ammonium sulfate as a source of nitrogen, produced a white exudation upon the upper portion of the blades which consisted almost entirely of glutamine. It appears that even in dilute concentrations glutamine exercises some selective influence on the permeability of the leaf cells of this plant.

Vickery, Pucher, and Clark (1936) found in beets supplied with ammonium sulphate that the maximum content of glutamine was 5.4 per cent of the dry tissue of the roots. They believed that glutamic acid is formed after the manner common to that of other amino acids, *i.e.*, the ammonium salt of glutamic acid is formed, and that from this compound glutamine is formed by subsequent dehydration.

3. Qualitative Reactions of the Proteins.—Most of the proteins show similar reactions with a large number of reagents. This is due to the fact that they are complex compounds built up in the same general manner from a large number of relatively simple molecules. None of the various chemical reactions of the proteins is characteristic of them alone, but if a substance gives several of these reactions it may be considered to belong to the protein group. Two of the more common reactions of the proteins are the precipitation reactions and the color reactions.

a. Precipitation.—The proteins are precipitated out of solution by the various mineral acids. In this regard, if nitric acid is allowed to flow gently into a protein solution a white ring forms at the junction of the acid and the solution. This is one of the most delicate protein reactions and is known as "Heller's test." The proteins are precipitated from solutions by the reagents that precipitate alkaloids from their solution. Among these reagents are phosphotungstic acid, tannic acid, picric acid, and phosphomolybdic acid.

The proteins are also precipitated from solution by the addition of small amounts of the salts of various heavy metals such as the chlorides, sulphates, and acetates of iron, copper, mercury, and lead. The precipitation reactions that have just been mentioned are due to the fact that a chemical reaction occurs between the protein and the reagents used. The protein is profoundly altered by these reactions and cannot again be dissolved except by treatment with some reagent that will remove the metal or acid radicals that have combined with the protein. With the exception of some of the mineral acids, the protein cannot be recovered in its original form after such precipitation. This type of precipitation is thus entirely different from the precipitation caused by the saturation of a protein solution with the salts of the alkali metals in which the precipitate proteins can again be readily redissolved and recovered in their original form.

b. Color.—The proteins give certain characteristic color reactions with certain reagents. This is due to the fact that certain radicals or groups are present in the protein molecule; accordingly, some proteins may respond with a color reaction to a certain reagent, while others will not. Certain of the decomposition products of proteins also give the color reactions, provided that disintegration has not progressed to a point where the reacting groups are destroyed. The following are the five most important color reactions of the proteins:

1. *Biuret Reaction.*—When a protein is treated with a solution of sodium hydroxide, and a dilute solution of copper sulphate is added drop by drop, a reddish-violet or violet-blue color is produced. When the protein has been hydrolyzed to peptone, a red coloration results with this test. This reaction is known as the "biuret test," since biuret, $NH_2CONHCONH_2$, gives this characteristic color with the reagents named. This reaction is also given by groups containing two—CONH—radicals connected by a carbon, nitrogen, or sulphur atom. Since most of the proteins contain several such groups, the biuret test is a very general one for proteins.

2. *Xanthoproteic Reaction.*—When proteins are treated with strong nitric acid, a yellow coloration is produced, which intensifies upon heating. If an excess of sodium hydroxide or ammonia is added, the color is changed to orange or orange red. The

production of this color is apparently associated with the presence of the benzene ring and in protein tests is evidently the effect of nitric acid on tyrosine.

3. *Millon's Reaction.*—When Millon's reagent is added to a solution or suspension of protein in water, there is obtained either in the cold or after boiling a pink coloration of the solution or a pink to brownish-red coloration of the precipitated protein. Millon's reagent is prepared by dissolving 1 part mercury in 2 parts concentrated nitric acid (sp. gr. 1.42), first cold and then warm, and after the complete solution of the mercury, one volume of the solution is diluted with two volumes of water. The Millon reaction is given by all benzene derivatives in which one of the hydrogen atoms has been replaced by a hydroxyl group, and thus the reaction is a test for proteins containing tyrosine.

4. *Adamkiewicz's or Hopkins-Cole's Reaction.*—If a protein solution is treated with one volume of concentrated sulphuric acid and two volumes of glacial acetic acid, a reddish-violet color is produced. It has been shown that this color is due to the reaction of the glyoxylic acid, which is present in the glacial acetic acid, upon the tryptophane group in the protein. A more intense reaction is obtained if glyoxylic acid is used instead of acetic acid.

5. *Sulphur Reaction.*—If a drop of a solution of lead acetate is added to a solution containing a protein, and sufficient sodium hydroxide is then added to dissolve the precipitate that is formed, a black or brown coloration will be produced upon heating to boiling, provided that the protein under consideration contains cystine, the amino acid containing sulphur. The reaction depends upon the splitting off of sulphur from the cystine and the subsequent formation of lead sulphide.

4. Amphoteric Nature of Proteins.—The proteins are amphoteric substances, *i.e.*, they are substances that may behave as either acids or bases (Loeb, 1924). The amphoteric nature of the proteins is due to the carboxyl (—COOH) and NH_2—linkages of their constituent amino acids. The behavior of a protein as an acid or as a base will depend upon the reaction of the medium in which it is dispersed, and there is one reaction of this medium at which the protein will behave neither as an acid nor as a base. This reaction is termed the "isoelectric point" of the protein. It is the pH value of the medium in which the protein is dispersed, at which the protein behaves as neither a cation nor an anion, or where the sum of the number of protein anions is equal to the number of protein cations present (Robbins, 1923). Since proteins as well as certain other colloids bear an electric charge when dispersed in water, the isoelectric point may be defined as that pH value of the dispersal medium at which the dispersed protein will behave as if uncharged (Pearsall and Priestley, 1923). The isoelectric point may be stated in yet another manner by saying that, as amphoteric electrolytes, proteins combine with either acids or bases, but at a particular hydrogen-ion concentration exist most nearly uncombined. Whether proteins are ionized at all at their isoelectric point or whether they are ionized equally as an acid or a base is a disputed point. The value of this singular point in ionization and its behavior is characteristic of each protein and is its isoelectric point (Cohn, Gross, and Johnson, 1919). If a pure protein is dispersed in a medium which contains electrolytes and which is more acid than its isoelectric point, the protein bears a positive charge, behaves as a base, combines with anions only, and thus forms a protein-acid salt. If the medium is more alkaline than the isoelectric point, the protein is negatively charged, behaves as an acid radical, combines with cations only, and forms salts of the base-protein type. The isoelectric points of plant proteins have been determined by Cohn, Gross, and Johnson (1919), Pearsall and Priestley (1923), Robbins (1923), Pearsall and Ewing (1924), and Csonka, Murphy, and Jones (1926). The following values are taken from Pearsall and Ewing (1924) and Csonka, Murphy, and Jones (1926):

Protein	Isoelectric point, pH	Protein	Isoelectric point, pH
Vicilin	3.4	Leucosin	4.5
Legumin	4.4 to 4.6	Tuberin	4.4
Legumelin	4.2	Edestin	5.6
Glutenin	4.4 to 4.5	Globulins	
Gliadin	3.5 to 5.5	Carrot	4.1
Globulins		Tomato seed	4.9
Cottonseed	5.4	Wheat bran	5.5
Navy bean	4.5	Pea	5.4
Squash	5.4	Georgia velvet bean	5.4
Flax seed	5.4	Locust bark	5.5

Since the cell sap of the parenchymatous tissues in plants is usually only slightly acid (pH 5.5 to 6.5), Pearsall and Ewing pointed out that the plant proteins are normally on the alkaline side of their isoelectric points and hence would behave as anions.

The position of the isoelectric point is one of the most significant properties of the proteins. At the isoelectric point the proteins are least soluble and exhibit a minimum tendency to swell in water. Thus at its isoelectric point a protein will most readily part with its water, a fact which is of great significance in the synthesis of substances in plants. In solutions of greater acidity or alkalinity than the isoelectric point, the swelling of proteins increases, as do their viscosity, osmotic pressure, and conductivity. Little or nothing is as yet known concerning the significance of the amphoteric nature of the proteins in the life activities of the plant.

C. Classification of Plant Proteins

The classification of the proteins is based on the little knowledge possessed concerning their chemical nature as derived from their products of hydrolysis and on their solubilities, precipitation by salts, and coagulation by heat. It has been made primarily upon the characteristics of those common to the animal kingdom, since they were the first examined and have been the most thoroughly investigated. Although many of the plant proteins show certain reactions not exactly characteristic of animal proteins, for the most part no separate classification has been made and they have been placed in those general groups to which they most nearly correspond in behavior. The following outline shows the groups of plant proteins that have so far been studied.

Classification of the proteins that have been found in plants

- The simple proteins
  - The albumins
    - Leucosin in seeds of wheat, rye, and barley
    - Legumelin in seeds of vetch, soybean, lentil, cowpea, and horse bean
    - Phaselin, in seeds of kidney bean
    - Ricin in seeds of castor bean
  - The globulins
    - Legumin in seeds of pea, bean, vetch, and lentil
    - Vignin in seeds of cowpea
    - Glycinin in seeds of soybean
    - Phaseolin (crystalline) in the seed of kidney bean (*Phaseolus vulgaris*)
    - Excelsin (crystalline) in the seed of Brazil nut
    - Edestin (crystalline) in the seed of hemp
    - Avenalin (crystalline) in the seed of oats
    - Cucurbitin (crystalline) in the seed of squash
    - Vicilin in seed of pea, lentil, horse bean
    - Arachin in seed of peanut
    - Corylin in seed of hazelnut
    - Amandin in seed of peach and almond
    - Juglansin in seed of walnut and butternut
    - Maysin in seed of corn
    - Tuberin in the potato tuber
    - Also globulins in various types from coconut and the seeds of flax, castor bean, cotton, sunflower, radish, rape, mustard, buckwheat, tomato, lima bean, and others
  - The glutelins
    - Glutenin in seed of wheat
    - Oryzenin in seed of rice
    - Maize glutelin in seed of corn
  - The prolamins
    - Gliadin in seed of wheat
    - Hordein in seed of rye
    - Zein in seed of corn
    - Kafirin in seed of sorghum (*Andropogon sorghum*)
- The conjugated proteins have not been isolated as yet in plants but considered to occur (see discussion in text)
- The derived proteins occur in plants in relatively small amounts as temporary intermediate products in the digestion or in the synthesis of proteins

1. Simple Proteins.—The simple proteins are those which yield only amino acids when they are hydrolyzed. They are practically the only plant proteins that have thus far been isolated and studied. There are four main groups of the simple plant proteins: (*a*) the albumins, (*b*) the globulins, (*c*) the glutelins, and (*d*) the prolamins.

a. Albumins.—The albumins are those proteins which are soluble in pure water and are coagulated by heat. The albumins of animal origin are not precipitated by saturating their neutral solutions with sodium chloride or with magnesium sulphate. The plant proteins that are classified as albumins, however, are often precipitated by saturation with one or the other of these salts but are included in the albumin group on the basis of their solubility in water at the neutral or slightly acid point and their coagulability by heat. The albumins occur in plants in small quantities, and on that account their nature has not been very thoroughly determined. According to Osborne (1924), most seeds and probably the cell sap in most cases contain proteins that belong in the albumin group. The plant albumins that have been isolated and studied are leucosin from the seeds of wheat, rye, and barley; legumelin from the seeds of soybeans, vetch, horse bean, lentil, and cowpea; phaselin from the seeds of kidney bean; and ricin from the castor bean.

b. Globulins.—A typical globulin is a protein that is insoluble in water but soluble in saline solutions (5 to 10 per cent) and is coagulated in solution by heat. The globulins of animal origin are precipitated from solution by saturation with magnesium sulphate or by half saturation with ammonium sulphate. The plant proteins do not always conform to these conditions of solubility. According to Osborne (1924), the plant globulins are precipitated by partial saturation with ammonium sulphate at very different degrees of saturation. Some are precipitated with half saturation, while others are not precipitated until their solutions are nearly saturated with this salt. Most of the seed globulins are only imperfectly coagulated by heating their solutions even to boiling, and some can be heated in this manner for a considerable time without showing any apparent change. Some of the plant globulins including edestin from hemp seed, excelsin from the Brazil nut, and globulins from the squash seed, flaxseed, oat kernel, and castor bean can be obtained in the crystalline form. Others are obtained in the form of spheroids that are sometimes mixed with crystals. The globulins include most of the proteins that thus far have been isolated and studied in plants. The names and sources of some of the most common globulins that have been studied are listed in the classification diagram.

c. Glutelins.—The glutelins represent a small group of proteins that are exclusively of plant origin. They are proteins that are not dissolved by neutral aqueous solution, by salt solutions, or by alcohol but are dissolved in dilute acid or alkali. The most characteristic protein of this type is the glutenin of wheat. Oryzenin and maize glutelin are two other glutelins that have been isolated from rice and corn, respectively. It is considered by Osborne that other glutelins may be present in the seeds of other cereals, but owing to the difficulty in extracting them no definite products have been obtained.

d. Prolamins.—The prolamins are proteins that are exclusively of plant origin and are known to occur only in the seeds of cereals. The proteins of this group are freely soluble in ethyl alcohol of 70 to 80 per cent, some dissolving in alcohol of 90 to 92 per cent, and the solutions are unaltered by boiling. They are insoluble in water or salt solutions but soluble in dilute acids or alkalies. On hydrolysis they yield a relatively large amount of proline and amide nitrogen and received their name on that account. The principal prolamins thus far isolated and studied are gliadin from the seeds of wheat and rye, hordein in the seed of barley, zein in the seed of corn, and kafirin in the seeds of sorghum (*Andropogon sorghum*). The glutelins and prolamins are collectively termed "glutens."

2. Conjugated Proteins.—The conjugated proteins are compounds of proteins with some other nonprotein group. They are nucleoproteins, glycoproteins, phosphoproteins, hemoglobins, and lecithoproteins. They have not been as yet definitely proved to occur in plants. According to Osborne (1924), some of the proteins in spinach and alfalfa leaves show behaviors in extraction which indicate that they may be a type of conjugated protein. It is frequently stated that nucleoproteins occur in abundance in plants, especially in the nuclei. The compounds, however, that occur in the nuclei of plant cells and in the embryos of many seeds are not true nucleoproteins but are salts or esters of protein and nucleic acid. A true nucleoprotein is one which, when subjected to peptic digestion or treated with dilute acid, gives a protein and a nuclein. This nuclein after treatment with caustic alkali breaks down into a second protein and nucleic acid (Haas and Hill, 1913). No nucleoproteins of this type have been isolated from plants.

3. Derived Proteins.—The term "derived proteins" is given to the decomposition or hydrolytic products of the simple proteins. Three of the most mentioned derived proteins are the proteoses, the peptones, and the peptides. The proteoses are the protein products of hydrolysis that are soluble in water, not coagulated by heat, but precipitated by the saturation of solution with ammonium sulphate. The peptones are products of further hydrolysis that are soluble in water, not coagulated by heat, not precipitated by ammonium sulphate, but give the biuret reaction. The peptides are the simplest products of the hydrolysis of the proteins and include the polypeptides and the individual amino acids. These compounds may or may not give the biuret reaction, depending upon the degree of hydrolysis, since amino acids do not give this test. The above-mentioned derived proteins have been observed in plants yet are not considered as permanent compounds but more as temporary intermediate products of the hydrolysis of proteins or as compounds from which proteins are being synthesized. Extensive work by Jodidi and Markley (1923), Jodidi (1924, 1925), and Jodidi and Wangler (1925) has shown that amino acids and polypeptides are present in considerable amounts in the ungerminated seeds of wheat, oats, corn, and rye. Thus in the case of Kanred, Fultz, Marquis, and Kubanka wheats the polypeptide nitrogen amounted, respectively, to 3.89, 4.67, 4.98, and 5.13 per cent of the total nitrogen of the seed. The ungerminated kernels of these varieties contained free amino acids, the nitrogen contained in these acids amounting to 1.4, 1.8, 1.8, and 2.3 per cent, respectively, of the total nitrogen content of the kernels of Kubanka, Fultz, Marquis, and Kanred.

In considering the kinds of proteins in plants it should be remembered that the investigations in this regard have been relatively few and that they have been confined, for the most part, to the reserve proteins of seeds and other storage organs. The proteins of the physiologically active tissue of the plant as the leaves and growing regions have been but little studied. It is highly probable that when such studies are made, the present ideas concerning the occurrence of conjugated proteins and derived proteins in plants will be greatly changed.

D. Synthesis of Proteins by the Green Plant

The general opinion is that proteins are formed by the linkage of amino acids. The evidence in this regard is that polypeptids have been formed artificially in the laboratory by linking together amino acids and that proteins yield amino acids upon hydrolysis. It has also been observed that in the maturing of seeds the proteins are formed at the expense of the amino acids. The origin of the amino acids, however, is not definitely known. It is known fairly definitely that proteins are not formed in the plant unless a supply of carbohydrates is present, but the manner in which the carbohydrates are changed to amino acids is not known. The formation of amino acids from the fatty acids is apparently a rather simple reaction, but the transformation of carbohydrates into fatty acids is accomplished, artificially at least, only with considerable difficulty. It was observed by Chibnall (1922, 1924) in the leaves of the bean that the nitric nitrogen and monoamino nitrogen varied directly with the protein nitrogen, which indicates that they may be connected with protein synthesis. Baly and Heilbron (1922, 1923) suggested as a theory of the formation of proteins that "activated" formaldehyde H—C—O—H, which they consider is photosynthetically formed in the leaves from carbon dioxide and water, reacts readily with potassium nitrite to give formhydroxamic acid, and the formhydroxamic acid at once reacts with more molecules of activated formaldehyde to produce a great variety of the complex substances that are found in the living plant. This reaction, they believe, takes precedence over the polymerization of the activated formaldehyde to reducing sugars, which they consider is produced only when the activated formaldehyde is produced at a rate greater than that at which it can react with the nitrite and the formhydroxamic acid, $\begin{matrix} \text{N—O—H} \\ \| \\ \text{H—C—OH} \end{matrix}$, thus formed.

1. Reduction of Nitrates in the Plant.—Since the nitrogen in the protein molecule is generally in the form of NH_2 groups, the nitrogen that has been absorbed by the plant in the form of nitrates must be reduced in order to convert the grouping NO_3 into the necessary NH_2 form. The first step in this reduction is the conversion of the nitrates to nitrites. The transition from nitrate to nitrite is a strongly endothermic reaction and can occur only by the transformation of other forms of energy such as that of light into chemical energy or by a linked chemical reaction with oxidation of previously formed reduced chemical substances, *e.g.*, the oxidation of carbohydrates. It is the intention here to mention the occurrence of nitrates in the plant and to discuss the conditions under which they are reduced both outside and inside the plant.

a. Occurrence.—As has previously been mentioned, a considerable portion of the nitrogen absorbed by plants is in the form of nitrates. The occurrence of nitrates in the plant, however, has for the most part been observed only at random, and the quantitative data in this regard are limited. Woo (1919) observed with *Amaranthus retroflexus* that the rate of nitrate absorption increased with the age of the plants until they were 20 in. high and near the blooming stage. At this stage the nitrate nitrogen amounted to 1.01, 1.94, 2.82, and 0.06 per cent of the dry weight of the roots, stem, branches, and leaves, respectively, as compared with 0.42, 0.22, and 0.3 per cent in the roots, stem, and leaves when the plants were only 1 to 4 in. high. Campbell (1924) determined the nitrate content of *A. retroflexus* and 25 other weeds just before the blooming stage and at maturity. He found that, although the nitrate nitrogen was prominent in some of these plants during the young and immature stages, it had completely disappeared at full maturity. In all species grown under normal conditions the highest percentage of nitrate was found in that stage of development designated as "just before blooming." Anderson (1924) found nitrates in the expressed sap of the shoots of a large number of plants including oats, lupine, wheat, and grasses. He observed that the amount of nitrate found in the plant would depend upon the time of day the examination was made and upon the soil in which the plants were grown. *Solanum dulcamara* showed considerably less nitrate in the morning than later in the day, and *Mercurialis perennis* gave positive nitrate reactions in October and negative in June. The amount of nitrate in the etiolated leaves of wheat, oats, and cabbage was higher than that found in the normal green leaves. Doneen (1934) mentioned that forest trees show different periods for the maximum absorption of nitrates ranging from early seasonal absorption, as in the pine, to late absorption in the autumn, as in the horse-chestnut. The most rapid absorption of nitrates does not always occur at the time of maximal terminal growth of the top. The French prune trees showed a primary peak of nitrate absorption near the end of June with a final secondary peak late in October followed by a decline to winter dormancy.

Woo (1919) observed in the root, stem, and leaves of *Amaranthus retroflexus* that there was a considerable accumulation of nitrates, especially in the stem and branches. In the soybean, Webster (1928) observed that nitrates, as a rule, are much higher in the stem and roots than in the leaves, while the various parts of the plant are lowest in nitrates at about the time of seed maturity. It was observed by Shmuk and Poliakov (1927) in *Sorghum saccharatum* that the nitrogen in the plant reached a maximum at flowering and thereafter rapidly decreased. It was observed by Frear (1930) in the beet that the sap of the midrib contained more nitrate than any other portion of the leaf. Dittrich (1930) noticed that some plants such as *Chenopodiaceae*, *Solanaceae*, and *Utricaceae* are high in nitrates, while others such as *Boraginaceae* and *Gramineae* are low in these salts. In the former group the stem contains more nitrates than the roots and leaves, while in the latter the nitrate content decreases from the roots to the top of the plant. Chapman (1933) found in the tulip tree that the nitrates were more abundant in the leaf, and decreased in order in the roots, bark, and wood.

Campbell (1924) reported that *A. retroflexus* and *Atriplex patula* grown upon manure piles and heaps of decaying hog hair at early maturity showed more than a trace of nitrate that at full maturity was still present. Webster (1928) observed that the addition of nitrates to the soil resulted in a temporary increase in the nitrate storage in all organs of the plant, but this was soon reduced to normal. The percentage of ammonia was very small, but there seem to be reasons for considering that it is one of the intermediate steps in both the synthesis and decomposition of proteins.

According to Strowd (1920) the nitrates in the cell sap of soybean plants increase to some extent with the increase of the nitrates in the soil, but this increase is not proportional to the increased nitrate supply. Thomas (1927) found that the application of sodium nitrate as a fertilizer to apple trees markedly increased the total nitrogen content of the leaves and growing twigs. Cook (1930) for small grains; McCool and Cook (1930) for barley, oats, and bluegrass; Williams (1932) for peach shoots; and Doneen (1934) for wheat found that the application of nitrates to the soil increased temporarily at least the concentration of nitrates in the cell sap. The rate of transformation of the nitrate nitrogen in the plant is very rapid as indicated by a decrease therein within 3 hr. after the source of nitrogen was removed. On the other hand Shmuk and Poliakov (1927) for *Sorghum saccharatum*, Chapman (1933) for the tulip tree, and Varadachar (1933) for the sunflower have reported that a variation of the concentration of nitrates in the soil had no effect on their concentration in the cell sap.

Nitrites have been found in small amounts only if at all in the plant tissues that have been examined (Aso and Sekine, 1914). They were detected by Webster (1928) in the leaves of the soybean in the earlier stages, but their presence in other parts was doubtful. Boncquet (1916) could detect no nitrites in any plant tissue that was normal. In the mosaic tissue of tobacco, however, considerable nitrites were found.

b. Conditions under Which Nitrates Are Reduced.—It was observed by Laurent (1890) that, when a sterilized solution of potassium nitrate was exposed to sunlight, oxygen and potassium nitrite were formed.

In investigations concerning the reduction of nitrates, Baudisch (1921, 1923) found that glucose solutions do not reduce nitrates or nitrites even when heated under pressure, but the smallest trace of iron salt is sufficient to reduce a large amount of nitrite on warming with glucose in weakly alkaline solution. Under these conditions, nitrates remain entirely unattacked. He found, however, that oxygen in the presence of ferrous salts reduces nitrates instantaneously even in the cold with the formation of nitrites and that there is a direct relation between the amount of oxygen dissolved in the water and the amount of nitrite formed. The reduction of an alkaline solution of nitrate to nitrite can be brought about in sunlight in the summer if the oxygen that is split off is taken care of chemically, a process that may be brought about by the addition of complex ferrous salts such as potassium ferrocyanide. Baudisch considered that the nitrite thus formed from nitrates by light energy or with ferrous hydroxide and oxygen is, in the presence of these same factors reduced to nitrosyl (R—NO), which will combine readily with aldehydes and produce formhydroxamic acid, $\begin{matrix} N\text{—}OH \\ \| \\ H\text{—}C\text{—}OH \end{matrix}$.

The conditions under which nitrates are reduced in the green plant are not very well defined. Apparently the process goes on in both light and darkness and in any part of the plant, but there is some little evidence that certain conditions are more favorable than others for the reaction. Thus Schimper (1888) found that nitrates were depleted in the green leaves exposed to daylight and were not destroyed in the leaves kept in the dark. He also observed that shade leaves were richer in nitrates than leaves in the sun, and that the disappearance of nitrates in the leaves in the light occurred only in green leaves and not in etiolated ones. Moore (1921) also considered that the reduction of nitrates to nitrites occurs in the leaves in the presence of sunlight. Warburg and Negelein (1920) transferred *Chlorella pyrenoidea* from Knop's solution to 0.1 N sodium nitrate and observed that reduction of nitrates took place in the dark but was increased by illumination. The rate of reduction, however, was independent of carbon assimilation. Dittrich (1930), Eisenmenger (1933), and Sommer (1936) could obtain little or no reduction of nitrates in the dark. Dittrich (1930) and Lease and Tottingham (1935) considered that the reduction of nitrates to nitrites is closely associated with ultraviolet radiation. Gautreret (1934) reported that red light is more effective in reducing nitrates in plants than any of the other visible rays of the same intensity. Tottingham and Lease (1934) reported that the blue to violet light increased the percentage of protein in the young wheat plant and caused a limited replacement of nitrate by nitrite.

Acqua (1899) and Thomas (1927) obtained evidence that some of the nitrates absorbed by the young roots are utilized directly in or near the root tips. It has been reported by Nightingale and Robbins (1928) for *Narcissus*, Davidson and Shive (1934) for peach trees, and Nightingale (1936) for apple and peach trees that the reduction of nitrates and the initial synthesis of amino acids and amides occurred for the most part in the roots. In the tomato, reduction of nitrates occurred in both the stem and the roots (Nightingale, 1936). Dittrich (1930) noted in numerous plants that the sap of the leaves and underground storage organs had a greater reducing activity than the sap of the stems. In tobacco, Eisenmenger (1933) believed that the midrib of the leaf is the region in which considerable reduction of nitrates occurs. Eckerson (1924) found further that the reduction of nitrates to nitrites and ammonia took place in tomato-plant extract of slightly alkaline reaction, in the presence of fructose or glucose and some free oxygen, in darkness as well as in light and that the reduction was most active in solutions having a pH value of approximately 7.6. Loehwing (1927) found in the tomato that an alkaline reaction and the presence of sugars are indispensable for nitrate reduction and for the formation of amino acids, while Dittrich (1930) found that the optimum pH value reported by Eckerson held in nitrate reduction over a wide range of plants. The most complete information that we have concerning the transformation of the nitrates after they enter the plant is afforded by the careful work of Eckerson (1924). This investigator grew tomato plants of the Bonny Best variety in rich soil until they were 8 in. high and then transferred them to quartz sand which was watered with a dilute nutrient solution lacking nitrogen. When the plants thus grown were ready for experimentation, they contained an abundance of glucose, some fructose, and a little sucrose and an abundance of starch in parenchyma cells of the stem and leaves. The tissues gave no reaction for nitrates, nitrites, or ammonia, and no amino acids could be detected. Calcium nitrate was then applied to the sand, and the subsequent chemical changes followed by microchemical means. Within 24 hr. after the nitrate was applied, nitrates were present in all parts of the plants. The tops of a few plants gave a slight reaction for nitrites but no reaction for ammonia. At the end of 36 hr. all the plants had considerable nitrite localized in the cortical cells at the tips of the stems, in the cortical cells near the phloem, and in the phloem parenchyma at the nodes of the stem. In all regions there was a trace of ammonia. After 48 hr. there was slightly less nitrite but more ammonia, and a slight decrease in the amount of starch could be detected in the cortical cells at the tips of the plant and in the youngest leaves. Within 3 to 5 days there was very much less nitrite, a little ammonia, but a great increase in amino acids. These amino acids were aspartic acid, alanine, leucine, cystine, and histidine and appeared at the nodes and in petioles and blades of young leaves and just behind the stem tips. Succinic acid, malic acid, and asparagin were also present.

c. Nitrate-reducing Substances.—Considerable experimental work has been done to determine the presence of nitrate-reducing enzymes in the plant, but the results are somewhat conflicting, especially in regard to the behavior of the extract to heat. Pozzi-Escot (1903) found that the aqueous extracts of the stem of the burdock have the power to reduce nitrates to nitrites and ammonia and concluded that the enzymes which reduce nitrates are very abundant in actively growing plants. Kastle and Elvove (1904) also found that the potato sprouts and eggplant contain a reducing substance or substances capable of effecting the reduction of nitrates to nitrites. It was found that the reduction takes place most rapidly at 40 to 50°C. and that it is augmented by an increase in the amount of nitrate present and also by an increase in the quantity of the reducing extract. The extracts capable of effecting this reduction lose this property when heated to boiling.

Irving and Haukinson (1908) claimed to have found a nitrate-reducing enzyme in *Elodea*, *Potamogeton*, *Iris*, *Vicia*, and numerous members of the grain family. They considered that the only conditions necessary for nitrate reduction seem to be the presence of the enzyme found in the roots, stem, and leaves and a suitable carbohydrate. Anderson (1924) detected nitrites in the shoots of 25 of the 105 species examined, and in the leafy parts of 23 of these, including sunflower, artichoke, pea, radish, tomato, clover, and wheat, the presence of a nitrate-reducing substance was confirmed. This nitrate-reducing substance was found to be thermolabile and an oxidizable substance rather than an enzyme. Eckerson (1924) reported that tomato-plant juice boiled and brought to a pH value of 7.6 reduced nitrates as rapidly as the unheated juice.

Loehwing (1927) considered that the reduction of nitrates is not caused by enzymatic action because the boiled, expressed sap reduces as effectively as the unboiled. Eckerson (1930, 1931) studied the weekly variations of the nitrate reductase in the various parts of the apple tree during the year. The ability of the tree to reduce nitrate was highest in early spring when the buds were swelling, and at zero during the 5 weeks following flowering. It was low during the summer but increased in the early autumn. It was high from late autumn to late winter but dropped extremely low during February, after which there was a rapid rise to the maximum in early spring. The high reductase content during the autumn and winter was localized in the fine roots. The maximal amount of reductase in early spring was in both the fine roots and buds. There was very little reductase in the leaves at any time.

In 1932 Eckerson found that the quantity of reductase in soybeans amounted to only 31 to 36 per cent of that in the unshaded plants when grown under conditions of only 34 per cent of total solar energy. When grown under an 8-hr. day and a 16-hr. night, the amount of reductase was only 1 to 5 per cent of that of the plants in full daylight.

Both potassium and phosphorus appear to be necessary for the synthesis of reductase, because when either is deficient there is little or no reductase formed. A deficiency of calcium and sulphate also decreases the production of reductase.

2. Protein Metabolism of the Green Leaf.—The observation of protein changes in the leaf is a difficult task. In the first place, many metabolic processes are continually taking place in the leaf, so that numerous nitrogenous substances are present at the same time. It is impossible to determine which of these substances are synthetic and which are deterioration products. In the second place, the methods for the extraction of proteins and protein products, especially from parenchymatous tissue, are not well developed. Then, too, the amount of protein in leaves is relatively small, and it is difficult to differentiate the extracted proteins into those which are uncombined in the cell and those which are constituent parts of the protoplasm.

a. Extraction of Proteins.—Several methods for the general extraction of proteins from leaves have lately been published. Thus Chibnall and Schryver (1920, 1921) treated the macerated leaves of spinach, cabbage, and scarlet runner bean with water saturated with ether and obtained, in such an extract, two-thirds of the total nitrogen of the leaves. Osborne and Wakeman (1920) by grinding the fresh leaves of spinach and centrifuging at high speed obtained solutions containing a certain portion of their protein. These same workers and Leavenworth (1921) found that by grinding and pressing fresh young alfalfa plants it was possible to obtain large quantities of extract suitable for protein determinations. In the case of the leaves of the sugar beet, Tottingham, Schulz, and Lepkovsky (1924) obtained results that indicated the desirability of extracting the macerated tissue with water as a general procedure in separating the nitrogenous constituents of plant cells. Lincoln and Mulay (1929) gave methods of extracting the nitrogenous material from the leaves, bark, and twigs of the pear. Chibnall, Miller, Hall, and Westall (1929) by the use of ether water obtained good yields of protein from the leaves of grass and forage crops. The above statements show that the methods for the extraction of proteins and nitrogenous products from leaves vary greatly, and the indications are that for the best results special methods of extraction must be applied to different types of leaves. Thus no one method is equally applicable in any considerable number of cases.

1. *Previous History of Tissue and Nature of Nitrogenous Extract.*—Much of the study that has been made on the nitrogenous changes in the leaves is open to criticism because of the methods used in the preparation of the material for analysis. For example, many of the results that have been obtained are based on the analysis of materials that were air dried or desiccated at low temperatures. The errors that are likely to occur from such a procedure have been stated by Chibnall (1922), who showed that proteolytic enzymes are present in the leaves of runner bean that were dried at 40 to 50°C., for 100 to 120 hr. He also observed evidences that indicated the presence of an asparaginase. A comparison of the distribution of the total nitrogen in the aqueous extract of fresh leaves and of leaves that have been dried at 40°C. for 120 hr. will indicate the changes that go on in the nitrogenous compounds of the leaves during the drying process.

Comparison of the Distribution of the Nitrogen in the Aqueous Extract from the Fresh and Dried Leaves of the Runner Bean, Percentage of Total Nitrogen

Material	Total water-soluble N	Protein-free and proteose-free water-soluble N	Ammonia	Amide N of asparagine	Nitric N	Humin N	Basic N	Amino N	Other N
Fresh ...	21.57	17.22	0.44	0.53	2.73	0.99	2.00	7.76	2.77
Dried, 40°C. .	33.68	29.55	5.32	1.51	1.62	0.82	2.84	13.22	4.22

Chibnall's work shows that, when leaves are dried at a low temperature, protein autolysis takes place, which brings about an increase in the simple water-soluble nitrogenous products consisting, for the most part, of ammonium salts, asparagin, and amino acids. There is a diminution in the amount of leaf proteins during the drying, but they are not appreciably changed in character.

The effect of the method of preparation of material upon the nitrogenous products obtained in extraction was shown by Tottingham, Schulz, and Lepkovsky (1924) in the case of the leaves of the sugar beet as follows:

Substance	Treatment of tissue		
	Extracted fresh, per cent	Extracted after drying at 40°C. without aeration, per cent	Extracted after freezing by ice salt mixture, per cent
Total soluble nitrogen......	4.0	2.2	3.3
Soluble protein nitrogen....	3.4	0.5	2.3

This has been especially studied in leaves affected with the mosaic disease. In this regard Jodidi (1918 to 1920) reported on spinach and cabbage, Dunlap (1930) on numerous plants, and Cordingley, Grainger, Pearsall and Wright (1934) on tobacco. Coons and Klotz (1925) noted that the nitrogenous constituents of celery plants affected by *Cercospora apii* and *Septoria apii* were different from those of the healthy plants.

2. *Separation of the Proteins of the Cell.*—The proteins in the cells of the leaf and of other parenchymatous tissue are those in solution in the vacuole, those held uncombined by the protoplasmic structure, and those combined in the structural material of protoplasm. By the ordinary methods of protein extraction, the proteins from these three sources are obtained in a general mixture. It is evident that before any knowledge can be gained in regard to the nitrogen metabolism of the leaf, methods must be devised to separate the uncombined proteins of the cell from the protoplasm. Chibnall (1923; see also Thomas, 1927) devised a method for extracting protein from leaves which he considered separates the protein of the vacuole of the cell from the protein of the protoplasm. This method consists of plasmolyzing the cells by means of certain organic agents, as ether or butyl alcohol, and then pressing out the major part of the vacuole content in a press. The remainder of the vacuole content can be washed out by repeatedly allowing the pressed residues to imbibe very dilute acid (0.002*N*) and subsequent pressing. This operation, he considered, does not rupture the leaf cells, and the protoplasm from which some of the water-soluble constituents may have been washed out is retained in them. After the removal of the vacuole contents the protoplasmic material remaining in the residue can be extracted by grinding with water. This material passes into colloidal solution and can be flocculated by the addition of acid. In the case of spinach leaves, the protein found in the vacuole amounted to from 1 to 2 per cent of the total protein of the leaves and had properties distinct from those proteins of the protoplasm.

Chibnall and Grover (1926) undertook to obtain the proteins of the protoplasm of the cells of the leaf as follows: The leaves were treated with ether, enclosed in filter cloth, and placed under pressure in a hand press, so as to remove the soluble proteins of the vacuole. The leaf residues were then washed free from the remainder of the vacuole material by alternate soaking in water and pressing. The protoplasm from which some water-soluble substances may have been removed was obtained in colloidal solution by grinding with water in a meat chopper, and the ground material filtered or strained through fine gauze. The colloidal solution thus contains proteins from the protoplasm of the leaf cells. The proteins thus obtained could be separated into (*a*) "combined" proteins, which are in loose combination with substances soluble in alcohol and (*b*) "soluble" proteins, which are uncombined and pass fairly readily into solution when the protoplasm is ground with water. These investigators examined these soluble proteins of the protoplasm of the leaves of *Spinacia oleracea*, *Vicia faba*, *Phaseolus multiflorus*, *Medicago sativa*, *Brassica oleracea*, and *Zea mays* and numerous others. It was found that these proteins are glutelins with very similar chemical properties. They have an isoelectric point from pH 4.0 to 5.0 at which their solubility is at a minimum. The hydrogen-ion concentration of the leaf cell sap was found in all cases to be alkaline with respect to the isoelectric point of the proteins so that they were probably present in the living cells as anions. Chibnall and Grover were, however, unable to obtain any "soluble" protein from the leaves of *Populus tremula*, *Wistaria chinensis*, *Rheum rhaponticum*, *Polygonum cuspidatum*, *Rumex acetosella*, and *Vitis vinifera* among others. In this regard it should be noted that Thomas (1927) found, in the case of apple leaves which had been collected at early bud formation, at the stage of active maximum growth, and at the period of chlorophyll degeneration, that the insoluble cytoplasmic proteins showed little or no variation in their nitrogen composition throughout the season.

b. Diurnal Variation of the Nitrogen in the Leaves.—In a consideration of the nitrogen metabolism of the leaves, a knowledge of the variation of their nitrogen content as to both quantity and quality during a 24-hr. period is of primary importance, since the changes in these two factors are indicators, at least, of the processes that are occurring.

1. *Methods of Determining.*—The determination of the changes of the nitrogen content of the leaves during a 24-hr. period is attended with considerable difficulty. This is due to the relatively small amount of nitrogen present, to the difficulty of separating the various nitrogenous compounds, and to the wide variation of the other more abundant constituents of the leaf during the period in question. Four methods, each of which has certain disadvantages, have been used to determine the variation of the nitrogen content of the leaves during the day and night: (*a*) Estimation of the nitrogen in percentage of the dry weight of the leaves. Most of the data on the diurnal variation of the nitrogen have been obtained by this method. This method is unreliable, since the total dry weight of the leaves changes markedly during the day, so that when the diurnal changes in the nitrogen content of the leaves are estimated in this manner, it is not the absolute amounts of nitrogen in the leaves that are being compared but only the concentrations of nitrogen in terms of total solids. (*b*) Estimation of the nitrogen by weight in terms of a certain number of leaves. This method is inaccurate, as shown by Chibnall (1924), for the reason that the error in sampling is high. Leaves differ considerably in texture, weight, and general composition, so that when the errors of the determination are taken into consideration, the changes observed in the nitrogen content cannot be considered reliable. These inaccuracies are partially but not entirely overcome by the twin-leaf method of Denny (1933). (*c*) Estimation of the nitrogen in percentage of the fresh weight of the leaves. Chibnall (1923) considered that this method gives the most reliable index to the daily fluctuations of the nitrogen in the leaves. It is evident, however, that this method

would be of value only under conditions that cause little or no fluctuation in the water content of the leaves. Under the climatic conditions under which Chibnall worked in England, the water content of the leaves remained almost constant. Such a constancy of the water content of the leaves is generally not the case, especially in regions of a relatively high evaporation. Miller (1917) observed in Kansas that the minimum amount of water in the leaves of corn and sorghums during the day may be from 88 to 97 per cent of the maximum amount. He also observed that the amount of water in the leaves of pumpkin, soybeans, and cowpeas at 1 P.M. may be only 66, 76, and 86 per cent, respectively, of the water content of the leaves at 8 A.M. It is evident, therefore, that the determination of the percentage of nitrogen on the fresh weight of leaves would in such cases not give a very accurate index to the actual changes of the nitrogen content. (*d*) Estimation of the nitrogen by weight in terms of a definite leaf area. This method has been used by Miller (1917, 1924) in the determination of the diurnal changes of carbohydrates, dry matter, and water in leaves. Its procedure is as follows: The nitrogen is determined in percentage of the dry weight of the leaves and this value is multiplied by the dry weight of a certain number of leaf areas that have been obtained by means of a calibrated punch (see Chap. VIII, Fig. 28). The two main objections to this method are the shrinkage and expansion of the leaves due to changes in the moisture content and to the errors in sampling due to lack of uniformity in the structure of the leaves. Experience has shown, however, that the errors from these two sources are comparatively small, so that it appears that this method is one of the most accurate of the four that have been mentioned.

2. *Total Nitrogen of the Leaves.*—The data of Suzuki (1897) showed that the total nitrogen content of the leaves of *Wistaria brachybotrys*, *Phaseolus mungo*, *P. vulgaris*, *Solanum tuberosum*, and *Polygonum fagopyrum* decreased during the night 16.6, 9.9, 10.9, 5.1, and 7.5 per cent, respectively, of the amount found in the leaves at the close of the day. The changes in the total nitrogen of the leaves of *Acer negundo* was determined by Schulze and Schütz (1909). The data showed that at all times of the growing season the absolute amount of nitrogen in the leaves was higher in the evening than in the morning, as shown in the following table:

VARIATION IN THE TOTAL NITROGEN OF THE LEAVES OF *Acer negundo*
After Schulze and Schütz

Date	Per cent of dry substance		Absolute amount in grams, 200 leaves	
	Morning	Evening	Morning	Evening
May 7	4.30	4.50	0.734	0.817
June 6	3.90	3.98	0.973	1.231
July 5	4.06	4.14	1.211	1.306
Aug. 2	3.74	3.75	0.864	0.898
Sept. 3 to 6	3.16	3.18	0.791	0.971

The total nitrogen of the leaves as expressed in percentage of the dry weight was reported by Kosutany (1897) for the grape and by Pigorini

(1914) for the mulberry to be higher in the morning than in the evening. By the same method Frank and Otto (1891) in the case of red clover and alfalfa and Otto and Kooper (1910) in the case of *Aesculus hippocastanum*, *Philadelphus coronarius*, *Syringa vulgaris*, and *Sambucus nigra* found that the total nitrogen was higher in the evening than in the morning. Chibnall (1924) in his investigations of the nitrogen metabolism of the leaves in the scarlet runner bean noted that the fall in the total nitrogen of the leaves expressed in percentage of fresh weight at night amounted to 2.5 per cent with a probable error of only ± 0.2 per cent.

Miller (1926) studied the daily variation of the total nitrogen in the leaves of various crop plants. The nitrogen was determined in percentage of the dry weight, and the results were reduced to the amount of nitrogen per unit of leaf area. A small portion of the data obtained in 1925 for the leaves of soybeans, cowpeas, and garden beans is shown in the table on page 682.

In 18 observations for soybeans in 1925, the total nitrogen content of the leaves expressed as grams per square meter of leaf at 8 P.M. showed fifteen times an increase and four times a decrease over the amount present at 8 A.M. The average nitrogen content of the leaves for the 18 cases at 8 P.M. showed an increase of 5.9 ± 0.9 per cent of the nitrogen content at 8 A.M. For the same year in 17 observations, the nitrogen content of the leaves of cowpeas, expressed in the same manner as above, showed at 8 P.M. an increase in 13 cases and a decrease in 4 cases over the amount of nitrogen present at 8 A.M. The average nitrogen content of the leaves of cowpeas at 8 P.M. for the 17 observations showed an increase of 6.7 ± 0.8 per cent over the amount of nitrogen present at 8 A.M. The leaves of garden beans in 16 observations showed eleven times an increase and five times a decrease of their nitrogen content at 8 P.M. as compared to the amount present at 8 A.M. The average nitrogen content at 8 P.M. showed an increase of only 2.9 ± 1.2 per cent over that present in the leaves at 8 A.M. The results in the case of garden beans do not show conclusively that the nitrogen content of the leaves increases during the day, at least under the conditions under which these observations were made. In 6 observations of the nitrogen changes in the leaves of Dwarf Milo in 4 different years, the amount of nitrogen in the evening showed an increase four times and a decrease two times, over the amount present in the morning. The results seem to indicate that in this sorghum there is little change in the total nitrogen content of the leaves during the day. The same statement can also be made for the nitrogen changes in the leaves of the corn. Denny (1933) by the use of the twin-leaf method could find no change in the amount of total nitrogen during the day and night in the leaves of beans and peanuts. The observed facts would seem to indicate that the total nitrogen variation in the leaves during the day may be marked in some plants and very little in others. The experimental work that has so far been done indicates that an actual increase in the total nitrogen content of the leaves occurs during the day, and that this increase disappears during the night.

3. *Nitrogenous Compounds of the Leaves.*—The information in this regard is meager and more or less contradictory. Suzuki (1897) reported

Daily Variation of the Total Nitrogen of the Leaves of Soybeans, Cowpeas, and Garden Beans at Manhattan, Kans., 1925

Plant	Time	Water per square meter of leaf, grams	Dry matter per square meter of leaf, grams	Total nitrogen per square meter of leaf, grams	Percentage of total nitrogen	
					Dry basis	Wet basis
July 10–11:						
Soybeans	8 a.m.	96.9	32.8	1.863	5.68	1.43
	8 p.m.	108.7	38.6	2.138	5.54	1.45
	8 a.m.	107.5	31.8	1.847	5.81	1.32
Cowpeas	8 a.m.	215.0	50.7	2.808	5.54	1.05
	8 p.m.	230.5	55.7	3.002	5.39	1.04
	8 a.m.	228.9	50.1	2.790	5.57	1.00
Garden beans	8 a.m.	163.9	38.3	1.758	4.59	0.86
	8 p.m.	162.0	43.6	1.979	4.54	0.96
	8 a.m.	167.5	38.7	1.880	4.86	0.91
July 13:						
Soybeans	8 a.m.	107.2	32.4	1.918	5.92	1.37
	8 p.m.	108.8	39.0	2.215	5.68	1.49
Cowpeas	8 a.m.	207.1	43.4	2.439	5.62	0.97
	8 p.m.	219.7	49.7	2.788	5.61	1.03
Garden beans	8 a.m.	166.3	42.3	1.941	4.59	0.93
	8 p.m.	175.5	47.7	2.027	4.25	0.90
July 17–18:						
Soybeans	8 a.m.	97.9	32.5	1.755	5.40	1.34
	8 p.m.	99.5	36.8	2.013	5.47	1.47
	8 a.m.	90.6	31.7	1.962	6.19	1.60
Cowpeas	8 a.m.	209.4	51.5	2.837	5.51	1.08
	8 p.m.	213.5	55.2	3.097	5.61	1.15
	8 a.m.	224.5	49.3	2.746	5.57	1.00
Garden beans	8 a.m.	172.9	52.2	2.176	4.17	0.96
	8 p.m.	174.2	53.0	2.178	4.11	0.95
	8 a.m.	186.3	50.4	2.192	4.35	0.92
July 24:						
Soybeans	8 a.m.	110.7	38.8	2.312	5.96	1.54
	8 p.m.	111.2	39.0	2.215	5.68	1.47
Cowpeas	8 a.m.	239.2	54.5	2.992	5.49	1.01
	8 p.m.	239.5	55.3	2.925	5.29	0.99
Garden beans	8 a.m.	199.3	52.5	2.136	4.07	0.84
	8 p.m.	209.8	52.5	2.168	4.13	0.82

that in the leaves of *Phaseolus* the asparagine nitrogen decreased during the night to 57 per cent and the amino nitrogen to 91 per cent of what it was during the day. He considered that the reserve proteins in the leaves are decomposed into amino compounds during the night and transferred to other parts of the plant. Schulze and Schütz (1909) in the case of the leaves of *Acer negundo* could observe little change in the amino acid content during the day. They observed, however, a greater amount of protein nitrogen in the evening than in the morning, and the protein nitrogen varied with the total nitrogen.

In *Phaseolus vulgaris* var. *multiflorus*, Chibnall (1924) reported that on the basis of the fresh weight of the leaves there was a fall in the protein nitrogen during the night of 1.8 per cent with a probable error of only ±0.2 per cent. The nonprotein nitrogen showed a definite decrease of 9 per cent with a probable error of only ±0.6 per cent. Both the ammonia nitrogen and amide nitrogen of asparagine remain unchanged at 0.001 and 0.005 per cent of the fresh weight, respectively. The experimental work all strongly indicates that protein translocation takes place in the leaf cells at night either as unchanged protein or as its decomposition products. This loss of protein is from the cytoplasm and not from the small amounts present in the vacuole. Chibnall (1924), in order to obtain data regarding the process of protein degradation in the leaves, cut leaves with long petioles from *P. vulgaris* var. *multiflorus* and allowed them to remain with their petioles in water for 4 or 5 days. At the same time that the leaves were removed, others were analyzed directly after cutting. It was found that the leaves with their petioles in water showed, in terms of the total leaf nitrogen, a large increase in nonprotein nitrogen with a corresponding decrease in the protein nitrogen, and that this increase in nonprotein nitrogen is due, in large part, to increases in asparagine and free amino nitrogen. Thus the amide nitrogen in the freshly plucked leaves constituted only 0.64 per cent of the total leaf nitrogen, while the detached leaves with their petioles in water contained 3.78 per cent of amide nitrogen on the same basis. Likewise the free amino nitrogen amounted to only 6 per cent of the total leaf nitrogen in the case of the freshly plucked leaves but to 14.1 per cent in the detached leaves after 4 days. Chibnall believed that there is a continuous production of asparagine from the reserve proteins of the leaves, that its role in the metabolism of the mature plant is that of a translocatory substance, and that it is the chief medium whereby nitrogen in a form suitable for subsequent metabolic processes can be transferred from one part of the plant to another.

It was found by Kishi and Monobe (1931) in the leaves of the mulberry that the total nitrogen, the albuminoid nitrogen, and the nonalbuminoid nitrogen in the fresh leaves showed practically no change during a 24-hr. period. On the basis of the dry matter of the leaves, these were greatest at sunrise, least at noon and 3 P.M., and less at sunset than at sunrise.

c. Formation of Protein in the Leaves.—The formation of protein in the leaves is indicated by the fact that (1) the amount of nitrate in the leaves is relatively small as compared with that in the stem and roots, as reported for *Vicia faba* by Emmerling (1880, 1887, 1900); (2) incised leaves with their petioles in nutrient solutions form protein, while those with their petioles in distilled water or in solutions lacking nitrogen do not (Chrapowicki, 1889; Sapoznikow, 1895), and (3) leaves can increase their protein content in the dark, provided that the petioles are placed in a nutrient solution containing the essential salts and sugar (Zaleski, 1897 to 1907). It has also been observed by Chibnall (1924), as previously mentioned, that the protein nitrogen of the leaves decreases during the night, a fact which indicates that the protein increases during the day and is translocated from the leaves during the night.

Work has been done by Molisch (1916), Lakon (1916), Meyer (1918), and Ullrich (1924) to determine what portion of the green cell is concerned in the formation of protein. All these workers concluded that the main portion of the protein formed in the leaves is synthesized in the chloroplasts. The general procedure of these workers may be illustrated by the work of Lakon (1916), who studied the variegated leaves of *Acer negundo, Acer pseudoplatanus, Sambucus nigra, Vinca major, Tradescantia zebrina, Abutilon vexillarium,* and *Aegopodium podagrària* among others to determine the distribution of protein in the differently colored parts. The leaves of these plants contain contrasts in color ranging from stripes of dark green and light green to stripes of dark green and pure white. The leaves were first placed in scalding water and then transferred to warm alcohol until they became colorless, after which they were tested for protein by the xanthoproteic, biuret, or Millon's reaction. In the leaves of *Acer negundo,* all three protein tests gave only a very slight reaction in the white portion of the leaf, while the green portion showed a very intense reaction, the contrast between the two portions being so great that it could be observed at a considerable distance. In the leaves of *Acer pseudoplatanus,* which have intense green, bright-green, and pure white stripes, the white stripes showed only a trace of coloration, the light green an intense coloration, and the dark-green regions a very intense coloration with both the biuret and Millon's reagents. In the pure white part of leaves there is generally no chlorophyll apparatus, since the plastids do not develop or else remain rudimentary. Since the intensity of the protein reaction increases from the white portions of the leaf to the dark-green parts, it is assumed that the intensity of the protein reaction depends upon the relative number of the chloroplasts and that the faint protein test observed in the colorless regions of the leaves is due to the reaction of the cytoplasm. Lakon thus concluded that the main part of the protein in the leaves is formed in the chloroplasts. When leaves of *Phaseolus, Lactuca, Brassica, Cucurbita, Zea,* and *Tropaeolum* are detached from plants (grown without nitrogen) and such leaves are placed under favorable conditions of light and furnished with a supply of nitrate, they show the formation of nitrogenous material that is proved by tests to be accumulated in the chloroplasts (Ullrich, 1924).

3. Light and Protein Synthesis.—Evidence has been submitted above to show that protein may be synthesized in the chloroplasts of the cells of the leaves. The question then arises as to whether the leaves are the only portion of the plant in which proteins are manufactured and as to what conditions are necessary for their formation. Suzuki (1897, 1898) grew young barley plants in the dark after the following manner: When the plants had reached a height of 15 cm. they were transferred to a complete nutrient solution that contained the nitrogen in the form of nitrates and allowed to remain for 7 days. One set was then allowed to remain in the nutrient solution while the other was transferred to a 10 per cent sugar solution that was daily renewed. After 7 days the two sets of seedlings were analyzed. It was found that the plants supplied with sugar had been completely exhausted of their nitrates and had greatly increased in their amount of protein and in their dry weight as compared to the plants grown in the solution lacking sugar. Similar results were also obtained in like experiments with beans and potatoes. It was concluded by Suzuki that his results indicated that plants can assimilate nitrates in darkness and form protein provided there is a sufficient supply of sugar present in the cells. This same conclusion was reached by Hansteen (1896) in nutrition experiments with *Lemna minor,* by Prianischnikow (1899) in the study of the regeneration of protein in the onion, and by Muenscher (1923) in a study of protein synthesis in *Chlorella.* Gouwentak (1929) found that the formation of protein may occur in leaves in the dark when the intake of nitrogen-containing substances is possible. Newby and Pearsall (1930) noted in the leaves of *Vitus* and *Rheum* that the ratio of protein to soluble nitrogen changes with the age of the leaf and increases when the content of water falls. Fujita (1931) observed that the lower the degree of illumination the less protein there was in the leaves.

There is considerable experimental evidence indicating that protein synthesis may occur in any part of the plant regardless of light. Thus Müller-Thurgau (1894) grew plants under such a condition that part of the roots of an individual plant extended into a complete nutrient solution containing assimilable nitrogen and the other part extended into a nutrient solution lacking the nitrogen. The roots in the nitrogen solution were profusely branched and showed a thrifty growth, while those growing in the solution lacking nitrogen were very poorly branched and showed lack of vigor. Müller-Thurgau believed this indicated that nitrogen can be assimilated in the plant without going to the leaves.

Iwanoff (1901) worked with the roots of *Brassica napus*, *Daucus carota*, and *Solanum tuberosum* and concluded that an increase of protein can take place in the roots of these plants in the absence of light only when certain conditions prevail. The conditions necessary are a small amount of protein, a large supply of amides, and a considerable quantity of usable carbohydrates. Bambacioni (1923) made chemical analyses of plants of *Vicia faba*, *Ricinus communis*, and *Cucurbita pepo*, which were grown in a full nutrient solution and in the same solution lacking nitrogen, and considered that his data indicated that all parts of the plant may manufacture organic nitrogenous substances. He found that the increase of these was greater in the roots than in the aerial parts and believed it probable that protein substances migrate from the roots to the aerial parts, since roots cut off and immersed in complete solutions contain more nitrogen than the roots of the intact plants immersed in such a solution.

It has been reported by Björksten (1930), Loose and Pearsall (1933), and Gile (1935) that light has no influence on the synthesis of proteins provided the necessary components are present in the plant. Platenius (1932) found an inverse relation betweem amino and protein nitrogen which indicated that protein is the result of a polymerization of amino acids. According to Loew (1933) this formation must be very rapid since intermediate products cannot be demonstrated when asparagine and like compounds are converted into protein.

The experimental evidence in nearly all cases indicates that protein formation may take place in any of the living cells of the plant, provided that a supply of carbohydrates and of the proper nitrogenous compounds and other constituents is present and that light is not directly essential to the process. Protein synthesis may take place to a greater extent in the leaves than in other parts of the plant, due primarily to the abundant supply of carbohydrate in them as a result of photosynthesis. Recent work by Tottingham and Lowsma (1928), however, indicates that the shorter visible light rays may greatly enhance the absorption of nitrate and significantly increase the synthesis of protein as evidenced by the early growth of wheat. Tottingham, Stephens, and Lease (1934) found with the young plants of Progress wheat that the absorption of nitrates was promoted by the longer ultraviolet radiations. Mothes (1932) found substances in the plants of tobacco and bean that act as regulators of the metabolism of proteins in the plant. One type accelerates protease activity during the blooming stage, while another type inhibits proteolysis during ripening.

4. The Seasonal Variation of Nitrogen.—In the apple tree, according to Murneek (1930), growth and development during the early spring are largely at the expense of the nitrogen stored during the previous year. Consequently all the woody structures of the tree including the roots show a progressive decrease in nitrogen from early spring until active growth has ceased. The nonbearing spurs have a maximum content of nitrogen at the time of bud swelling and a minimum when vegetative elongation has ceased. The bearing spurs draw heavily on the nitrogen reserves of the older parts of the branches and possibly on those of the roots.

An unusually large proportion of the supply of nitrogen in the tree is utilized for the growth of leaves. There is a seasonal percentage decrease of nitrogen in leaves from 4 to a fraction of 1 per cent. Murneek found that 35 to 45 per cent of the total nitrogen of the leaves is reabsorbed by the tree prior to their abscission. The soluble nitrogen of the leaves usually increases at this period, while the insoluble fraction decreases.

In a 6-year-old Bartlett pear tree (Mulay, 1931, 1932), the total nitrogen in the shoots began to increase at the end of October, reached a peak in December, remained constant until February, and showed a sharp fall in March when new growth began. In May it had reached a new low. When absolute amounts are considered, the nitrogen changes in the wood about equaled those in the bark. The soluble nitrogen in the bark constituted about 20 to 30 per cent of the total nitrogen, and both types of nitrogen showed the same general trend. In December, insoluble nitrogen increased at the expense of the soluble nitrogen. Between February and March, the rate of proteolysis was much faster than the rate of transport, and there was a temporary accumulation of soluble nitrogen. The soluble nitrogen in the wood followed the same trend as the total nitrogen.

In beet leaves Pearsall (1931) found that the basic nitrogen fraction was relatively abundant in their youngest stages of growth but was sparse in the older stages. The amide nitrogen increased very rapidly at the beginning of the photosynthetic period. According to Richards and Templeman (1936), nitrogen content in the leaves of barley decreased with age in the earlier leaves but increased in the later leaves for some time after their expansion.

5. Formation of Protein in Seeds.—Since the greater amount of the protein that occurs in plants is stored as a reserve in seeds, it is of interest to consider the question of its origin. Wassilieff (1908) observed that the disappearance of asparagine at the maturity of seeds is accompanied by an increase in protein material. The production of this amide nitrogen is accompanied by a decrease in amino nitrogen. It was noted by Schulze and Winterstein (1910) and Schulze (1911) in the case of legumes that in the unripe seed there were found along with the proteins small quantities of asparagine, monoamino acids, arginine, and histidine. They also observed that in the hulls of the unripe seeds tryptophane occurred in appreciable quantities, while in the developing seed but little occurred. In the leaves and stems, asparagine occurred in considerable amounts, while in the maturing seed it occurred in only very small quantities. These investigators considered these data to indicate that the above-mentioned nitrogenous compounds are the materials from which the protein of the seed is synthesized. Zaleski (1911) observed in the maturing seeds of the pea and corn which had been taken from the plant and kept in moist air for varying periods that the protein increased in amount while the other nitrogenous compounds decreased as illustrated in the following data in the case of ripening peas (Raber, 1928):

Time	Protein, per cent	Amino acids, per cent	Nitrogen bases, per cent	Other nitrogen compounds, per cent
Beginning..........	79.2	8.7	10.8	1.4
After 5 days........	89.2	4.6	5.6	0.8

Teller (1935) harvested wheat in Arkansas daily during the development of the grain and for several days after ripening he found that the larger proportion of the nonprotein, nitrogenous compounds, which are predominant at the earliest stage of kernel formation, are quickly changed into the different types of proteins characteristic of the developed grain. Zeleny (1935) examined the grain of corn at four stages of development. He found that during these stages of development the nonprotein nitrogen decreased from 41 to 4.6 per cent, and he considered that the simpler amino compounds undergo rapid condensation as the grain approaches maturity. All the available evidence indicates that the simple organic compounds furnish the materials for the formation of the proteins.

The development of the wheat grain has been studied more in detail than the development of any other seed, and considerable information has been obtained concerning the formation of its protein. It will be necessary to discuss here in detail the development of the wheat grain, since the reactions involving protein formation are closely involved with and cannot be separated from the reactions of other processes. In the formation of the wheat grain, three stages may be distinguished (Brenchley and Hall, 1908 to 1910): (*a*) a period during which the pericarp is the most prominent feature, (*b*) a main period during which the endosperm is filled, and (*c*) the ripening period characterized by the desiccation of the grain.

According to Eckerson (1917), at the time of spike formation the largest amount of potassium nitrate is found in the tissues of the root and stem. A continuous stream of sugars and amino acids moves from the leaves of the culms into the young spike. Fructose, glucose, some arginine, histidine, considerable asparagine, and a large amount of potassium nitrate are present in the vascular elements of the culms. The cells of the primordia of the flower contain much fructose and asparagine. The primordia of the stamens, pistils, and glumes are alike chemically, but when the sporogenous tissue is developing, phosphates begin to enter the stamens and pistils while the magnesium oxalate crystals in the spike disappear and magnesium appears in the sporogenous cells. Phosphates continue to move into the sporogenous tissue until the pollen grain and egg are formed. It appears that the greatest absorption of phosphates is during the shooting period. It seems thus that the greatest absorption of phosphates is at the time that they are being assimilated most actively, while nitrates are absorbed in large quantities by the young plant and are utilized much later in the development.

After the fertilization of the egg there is a continuous stream of nutrient materials moving into the endosperm from the leaves and glumes. These materials include fructose and glucose, asparagine, arginine, histidine, and leucine. As the outer membrane of the nucellus becomes suberized, the current of sugar and amino acids passes from the base of the grain up through the raphe, enters the embryo sac at the chalazal region, and passes down through the endosperm cells to the embryo. Starch is formed in the endosperm cells soon after wall formation. It continues to increase in amount until desiccation begins or as long as the leaves and glumes are green and form an excess of sugar. The nitrogen compounds present, aside from aleurone and protoplasm in the endosperm, just before the ripening of the grain are a large amount of asparagine, considerable arginine, histidine, and some leucine but no glutamine. Thatcher (1913, 1915) found that there was an increase in the actual quantity of all the materials in the kernel with the exception of sugar during each successive period of growth. The decrease in the amount of sugar is due to its condensation into starch. The carbohydrate/protein ratio is at first greater and then becomes less in the developing kernel than in the pericarp material at the beginning of the experiment.

Eckerson (1917) stated that in the full-grown, still green wheat kernel containing about 90 per cent moisture there is no storage protein in the endosperm. The aleurone layer and the layer of cells immediately below it contain more protoplasm than the other endosperm cells and give a protein reaction, but this is not storage protein. No storage protein is formed in the endosperm until desiccation begins. The main feature of the ripening process is thus desiccation, during which the condensation of nitrogenous compounds to proteins occurs. The percentage of water in barley was found by Harlan (1920) to be the highest at flowering time, when 80 per cent of the caryopsis was water. From flowering time until maturity the water content gradually decreased until at maturity it amounted to 40 per cent. This percentage decrease is very uniform, and Harlan found in his experiments that it amounted to 2 per cent per day, while Brenchley (1912) found that it averaged about 1 per cent per day. The maximum dry weight of grain is attained a day or two before the grain should be regarded as ripe in practice. This is in agreement with the observations of Spitzer, Carr, and Epple (1919), who found that the total nitrogen of soft corn is only slightly lower than that of mature corn but that the amide nitrogen is much higher in the former than in the latter. It is also in agreement with the observation of Olson (1917), who stated that the nitrogenous compounds of the wheat kernel are at first very simple but change to the more complex forms as the period of desiccation advances.

6. Factors That Influence the Percentage of Protein in Grains.—The amount of protein in seeds and grains varies with different species and varieties of plants and with the conditions under which the plants are grown. The factors that influence the percentage of proteins in the cereals have received considerable attention, since the amount of protein in the grain, especially in wheat, determines to a certain degree its market value. A certain amount of protein is necessary in the wheat grain in order to produce a high quality of flour. In certain regions the wheats are especially low in protein so that high-protein wheats must be mixed with them in order to obtain a flour of good baking qualities.

The factors or causes that influence the percentage of protein in grains are apparently numerous and include the general weather conditions prevailing during the growing season, the time of nitrogen application, the available nitrogen, length of the growing season, available water, and certain unknown genetic factors. These factors are all more or less interrelated, so that in any discussion concerning them it is impossible to separate one from the other.

a. Time of Application of Nitrogen.—It is generally agreed that the available nitrogen is a very important and in many cases the greatest factor in determining the yield and quality of wheat (Burke, 1925; Ames, 1910; Whitson, Wells, and Vivian, 1902). As stated by Gericke

(1927), however, the peculiarities of the varieties may determine the effect of fertilizer upon the protein content of the grain. The properties of wheat varieties can and do markedly affect the efficiency of any fertilizer treatment.

Davidson and LeClerc (1917, 1918, 1923) applied nitrogen to wheat plants when they were 2 in. high, at heading, and at the milk stage. They found that the application of nitrogen in any of the inorganic forms used at the early stages of growth was instrumental in producing the highest yields of wheat, while the application of nitrogen in any form at the time of heading produced the highest protein content. When nitrogen was applied at the milk stage, it had no effect on the yield or upon the composition or quality of the grain. The period between the resumption of growth of wheat in the spring and at the time of heading was divided into three parts (Davidson, 1922), each of three corresponding sets of plots receiving nitrates at one of these subperiods. It was found that the effectiveness of increasing yields decreased consistently as the time of the application of nitrates approached the heading stage, while the reverse was true as regards the effectiveness of the nitrates in increasing the protein content of the grain.

Gericke (1920, 1922) applied nitrogenous fertilizers to the soil at planting time of wheat, oats, and rye in some cases and at different periods thereafter in others. In experiments with spring wheat, nitrogen was applied at planting time, at 17, 33, 48, 72, and 110 days after planting. The protein content of the grain produced under each of these applications taken in the same order as above was 8.6, 9.3, 10.4, 11.8, 13.2, and 15.2 per cent of the dry weight. The data thus show an increase of 77 per cent in the protein content of the grain obtained from plants that received their nitrogen 110 days after planting over those which were treated with nitrogen at the time of planting. Practically the same results were obtained with oats and rye. Later, as mentioned above, it was found that the response in the protein content of the grain was different for different varieties of plants. The observations of Watson (1936) regarding the time of application of nitrogen and its percentage in the grain agreed with those of Gericke above mentioned.

Gericke (1930) sowed wheat in a soil deficient in nitrogen and thus restricted the stalk formation of the early growth to one culm per plant. After 90 days from this planting a heavy application of nitrogen as sodium nitrate was added to the soil. Soon thereafter new culms arose from these plants and eventually produced grain. The grain of the original culm ripened before that of the newly formed ones. The highest percentage of protein was in the grain from the newly produced culms. The variation in the percentage of protein in the grains from older and from younger culms amounted to 30, 39, 57, 59, and 119 per cent respectively for the varieties Bunyip, Fulcaster, Cedar, Hard Federation, and Sonora. McCalla (1933) found that the organic nitrogen produced in the vegetative parts of the wheat plant after heading was not synthesized to protein but accumulated in the vegetative parts. It was noted by Doneen (1934) that if sufficient quantities of nitrogen for large yields of grain were present in the soil, the addition of sodium nitrate only retarded growth and did not increase the yield or the content of nitrogen in the grain. When, however, the nitrogen in the soil was limited, the addition of this element stimulated growth and increased the yield and the amount of nitrogen in the grain. The composition of the soil, however, was found by LeClerc (1910), Shaw and Walters (1911), Thatcher (1913), and LeClerc and Yoder (1914) to have little effect on the protein content of the grain under the conditions of their experiments and with the varieties with which they worked. In this connection it might also be mentioned that Lipman and Blair (1916) found that the liming of the soil increased the percentage of protein in soybeans. Stark (1924) in the case of soybeans noted that the application of limestone and organic matter increased the percentage of protein, while potassium in addition to these compounds gave a decrease in the percentage of protein.

b. Soil Moisture.—In general, it may be said that the protein content of grains varies inversely with the total rainfall (Hopkins, 1935). Neidig and Snyder (1922, 1924, 1926) found in the case of Marquis and Palouse bluestem wheats that under field conditions available nitrogen shows its greatest effect on protein content and yield of wheat when climatic factors are most favorable, and that both the climatic factors and available nitrogen play an important part in the quality of the wheat. It is considered that the importance of climate is chiefly due to its effect upon the availability of the nutrients in the soil, which, in turn, affect the nutrition of the plant. Neidig and Snyder (1924) noted that under field conditions a high moisture content properly distributed during the growing season in an average soil will produce a high-yielding wheat with a low protein content. Thatcher (1913) found that the increase in protein content of wheat in eastern Washington decreased with an increase in rainfall. Greaves and Carter (1923) observed a decrease in the nitrogen content of wheat, oats, and barley as the irrigation water used in their growth was increased. The decrease in the nitrogen content of the grain of wheat, oats, and barley amounted to 21, 40, and 19 per cent, respectively. Stewart and Greaves (1909) also observed that wheat grown on arid nonirrigated land contained more protein than was found in wheat on adjoining irrigated land. Greaves and Nelson (1925) showed that corn grown with and without irrigation water and manure gave a decrease in the nitrogen content of the kernel due to irrigation water and an increase due to the manure, the nitrogen content of the grain being a function of the available nitrogen content of the soil.

As a rule, however, the composition of corn is modified little if at all by variations of nutrient treatments or of climatic factors, as is indicated by the fact that the nitrogen content of corn seed from widely separated sections is approximately the same.

c. *Kind of Plant.*—The effect of changes in soil and climate upon the amount of protein in grain or seed depends to a great extent upon the kind of plant. Thus Tottingham (1924) and Tottingham and Kerr (1926) found in the case of Leaming Yellow Dent corn grown in soil in the greenhouse that variations in the amounts and time of application of sodium nitrate did not modify the nitrogenous content of the cured seed.

Dewiche and Tottingham (1930) grew corn, barley, and clover at two stations in Wisconsin with a difference of 3.5° in latitude. The crude protein varied but little for the grain of corn and barley under these two conditions, while that in the seed of the clover was significantly different.

Ivanov (1927) reported that peas, corn, lentils, and vetches grown under different conditions of soil moisture and climate showed no variation in the content of protein of their seeds, and that there was maintained a definite relationship between proteins and carbohydrates. Schuster and Graham (1927) found indications that the composition of the soybean cannot be changed by soil treatment.

Tottingham (1923) found that the composition of red clover (*Trifolium pratense*) and buckwheat was greatly altered by changes in the environmental conditions, while Waldron (1933) in North Dakota reported that the later and lower yielding wheat had the highest content of protein.

Tottingham and his workers found that the leaves of corn are characterized by low proportions of total soluble nitrogen and soluble protein as contrasted with high values for these factors in wheat and sugar beets, plants whose composition responds readily to changes of climatic conditions. Corn leaves are characterized by low proportions of reducing sugars, while the sugar-beet leaf contains much more reducing sugar than sucrose in the tests that have been made. They believed that sucrose and less soluble forms of protein are quite likely to be less altered by the effects of temperature and other climatic factors than are such reactive compounds as glucose, soluble proteins, and other soluble nitrogenous compounds.

7. Yellow Berry in Hard Winter Wheats.—In connection with the protein content of wheat, the nature of yellow berry and the factors that influence it should be taken into consideration. The term "yellow berry" has been defined by Roberts and Freeman (1908) as the appearance in hard, flinty wheats of grains of a light-yellow color, opaque, soft, and starchy. These opaque yellow grains may have this character throughout, or sometimes from a small fraction to half of a grain will be yellow and starchy while the remainder of the kernel will be hard, flinty, and translucent. The difference in color between the flinty grains and the "yellow berries" is due to differences in the structure and content of the cells of the endosperm. Considerable attention has been given to the causes of yellow berry. Lyon and Keyser (1905) concluded that the amount of yellow berry increases with the lateness of ripening and that crops of large yield and low nitrogen content contain more yellow berries than do crops of opposite kinds. Roberts and Freeman (1908) found that there was a diminution in the amount of yellow berry corresponding to the shortening of the fall growing period on account of late planting. They found, in general, that late ripening increased it and that higher mean temperatures 3 weeks before ripening were found to be correlated with low percentage of yellow berry. Headden (1915) reported that the application of nitrogen in the form of sodium nitrate greatly reduced the amount of yellow berry and in some cases prevented it altogether under the conditions prevailing in Colorado. He found also that yellow berry could be greatly increased by the application of available potassium. He considered that the occurrence of yellow berry indicates that potassium is present in excess of that necessary to form a potassium/nitrogen ratio favorable to the formation of hard, flinty kernels. Roberts (1919) concluded that the operation of common causes for the production of yellow berry overshadows any differences that may be due to hereditary tendencies and precludes a definite statement concerning the influence of hereditary factors in this regard. Some isolated forms of wheat are, however, apparently freer from the condition of yellow berry than others growing in the same field. Jones and Mitchell (1926) found that thorough tillage of summer fallow in contrast to poor tillage resulted in larger yields and correspondingly less yellow berry. They considered that yellow berry is the manifestation of nutritional disturbances resulting from an insufficiency of nitrogen and other elements for adequately meeting the requirements of a normally developing crop. Since no means appear feasible as yet for protecting dry-farmed lands against the gradual depletion of their native supply of nitrogen, high efficiency in the control of yellow berry cannot be maintained indefinitely by tillage.

In conclusion it should be stated that yellow berry is apparently different from ordinary soft wheat, since it is produced under apparently the same conditions as the flinty kernels, not merely in the same field, but on the same plant or in the same head.

IV. NITROGEN BASES IN PLANTS

The nitrogen-containing compounds in plants may, for the most part, be regarded as derived from ammonia by the replacement of one or more of the hydrogen atoms by organic radicals of various types. The nature of these replacements in the formation of amino acids and amides has already been discussed, and it is the intention here to make a statement concerning the general nature of the amines. The replacement of one or more hydrogen ions of ammonia by alkyl groups gives rise to compounds strongly basic in nature and known as "amines." There are three different classes of amines designated as primary, secondary, and tertiary according as one, two, or three of the hydrogen atoms of ammonia have been replaced by the organic radicals mentioned above. The nitrogen bases in plants are amines of these three classes and may be divided into three main groups, (*a*) the plant amines, (*b*) the alkaloids, and (*c*) the purine bases.

A. Plant Amines or Natural Bases

These are simple, open, chain amines. Some of the plant amines are trimethyl amine, a volatile compound that occurs in the seeds of *Mercurialis annua* and in the flowers of *Crataegus oxyacantha* and in the leaves of *Chenopodium vulvaria;* and betaine and choline, which occur together frequently in the embryo of *Hordeum sativum, Triticum sativum, Vicia sativa,* and other plants. Betaine occurs also in the juice of the beet and in the tubers of the Jerusalem artichoke, while choline occurs in the root of *Acorus calamus,* in the endosperm of *Cocos nucifera,* and in many other plants (Haas and Hill, 1913). There is no known physiological use for these simple amines in the plant. They are regarded by some as intermediate products in the synthesis or decomposition of proteins, but there are no data to warrant such a statement.

B. Alkaloids

The alkaloids are compounds that for the most part are composed of carbon, hydrogen, oxygen, and nitrogen, but a few, as coniine and nicotine, contain no oxygen. The alkaloids differ widely in structure but are related, for the most part, to heterocyclic compounds, as pyridine, quinoline, and isoquinoline. The term "alkaloid" literally means an alkali-resembling substance, since the compounds of this type have properties similar to those of the alkalies in being able to form salts with acids that are usually soluble in water.

The alkaloids are precipitated from their solutions by the so-called "alkaloid reagents" among which are tannins, phosphomolybdic acid, phosphotungstic acid, picric acid, and potassium mercuric iodide. The majority of the alkaloids are optically active, rotating the plane of polarized light to the left, although a few, such as coniine, are dextrorotatory. The alkaloids, in general, are colorless, odorless, crystalline, and have a bitter taste, although there are a number of exceptions in one or more of these regards. They are generally insoluble in water but are easily soluble in organic solvents as chloroform, carbon tetrachloride, and ether. The alkaloids generally do not occur in the plant as such but are combined with acids in the form of a salt. Some of the acids that are combined in this manner are tannic, malic, citric, succinic, and oxalic. The alkaloids are generally set free in extraction by the addition of an alkali as lime or barium, since only the free bases and not their salts are soluble in the solvents mentioned above.

The alkaloids are very limited in their distribution in the plant kingdom, occurring, for the most part, in the *Leguminosae, Papaveraceae, Ranunculaceae, Rubiaceae,* and

Solanaceae. They may occur in solution in the cell sap in the young parenchyma or may be stored in older tissue in the solid state. They are generally found in the seeds and fruits, but some occur in the leaves, stem, and roots (Haas and Hill, 1913).

Some of the alkaloids are: coniine in *Conium maculatum;* nicotine in tobacco; atropine, which is the principal alkaloid in the deadly nightshade; cocaine in cocoa leaves; quinine, which is the most important alkaloid of the 24 found in cinchona bark; strychnine in the seeds of *Strychnos nux vomica;* and morphine, which is the principal alkaloid of the 20 that are found in the juice of the poppy. According to McNair (1931) the ratio of the number of tropical plant families containing alkaloids to the total number of tropical families is 0.16 as compared to the ratio of 0.12 between such families in the temperate zone. For the tropical alkaloids the melting point is between 200 and 250°C., while in the temperate group it is between 100 and 150°C. The number of carbon atoms on the alkaloid molecule increases from the tropics to the temperate region. The average and minimum number of nitrogen atoms increases from the tropics to the temperate regions but the maximum number decreases. The maximum number of oxygen atoms increases and the minimum number decreases as one proceeds from the tropics. The alkaloids of tropical origin are generally less toxic to man than those of the temperate region.

The origin of the alkaloids in the plant is not definitely known. Some consider that they arise in the formation of proteins, while others consider that they are formed in the disintegration of the proteins. In general, they are considered as nitrogenous waste products that the plant, although it is incapable of eliminating them, renders noninjurious by storing in this condition (Weevers, 1930). It would seem, however, that the connection of alkaloids with protein metabolism is not a common relationship, since it is manifested by such a limited number of species. Emde (1929) considered that the formation of alkaloids is dependent upon the activity of photosynthesis, because the amount of photosynthesis decreases progressively from the equator to the poles. The maximum of plant alkaloids is produced in the tropics, while the plants of the polar regions produce no alkaloids.

C. The Purine Bases

The purine bases are complex compounds containing a nucleus with four carbon atoms and four nitrogen atoms arranged alternately to form a double-ring group. They are a group of compounds, all of which are derivatives of the compound purine ($C_5H_4N_4$). Under this list are included caffeine or theine in coffee and tea; theobromine in the fruit of *Theobroma cacao;* xanthine; hypoxanthine; guanine in sprouting seeds; and adenine, which occurs in the juice of beets. Uric acid, a purine derivative which does not occur in plants but which is a waste product of the metabolism of animals, is of interest in regard to the nature of the purine bases found in plants. The close relationship between this substance and the purine bases found in plants suggests that the latter might be considered as waste products in the protein metabolism of the plant. Weevers (1930) believed that the xanthine derivatives have their origin in the decomposition of proteins, accumulate for a time, and are again used for new proteins.

V. LOSS OF NITROGEN FROM PLANTS

One of the most striking differences between the metabolism of animals and plants is that the former continually excrete nitrogen compounds to the outside world, while plants rarely if ever excrete or eliminate nitrogen in any form. The nitrogenous compounds eliminated by animals are chiefly urea, uric acid, ammonia, and others, all of which result from the breaking down of proteins and the protoplasm. The same compounds are apparently formed in the life processes of the plant cell but are again directly utilized in the formation of new protein compounds and not eliminated as in animals.

Fosse (1913) proved that urea is present in the leaves of carrot, spinach, in potato tubers, root of the turnip, and in the seedlings of pumpkin, wheat, rye, clover, beet, pea, and corn. In the resting seed of wheat, corn, and pea it was present in amount equal to 1 cg. per kilogram of weight. Fosse has proved that the urea detected was formed within the plant and was not absorbed directly from the soil where it is known to be present. Chibnall (1922), in working with the changes of protein in the leaves of the runner bean, found that their products of protein disintegration pass into urea derivatives that have a striking analogy to what is found in the animal kingdom.

Klein and Tauböck (1927, 1931, 1932) and Klein, Tauböck, and Linser (1930) found an abundance of urea in seedlings but none in the mature seeds. Young leaves, petioles, and leaf buds usually gave positive tests. In herbaceous plants urea is present in the largest amount in the roots. It occurs usually in the greatest amount in the more actively growing parts of the plant. These investigators concluded that urea is formed by the decomposition of arginine or of argininelike bodies. When arginine is taken up by plants in sterile cultures it is broken down and an increase in the amount of urea occurs. The etiolated seedlings of soybeans have 30 per cent more urea than the green ones of the same age.

In the germination of seeds where the processes of metabolism are very intense, the question of the loss of nitrogen in the gaseous form is somewhat in doubt. Schulz (1862) and Atwater and Rockwood (1886) reported appreciable losses of nitrogen during germination, but Boussingault (1838) and Hellriegel (1855) and more recently Davidson (1923) found only negative evidence of nitrogen loss. Davidson (1923) grew cowpeas and two varieties of soft winter wheat under sterile conditions in Kjeldahl flasks so that no transference of seedlings was necessary in the analyses. The seedlings were grown for 15 days, and the nitrogen content of the growing seedlings and that of the sterilized seeds were found to be identical. One is thus justified in concluding that no nitrogen in the gaseous form is lost during the early stages of these seedlings. Davidson (1926) found that wheat seedlings floating on distilled water differ in composition from the stock seed from which they were obtained. In 7 days from the time the seeds were set to germinate, or 3 to 4 days after germination, the nitrogen content of the seedlings was approximately 10 per cent higher than the nitrogen content of the stock seeds. This fact seems to be due to the leaching of the nitrogen from the ungerminated seeds and its reabsorption by the growing seedlings. The reserve in these seeds is mostly carbohydrate and it would seem advisable that the loss of nitrogen should be investigated in the germination of seeds in which the major portion of the reserve material is of an oily nature.

Miller (1910) in studying the chemical changes in the germination of the sunflower seed found evidence indicating that there might be a loss of nitrogen from these seeds during the first 3 days of their germination. The total nitrogen in 100 seeds before germination amounted to 346 mg. and at the end of the 3-day period, when the hypocotyls were 2.5 to 3.5 cm. in length, the total nitrogen of 100 seedlings amounted to 292 mg.—a loss amounting to approximately 15 per cent of the total nitrogen present in the seed. The total nitrogen in the seedlings at four other more advanced stages showed no loss of nitrogen whatsoever. Newcomb and Miller (1927) determined the nitrogen content of the seeds and seedlings of the sunflower and squash. They obtained data indicating that a loss of nitrogen occurred during the germination of these seeds, the loss amounting to from 5 to 6 per cent of the nitrogen content of the seed. This loss occurred while the hypocotyl and radicle were attaining a length of 4 to 5 cm. Several sources of error were overlooked, however, and a more careful study of this subject is needed before any definite statements can be made. In the squash plant Reid (1930) suggested that a relatively small amount of nitrogen might be lost as a result of the respiratory process in the leaves. Although the question of the loss of nitrogen from the germinating seed seems as yet not to be definitely settled, the loss of nitrogen from plants growing in the field seems to be confined wholly to the diffusion outward of nitrogenous salts into the soil, to the leaching of the stems and leaves by rains, and to the falling off of certain parts of the plants.

VI. CARBON/NITROGEN RELATIONS

Reproduction in plants, as well as their vegetative growth, may be controlled, to some extent at least, by varying their external and internal conditions. Recently it has been found that rather definite carbon and nitrogen relations in the plant influence its response in regard to vegetative growth and reproduction. The relationship of the carbon and nitrogen content of the plant has come to be expressed as the "carbon/nitrogen ratio," a term, however, that has been rather loosely used. To some it is the carbohydrate/nitrogen ratio; to others the carbohydrate/insoluble-nitrogen ratio is the important one; others consider the effective ratio to be the starch/nitrogen; while yet others express the relationship as the ratio of the total carbon to the total nitrogen.

In 1916 Fisher reported that the végetative condition was characterized by a carbohydrate content relatively low in proportion to the nitrogen or, in other words, by a low carbohydrate/nitrogen ratio. He found that the reproductive condition was characterized by a carbohydrate content relatively high in proportion to the nitrogen content, a condition that is designated as a high carbohydrate/nitrogen ratio. Kraus and Kraybill (1918) in their nutrition studies of the tomato plant brought out clearly that the carbohydrate/nitrogen relation influences its growth and reproduction. They recognized four conditions that had a decided effect upon the behavior of this plant. These may be summarized as follows:

(1) A very high carbohydrate/nitrogen ratio accompanying a weakly vegetative condition. Here nitrogen appears to be a limiting factor of growth and the high ratio is apparently due to the small amount of nitrogen present. (2) A high carbohydrate/nitrogen ratio accompanying abundant fruit production. In this type, nitrogen compounds are available, but the high ratio is due to an excess of carbohydrates. (3) A low carbohydrate/nitrogen ratio accompanying a vigorous vegetative condition. In this type there appears to be an available supply of both carbohydrate and nitrogen and the balance between them is such as to produce the best vegetative conditions without leaving a residue of carbohydrate. (4) An exceedingly low carbohydrate/nitrogen ratio accompanying a weakly vegetative condition. In this type carbohydrates appear to be the limiting factor of growth, and the low ratio is due to the small amount of carbohydrate present, while the amount of nitrogen appears to be an indifferent factor.

Nightingale (1922) in experiments with salvia, buckwheat, soybeans, and radish concluded that the carbohydrate/insoluble-nitrogen ratio is the effective one in relation to vegetative growth and reproduction in these plants. He considered that nitrates may be stored in the plant until the proper conditions arise for synthesis to other forms of nitrogen and that the presence of nitrates as such in the plant does not appear to affect materially the type of growth of the plant. Gurjar (1920) noted in the case of the tomato that the carbon/nitrogen ratio may be as high as 19 and as low as 2 but that the fruiting took place between the ratios 4 and 6. Work (1924) considered that a nitrogen content of 0.3 per cent on a green basis in this plant is conducive to a vigorous vegetative growth.

Kraus and Kraybill (1918) also found that withholding moisture from plants grown under conditions of relative abundance of available nitrogen results in much the same condition of fruitfulness and carbohydrate storage as the limiting of the supply of available nitrogen. They further concluded that fertilizers containing available nitrogen or that which may be readily made available are mainly effective in producing vegetative response and that they may either increase or decrease fruitfulness according to the relative available carbohydrate supply. They also pointed out that pruning and girdling are largely effective in promoting or retarding fruitfulness by their effects in balancing the carbohydrate supply within the plant or the means for its manufacture with the available moisture and nitrogen supply. These observations of Kraus and Kraybill have greatly stimulated investigations in regard to the carbohydrate/nitrogen relation, since it offers a means of outlining methods of practice in regard to fertilizing, pruning, and ringing based upon physiological relations. It is not the intention here, however, to consider any of the methods of agricultural practice but to mention only some of the carbohydrate/nitrogen relationships that so far have been observed.

A. Fruit-bud Formation

The effects of the amount of nitrogen, and the time and manner of its application upon fruit-bud production have been extensively studied. Only a brief résumé of some of the work will be given here because a detailed consideration of this topic belongs to the field of practical horticulture rather than to the field of plant physiology.

1. The Carbohydrate/Nitrogen Relation.—The relationship of carbohydrate and nitrogen in regard to fruit-bud formation has been extensively studied in the apple by Hooker (1920 to 1924), Roberts (1920), Harvey and Murneek (1921), Harvey (1923), and Kraybill (1923).

Hooker (1920 to 1924) in his investigations of the seasonal changes in the chemical composition of apple spurs found that conditions leading to high starch and low nitrogen content at the time of fruit-bud differentiation appear to be essential for productivity. Fruit-bearing spurs that develop leaf buds have a low starch and a high nitrogen content, and barren spurs, which neither blossom nor produce fruit buds, have a low starch and a low nitrogen content. The starch/nitrogen ratio was more indicative than the total carbohydrate/nitrogen ratio. Starting with an apple spur in the off year, it contains slightly less ash including potassium and phosphorus, less nitrogen, and less starch than a spur at the beginning of the bearing year, but it is higher in dry weight, reducing sugars, and polysaccharoses. During the spring, water is absorbed, the stored starch is hydrolyzed to sugar, and the sugar is utilized along with phosphorus and nitrogen in the production of new growth. During this period of the utilization of reserves and production of new vegetative tissue the acidity, polysaccharoses, and, to some extent, the potassium content increase. Eventually the supply of available carbohydrates is reduced to a minimum, whereupon terminal-bud formation takes place on spurs. After this, growth practically stops and is accompanied by a falling off of acidity and polysaccharose content. By the photosynthetic activity of the newly formed leaves a fresh supply of reducing sugar is formed, some of which is stored in the form of starch and other polysaccharoses, resulting in an increase of dry weight. At the same time, the potassium and phosphorus content increase somewhat while the nitrogen content continues to fall off. As a result of this condition, leading to a high starch and a low nitrogen content late in June, fruit-bud differentiation occurs.

It was observed by Roberts (1921), under conditions of low nitrogen nutrition, that the type and appearance of foliage and growth of the apple tree are more influenced by the composition of the wood as a result of previous treatment than they are by the current seasonal conditions. Thus, for example, trees that were previously poor vegetatively made little growth when maintained in a low nitrogen nutrient, while trees that were previously very vegetative made an excellent growth after being transferred to a low nitrogen nutrient.

Harvey and Murneek (1921) and Harvey (1923) investigated the effects of defoliation and ringing of apple twigs and spurs with especial reference to the carbohydrate/nitrogen ratio. In the case of defoliation, it was found that the defoliated spurs, as compared to the checks, contained more nitrate nitrogen, total nitrogen, and insoluble nitrogen, more reducing sugars, and less total carbohydrates and a smaller value for the carbohydrate/nitrogen ratio. In general, the bearing and sterile spurs showed extreme values, while the nonbearing spurs assumed an intermediate position between them. Howlett (1923) considered that the lack of an adequate supply of nitrogen, rather than a lack of carbohydrates, is more often the limiting factor to normal flower development in the case of the apple.

It was observed by Potter and Phillips (1930) for the Baldwin apple that the insoluble nitrogen was the constituent which was most consistently associated with the formation of fruit buds. Its accumulation accompanied their formation, while the accumulation of carbohydrates depressed their development.

Finch (1935) noted in apple trees that the degree of vegetativeness is closely related to the chemical composition of the tree especially as regards the amount of carbohydrates and nitrogen. The starch/nitrogen ratio and the total carbohydrate/nitrogen ratio were highest in the fruitful terminal shoots of trees of biennially bearing varieties. These ratios were the lowest in the unfruitful, terminal shoots of the trees of biennially bearing varieties.

2. The Application of Nitrogen.—Hooker also found that the chief effects of spring applications of nitrogenous fertilizers to healthy apple trees are, on bearing trees, an increased set of fruit associated with a greater nitrogen content in the spurs during the period of fruit setting and, in nonbearing trees, an increased rate of growth. Spring applications of nitrogenous fertilizers do not favor starch accumulation at the period of fruit-bud differentiation, and consequently they could not be expected to favor the process. The later in the season nitrogenous fertilizers are applied the greater is the nitrogen content of the spurs the following spring immediately before growth begins.

Hofman (1930) believed that the application of nitrogen in the autumn to orchards in Virginia produced the best growth and yields. Harley, Masure, and Magness (1932) believed that the principal factor in the initiation of fruit-bud formation in apple is the ratio of the amount of foliage to the amount of fruit. In Delicious apples the time of bud differentiation extends over a relatively long period during the summer. Thus apparently some buds are differentiated as early as June 17, while the formation of others could be influenced as late as July 29 by some treatments. Harlan and Collison (1933) noted that under the conditions of low fertility the use of nitrogen fertilizer produced increased yields of apples. Applications of nitrogen in the early spring produced larger yields than did the application in summer. The application of sodium nitrate after blooming did not produce any greater yield than did the application in the spring.

Lagassé (1935) reported that the application of nitrogen over a 5-year period to Yellow Transparent apple trees increased the diameter and the terminal growth of the tree but had no effect on the total yield of fruit.

It was noticed by Plagge (1930) that single or successive, annual applications of sodium nitrate to Jonathan and Grimes apple trees increased the susceptibility of the fruit to soggy breakdown. Potter and others (1930) found that at the time of the maximum increase in growth of the apple in July, each fruit absorbed daily approximately 1 mg. of nitrogen and about 300 mg. of carbohydrate. When nitrogen is applied to apple trees, Marth (1934) obtained the best results when the fertilizer was spread just outside the branches where the greater proportion of the fibrous roots were located in the upper soil. Gardner (1923), in the case of the strawberry, reported that when moisture and temperature are not limiting factors, the number of flower clusters, number of flowers, and size of berries are dependent on nutritive conditions within the plant during the preceding fall and winter and are practically independent of soil-fertility conditions during the spring and at the time of fruiting. Treatments that would increase production through modifying fertility, therefore, should be given during the summer and fall months. He further stated that the maximum production of flower clusters, flowers, and berries was associated with those summer and fall treatments that led to the greatest accumulation of starch and total carbohydrates at the time of fruit-bud differentiation. Taylor (1932) found in Alabama that the application of nitrogen in the autumn to strawberry plants, and then again about 90 days prior to the first harvest gave the best production of a large number of flower clusters effective in producing a crop. Schilletter (1932) considered that low temperature or lack of moisture taken separately or in combination are associated with the time of fruit formation of the strawberry. Gardner also noted that low carbohydrate and low starch content at the time of fruit-bud differentiation led to the production of female flowers in a variety that is normally hermaphroditic. In the strawberry, a low carbohydrate content is apparently associated with the female condition, high carbohydrate content with the male condition, and an intermediate carbohydrate content with hermaphroditism. Talley (1934) analyzed the aerial portions of the staminate and pistillate plants of hemp at flowering. The staminate plants were higher in total carbohydrates, polysaccharides, and sugars than the pistillate plants. Nitrogen was more abundant in the pistillate than in the staminate regions of the respective plants. Platenius (1932) considered that the formation of the reproductive organs of celery is not determined by nutritional factors that involve the entire plant. He thought it possible that the ultimate cause of the formation of the seed stalk is localized accumulation of certain chemical compounds in the meristematic tissue possibly involving only a few cells.

B. Length of Day

It was observed by Garner and Allard (1920) in their investigations on the effect of the length of day and night upon growth and reproduction, that there are some plants which bloom and produce seed under light conditions of relatively short duration, but which when the length of day is increased become strongly vegetative and unfruitful. Other plants, however, require a long day to be reproductive and become weakly vegetative when the length of day is shortened. These observations led to the assumption by some that the light requirements might be associated in some manner with the quantity of carbohydrates manufactured during the light period and its relationship to the nitrogen supply. A survey of the light responses, however, indicates that the problem is a complicated one and is difficult to interpret on the basis of photosynthetic activity. Thus the effects produced are due not to the total quantity of radiation received but rather to the actual length of the exposure period. Plants exposed for long daily periods to sunlight of only one-fourth full intensity behaved similarly to plants exposed to full intensity for the same period and not in the same manner as plants exposed to full intensity for one-fourth the length of time. It is not known, however, whether the difference in total radiation was accompanied by differences in the photosynthetic activity, and other factors might have regulated or influenced the rate of photosynthesis.

The effect of the light period on the fertilizer requirements of plants was studied by Nightingale and Kraus (1924). They found in the case of tomatoes that light, within the limits of a 6-hr. day, did not appear markedly to limit the building up of nitrates to insoluble forms of nitrogen, provided there was present an available supply of carbohydrates. Buckwheat, soybeans, radish, and salvia of the varieties used were limited, however, in the building of nitrates to insoluble forms of nitrogen by a 7-hr. day, as it occurred in the greenhouse, even though there was present an available supply of carbohydrates.

Werner (1934) reported for the potato plant that high temperatures, long days, and an abundant supply of nitrogen favored vegetative growth in all plant parts except the tubers. Early tuberization was induced with low temperature, short days, and a deficiency of nitrogen. Maximum tuberization occurred with days of intermediate length, low temperature, and an abundant supply of nitrogen.

C. Different Stages of Growth

The value of the total-carbon/total-nitrogen ratio was determined by Hicks (1928) for different stages of growth of Starling winter wheat and of Nevin and Marquis spring wheats. The stages considered were (1) the seedling stage up to the active photosynthetic action of the first leaf and the exhaustion of the seed's store of food, (2) the vegetative cycle up to the heading period, and (3) the fruiting stage.

The seedling stage is characterized by a rapid drop in the carbon and nitrogen percentage. Carbon is lost by respiration, but most of the reserve in the endosperm is taken into the embryo. No nitrogen is lost, but the actual amount is increased by the withdrawal of the reserves from the endosperm, although the percentage is decreased owing to the increased dry weight of the young plant. The carbon/nitrogen ratio in the seedling stage remains low, is constant, and is of practically the same value as that of the ungerminated embryo. The vegetative cycle opens with a low carbon and fairly high nitrogen and with a low carbon/nitrogen balance. After the emergence of the first leaf and the beginning of active photosynthesis, there is a rise in the carbon curve. The carbon/nitrogen ratio shows a marked increase throughout the whole vegetative period. At the time of the highest carbon/nitrogen ratio, flower initials appear, and a general movement in the plant of the carbohydrates and the soluble nitrogen constituents through the stem and into the reproductive parts occurs. After fertilization, the carbon/nitrogen ratio decreases in the developing organs until a very low value is shown by the mature embryo. Hicks further observed that the three strains of wheat showed differences in the rate of carbon accumulation. In winter wheat it accumulates very slowly, the plant maintaining an intermediate carbon/nitrogen ratio. A much higher carbon/nitrogen ratio is required to produce flowers in the winter wheat than in the spring types. Thus a carbon/nitrogen ratio of 14 to 17 covers the range of conditions favorable to flowering in the spring wheats, while a ratio of 31 was required by the winter wheat. Hicks concluded that although each strain examined had its own initial carbon/nitrogen ratio value at which flowers are initiated, it represents in every case the maximum of the ascending carbon/nitrogen ratio curve.

D. Variations of Ratio in Different Organs of the Plant

The carbon/nitrogen ratio for different parts of the wheat plant was determined by Hicks (1928) at different stages of growth. In the case of a plant in the vegetative phase at the tenth leaf stage, the carbon/nitrogen ratio at the base of the stem was 13.7, at the middle of the stem 12.4, and at the upper portion 11.9. In the case of the tenth leaf, the lower half had a carbon/nitrogen ratio of 8.1 while the upper half had a ratio of 6.5. The carbon content was practically constant throughout the length of the stem, but the nitrogen increased from the base upward. In the case of the roots of plants in the fruiting stage, the carbon/nitrogen ratio of the secondary roots was 19, while that of the root hairs was 15. Hicks concluded from these observations that as a general rule in developing annual plants "the younger the tissue the lower the carbon/nitrogen ratio."

E. Effect on Root and Shoot Growth

Much study has been made on the effect of the relation of nitrogen and carbohydrates to root and shoot growth. Chandler (1919), in peach trees, found that root development is increased less than top growth by the addition of nitrates, and Gericke (1922) stated that an abnormally large root development of wheat seedlings, in proportion to that of tops, is primarily associated with a deficiency of nitrogen in the medium in which the plants are rooted. As mentioned in Chap. III, Turner (1922) found that barley and corn showed significant increases in ratios of tops to roots as the nitrate concentration of the solution was increased, but that flax plants did not show such an increased ratio. When nitrogen is lacking in the nutrient medium, the plant is able to utilize in new growth the nitrogen that is stored within the plant. It has been shown by Roberts (1921) that apple trees can absorb nitrogen, store it as a reserve, and later utilize it in growth. An abundant supply of carbohydrates stimulates root development. Thus it has been observed by Dachnowski (1914), Knudson (1916), Curtis (1918), and others that when twigs, cuttings, or plants are grown in sugar solutions an increased root development results.

It was observed by Davies (1931) that willow shoots develop in the area of highest total nitrogen per gram of dry weight of the cutting, while the roots regenerate in the area of lowest total nitrogen per gram of dry weight of cutting. Harrison (1934) found that it was possible to influence the amounts and relative proportions of the various parts of bluegrass by limiting the supply of nitrogen. As the supply of nitrogen was decreased, the relative amount of top growth diminished, while that of the roots and rhizomes increased.

Starring (1923) studied the effect of the carbohydrate/nitrogen content upon the production of roots on the cuttings of tomato and *Tradescantia* and found that the best production of roots is obtained from those cuttings which have a high content of carbohydrate. When carbohydrates are absent or low in amount, the cuttings develop no roots; and if there is sufficient carbohydrate merely to initiate the growth of roots, they make little or no growth. No wide differences in root development could be secured by varying the nitrogen content.

Reid (1924, 1926) investigated the behavior of cuttings taken from tomato plants that had been grown under conditions to produce the extremes in the carbohydrate/nitrogen ratio. Her results indicated that a high-nitrogen supply plus a readily available supply of carbohydrates appears to furnish favorable conditions for shoot growth. A somewhat limited nitrogen supply plus a readily available supply of carbohydrates appears to furnish conditions for root growth, and, in general, the cutting has a tendency to do what the plant, from which it is taken, has been doing. She observed also that shoots are produced in greater number in light than in darkness. A greater quantity of roots is produced in darkness than in light by high-carbohydrate cuttings having a moderately high internal nitrogen reserve and growing in solutions lacking nitrates. If, however, high-carbohydrate cuttings with a lower nitrogen reserve are grown under the same conditions, a greater quantity of roots is produced in light than in darkness. Hicks (1928) obtained similar results in the case of normal cuttings of *Salix viminalis* and in those injected with potassium nitrate and various sugars. She considered that the initiation of growth is due to stimulated respiration giving energy for the withdrawal of nitrogen into the bast and its consequent upward translocation, particularly to the buds. The injected sugars hasten this considerably, while potassium nitrate in excess prevents the commencement of growth. Hicks concluded that shoots grow at the area of the lowest carbon/nitrogen ratio and roots at the highest. Reid (1926) also found that different kinds of seedlings show very different growth responses, which are often related to the chemical composition of the seed. Thus the higher the nitrogen in proportion to the carbohydrate content of the seed the higher the shoot/root ratios of the seedlings. The shoot/root ratios in seedlings ranged from 2.01 for low-protein wheat to 8.37 for sunflower. In the case of high-protein corn and high-protein wheat, the shoot/root ratios are higher than the corresponding types that are low in protein. It was also found that with the exception of cotton seedlings, the shoot/root ratios of all types were increased by the addition of nitrates, but that the seedlings of *Leguminosae* were the least responsive in this respect. Reid makes the significant statement that it is apparently inadvisable to draw conclusions as to the effect of mineral nutrients upon the subsequent growth of plants when the observations are based on growth responses during the first 3 weeks of growth only. Before studying the effect of an element or compound on growth it would therefore seem desirable to conduct experiments in which the storage supply of the elements or compound in question has been at least partially exhausted by the seedling.

F. Significance in Agricultural Practice

The investigations of the carbon/nitrogen ratio indicate its importance upon the vegetative growth and reproduction of plants. When, however, an attempt is made to formulate methods of agricultural practice based upon the carbon/nitrogen ratio, the complexity of the problem and the lack of definite information on this subject become evident. Little or nothing is known concerning the question of cumulative and reciprocal influences or the effect of the length of the growing season as influenced by weather upon the relations of carbon to nitrogen. In this regard it is necessary to consider not only the accumulation of reserves but also the relative rates of nitrogen absorption and of carbohydrate synthesis at the critical periods of growth (Knight, 1924). Hooker (1925) enumerated various ways in which the carbohydrate/nitrogen relations may be varied. Thus the carbohydrate content may be increased by girdling, by thinning, and by the application of nitrogen at certain times. It can be decreased by shading, by shortening the daily period of illumination, by defoliation, by heading, and by manuring with nitrogen. The nitrogen content, on the other hand, can be increased by manuring, by shading, by defoliation, and by certain types of pruning. It may be decreased by girdling or defoliation early in the season or by local suppression of growth through pruning, and in some cases the insoluble nitrogen may be increased by shortening the day. The nitrogen content may also be decreased by sod or intercrops.

In conclusion it may be stated that the facts that have been observed concerning the carbon/nitrogen ratio have thrown light only on many established practices, as, for example, manuring, pruning, and girdling, and have thus shown that certain fairly definite physiological processes occur as a result of these practices. The knowledge concerning the carbon/nitrogen ratio is thus at present not sufficient to formulate any methods of agricultural practice other than those which have long been established. The information that has been obtained in regard to the carbon/nitrogen ratio has helped to a certain extent to account for some of the conflicting results that have been obtained from certain agricultural practices. It is now known that the results obtained from agricultural practices will depend upon both the internal and external conditions that prevail both before and after the plant has been treated.

Bibliography

ACQUA, C., 1910: The place in which nitrates are utilized by plants, *Exp. Sta. Rec.*, **24**: 531.

ADDOMS, R. M., and F. C. MOUNCE, 1931: Notes on the nutrient requirements and the histology of the cranberry (*Vaccinium macrocarpon*) with special reference to mycorrhiza, *Plant Physiol.*, **6**: 653–666.

——— and ———, 1932: Further notes on the nutrient requirements and the histology of the cranberry, with special reference to the sources of nitrogen, *Plant Physiol.*, **7**: 643–656.

ALLISON, F. E., and H. J. MORRIS, 1930: Nitrogen fixation by blue-green algae, *Sci.*, **71**: 221–223.

ALWAY, F. J., and G. H. NESOM, 1930: Protein content of reed canary grass on peat soils, *J. Agr. Res.*, **40**: 297–321.

AMES, J. W., 1910: The composition of wheat. Influence of various factors on the phosphorus, potassium, and nitrogen content of the wheat plant, *Ohio Sta. Bull.* 221.

ANDERSON, V. L., 1924: Some observations on the nitrate-reducing properties of plants, *Ann. Bot.*, **38**: 699–706.

ARMSTRONG, G. M., and W. B. ALBERT, 1931: A study of the cotton plant with especial reference to its nitrogen content, *J. Agr. Res.*, **42**: 689–703.

ARRINGTON, L. B., and J. W. SHIVE, 1935: Rates of absorption of ammonium and nitrate nitrogen from culture solutions by ten-day-old tomato seedlings at two pH levels, *Soil Sci.*, **39**: 431–435.

ASHBY, E., 1929: The interaction of factors in the growth of *Lemna*. IV, The influence of minute quantities of organic matter upon growth and reproduction, *Ann. Bot.*, **43**: 805–816.

ASO, K., and T. SEKINE, 1914: Nitrites in plants. *Beih. bot. Centrbl.*, **32**: 146–147; *Exp. Sta. Rec.*, **33**: 627.

ATWATER, W. O., and E. W. ROCKWOOD, 1886: On the loss of nitrogen by plants during germination and growth, *Am. Chem. J.*, **8**: 327–343.

BALY, E. C. C., I. M. HEILBRON, and D. P. HUDSON, 1922: Photocatalysis. II, The photosynthesis of nitrogen compounds from nitrates and carbon dioxide, *J. Chem. Soc.* (London), **121**: 1078–1088.

———, ———, and H. J. STERN, 1923: Photocatalysis. III, The photosynthesis of naturally occurring nitrogen compounds from carbon dioxide and ammonia, *J. Chem. Soc.* (London), **123**: 185–197.

BAMBACIONI, V., 1923: Contribuzione alla conoscenza del luogo di formazione del sostanza organiche azotate nei vegetali, *Atti R. Accad. Lincei Roma Rendiconte Cl. Sci. Mat. e. Nat.*, **32**: 108–110.

———, 1926: Ulteriori osservazioni sul luogo in cui si compie l'organizzazione dell'-azoto nei vegetali superiori, *Ann. Botanica*, **17**: 4–23; *Biol. Abst.*, **2**: 873.

BARBERA, G., 1933: Proteine e sostanze azotate non proteiche contenute nel succo di erba medica, *Ann. Chim. Applicata*, **23**: 462–470; *Biol. Abst.*, **10**: 27.

BAUDISCH, O., 1921: The mechanism of reduction of nitrates and nitrites in process of assimilation, *J. Biol. Chem.*, **48**: 489–502.

———, 1923: On the formation of organic compounds from inorganic by the influence of light, *Sci.*, **57**: 451–457.

BEAUMONT, A. B., C. J. LARSINOS, P. PIEKENBROCK, and P. R. NELSON, 1931: The assimilation of nitrogen by tobacco, *J. Agr. Res.*, **43**: 559–567.

———, W. S. EISENMENGER, and W. J. MOORE, 1933: Assimilation of fixed nitrogen by grasses and clovers, *J. Agr. Res.*, **47**: 495–503.

——— and W. J. MOORE, 1933: The absorption and assimilation of ammonic and nitric nitrogen by plants, *Am. Fertilizer*, **79**: 7–9, 24–27.

BENNET-CLARK, T. A., 1933: The role of the organic acids in plant metabolism, *New Phytol.*, **32**: 197–230.

BEYERINCK, M. W., 1888: Die Bacterien der Papilionaceen-Knöllchen, *Bot. Ztg.*, **46**: 725–735, 741–750, 757–771, 781–790, 797–802.

BJÖRKSTEN, J., 1930: Zur Kenntnis der Synthese von Eiweissstoffen und ihrer Bausteine bei höheren Pflanzen, *Biochem. Z.*, **225**: 1–80.

BLACKMAN, G. E., 1934: The ecological and physiological action of ammonium salts on the clover content of turf, *Ann. Bot.*, **48**: 975–1001.

BONCQUET, P. A., 1916: Presence of nitrites and ammonia in diseased plants, *J. Am. Chem. Soc.*, **38**: 2572–2576.

BOTTOMLEY, W. B., 1917: Some effects of organic growth promoting substances (auximones) on the growth of *Lemna minor* in mineral culture solutions, *Proc. Roy. Soc.*, B, **89**: 481–508.

———, 1919: The isolation from peat of certain nucleic acid derivatives, *Proc. Roy. Soc.*, B, **90**: 39–44.

———, 1920: The effect of nitrogen-fixing organisms and nucleic acid derivatives on plant growth, *Proc. Roy. Soc.*, B, **91**: 83–95.

———, 1920: The growth of *Lemna* plants in mineral solutions and in their natural medium, *Ann. Bot.*, **34**: 345–352.

———, 1920: The effect of organic matter on the growth of various water plants in cultural solutions, *Ann. Bot.*, **34**: 353–365.

BOUSSINGAULT, J., 1854–1855: *Ann. Chim. et Phys.*, 3 ser., tomes 41, 43.

———, 1838: Recherches chimiques sur la végétation entreprises dans le but d'examiner si les plantes prennent l'azote à l'atmosphère, *Ann. Chim. et Phys.*, **67**: 5–54.

BOUSSINGAULT, M., 1864: De la végétation dans l'obscurité, *C. R. Acad. Sci. Paris*, **58**: 917–922.

BRENCHLEY, W. E., and A. D. HALL, 1908–1910: The development of the grain of wheat, *J. Agr. Sci.*, **3**: 193–217.

———, 1909: On the strength and development of the grain of wheat (*Triticum vulgare*), *Ann. Bot.*, **23**: 117–140.

———, 1912: The development of the grain of barley, *Ann. Bot.*, **26**: 903–928.

BRIGHAM, R. O., 1917: Assimilation of organic nitrogen by *Zea mays* and the influence of *Bacillus subtilis* on such assimilation, *Soil Sci.*, **3**: 155–197.

BRISTOL, B. M., and H. J. PAGE, 1923: A critical enquiry into the alleged fixation of nitrogen by green algae, *Ann. App. Biol.*, **10**: 378–409.

BROWN, R., 1933: Nitrogen fixation in the genus *Lolium*, *Nature*, **131**: 169–170.

BURK, D., 1927: Does the pea plant fix atmospheric nitrogen? *Plant Physiol.*, **2**: 83–90.

BURKE, E., 1925: The influence of nitrate nitrogen upon the protein content and yield of wheat, *J. Agr. Res.*, **31**: 1189–1199.

BURKHART, L., 1934: Metabolism of etiolated seedlings as affected by ammonium nutrition, *Plant Physiol.*, **9**: 351–358.

BURRELL, R. C., 1926: Effect of certain deficiencies on nitrogen metabolism of plants, *Bot. Gaz.*, **82**: 320–328.

CAMERON, S. H., and D. APPLEMAN, 1933: The distribution of total nitrogen in the orange trees, *Proc. Am. Soc. Hort. Sci.*, **30**: 341–348.

CAMPBELL, E. G., 1924: Nitrogen content of weeds, *Bot. Gaz.*, **78**: 103–115.

CHANDLER, W. H., 1919: Some results as to the response of fruit trees to pruning, *Proc. Am. Soc. Hort. Sci.*, **16**: 88–101.

CHANNON, H. J., and C. A. M. FOSTER, 1934: The phosphatides of the wheat germ, *Biochem. J.*, **28**: 853–864.

CHAPMAN, A. G., 1933: Some effects of varying amounts of nitrogen on the growth of tulip poplar seedlings, *Ohio J. Sci.*, **33**: 164–181.

CHIBNALL, A. C., and S. B. SCHRYVER, 1920: The isolation of proteins from leaves, *Proc. Physiol. Soc., J. Physiol.*, **54**: 1–2.

——— and ———, 1921: Isolation of proteins from leaves, *Biochem. J.*, **15**: 60–75.

———, 1922: The distribution of nitrogen in the leaves of the runner bean, *Biochem. J.*, **16**: 344–362.

———, 1922: The effect of low-temperature drying on the distribution of nitrogen in the leaves of the runner bean, *Biochem. J.*, **16**: 599–607.

———, 1922: Distribution of nitrogen in the dead leaves of the runner bean, *Biochem. J.*, **16**: 608–610.

———, 1923: A new method for the separate extraction of vacuole and protoplasmic material from the leaf cells, *J. Biol. Chem.*, **55**: 333–342.

———, 1923: Diurnal variations in the total nitrogen content of foliage leaves, *Ann. Bot.*, **37**: 511–518.

———, 1924: Investigation on the nitrogenous metabolism of the higher plants. V, Diurnal variations in the protein nitrogen of runner bean leaves, *Biochem. J.*, **18**: 387–394.

———, 1924: The role of asparagine in the metabolism of the mature plant, *Biochem. J.*, **18**: 395–404.

———, 1924: Leaf protein metabolism in normal and abnormal runner bean plants, *Biochem. J.*, **18**: 405–407.

——— and C. E. GROVER, 1926: A chemical study of leaf cell cytoplasm. I, The soluble proteins, *Biochem. J.*, **20**: 108–118.

———, 1926: Leaf cytoplasmic proteins, *J. Am. Chem. Soc.*, **48**: 728–732.

———, E. J. Miller, D. H. Hall, and R. G. Westall, 1933: The proteins of grasses. II, A new method of preparation, *Biochem. J.*, **27**: 1879–1884.

Chrapowicki, W., 1889: Beobachtungen über die Eiweissbildung in den chlorophyllführenden Pflanzen, *Arbeiten St. Petersburger Natur. Ges.*, **18**: 1–27.

Ciamician, G., and C. Ravenna, 1919 and 1920: Sulla influenza di alcune sostanze organiche sullo sviluppo della piante, *Atti R. Accad. Lincei Rend*, **28**: 13–20; **29**: 7–13; *Bot. Abst.*, **6**: 194; **7**: 309.

——— and ———, 1919 and 1920: Sul contegno di alcune sostanze organiche nei vegetali, *Gaz. Chim. Italiana*, **49**: 83–126; **50**: 13–46; *Bot. Abst.*, **5**: 292; **7**: 308.

Clark, H. E., and J. W. Shive, 1934: The influence of the pH of a culture solution on the rates of absorption of ammonium and nitrate nitrogen by the tomato plant, *Soil Sci.*, **37**: 203–226.

——— and ———, 1934: The influence of the pH of a culture solution on the assimilation of ammonium and nitrate nitrogen by the tomato plant, *Soil Sci.*, **37**: 459–476.

———, 1936: Effect of ammonium and of nitrate nitrogen on the composition of the tomato plant, *Plant Physiol.*, **11**: 5–24.

Clark, J. H., 1933: Reaction of the nutrient medium as affecting growth of strawberry plants, *Proc. Am. Soc. Hort. Sci.*, **30**: 283–287.

Clark, N. A., 1924: The soil organic matter and growth-promoting accessory substances, *Ind. and Eng. Chem.*, **16**: 249–250.

——— and E. M. Roller, 1924: "Auximones" and the growth of the green plant, *Soil Sci.*, **17**: 193–199.

———, 1930: "Auximones" and the stimulation of *Lemna* by organic matter, *Sci.*, **71**: 268–269.

——— and E. M. Roller, 1931: The stimulation of *Lemna major* by organic matter under sterile and non sterile conditions, *Soil Sci.*, **31**: 299–310.

Cohn, E. J., J. Gross, and O. C. Johnson, 1919: The isoelectric points of the proteins in certain vegetable juices, *J. Gen. Physiol.*, **2**: 145–160.

Colby, H. L., 1933: Seasonal absorption of nutrient salts by the French prune grown in solution culture, *Plant Physiol.*, **8**: 1–34.

Conrad, J. P., 1934: Physiological acidity and alkalinity of inorganic nitrogenous compounds in solution cultures, *J. Am. Soc. Agron.*, **26**: 364–372.

Cook, R. L., 1930: Effect of soil type on the nitrate content of the expressed sap and the total nitrogen content of the tissue of the small grains, *J. Am. Soc. Agron.*, **22**: 393–409.

Coons, G. H., and L. J. Klotz, 1925: The nitrogen constituents of celery plants in health and disease, *J. Agr. Res.*, **31**: 287–300.

Copeland, J. J., 1932: Nitrogen fixation by *Myxophyceae*, abst., *Am. J. Bot.*, **19**: 844.

Cordingley, H., J. Grainger, W. H. Pearsall, and A. Wright, 1934: The effect of mosaic disease upon certain metabolic products in the tobacco plant, *Ann. App. Biol.*, **21**: 78–89.

Coville, F. V., 1926: Buttermilk as a fertilizer for blueberries, *Sci.*, **64**: 94–96.

Crowther, E. M., 1925: A note on the availability of organic nitrogen compounds in pot experiments, *J. Agr. Sci.*, **15**: 300–302.

———, 1935: Comparative trials of calcium cyanamide and other nitrogenous fertilizers on arable crops, *Empire J. Exp. Agr.*, **3**: 129–143.

Crowther, F., 1914: Studies in growth analysis of the cotton plant under irrigation in the Sudan. I, The effects of different combinations of nitrogen applications and water supply, *Ann. Bot.*, **48**: 877–913.

CSONKA, F. A., J. S. MURPHY, and D. B. JONES, 1926: The isoelectric points of various proteins, *J. Am. Chem. Soc.*, **48**: 763–768.

——— and D. B. JONES, 1934: The cystine, tryptophane and tyrosine content of the soybean, *J. Agr. Res.*, **49**: 279–282.

CURTIS, O. F., 1918: Stimulation of root growth in cuttings by treatment with chemical compounds, *N. Y. Sta. (Cornell) Mem.* 14.

DACHNOWSKI, A., 1914: The effects of acid and alkaline solutions upon the water relation and the metabolism of plants, *Am. J. Bot.*, **1**: 412–439.

DAIKUHARA, G., 1905: On the application of magnesium in the form of magnesium sulphate for the needs of the rice plant, *Bull. Imp. Cent. Agr. Expt. Sta. Japan*, **1**: 24–29.

DAS, U. K., 1936: Nitrogen nutrition of sugar cane, *Plant Physiol.*, **11**: 251–317.

DASTUR, R. H., and T. J. MALKANI, 1933: The intake of nitrogen by the rice plant (*Oryza sativa*), *Indian J. Agr. Sci.*, **3**: 157–206; *Biol. Abst.*, **9**: 43; *Exp. Sta. Rec.*, **69**: 796.

DAVIDSON, J., and J. A. LECLERC, 1917, 1918: The effect of sodium nitrate applied at different stages of growth on the yield, composition, and quality of wheat. I, II, *J. Am. Soc. Agron.*, **9**: 145–154; **10**: 193–198.

———, 1922: The effect of nitrates applied at different stages of growth on the yield, composition, and quality of wheat, *J. Am. Soc. Agron.*, **14**: 118–122.

———, 1923: Is gaseous nitrogen a product of seedling metabolism? *Bot. Gaz.*, **76**: 95–102.

——— and J. A. LECLERC, 1923: Effect of various inorganic nitrogen compounds, applied at different stages of growth on the yield, composition, and quality of wheat, *J. Agr. Res.*, **23**: 55–69.

———, 1926: Changes in nitrogen, potassium, and phosphorus content of wheat seedlings during germination and early stages, *Bot. Gaz.*, **81**: 87–95.

DAVIDSON, O. W., and J. W. SHIVE, 1934: The influence of the hydrogen ion concentration of the culture solution upon the absorption and assimilation of nitrate and ammonium nitrogen by peach trees grown in sand cultures, *Soil Sci.*, **37**: 357–386.

DAVIES, P. A., 1931: Distribution of total nitrogen in regeneration of the willow, *Bot. Gaz.*, **91**: 320–326.

DENNY, F. E., 1933: Bases for calculations in measuring changes in leaves during the night, *Contr. Boyce Thompson Inst.*, **5**: 181–194.

DEWICHE, E. J., and W. E. TOTTINGHAM, 1930: Effect of climate on nitrogen content of maize, barley and red clover, *J. Am. Soc. Agron.*, **22**: 681–689.

DHAR, N. R., A. K. BHATTACHARYA, and N. N. BISWAS, 1933: Photonitrification of soil, *Soil Sci.*, **35**: 281–284.

——— and S. K. MUKHERJEE, 1934: Photosynthesis of amino acids *in vitro*, *Nature*, **134**: 499.

DITTRICH, W., 1930: Zur Physiologie des Nitratumsatzes in höheren Pflanzen (unter besonderer Berücksichtigung der Nitratspeicherung), *Planta*, **12**: 69–119.

DOMONTOVICH, SHESTAKOV, and POLOSSIN, 1933: Ueber die Änderung der Wasserstoffionenkonzentration der Nährlösung durch die Tätigkeit der Lupinenwurzeln, *Abh. Sowiet Sekt., Int. Bodenk. Gesells. K.*, **4**: 214. Quoted by Nicol, 1934.

DONEEN, L. D., 1934: Nitrogen in relation to composition, growth and yield of wheat, *Wash. Sta. Bull.* 296.

DREWES, K., 1928: Über die Assimilation des Luftsticksstoffs durch Blaualgen, *Cent. Bakt. Par., Abt.* 2, **76**: 88–101.

DUNLAP, A. A., 1930: The total nitrogen and carbohydrates, and the relative rates of respiration in virus infected plants, *Am. J. Bot.*, **17**: 348–357.

ECKERSON, S., 1917: Microchemical studies in the progressive development of the wheat plant, *Wash. Sta. Bull.* 139.

———, 1924: Protein synthesis by Plants. I, Nitrate reduction, *Bot. Gaz.*, **77**: 377–390.

———, 1930: Seasonal distribution of reductase in the various organs of an apple tree, *Am. J. Bot.*, **17**: 1045–1046.

———, 1931: Seasonal distribution of reductase in the various organs of an apple tree, *Contr. Boyce Thompson Inst.*, **3**: 405–412.

———, 1932: Conditions affecting nitrate reduction by plants, *Contr. Boyce Thompson Inst.*, **4**: 119–130.

EGGLETON, W. G. E., 1935: The assimilation of inorganic nitrogenous salts, including sodium nitrite by the grass plant, *Biochem. J.*, **29**: 1389–1397.

EISENMENGER, W. S., 1933: The distribution of nitrogen in tobacco when the supplies of nitrogen and of light are varied during the growing period, *J. Agr. Res.*, **46**: 255–266.

ELLETT, W. B., H. H. HILL, and W. G. HARRIS, 1915: The effect of association of legumes and non legumes, *Va. Sta. Tech. Bull.* 1.

EMDE, H., 1929: Alkaloid und Kohlensäureassimilation, *Naturwiss.*, **17**: 699–703; *Biol. Abst.*, **5**: 2666.

EMMERLING, A., 1880: Studien über die Eiweissbildung in der Pflanze. I, *Landw. Versuchs-Stat.*, **24**: 113–160.

———, 1887: Studien über die Eiweissbildung in der Pflanze. VII, *Landw. Versuchs-Stat.*, **34**: 1–91.

———, 1900: Studien über die Eiweissbildung in der Pflanze, *Landw. Versuchs-Stat.*, **54**: 215–281.

EMMERT, E. M., 1929: The determination of nitrate in green tomato and lettuce tissues, *Plant Physiol.*, **4**: 519–528.

———, 1936: Effect of drouth on the nutrient levels in the tomato plant, *Soil Sci.*, **41**: 67–70.

ENGEL, H., 1929: Beiträge zur Kenntnis des Stickstoffumsatzes grüner Pflanzen, *Planta*, **7**: 133–163; *Biol. Abst.*, **5**: 1616.

ENLOW, C. R., and J. M. COLEMAN, 1929: Increasing the protein content of pasture grasses by frequent light applications of nitrogen, *J. Am. Soc. Agron.*, **21**: 845–853.

ESPINO, R. B., 1920: Some aspects of the salt requirements of young rice plants, *Philippine J. Sci.*, **16**: 455–525.

EVANS, M. V., 1916: Some effects of legumes on associated non legumes, *J. Am. Soc. Agron.*, **8**: 348–357.

FAGAN, T. W., 1925: The variation in the moisture and nitrogen content of the potato during growth and storage, *Welsh J. Agr.*, **1**: 110–115; *Bot. Abst.*, **14**: 1441.

FEHER, D., and I. VAGI, 1924, 1926: Untersuchungen über die Einwirkung von Nitriten auf das Wachstum der Pflanzen, *Biochem. Z.*, **153**: 156–158; **174**: 262–270.

FINCH, A. H., 1935: Physiology of apple varieties, *Plant Physiol.*, **10**: 49–72.

FISCHER, E., 1899–1906: "Untersuchungen über Aminosäuren, Polypeptide, und Proteine," Julius Springer, Berlin, 770 pp.

FISHER, H., 1916: Zur Frage der Kohlensäureernährung der Pflanze, *Gartenflora*, **65**: 232–237.

———, 1917: Das Problem der Stickstoffbindung, Festlegung des Luftstickstoffs bei niederen Pflanzen, *Ber. bot. Ges.*, **35**: 423–454.

FISHER, P. L., 1935: Response of the tomato in solution cultures with deficiencies and excesses of certain essential elements, *Md. Sta. Bull.* 375.

FOSSE, M. R., 1912: Recherches sur l'urée, *C. R. Acad. Sci. Paris*, **155**: 851–852.

———, 1913: Formation de l'urée par deux moisissures, *C. R. Acad. Sci. Paris*, **156**: 263–265.

———, 1913: Formation de l'urée par les végétaux supérieurs, *C. R. Acad. Sci. Paris*, **156**: 567–568.

———, 1913: Recherche de l'urée dans les végétaux, *C. R. Acad. Sci. Paris*, **156**: 1938–1941.

———, 1914: Présence simultanée de l'urée et de l'uréase dans le même végétal, *C. R. Acad. Sci. Paris*, **158**: 1374–1376.

FRANK, B., 1888: Untersuchungen über die Ernährung der Pflanze mit Stickstoff und über den Kreislauf desselben in der Landwirthschaft, *Landw. Jahrb.*, **17**: 421–553.

———, 1889: Ueber den experimentellen Nachweis der Assimilation freien Stickstoffs durch erdbodenbewohnende Algen, *Ber. bot. Ges.*, **7**: 34–42.

——— and R. OTTO, 1891: New experiments concerning the assimilation of nitrogen by plants, *Exp. Sta. Rec.*, **3**: 64.

FREAR, D. E., 1930: The clarification of plant juices: Nitrate concentration in large and small leaves, *Sci.*, **72**: 634–635.

———, 1930: Estimation of the nitrate nitrogen in plant juice: A study of the expression and clarification of the juice, *Plant Physiol.*, **5**: 359–371.

———, 1931: A negative correlation observed between the nitrate nitrogen in the juice of beet leaves and the weight of the leaves, *J. Agr. Res.*, **42**: 53–56.

FUJITA, T., 1931: Über die Beziehungen zwischen dem Eiweissgehalt der Blätter und dem Grad der Sonnenbeleuchtung, *Bull. Kjusu. Imp. Univ. Fukuoka*, **4**: 358–368; *Biol. Abst.*, **6**: 2515.

GAINEY, P. L., and M. C. SEWELL, 1932: The role of nitrogen in the production of wheat fields, *J. Agr. Res.*, **45**: 129–148.

GARDNER, V. R., 1923: Studies in the nutrition of the strawberry, *Mo. Sta. Res. Bull.* 57.

GARNER, W. W., and H. A. ALLARD, 1920: Effect of the relative length of day and night and other factors of the environment on growth and reproduction in plants, *J. Agr. Res.*, **18**: 553–607.

GAUTRERET, R., 1934: Recherches sur la réduction du nitrate d'argent par les chloroplastes, *C. R. Acad. Sci. Paris*, **198**: 1252–1254; *Biol. Abst.*, **9**: 1012.

GEORGI, C. E., 1935: Influence of the carbohydrate-nitrogen relation on nodule production by red clover, *J. Agr. Res.*, **51**: 597–612.

GERICKE, W. F., 1920: On the protein content of wheat, *Sci.*, **52**: 446–447.

———, 1922: Certain relations between the protein content of wheat and the length of the growing period of the head-bearing stalks, *Soil Sci.*, **13**: 135–139.

———, 1922: Differences effected in the protein content of grain by applications of nitrogen made at different growing periods of the plants, *Soil Sci.*, **14**: 103–109.

———, 1922: Certain relations between root development and tillering in wheat; significance in the production of high-protein wheat, *Am. J. Bot.*, **9**: 366–369.

———, 1927: Why applications of nitrogen to land may cause either increase or decrease in the protein content of wheat, *J. Agr. Res.*, **35**: 133–141.

———, 1930: Variation in the percentage of protein in the grain of a single wheat plant, *Sci.*, **71**: 73–74.

GERLACH, M., and J. VOGEL, 1905: Ammoniakstickstoff als Pflanzennahrstoff, *Cent. Bakt. und Parasit.* II, **14**: 124–138.

GILE, P. L., 1935: Absorption of nitrates by corn in the dark, *Sci.*, **81**: 520–521.

GOURLEY, J. H., 1930: The relation of nitrogen to the storage quality of fruit, *Sci. Agr.*, **11**: 130–136.

GOUWENTAK, C. A., 1929: Untersuchungen über den N-Stoffwechsel bei *Helianthus annuus*, *Rec. trav. bot. Néerl.*, **26**: 19–96.

GRĂCANIN, M., 1932: Forschungen über die Beziehung zwischen Langenwachstum der Wurzeln und dem Stickstoffgehalt im Nährsubstrat, *Arbeiten der südslav. Akad. Wiss. u. Kunst.*, Bd. 244, Zagreb.

GREAVES, J. E., and E. G. CARTER, 1923: The influence of irrigation water on the composition of grains and the relationship to nutrition, *J. Biol. Chem.*, **58**: 531–541.

——— and D. H. NELSON, 1925: The influence of irrigation water and manure on the composition of the corn kernel, *J. Agr. Res.*, **31**: 183–191.

GREENHILL, A. W., and A. C. CHIBNALL, 1934: The exudation of glutamine from perennial rye grass, *Biochem. J.*, **28**: 1422–1427.

GRIFFITHS, A., 1891: On the direct absorption of ammoniacal salts by certain plants, *Chem. News*, **64**: 147.

GURJAR, A. M., 1920: Carbon nitrogen ratio in relation to plant metabolism, *Sci.*, **51**: 351–352.

HAAS, A. R. C., 1929: Effect of nitrate salt upon the growth and composition of tobacco leaves, *Bot. Gaz.*, **88**: 96–102.

HAAS, P., and T. G. HILL, 1913: "An Introduction to the Chemistry of Plant Products," Longmans, Green and Company, New York, 401 pp.

HAMNER, K. C., 1936: Effects of nitrogen supply on rates of photosynthesis and respiration in plants, *Bot. Gaz.*, **97**: 744–764.

HANSTEEN, B., 1896: Beiträge zur Kenntniss der Eiweissbildung und der Bedingungen der Realisirung dieses Processes in phanerogamen Pflanzenkörper, *Ber. bot. Ges.*, **14**: 362–371.

HARLAN, H. V., 1920: Daily development of kernels of Hannchen barley from flowering to maturity at Aberdeen, Idaho, *J. Agr. Res.*, **19**: 393–429.

HARLAN, J. D., and R. C. COLLISON, 1933: Experiments with commercial nitrogenous fertilizers on apple orchards, *N. Y. Sta. (Geneva) Bull.* 623.

HARLEY, C. P., M. P. MASURE, and J. R. MAGNESS, 1932: Effects of leaf area, nitrate of soda, and soil moisture on fruit bud formation in the Delicious apple, *Proc. Am. Soc. Hort. Sci.*, **29**: 193–198.

HARRISON, C. M., 1934: Responses of Kentucky blue grass to variations in temperature, light, cutting and fertilizing, *Plant Physiol.*, **9**: 83–106.

HARTLEY, K. T., and M. GREENWOOD, 1933: The effect of small applications of farm yard manure on the yield of cereals in Nigeria, *Empire J. Exp. Agr.*, **1**: 113–121.

HARVEY, E. M., and A. E. MURNEEK, 1921: The relation of carbohydrates and nitrogen to the behavior of apple spurs, *Ore. Sta. Bull.* 176.

———, 1923: A study of growth in summer shoots of the apple with special consideration of the rôle of carbohydrates and nitrogen, *Ore. Sta. Bull.* 200.

HEADDEN, W. P., 1915: Yellowberry in wheat, its cause and prevention, *Colo. Sta. Bull.* 205.

HELLRIEGEL, H., 1855: Beiträge zur Keimungsgeschichte der ölgebenden Samen, *J. Prakt. Chem.*, **64**: 94–107.

——— and H. WILFARTH, 1888: Untersuchungen über die Stickstoffnahrung der *Gramineen* und *Leguminosen*, *Beilage Z. Rüben zucker-Ind. Reich*, 234 pp.

HICKS, P. A., 1928: The carbohydrate/nitrogen ratio in the wheat plant, *New Phytol.*, **27**: 1–46.

———, 1928: Distribution of carbon/nitrogen ratio in the various organs of the wheat plant at different periods of its life history, *New Phytol.*, **27**: 108–116.

———, 1928: Chemistry of growth as represented by carbon/nitrogen ratio, *Bot. Gaz.*, **86**: 193–209.

HILL, H. H., 1930: Plant juice clarification for nitrate nitrogen determinations, *Sci.*, **71**: 540.

HOFMAN, F. W., 1930: Time of applying nitrogen to apple trees, *Proc. Am. Soc. Hort. Sci.*, **27**: 19–22.

HOLLEY, K. T., T. A. PICKETT, and T. G. DULIN, 1931: A study of ammonia and nitrate nitrogen for cotton. I, Influence on absorption of other elements, *Ga. Sta. Bull.* 169.

HOOKER, H. D., 1920: Seasonal changes in the chemical composition of apple spurs, *Mo. Sta. Res. Bull.* 40.

———, 1922: Certain responses of apple trees to nitrogen applications of different kinds and at different seasons, *Mo. Sta. Res. Bull.* 50.

———, 1922: Some effects of fall application of nitrogen to apple trees, *Proc. Am. Soc. Hort. Sci.*, **19**: 241–243.

———, 1924: Changes produced in apple trees by various types of pruning, *Mo. Sta. Res. Bull.* 72.

———, 1925: A survey of investigations by American horticulturists on carbohydrate-nitrogen relations, *J. Pom. and Hort. Sci.*, **5**: 34–42.

HOPKINS, E. F., and J. H. GOURLEY, 1930: The effect of nitrate applications on the soluble carbohydrate in apples, *Proc. Am. Soc. Hort. Sci.*, **27**: 32–36.

——— and E. W. GREVE, 1931: The effect of nitrate applications on the soluble carbohydrates in apples, *Proc. Am. Soc. Hort. Sci.*, **28**: 501–506.

HOPKINS, E. W., P. W. WILSON, and W. H. PETERSON, 1932: Influence of potassium nitrate on nodule formation and nitrogen fixation by clover, *Plant Physiol.*, **7**: 597–611.

HOPKINS, J. W., 1935: Influence of weather conditions on the nitrogen content of wheat, *Can. J. Res.*, **12**: 228–237.

HOWLETT, F. S., 1923: Nitrogen and carbohydrate composition of the developing flowers and young fruits of the apple, *Proc. Am. Soc. Hort. Sci.*, **20**: 31–37; *N. Y. Sta.* (*Cornell*) *Mem.* 99.

HULME, A. C., 1936: Biochemical studies in the nitrogen metabolism of the apple fruit. II, The course followed by certain nitrogen fractions during the development of the fruit on the tree, *Biochem. J.*, **30**: 258–268.

HUTCHINSON, H. B., and N. H. J. MILLER, 1909: Direct assimilation of ammonium salts by plants, *J. Agr. Sci.*, **3**: 179–195.

——— and ———, 1911: The direct assimilation of inorganic and organic forms of nitrogen by higher plants, *Cent. Bakt.* II, *Abt.*, **30**: 513–548.

IRVING, A. A., and R. HAUKINSON, 1908: The presence of a nitrate reducing enzyme in green plants, *Biochem. J.*, **3**: 87–96.

IVANOV, N. N., 1927: On the stability of the chemical composition of leguminous plants and corn, *Bull. App. Bot. and Plant Breeding*, **17**: 225–259; *Biol. Abst.*, **4**: 694.

IWANOFF, M., 1901: Versuche über die Frage, ob in den Pflanzen bei Lichtabschluss Eiweissstoffe sich bilden, *Landw. Versuchs-Stat.*, **55**: 78–94.

JODIDI, S. L., E. H. KELLOGG, and R. H. TRUE, 1918: Nitrogen metabolism in normal and in blighted spinach, *J. Agr. Res.*, **15**: 385–404.

———, S. C. MOULTON, and K. S. MARKLEY, 1920: The mosaic disease of spinach as characterized by its nitrogen constituents, *J. Am. Chem. Soc.*, **42**: 1061–1070.

———, 1920: A mosaic disease of cabbage as revealed by its nitrogen constituents, *J. Am. Chem. Soc.*, **42**: 1883–1893.

——— and K. S. Markley, 1923: The occurrence of polypeptides and free amino acids in the ungerminated wheat kernel, *J. Am. Chem. Soc.*, **45**: 2137–2144.

———, 1924: Physiological studies on cereals. II, The occurrence of amino acids and polypeptides in the ungerminated oat kernel, *J. Franklin Inst.*, **198**: 201–211.

———, 1925: Physiological studies on cereals. III, The occurrence of polypeptides and amino acids in the ungerminated maize kernel, *J. Agr. Res.*, **30**: 587–592.

——— and J. G. Wangler, 1925: Physiological and biochemical studies on cereals. IV, On the presence of amino acids and polypeptides in the ungerminated rye kernel, *J. Agr. Res.*, **30**: 989–994.

———, 1930: Isolation and purification of the alcohol-soluble protein (prolamin) occurring in English rye grass (*Lolium perenne*), *J. Agr. Res.*, **40**: 361–370.

———, 1931: The non protein nitrogen of the Alaska pea with special reference to the chemical nature of humin nitrogen, *J. Agr. Res.*, **43**: 811–825.

Jones, J. S., and G. A. Mitchell, 1926: The cause and control of yellowberry in Turkey wheat grown under dry farming conditions, *J. Agr. Res.*, **33**: 281–293.

Jones, L. H., 1936: Diagnosis of plant troubles with diphenylamine, *Plant Physiol.*, **11**: 207–209.

Karmarkar, D. V., 1934: The seasonal cycles of nitrogenous and carbohydrate materials in fruit trees, *J. Pom. and Hort. Sci.*, **12**: 177–221.

Kastle, J. H., and E. Elvove, 1904: On the reduction of nitrates by certain plant extracts and metals, and the accelerating effect of certain substances on the progress of the reduction, *Am. Chem. J.*, **31**: 606–641.

Kelley, W. P., 1911: The assimilation of nitrogen by rice, *Hawaii Sta. Bull.* 24.

Kellner, O., 1884: Agriculturchemische Studien über die Reiscultur, *Landw. Versuchs-Stat.*, **30**: 18–41.

Kezer, A., and D. W. Robertson, 1927: The critical period of applying irrigation water to wheat, *J. Am. Soc. Agron.*, **19**: 80–116.

Kinoshita, Y., 1897: On the assimilation of nitrogen from nitrates and ammonium salts by phanerogams, *Bull. Coll. Agr. Tokyo*, **2**: 200–202.

Kishi, Y., and S. Monobe, 1931: On the quantitative changes of the chemical constituents of mulberry leaves during 24 hours. (In Japanese.) *Kjusu. Imp. Univ. Fukuoka Bull.*, **4**: 531–599; *Biol. Abst.*, **8**: 335.

Klein, G., and K. Tauböck, 1927: Physiologie des Harnstoffs in der höheren Pflanze. II, *Österr. Bot. Z.*, **76**: 195–221; *Biol. Abst.*, **6**: 693.

———, ———, and H. Linser, 1930: Harnstoff und Ureide bei den höheren Pflanzen. I, Das Vorkommen von Harnstoff im Pflanzenreich und sein Wandel im Laufe der Vegetationsperiode, *Jahrb. wiss. Bot.*, **73**: 193–225.

———, 1930: Changes in the nitrogen of green plants, *Ergeb. Agr.-Chem.*, **2**: 143; *Chem. Abst.*, **26**: 2484.

——— and K. Tauböck, 1931: Harnstoff und Ureide bei den höheren Pflanzen. II, Untersuchungen über das Auftreten und Verschwinden von Harnstoff bei der Pflanze, *Jahrb. wiss. Bot.*, **74**: 429–458.

——— and ———, 1931: Harnstoff und Ureide bei den höheren Pflanzen. III, Das Vorkommen von Ureiden. Quantitative Bestimmung von freiem und gebundenem Harnstoff, *Biochem. Z.*, **241**: 413–459; *Biol. Abst.*, **8**: 1919.

——— and ———, 1932: Argininstoffwechsel und Harnstoffgenese bei höheren Pflanzen, *Biochem. Z.*, **251**: 10–50.

——— and ———, 1932: Argininstoffwechsel und Harnstoffgenese bei höheren Pflanzen. II, *Biochem. Z.*, **255**: 278–286.

KNIGHT, R. C., 1924: The carbohydrate/nitrogen ratio, *Sci. Prog.*, **19**: 34–42.

KNOWLTON, H. E., and M. B. HOFFMAN, 1930: Nitrogen fertilization and keeping quality of apples, *Proc. Am. Soc. Hort. Sci.*, **27**: 28–31.

KNUDSON, L., 1916: Influence of certain carbohydrates on green plants, *N. Y. Sta. (Cornell) Mem.* 9.

———, 1933: Investigation on the use of certain amino acids by green plants, abst., *Am. J. Bot.*, **20**: 680.

KOSSOWITSCH, P., 1894: Untersuchungen über die Frage ob die Algen freien Stickstoff fixiren, *Bot. Ztg.*, **52**: 97–116.

KOSUTANY, T., 1897: Untersuchungen über die Entstehung des Pflanzeneiweisses, *Landw. Versuchs-Stat.*, **48**: 13–32.

KRAUS, E. J., and H. R. KRAYBILL, 1918: Vegetation and reproduction with special reference to the tomato, *Ore. Sta. Bull.* 149.

KRAYBILL, H. R., 1923: Effect of shading and ringing upon the chemical composition of apple and peach trees, *N. H. Sta. Tech. Bull.* 23.

———, 1932: Effect of plant nutrition on the composition of wheat, *Cereal Chem.*, **9**: 71–80.

KRÜGER, W., 1905: Ueber die Bedeutung der Nitrifikation für die Kulturpflanzen, *Landw. Jahrb.*, **34**: 761.

KULTZSCHER, M., 1931, 1932: Die biologische NH_3-Entgiftung in höheren Pflanzen in ihrer Abhängigkeit von der Wasserstoffionenkonzentration des Zellsaftes, *Planta*, **14**: 782–783; **17**: 699–757.

LAGASSÉ, F. S., 1935: Some responses of Yellow Transparent apple trees in Delaware to various nitrogen treatments, *Del. Sta. Bull.* 195.

LAKON, G., 1917: Der Eiweissgehalt panachierter Blätter geprüft mittels des makroskopischen Verfahrens von Molisch, *Biochem. Z.*, **78**: 145–154.

LATSHAW, W. L., and E. C. MILLER, 1924: Elemental composition of the corn plant, *J. Agr. Res.*, **27**: 845–861.

LAURENT, E., 1890: Expériences sur la réduction des nitrates par les végétaux, *Ann. Inst. Pasteur*, **4**: 722–744.

LAWES, J. B., J. H. GILBERT, and E. PUGH, 1860: On the sources of nitrogen of vegetation; with special reference to the question whether plants assimilate free or uncombined nitrogen, *Phil. Trans. Roy. Soc.*, **151**: 431–578.

LEASE, E. J., and W. E. TOTTINGHAM, 1935: Photochemical responses of the wheat plant to spectral regions, *J. Am. Chem. Soc.*, **57**: 2613–2616.

LEATHER, J. W., 1934: Final report of the agricultural chemist to the government of India. 99 pp. Quoted by Nicol, 1934.

LECLERC, J. A., 1910: Tri-local experiments on the influence of environment on the composition of wheat, *U. S. Dept. Agr. Bull.*, **128**: 7–18.

———, and P. A. YODER, 1914: Environmental influences on the physical and chemical characteristics of wheat, *J. Agr. Res.*, **1**: 275–291.

LEWIS, A. H., 1936: The effects of ammonium and nitrate nitrogen on the growth of perennial rye grass, *J. Agr. Sci.*, **26**: 247–257.

LI, H. W., and T. N. LIU, 1935: Defoliation experiments with kaoliang, *J. Am. Soc. Agron.*, **27**: 486–491.

LINCOLN, F. B., and A. S. MULAY, 1929: The extraction of nitrogenous materials from pear tissues, *Plant Physiol.*, **4**: 233–250.

LIPMAN, C. B., and J. K. TAYLOR, 1922: Proof of the power of the wheat plant to fix atmospheric nitrogen, *Sci.*, **56**: 605–606.

——— and ———, 1924: Do green plants have the power of fixing elementary nitrogen from the atmosphere? *J. Franklin Inst.*, October, **1924**: 475–506.

Lipman, J. G., 1910: A method for the study of soil fertility problems, *J. Agr. Sci.*, **3**: 297–300.

———, 1912: The associative growth of legumes and non-legumes, *N. J. Sta. Bull.* 253.

———, 1913: A further discussion of certain methods used in the study of "The associative growth of legumes and non legumes," *J. Am. Soc. Agron.*, **5**: 72–79.

——— and A. W. Blair, 1916: Factors influencing the protein content of soybeans, *Soil Sci.*, **1**: 171–178.

Loeb, J., 1924: "Proteins and the Theory of Colloidal Behavior," McGraw-Hill Book Company, Inc., New York, 380 pp.

Loehwing, W. F., 1927: Preliminary report on amino acid synthesis in plants, *Proc. Iowa Acad. Sci.*, **34**: 115–118.

Loew, O., 1933: Über die Bildung von Eiweiss in den Pflanzen, *Angew. Bot.*, **15**: 518–539; *Biol. Abst.*, **10**: 31.

Loo, T. L., 1931: Studies on the absorption of ammonia and nitrate by the roots of *Zea mais* seedlings in relation to the concentration and the actual acidity of the culture solution, *J. Faculty Agr. Hokkaido Imp. Univ.*, **30**: 1–118; *Exp. Sta. Rec.*, **68**: 458.

Loose, L., and W. H. Pearsall, 1933: Synthesis of protein by green plants, *Nature*, **131**: 362–363.

Ludwig, C. A., 1934: Do germinating willow cuttings fix atmospheric nitrogen? *Am. J. Bot.*, **21**: 557–561.

Lyon, T. L., and A. Keyser, 1905: Nature and causes of "yellow-berry" in hard winter wheat, *Neb. Sta. Bull.*, **89**: 23–36.

——— and J. A. Bizzell, 1911: A heretofore unnoted benefit from the growth of legumes, *N. Y. Sta.* (*Cornell*) *Bull.* 294.

——— and ———, 1913: A discussion of certain methods used in the study of "The associative growth of legumes and non legumes," *J. Am. Soc. Agron.*, **5**: 65–72.

Macht, D. I., 1934: Growth of *Lupinus albus* seedlings in solutions of some amino acids, *Am. J. Bot.*, **21**: 72–76.

Mameli de Calvino, E., and G. Pollacci, 1911: Sull' assimilazione diretta dell' azoto atmosferico libero nei vegetali, *Atti dell' Instituto Bot. di Pavia*, Ser. II, **14**: 159–257.

——— and ———, 1911: Ancora sull' assimilazione diretta dell' azoto atmosferico libero nei vegetali, *Atti dell' Instituto Bot. di Pavia*, Ser. II, **16**: 197–203.

———, 1923: The direct assimilation of free nitrogen by plants. A review of recent work on the subject, *Torreya*, **23**: 99–104.

———, 1923: Sobre la assimilacion directa del nitrogeno libre por las plantas, *Estoc. Exp. Agron.* (Cuba) *Circ.* **59**: 3–7.

Mangel, C. E., 1927: Pre-harvest factors which affect wheat quality, *Cereal Chem.*, **4**: 376–388.

Marañon, J., 1932: Nitrogen distribution in the leaves of Philippine camphor trees, *Philippine J. Sci.*, **49**: 461–468.

Marth, P. C., 1934: Response of nitrogen fertilizers applied in different areas under Rome apple trees, *Proc. Am. Soc. Hort. Sci.*, **32**: 73–75.

Mazé, P., 1898: L'assimilation de l'azote nitrique et de l'azote ammoniacal par les végétaux supérieurs, *C. R. Acad. Sci. Paris*, **127**: 1031–1033.

———, 1900: Recherches sur l'influence de l'azote nitrique et de l'azote ammoniacal sur le développement du maïs, *Ann. Inst. Pasteur*, **14**: 26–45.

McCalla, A. G., 1933: The effect of nitrogen nutrition on the protein and non protein nitrogen of wheat, *Can. J. Res.*, **9**: 542–570.

———, 1934: Amide nitrogen in germinating seeds, *Can. J. Res.*, **10**: 430–434.

McCool, M. M., and R. L. Cook, 1930: Rate of intake, accumulation and transformation of nitrate nitrogen by small grains and Kentucky blue grass, *J. Am. Soc. Agron.*, **22**: 757–765.

———, 1932: Use of peats in composts to increase nitrification and plant growth, *Contr. Boyce Thompson Inst.*, **4**: 257–271.

McGeorge, W. T., 1923: The assimilation of nitrogen by sugar cane, nitrates *vs.* ammonium salts, *Planter's Rec.*, **27**: 347–352.

McKie, P., and J. Barnett, 1936: The nitrogen metabolism of the pea seedling, *Biochem. J.*, **30**: 1010–1013.

McNair, J. B., 1931: Some properties of alkaloids in relation to climate or habitat, *Am. J. Bot.*, **18**: 416–424.

Metzger, W. H., 1935: The residual effect of alfalfa cropping periods of various lengths upon the yield and protein content of succeeding wheat crops, *J. Am. Soc. Agron.*, **27**: 653–659.

Mevius, W., and I. Dikussar, 1930: Nitrite als Stickstoffquellen für höhere Pflanzen. Ein Beitrag zur Frage nach der Assimilation des Nitratstickstoffs, *Jahrb. wiss. Bot.*, **73**: 633–703.

Meyer, A., 1918: Eiweissstoffwechsel und Vergilben der Laubblätter von *Tropaeolum majus*, *Flora*, **11-12**: 85–127.

Miller, E. C., 1910: A physiological study of the germination of *Helianthus annuus*, *Ann. Bot.*, **24**: 693–726.

———, 1917: Daily variation of water and dry matter in the leaves of corn and the sorghums, *J. Agr. Res.*, **10**: 11–47.

———, 1924: Daily variation of the carbohydrates in the leaves of corn and the sorghums, *J. Agr. Res.*, **27**: 785–808.

———, 1926: Daily variation of the nitrogen in the leaves, unpub. data, *Kans. Sta.*

———, 1929: Nitrogen in the leaves of crop plants, unpub. data, *Kans. Sta.*

Miller, J. E., and A. C. Chibnall, 1932: The proteins of grasses. I, Preliminary communication, *Biochem. J.*, **26**: 392–402.

Mockeridge, F. A., 1917: Some effects of organic growth-promoting substances (auximones) on the soil organisms concerned in the nitrogen cycle, *Proc. Roy. Soc.*, B, **89**: 508–534.

———, 1924: The formation of plant growth-promoting substances by microorganisms, *Ann. Bot.*, **38**: 723–734.

Molisch, H., 1916: Die Eiweissproben makroskopisch angewendet auf Pflanzen, *Z. Bot.*, **8**: 124–131.

Moore, B. and T. A. Webster, 1919: The formation of nitrites from nitrates in aqueous solution by the action of sunlight and the assimilation of the nitrites by green leaves in sunlight, *Proc. Roy. Soc.*, B, **90**: 158–167.

———, 1920: Studies of photosynthesis in fresh water algae. I, The fixation of both carbon and nitrogen from the atmosphere to form organic tissue by the green plant cell. II, III, *Proc. Roy. Soc.*, B, **91**: 201–215.

———, E. Whitley, and T. A. Webster, 1921: Studies of photosynthesis in marine algae. I, Fixation of carbon and nitrogen from inorganic sources in sea water. II, *Proc. Roy. Soc.*, B, **92**: 51–60.

Morgan, M. F., and O. E. Street, 1935: Rates of growth and nitrogen assimilation of Havana seed tobacco, *J. Agr. Res.*, **51**: 163–172.

Mothes K., 1926: Ein Beitrag zur Kenntnis des N-Stoffwechsels höherer Pflanzen, *Planta*, **1**: 472–552.

———, 1931: Zur Kenntnis des N-Stoffwechsels höherer Pflanzen. III. Beitrag, *Planta*, **12**: 686–731.

———, 1932: Natural regulation of the vegetable protein metabolism. *Naturwiss.*, **20**: 102–103; *Chem. Abst.*, **26**: 3820.

Muenscher, W. C., 1923: Protein synthesis in *Chlorella*, *Bot. Gaz.*, **75**: 249–268.

Mulay, A. S., 1931: Seasonal changes in total, soluble, soluble protein, non protein, and insoluble nitrogen in current year's shoot of Bartlett pear, *Plant Physiol.*, **6**: 519–529.

———, 1932: Seasonal changes in the composition of the non protein nitrogen in the current year's shoots of Bartlett pear, *Plant Physiol.*, **7**: 107–118.

———, 1932: Seasonal changes in the composition of the insoluble nitrogen fraction in the current year's shoots of Bartlett pear, *Plant Physiol.*, **7**: 323–327.

Müller-Thurgau, H. 1894: Einfluss des Stickstoffs auf die Wurzelbildung, *Jahresbericht Versuchs-Stat. Wädensweil*, **4**: 48–52.

Müntz, A., 1889: Sur le rôle de l'ammoniaque dans la nutrition des végétaux supérieurs, *C. R. Acad. Sci. Paris*, **109**: 646–648.

Murneek, A. E., 1930: Quantitative distribution and seasonal fluctuation of nitrogen in apple trees, *Proc. Am. Soc. Hort. Sci.*, **27**: 228–231.

———, 1935: Physiological rôle of asparagine and related substances in nitrogen metabolism of plants, *Plant Physiol.*, **10**: 447–464.

Naftel, J. A., 1931: The absorption of ammonium and nitrate nitrogen by various plants at different stages of growth, *J. Am. Soc. Agron.*, **23**: 142–158.

Nagaoka, M., 1904: On the behavior of the rice plant to nitrates and ammonium salts, *Bull. Col. Agr. Tokyo Imper. Univ.*, **6**: 285–334; *Exp. Sta. Rec.*, **16**: 560.

Neidig, R. E., and R. S. Snyder, 1922: The effect of available nitrogen on the protein content and yield of wheat, *Idaho Exp. Sta. Bull.* 1.

——— and ———, 1924: The relation of moisture and available nitrogen to the yield and protein content of wheat, *Soil Sci.*, **18**: 173–181.

——— and ———, 1926: The relation of the yield and protein content of wheat to the nitrogen content of the soil under ten years of different systems of cropping, *Idaho Sta. Res. Bull.* 5.

Newby, H. L., and W. H. Pearsall, 1930: Observations on nitrogen metabolism in the leaves of *Vitis* and *Rheum*, *Proc. Leeds Phil. and Lit. Soc., Sci. Sec.*, **2**: 81–85.

Newcomb, M. A., 1927: The loss of nitrogen from oily seeds, unpub. data, *Master's thesis, Kans. State Col.*

Nicol, H., 1934: The derivation of the nitrogen of crop plants with special reference to associated growth, *Biol. Rev.*, **9**: 383–410.

Nightingale, G. T., 1922: Light in relation to the growth and chemical composition of some horticultural plants, *Proc. Am. Soc. Hort. Sci.*, **19**: 18–29.

——— and E. J. Kraus, 1924: Does light affect the fertilizer requirements of plants? *Wis. Sta. Bull.* **362**: 52–54.

———, L. G. Schermerhorn, and W. R. Robbins, 1928: The growth status of the tomato as correlated with organic nitrogen and carbohydrates in roots, stem and leaves, *N. J. Sta. Bull.* 461.

———, and W. R. Robbins, 1928: Some phases of nitrogen metabolism in polyanthus narcissus (*Narcissus tazetta*), *N. J. Sta. Bull.* 472.

——— and L. G. Schermerhorn, 1928: Nitrate assimilation by asparagus in the absence of light, *N. J. Sta. Bull.* 476.

———, 1934: Ammonium and nitrate nutrition of dormant Delicious apple trees at 48°F., *Bot. Gaz.*, **95**: 437–452.

———, 1936: The biochemistry of the nitrogenous constituents of the green plants, *Ann. Rev. Biochem.*, **5**: 513–524.

Olson, G. A., 1917: Gluten formation in the wheat kernel, *Wash. Sta. Bull.* 142.

———, 1923: A study of factors affecting the nitrogen content of wheat and of the changes that occur during the development of wheat, *J. Agr. Res.*, **24**: 939–955.

ORCUTT, F. S., and E. B. FRED, 1935: Light intensity as an inhibiting factor in the fixation of atmospheric nitrogen by Manchu soybeans, *J. Am. Soc. Agron.*, **27**: 550–558.

OSBORNE, T. B., and A. J. WAKEMAN, 1920: The proteins of green leaves. I, Spinach leaves, *J. Biol. Chem.*, **42**: 1–26.

———, ———, and C. S. LEAVENWORTH, 1921: The proteins of the alfalfa plant, *J. Biol. Chem.*, **49**: 63–91.

———, 1924: "The Vegetable Proteins," mon., Longmans, Green and Company, New York, 151 pp.

OTTO, R., and W. D. KOOPER, 1910: Beitrag zur Abnahme bezw. Rückwanderung der Stickstoffverbindungen aus den Blättern während der Nacht sowie zur herbstlichen Rückwanderung von Stickstoffverbindungen aus den Blättern, *Landw. Jahrb.*, **39**: 167–172.

PANTANELLI, E., and G. SEVERINI, 1910, 1911: Some experiments on the utilization of ammonium salts by green plants, *Staz. Sper. Agr. Ital.*, **43**: 449–544; **44**: 873–908; *Exp. Sta. Rec.*, **25**: 223; **27**: 634.

PARDO, J. H., 1930: Utilization of certain nitrogen compounds by the sugar cane, *Int. Sugar J.*, **32**: 11–19.

———, 1933: Ammonia vs. nitrate as nitrogen sources for sugar cane, *Proc. Fourth Cong. Int. Soc. Sugar Cane Tech. Bull.* 13; *Chem. Abst.*, **27**: 2712.

———, 1933: A note on the utilization of ammonium and nitrate by higher plants, *New Phytol.*, **32**: 308–310.

———, 1935: Ammonium in the nutrition of higher green plants, *Quart. Rev. Biol.*, **10**: 1–31.

PEARSALL, W. H., and J. H. PRIESTLEY, 1923: Meristematic tissues and protein isoelectric points, *New Phytol.*, **22**: 185–191.

——— and J. EWING, 1924: The isoelectric points of some plant proteins, *Biochem. J.*, **18**: 329–339.

——— and ———, 1929: The relation of nitrogen metabolism to plant succulence, *Ann. Bot.*, **43**: 27–33.

———, 1931: The distribution of the insoluble nitrogen in *Beta* leaves of different ages, *J. Exp. Biol.*, **8**: 279–285.

PERCIABOSCO, F., and V. ROSSO, 1909: L'assorbimento diretto dei nitrite nelle piante, *Staz. Sper. Agrar. Ital.*, **42**: 5–36; *Exp. Sta. Rec.*, **23**: 724.

PIGORINI, L., 1914: Studi sulla foglia di gelso; sulla composizione chimica della foglia al mattino e alla sera, *Atti dei. Lincei.*, **23**: 433–437.

PIRSCHLE, K., 1929: Zur Assimilation des Harnstoffes durch die höhere Pflanze, *Biochem. Z.*, **212**: 466–474.

———, 1929: Nitrate und Ammonsalze als Stickstoffquellen für höhere Pflanzen bei konstanter Wasserstoffionenkonzentration, *Ber. bot. Ges.*, **47**: 86–92.

———, 1931: Nitrate und Ammonsalze als Stickstoffquellen für höhere Pflanzen bei konstanter Wasserstoffionkonzentration. III, *Planta*, **14**: 583–676; *Biol. Abst.*, **9**: 289.

——— and H. MENGDEHL, 1931: Ionenaufnahme aus Salzlösungen durch die höhere Pflanze, *Jahrb. wiss. Bot.*, **74**: 297–363.

PITSCH, O., 1887, 1893, 1896: Versuche zur Entscheidung der Frage, ob salpetersäure Salze für die Entwickelung unserer landwirtschaftlichen Kulturgewächse unentbehrlich sind oder nicht, *Landw. Versuchs-Stat.*, **34**: 217–258; **42**: 1–95; **46**: 357–370.

PLAGGE, H. H., 1930: Do successive applications of nitrogenous fertilizers influence the development of physiological disorders of apples in cold storage, *Proc. Am. Soc. Hort. Sci.*, **27**: 23–27.

PLATENIUS, H., 1932: Carbohydrate and nitrogen metabolism in the celery plant as related to premature seeding, *N. Y. Sta.* (*Cornell*) *Mem.* 140.

POLLARD, A., and A. C. CHIBNALL, 1934: The proteins of grasses. III, The cystine content of certain grasses and other pasture plant proteins, *Biochem. J.*, **28**: 326–336.

POPOFF, M., 1933: Ueber die pflanzlichen Auxine und ihre Wirkung auf Einzellige, *Biol. Zent.*, **53**: 661–668.

POTTER, G. F., H. R. KRAYBILL, S. W. WENTWORTH, J. T. SULLIVAN, and P. T. BLOOD, 1930: Some effects of defloration on fruit spur composition and fruit bud formation in the Oldenburg apple, *N. H. Sta. Tech. Bull.* 41.

——— and T. G. PHILLIPS, 1930: Composition and fruit bud formation in non bearing spurs of the Baldwin apple, *N. H. Sta. Tech. Bull.* 42.

POZZI-ESCOT, M-EMM, 1903: The reducing enzymes, *Am. Chem. J.*, **29**: 517–563.

PRAZMOWSKI, A., 1890: Die Wurzelknöllchen der Erbse. I, Die Aetiologie und Entwickelungsgeschichte der Knöllchen, *Landw. Versuchs-Stat.*, **37**: 161–238.

PRIANISCHNIKOW, D. N., 1899: Die Rückbildung der Eiweissstoffe aus deren Zerfallsprodukten, *Landw. Versuchs-Stat.*, **52**: 347–382.

———, 1908: Zur physiologischen Characteristik der Ammoniumsalze, *Ber. bot. Ges.*, **26**: 716–724.

———, 1922: Ueber den Aufbau und Abbau des Asparagins in den Pflanzen, *Ber. bot. Ges.*, **40**: 242–248; *Bot. Abst.*, **12**: 751.

———, 1923: Sur l'assimilation de l'ammoniaque par les plantes supérieures, *C. R. Acad. Sci. Paris*, **177**: 603–606.

———, 1924: Asparagin und Harnstoff (Physiologische Parallele), *Biochem. Z.*, **150**: 407–423.

PRIESTLEY, J. H., 1922: Some recent work on proteins in its relation to physiology, *Sci. Prog.*, **16**: 201–207.

RABER, O., 1928: "Principles of Plant Physiology," The Macmillan Company, New York, 362 pp.

RAHN, H., 1932: Untersuchungen über den N-Stoffwechsel pflanzlicher vegetativer Speicherorgane, *Planta*, **18**: 1–51.

REID, M. E., 1924: Relation of kind of food reserves to regeneration in tomato plants, *Bot. Gaz.*, **77**: 103–111.

———, 1924: Quantitative relations of carbohydrates to nitrogen in determining growth responses in tomato cuttings, *Bot. Gaz.*, **77**: 404–418.

———, 1926: Growth of tomato cuttings in relation to stored carbohydrate and nitrogenous compounds, *Am. J. Bot.*, **13**: 548–575.

———, 1926: Growth of seedlings in relation to composition of seed, *Bot. Gaz.*, **81**: 196–203.

———, 1929: Growth of seedlings in light and in darkness in relation to available nitrogen and carbon, *Bot. Gaz.*, **87**: 81–117.

———, 1929: Effect of variations in the amounts of available carbon and nitrogen on the growth of wheat seedlings, *Am. J. Bot.*, **16**: 770–779.

———, 1930: Growth and nitrogen metabolism of squash seedlings. II, With respect to stages of development and the influence of light, *Am. J. Bot.*, **17**: 396–416.

RICHARDS, F. J., and W. G. TEMPLEMAN, 1936: Physiological studies in plant nutrition. IV, Nitrogen metabolism in relation to nutrient deficiency and age in barley leaves, *Ann. Bot.*, **50**: 367–402.

Richardson, A. E. V., and H. C. Gurney, 1933: The effect of nitrogenous fertilizers on the growth and yield of wheat and barley in South Australia. I, Wheat grown after fallow and after stubble. II, The effect of a previous crop in the response of wheat to nitrogen fertilizers and the effect of increasing amounts of nitrogen on barley, *Empire J. Exp. Agr.*, **1**: 193–205, 325–332.

——— and ———, 1935: Nitrogen in relation to cereal culture, *J. Dept. Agr. So. Australia*, **28**: 954–971.

Richardson, G. M., 1934: Critique on the biological estimation of amino nitrogen, *Proc. Roy. Soc.*, B, **115**: 142–169.

Robbins, W. J., 1923: An isoelectric point for plant tissue and its significance, *Am. J. Bot.*, **10**: 412–440.

Roberts, H. F., and G. F. Freeman, 1908: The yellow berry problem in Kansas hard winter wheats, *Kans. Sta. Bull.* 156.

———, 1919: Yellow berry in hard winter wheat, *J. Agr. Res.*, **18**: 155–171.

Roberts, R. H., 1920: Off year apple bearing and apple spur growth, *Wis. Sta. Bull.* 317.

———, 1921: Nitrogen reserves in apple trees, *Proc. Am. Soc. Hort. Sci.*, **18**: 143–145.

———, 1923: Effect of defoliation upon blossom bud formation, *Wis. Sta. Res. Bull.* 56.

Robinson, M. E., 1929: The protein metabolism of the green plant, *New Phytol.*, **28**: 117–150.

Russell, E. J., and E. H. Richards, 1919: The amount and composition of rain falling at Rothamsted, *J. Agr. Sci.*, **9**: 309–337.

Saeger, A., 1925: The growth of duckweeds in mineral nutrient solutions with and without organic extracts, *J. Gen. Physiol.*, **7**: 517–526.

Sampson, A. W., 1935: Growth and seasonal changes in composition of oak leaves, *Plant Physiol.*, **10**: 739–751.

Sapoznikow, W., 1895: "Eiweisstoffe und Kohlenhydrate der grünen Blätter als Assimilationsproducte," 61 pp., Tomsk (1894); (Russian) *Bot. Cent.*, **63**: 246–251.

Schiletter, J. C., 1932: Time of bud differentiation in the Dunlap strawberry, *Proc. Am. Soc. Hort. Sci.*, **29**: 325–329.

Schramm, J. R., 1914: The relation of certain grass-green algae to elementary nitrogen, *Ann. Mo. Bot. Gard.*, **1**: 157–184.

Schreiner, O., and J. J. Skinner, 1912: Nitrogenous soil constituents and their bearing on soil fertility, *U. S. Bur. Soils Bull.* 87.

Schultz, M., 1903: "Studien über den Einfluss von Nitriten auf die Keimung von Samen und auf das Wachstum von Pflanzen," *Inaug-Diss., Königsberg.*

Schulz, M., 1862: Chemische Beiträge zur Kenntniss des Keimprocesses bei einigen Phanerogamen, *J. Prakt. Chemie*, **71**: 129–173.

Schulze, B., and J. Schütz, 1909: Die Stoffwandlungen in den Laubblättern des Baumes, insbesondere in ihren Beziehungen zum herbstlichen Blattfall, *Landw. Versuchs-Stat.*, **71**: 299–352.

Schulze, E., 1897: Über die Verbreitung des Glutamins in den Pflanzen, *Landw. Versuchs-Stat.*, **48**: 33–55.

———, and E. Winterstein, 1910: Studien über die Proteinbildung in reifenden Pflanzensamen, *Z. physiol. Chem.*, **66**: 431–476; *Bot. Cent.*, **116**: 63.

———, 1911: Studien über die Proteinbildung in reifenden Pflanzensamen, *Z. physiol. Chem.*, **71**: 31–48.

Schuster, G. L., and J. M. Graham, 1927: Effect of various fertilizers and lime on composition of soybeans, *J. Am. Soc. Agron.*, **19**: 574–577.

Sessions, A. C., and J. W. Shive, 1933: The effect of culture solutions on growth and nitrogen fractions of oat plants at different stages of their development, *Soil Sci.*, **35**: 355–374.

Shaw, G. W., and E. H. Walters, 1911: A progress report upon soil and climatic factors influencing the composition of wheat, *Calif. Sta. Bull.* 216.

Shear, G. M., 1933: Field and laboratory studies on frenching of tobacco, *Va. Sta. Tech. Bull.* 49.

Shmuk, A., and M. Poliakov, 1927: The accumulation of nitrates in plants, *Arb. Kubansch. Landw. Inst.*, **5**: 161–173; *Biol. Abst.*, **3**: 478.

Shull, C. A., and J. W. Mitchell, 1933: Some physico-chemical properties of seed extracts, *Bot. Gaz.*, **95**: 258–278.

Shulov, I., 1912: Sterile cultures of higher plants. Assimilation of nitrogen as ammonia and nitrates, *J. Exp. Landw.*, **13**: 200–206.

Smirnow, A. I., 1923: Über die Synthese der Säureamide in der Pflanzen bei Ernährung mit Ammoniaksalzen, *Biochem. Z.*, **137**: 1–34; *Bot. Abst.*, **13**: 67.

Sommer, A. L., 1936: Reduction of nitrites by the expressed juice of higher green plants, *Plant Physiol.*, **11**: 429–436.

Spitzer, G., R. H. Carr, and W. F. Epple, 1919: Soft corn, its chemical composition and nitrogen distribution, *J. Am. Chem. Soc.*, **41**: 1212–1221.

Spoehr, H. A., 1911: The relation between photosynthesis of CO_2 and nitrate reduction, *Sci.*, **34**: 63–64.

Stahl, A. L., and J. W. Shive, 1933: Studies on nitrogen absorption from culture solutions: I, Oats, *Soil Sci.*, **35**: 373–400.

——— and ———, 1933: Further studies on nitrogen from culture solutions. II, Buckwheat, *Soil Sci.*, **35**: 469–483.

Stallings, J. H., 1926: The form of legume nitrogen assimilated by non legumes when grown in association, *Soil Sci.*, **21**: 253–276.

Stark, O. K., 1924: Environmental factors affecting the protein and oil content of soybeans and the iodine number of soybean oil, *J. Am. Soc. Agron.*, **16**: 636–646.

Starring, C. C., 1923: Influence of the carbohydrate-nitrate content of cuttings upon the production of roots, *Proc. Am. Soc. Hort. Sci.*, **20**: 288–292.

Steiner, M., 1929: Weitere Untersuchungen über flüchtige Stickstoffbasen bei höheren Pflanzen, *Beitr. Biol. Pflanzen*, **17**: 247–258; *Biol. Abst.*, **5**: 2675.

Stewart, C. R., E. C. Thomas, and J. Horner, 1925: The comparative growth of pineapple plants with ammonia and nitrate nitrogen, *Soil Sci.*, **20**: 227–243.

Stewart, R., and J. E. Greaves, 1909: A study of the production and movement of nitric nitrogen in an irrigated soil, *Utah Sta. Bull.* 106

Strowd, W. H., 1920: The relation of nitrates to nodule production, *Soil Sci.*, **10**: 343–356.

Stuart, N. W., 1932: Nitrogen and carbohydrate metabolism of young apple trees as affected by excessive applications of sodium nitrate, *N. H. Sta. Bull.* 50.

——— and C. O. Appleman, 1935: Nitrogenous metabolism in Irish potatoes during storage, *Md. Sta. Bull.* 372.

Stutzer, A., 1906: Die Wirkung von Nitrit auf Pflanzen, *Bot. Cent.*, **105**: 569–570.

Suzuki, U., 1897: The formation of asparagin in plants under different conditions, *Imp. Univ. Col. Agr. Tokyo Bull.*, **2**: 409–457.

———, 1897: An important function of leaves, *Imp. Univ. Col. Agr. Tokyo Bull.*, **3**: 241–252.

———, 1898: On the formation of proteids and the assimilation of nitrates by Phanerogams in the absence of light, *Imp. Univ. Col. Agr. Tokyo Bull.*, **4**: 488–587.

———, 1898: Ueber die Assimilation der Nitrate in Dunkelheit durch Phanerogamen, *Bot. Cent.*, **75**: 289–292.

Talley, P J., 1934: Carbohydrate-nitrogen ratios with respect to the sexual expression of hemp, *Plant Physiol.*, **9**: 731–748.

TAYLOR, R. W., 1932: Influence of nitrogenous fertilizers applied at different dates on the number of flower clusters, flowers, and fruits of the strawberry, *Proc. Am. Soc. Hort. Sci.*, **29**: 311–317.

TELLER, G. L., 1935: Changes in nitrogen compounds in the wheat grain at different stages of development, *Plant Physiol.*, **10**: 499–509.

THATCHER, R. W., 1913: A report on the investigations concerning the chemical composition of wheat, 1906 to 1912 inclusive, *Wash. Sta. Bull.* 111.

———, 1913: The progressive development of the wheat kernel, *J. Am. Soc. Agron.*, **5**: 203–213.

———, 1915: The progressive development of the wheat kernel. II, *J. Am. Soc. Agron.*, **7**: 273–283.

———, 1921: "The Chemistry of Plant Life," McGraw-Hill Book Company, Inc., New York, 268 pp.

THELIN, G., and A. B. BEAUMONT, 1934: The effect of some forms of nitrogen on the growth and nitrogen content of wheat and rice plants, *J. Am. Soc. Agron.*, **26**: 1012–1017.

THOMAS, W., 1927: Nitrogenous metabolism of *Pyrus malus*. I, Influence of temperature of desiccation on water-soluble nitrogenous constituents and separation of water-soluble protein from non-protein constituents, *Plant Physiol.*, **2**: 55–67.

———, 1927: Nitrogenous metabolism of *Pyrus malus*. II, The distribution of nitrogen in the insoluble cytoplasmic proteins, *Plant Physiol.*, **2**: 67–71.

———, 1927: Nitrogenous metabolism of *Pyrus malus*. III, The partition of nitrogen in the leaves, one and two year branch growth and non-bearing spurs throughout a year's cycle, *Plant Physiol.*, **2**: 109–137.

———, 1927: Nitrogenous metabolism of *Pyrus malus*. IV, The effect of sodium nitrate applications on the total nitrogen and its partition products in the leaves, new and one year branch growth throughout a year's cycle, *Plant Physiol.*, **2**: 245–271.

———, 1927: The seat of formation of amino acids in *Pyrus malus* L., *Sci.*, **66**: 115–116.

TIDMORE, J. W., 1933: Ammonium hydroxide versus calcium nitrate for cotton seedlings, *J. Am. Soc. Agron.*, **25**: 617–622.

TIEDJENS, V. A., and W. R. ROBBINS, 1931: The use of ammonia and nitrate nitrogen by certain crop plants, *N. J. Sta. Bull.* 526.

———, 1932: Growing cotton and other crop plants with ammonium nitrogen, *Sci.*, **75**: 648.

——— and M. A. BLAKE, 1932: Factors affecting the use of nitrate and ammonium nitrogen by apple trees, *N. J. Sta. Bull.* 547.

———, 1934: Factors affecting assimilation of ammonium and nitrate nitrogen, particularly in tomato and apple, *Plant Physiol.*, **9**: 31–57.

TOTTINGHAM, W. E., 1923: Temperature effects in plant metabolism, *J. Agr. Res.*, **25**: 13–31.

———, E. R. SCHULZ, and S. LEPKOVSKY, 1924: The extraction of nitrogenous constituents from plant cells, *J. Am. Chem. Soc.*, **46**: 203–208.

———, 1924: Physiological stability in maize, *Sci.*, **59**: 69–70.

——— and H. W. KERR, 1926: Climatic effects in the metabolism of maize, *Plant Physiol.*, **1**: 415–416.

——— and H. LOWSMA, 1928: Effects of light upon nitrate assimilation in wheat, *J. Am. Chem. Soc.*, **50**: 2436–2445.

——— and E. J. LEASE, 1934: A photochemical aspect of nitrate assimilation in plants, *Sci.*, **80**: 615–616.

———, H. L. STEPHENS, and E. J. LEASE, 1934: Influence of shorter light rays upon absorption of nitrate by the young wheat plant, *Plant Physiol.*, **9**: 127–142.

TREBOUX, O., 1904: Zur Stickstoffernährung der grünen Pflanze, *Ber. bot. Ges.*, **22**: 570–572.

TRELEASE, S. F., and P. PAULINO, 1920: The effect on the growth of rice of the addition of ammonium and nitrate salts to soil cultures, *Philippine J. Agr.*, **8**: 293–313.

TYAGNY-RYADNO, M., 1933: The relations of *Bacillus mycoides* with ammonification, nitrification and soil fertility, *J. Agr. Sci.*, **23**: 335–358.

ULLRICH, H., 1924: The role of chloroplasts in protein formation in green plants, *Z. Bot.*, **16**: 513–562; *Exp. Sta. Rec.*, **56**: 814.

VALLEAU, W. D., and E. M. JOHNSON, 1927: Tobacco frenching—a nitrogen deficiency disease, *Ky. Sta. Bull.* 281.

VARADACHAR, K. S., 1933: Synthesis of proteins in plants. I, Conversion of nitrates into protein in *Helianthus annuus*, *J. Indian Inst. Sci.*, 16A, **12**: 129–138.

VERNER, L., 1933: Effect of nitrate fertilization on apple fruits, *Proc. Am. Soc. Hort. Sci.*, **30**: 32–36.

VICKERY, H. B., and G. W. PUCHER, 1931: The chemical changes that occur during the curing of Connecticut shade grown tobacco, *Conn. Sta. Bull.* 324.

———, ——— and H. E. CLARK, 1934: Glutamine in the tomato plant, *Sci.*, **80**: 459–461.

———, ——— and ———, 1936: Glutamine metabolism of the beet, *Plant Physiol.*, **11**: 413–420.

VILLE, M. G., 1853–1857: "Recherches expérimentales sur la végétation," Paris.

VIRTANEN, A. I., and S. VON HAUSEN, 1930: The capability of grass plants to take advantage of the nitrogen fixed by the nodule bacteria of leguminous plants, *Contr. Lab. Valio, Helsinki.* (Finnish with English summary.) Quoted by Nicol, 1934.

———, ——— and H. KARSTRÖM, 1933: Untersuchungen über die Leguminose-Bakterien und -Pflanzen. XII, Die Ausnutzung der aus den Wurzelknöllchen der Leguminosen herausdiffundierten Stickstoffverbindungen durch Nichtleguminosen, *Biochem. Z.*, **258**: 106–117.

——— and S. SAASTAMOINEN, 1933: Ueber die Stickstoffbindung bei Erlen (*Alnus*), *Acta Chem. Fenn. B.*, 6. Quoted by Nicol, 1934.

WALDRON, L. R., 1933: Yield and protein content of hard red spring wheat under conditions of high temperature and low moisture, *J. Agr. Res.*, **47**: 129–148.

WANN, F. B., 1920: The fixation of free nitrogen by green plants, *Sci.*, **51**: 247–248.

———, 1921: The fixation of free nitrogen by green plants, *Am. J. Bot.*, **8**: 1–30.

WARBURG, O., and E. NEGELEIN, 1920: Über die Reduktion der Salpetersäure in grünen Zellen, *Biochem. Z.*, **110**: 66–115.

WASSILIEFF, N., 1908: Eiweissbildung im reifenden Samen, *Ber. bot. Ges.*, **26**: 454–467.

WATSON, D. J., 1936: The effect of applying a nitrogenous fertilizer to wheat at different stages of growth, *J. Agr. Sci.*, **26**: 391–414.

WEBSTER, J. E., 1928: Nitrogen metabolism in the soybean, *Plant Physiol.*, **3**: 31–43.

WEEVERS, T., 1930: Die Funktion der Xanthinderivate im Pflanzenstoffwechsel, *Arch. Néerl. Sci. Exactes et Nat. Sér.*, 3B, **5**: 111–195; *Biol. Abst.*, **5**: 2676.

WEINBERGER, J. H., and F. P. CULLINAN, 1934: Nitrogen intake and growth response in peach trees following fall and spring fertilizer applications, *Proc. Am. Soc. Hort. Sci.*, **32**: 65–69.

WELTON, F. A., and V. H. MORRIS, 1930: Effect of fertility in the carbohydrate-nitrogen relation in the soybean, *Plant Physiol.*, **5**: 607–612.

WERNER, H. O., 1934: The effect of a controlled nitrogen supply with different temperatures and photoperiods upon the development of the potato plant, *Neb. Sta. Res. Bull.* 75.

WESTGATE, J. M., and R. A. OAKLEY, 1914: Percentage of protein in non legumes and legumes when grown alone and in association with field mixtures, *J. Am. Soc. Agron.*, **6**: 211–215.

WHITE, H. L., 1936: The interaction of factors in the growth of *Lemna.* VIII, The effect of nitrogen on growth and multiplication, *Ann. Bot.*, **50**: 403–417.

WHITSON, A. R., F. J. WELLS, and A. VIVIAN, 1902: Influence of the soil on the protein content of crops, *Wis. Sta. 19th Ann. Rept.*, **1902**: 192–209.

WILLIAMS, C. F., 1932: Seasonal variations in nitrogen concentration in twigs of peach trees under sand hill conditions, *Proc. Am. Soc. Hort. Sci.*, **28**: 39–44.

WILLIAMS, R. J., and E. ROHRMAN, 1935: Pantothenic acid as a nutrilite for green plants, *Plant Physiol.*, **10**: 559–563.

WILLIS, L. G., and J. O. CARRERO, 1923: Influence of some nitrogenous fertilizers on the development of chlorosis in rice, *J. Agr. Res.*, **24**: 621–640.

——— and W. H. RANKIN, 1930: Free-ammonia injury with concentrated fertilizers, *Ind. and Eng. Chem.*, **22**: 1405–1407.

——— and ———, 1932: Is ammonium hydroxide toxic to cotton plants? *Sci.*, **76**: 214–215.

WILSON, B. D., 1921: Nitrogen in the rainwater at Ithaca, N. Y., *Soil Sci.*, **11**: 101–110.

WILSON, R. W., E. B. FRED, and M. R. SALMON, 1933: Relation between carbon dioxide and elemental nitrogen assimilation in leguminous plants, *Soil Sci.*, **35**: 145–166.

WOLFE, H. S., 1926: The auximone question, *Bot. Gaz.*, **81**: 228–231.

WOO, M. L., 1919: Chemical constituents of *Amaranthus retroflexus*, *Bot. Gaz.*, **68**: 313–344.

WORK, P., 1924: Nitrate of soda in the nutrition of the tomato, *N. Y. Sta.* (*Cornell*) *Mem.* 75.

YAMAGUCHI, S., 1930: Studies on the resorption of urea by the root of *Zea mays* seedlings in sterile culture, *J. Fac. Sci. Hokkaido Imp. Univ.*, Ser. 5, Bot. 1, 37–55; *Biol. Abst.*, **6**: 2516.

ZAHNLEY, J. W., and F. L. DULEY, 1934: The effect of nitrogenous fertilizers on the growth of lawn grasses, *J. Am. Soc. Agron.*, **26**: 231–234.

ZALESKI, W., 1897: Zur Kenntniss der Eiweissbildung in den Pflanzen, *Ber. bot. Ges.*, **15**: 536–542.

———, 1898: Zur Keimung der Zwiebel von *Allium cepa* und Eiweissbildung, *Ber. bot. Ges.*, **16**: 146–151.

———, 1901: Die Bedingungen der Eiweissbildung in den Pflanzen, *Bot. Cent.*, **87**: 277–282.

———, 1907: Über die autolytische Ammoniakbildung in den Pflanzen, *Ber. bot. Ges.*, **25**: 357–360.

———, 1907: Über den Aufbau der Eiweissstoffe in den Pflanzen, *Ber. bot. Ges.*, **25**: 360–368.

———, 1909: Über die Rolle des Lichtes bei der Eiweissbildung in den Pflanzen, *Ber. bot. Ges.*, **27**: 56–62.

———, 1911: Zur Kenntnis der Stoffwechselprozesse in reifenden Samen, *Beih. Bot. Cent.*, **27**: 63–82; *Bot. Cent.*, **117**: 57.

——— and W. SHATKIN, 1913: Untersuchungen über den Eiweissaufbau in den Pflanzen. I, Über den Eiweissaufbau in den Zwiebeln von *Allium cepa*, *Biochem. Z.*, **55**: 72–78.

ZELENY, L., 1935: The distribution of nitrogen in the seed of *Zea mays* at different stages of maturity, *Cereal Chem.*, **12**: 536–542.

CHAPTER X

THE FAT METABOLISM OF THE GREEN PLANT

I. FATTY SUBSTANCES IN PLANTS. CRUDE LIPIDES

When dry plant tissues are extracted with ethyl ether, chloroform, petroleum ether, carbon disulphide, benzene, acetone, or any of the other "fat solvents," a large number of substances are obtained which are designated collectively as the "ether extract," the "chloroform extract," etc., according to the particular solvent that has been used in the extraction. These substances are also frequently termed the "fatty substances" of the plant. Recently Sando (1928) in order to simplify the classification of the fatty substances suggested the name "crude lipides" for the tissue constituents obtained by extraction with the fat solvents, and that term will be used in the following discussion.

The crude lipides that have thus been extracted may be divided into two main groups: (*a*) Those substances which contain in their chemical constitution the fatty acids and which yield these acids upon hydrolysis. This group of substances includes the fats, fatty oils, waxes, sterol esters, phospholipides, and galactolipides. Until 1925, however, there was no comprehensive name to include all such substances. In that year Bloor proposed the name "lipides" to designate these types of compounds, and this term will be used in the following classification of the fatty substances of plants. (*b*) Those substances which are not compounds of fatty acids. These include the essential oils, hydrocarbons, resins, and coloring matters. Although some of these substances are similar to the lipides in possessing a greasy feel, they have little or no resemblance to them from a chemical standpoint.

The classification of the crude lipides that may occur in plant tissue is given in the outline on page 727.

A. Lipides

The lipides are the most abundant, the most widely distributed throughout the plant, and apparently are the most important, from a biological standpoint, of the fatty substances that occur in plants. As defined by Bloor (1925), they include those substances in plants and animals which are insoluble in water but soluble in ether, chloroform, benzene, or other fat solvents and which have a relationship to the fatty acids as esters either actual or potential. The compounds included under the term "lipides" form a group which is as strictly defined as either the proteins or carbohydrates and which are practically of the same physiological importance.

- The crude lipides: The fatty substances which may be extracted from plant tissues by ether, chloroform, benzene, and other fat solvents
  - The lipides: Esters of fatty acids and alcohols and their hydrolytic products which are soluble in fat solvents
    - The simple lipides
      - The fats or fatty oils: Esters of the fatty acids with glycerol
      - The waxes: Esters of fatty acids with monohydric alcohols
    - The compound lipides: Esters of the fatty acids containing groups in addition to alcohols and fatty acids
      - The phospholipides
        - Lecithin
        - Cephalin
      - Galactolipides
        - Phreosin
        - Kerasin
    - The derived lipides: Substances derived from the simple and compound lipides by hydrolysis
      - The fatty acids
        - The saturated fatty acids
        - The unsaturated fatty acids
      - Sterol alcohols
      - Wax alcohols
  - Substances not compounds of fatty acids
    - Resins
    - Hydrocarbons
    - Essential oils
    - Coloring matters
    - Sterols: Not derived from hydrolysis of esters

1. Composition.—The fatty acids and various types of alcohols are always component parts of the lipides and should be discussed here in some detail, since the reactions of the lipides are due in a large part to the character of these two types of compounds that enter into their composition.

a. Fatty Acids.—According to their position in the scheme of classification, the fatty acids should be considered under the heading of the derived lipides. In order to give the student a clear understanding of the nature of the lipides, however, and the part that the fatty acids play in determining their characteristics, a discussion of the fatty acids is given here. The fatty acids are monobasic and are so named because they occur in natural fats and because in the free state they resemble the fats in physical properties. The lower fatty acids as formic, acetic, and propionic are widely distributed in the various cells throughout the plant, either in the free or in the combined form. The higher fatty acids with which we are here more particularly concerned occur in the free state to a considerable extent in germinating seeds and perhaps to a limited extent in other plant parts. By far the greater portion that occurs in plants, however, is combined with the alcohols to form the various types of esters that are designated as lipides. The classification and identification of a large proportion of the lipides are based upon the fatty acids that they contain. The fatty acids may be divided into two main series: (1) the saturated and (2) the unsaturated.

1. *Saturated.*—The saturated fatty acids have the general formula $C_nH_{2n}O_2$ and contain the maximal hydrogen possible. A saturated acid is thus saturated with respect to its hydrogen. The more important saturated acids are shown in the following table:

THE SATURATED FATTY ACIDS

Name of the acid	Formula
Formic	$HCOOH$
Acetic	CH_3COOH
Propionic	C_2H_5COOH
n Butyric	C_3H_7COOH
Isobutyric	$(CH_3)_2CHCOOH$
n Valeric	C_4H_9COOH
n Caproic	$C_5H_{11}COOH$
Caprylic	$C_7H_{15}COOH$
Capric	$C_9H_{19}COOH$
Lauric	$C_{11}H_{23}COOH$
Myristic	$C_{13}H_{27}COOH$
Palmitic	$C_{15}H_{31}COOH$
Stearic	$C_{17}H_{35}COOH$
Arachidic	$C_{19}H_{39}COOH$
Lignoceric	$C_{23}H_{47}COOH$
Cerotic	$C_{25}H_{51}COOH$

The acids of this series up to capric acid are liquid at ordinary temperatures, while the members containing 10 or more carbon atoms are solids. The lowest members of this saturated series containing four or less carbon atoms are miscible with water in all proportions. As the molecular weight increases beyond this, however, the solubility of the acids in water rapidly diminishes to zero. The acids of this series from capric acid down are easily distilled with steam and are termed the "volatile fatty acids." The acids next above capric pass over in a current of steam only in traces, while the acids higher distill scarcely at all. Practically all these saturated acids above normal valeric occur, for the most part, in the form of glycerides in various plants. Thus caproic, caprylic, and capric acids occur as glycerides in coconut and palm-nut oils. Lauric acid occurs as a glyceride in laurel oil, coconut oil, palm oil, and myrtle wax. Myristic acid occurs as a glyceride in palm-kernel oil. Palmitic acid is found as glycerides in barberry wax and in palm oil. Stearic acid occurs in the form of glyceride in shea butter and cacao butter while arachidic acid is found in relatively large amounts as glycerides in peanut oil.

2. *Unsaturated.*—The organic chemist designates these acids as the unsaturated acids, but since the term "unsaturated fatty acids" is used extensively by biologists, it was thought best to designate them by this name in this text. When the fatty acid molecule does not contain the maximum amount of hydrogen possible, the acid is said to be unsaturated. This means that at some point in the chain one or more pairs of carbon atoms are united by a double union. This double union may occur in a number of different positions, and the properties of the acid differ with the different positions of the double unions. The unsaturated fatty acids may be made to combine with hydrogen, halogens, or oxygen by chemical means. The greater the degree of unsaturation the more unstable is the acid and the more readily does it combine with the elements mentioned above. The unsaturated acids are liquids at ordinary temperatures. They fall into different series according to their degree of unsaturation. The more important ones are given in the following table:

THE UNSATURATED FATTY ACIDS

Name of the acid		Formula
Oleic series:		$C_nH_{2n-2}O_2$
	or	$C_nH_{2n-1}COOH$
Tiglic		C_4H_7COOH
Hypogeic		$C_{15}H_{29}COOH$
Oleic		$C_{17}H_{33}COOH$
Isomer of oleic:		
Rapic		$C_{17}H_{33}COOH$
Erucic		$C_{21}H_{41}COOH$
Linolic series:		$C_nH_{2n-4}O_2$
	or	$C_nH_{2n-3}COOH$
Linolic		$C_{17}H_{31}COOH$
Linolenic series:		$C_nH_{2n-6}O_2$
	or	$C_nH_{2n-5}COOH$
Linolenic		$C_{17}H_{29}COOH$
Hydroxy series:		$C_nH_{2n-2}O_3$
	or	$C_nH_{2n-1}OCOOH$
Ricinoleic acid		$C_{17}H_{33}OCOOH$

The oleic series takes its name from oleic acid, which occurs as glyceride in most fats and oils. Tiglic acid occurs as a glyceride in croton oil, while hypogeic acid is found in the form of glyceride in peanut and maize oil. Oleic is the most widespread and most abundant of any of the fatty acids that occur in the plant. The glyceride of this acid is found in the fats and oils of the coconut, palm kernel, olive, peanut, cotton seed, maize, flax seed, soybean, and many other seeds. Linolic acid occurs in the combined form in linseed oil, cotton-seed oil, olive oil, peanut oil, soybean oil, and maize oil, while linolenic acid and its isomers are found in linseed oil, hemp oil, sunflower oil, soybean oil, and other plant oils.

The hydroxy-fatty acids have one or more hydroxyl groups that replace hydrogen in the chain. One of the common hydroxy-fatty acids is ricinoleic, which is unsaturated and forms the glyceride that is the principal constituent of castor oil.

b. Glycerol and Other Alcohols.—Alcohols of various kinds are combined with the fatty acids to form numerous types of lipides. Of these alcohols, the trihydroxyalcohol, glycerol, or glycerin ($C_3H_5(OH)_3$), is by far the most abundant and forms esters or glycerides with many different fatty acids. At ordinary temperatures, it is a viscid fluid and mixes with water in all proportions. It is miscible with ethyl alcohol, but only slightly soluble in ether and is insoluble in chloroform, petroleum ether, and carbon disulphide. It is highly hygroscopic, absorbing more than one-half its weight of water from the air and cannot be completely freed from water *in vacuo* over sulphuric acid. Glycerol is formed in the alcoholic fermentation of sugar. It was discovered during the World War that glycerol can be prepared from sugar by the action of yeast in the presence of large amounts of sodium sulphite and large quantities were obtained in this manner.

The alcohols that are combined with the fatty acids to form waxes or sterol esters are monohydric and are insoluble in water. Some of these which are found in plants are ceryl alcohol ($C_{26}H_{53}OH$), which occurs in the combined state as ceryl palmitate in poppy wax; myricyl alcohol ($C_{30}H_{61}OH$), which occurs free and as the ester of cerotic acid in carnauba wax, which is obtained from the leaves of the Brazil palm; and cholesterol ($C_{27}H_{45}OH$), which is a cyclic, monohydric alcohol. Such compounds are sometimes termed "sterols." Cholesterol is found in animal tissue, but so far has not been detected in plants. It is of interest here, however, since phytosterol, which is apparently an isomer of cholesterol, is found in practically all the fatty materials of plants, constituting from 0.13 to 0.30 per cent of such materials. The term "phytosterol," however, is now used generically, since phytosterol is considered to be composed of a mixture of two substances: sitosterol ($C_{27}H_{45}OH$), which has been obtained from the oil of wheat, rye, and maize; and stigmasterol ($C_{30}H_{47}OH$), which has been found in the phytosterol of rape oil and cacao butter.

Anderson and Moore (1923) found that corn oil contains 2 per cent of unsaponifiable matter, largely of phytosterol, which is identical with sitosterol. Both cottonseed oil and linseed oil contain at least two phytosterols differing in optical properties. The corn pollen of white flint corn contains phytosterol palmitate (Anderson, 1923). The fat extracted from this pollen with absolute alcohol contains 25 per cent unsaponifiable matter, primarily a mixture of optically inactive phytosterols, which are free from water of crystallization. Anderson (1924) also found that the unsaponifiable matter derived from the endosperm of corn contained considerable quantities of ordinary sitosterol associated with dihydrositosterol (see Anderson and others, 1926; Terrone and others, 1927; Matlack, 1935; and Moyer, 1935).

2. Classification.—According to Bloor (1925), the lipides may be divided into three main groups: (*a*) the simple, (*b*) the compound, and (*c*) the derived.

a. Simple.—The simple lipides include those compounds which are the esters of the fatty acids with various alcohols. The fats and fatty oils and the waxes are the main groups of the simple lipides.

1. *Fats and Fatty Oils.*—This group of compounds is composed of esters of the fatty acids with glycerol, termed the "triglycerides" of fatty acids. These compounds are commonly called "oils" if they remain liquid at ordinary temperatures and "fats" when they are solid at such temperatures. The oils of this type are frequently designated as "fatty oils" to distinguish them from the volatile oils and others that have no chemical relation to the triglycerides. In this discussion the term "fat" will be used in the general sense as including all the triglycerides. The fats as they occur in nature are practically always mixtures in varying proportions of triglycerides. In some fats one triglyceride predominates, in others another, and in still others several are present in considerable amounts, so that probably no natural fat consists solely of a single triglyceride. Furthermore, the individual fatty-acid radicals of any single glyceride may be different (Collin and Hilditch, 1929; and Bengis and Anderson, 1934). Thus each of the three fatty-acid radicals may be different, two may be of one type and the third another, or all three may be of the same kind. The type of glyceride that predominates in a given fat gives that fat its more pronounced characteristics. Although a large number of triglycerides occur in nature, those of myristic acid, lauric acid, palmitic acid, stearic acid, oleic acid, linolic acid, and linolenic acid make up the great bulk of the natural fats and oils. This fact, as well as the mixed nature of the fats and oils from plants, is shown in the table on page 732, adapted from Alsberg and Taylor (1928), Baughman and Jamieson (1920, 1921, 1922), and Jamieson, Baughman, and Brauns (1921, 1922).

(*a*) *Physical Properties.*—The triglycerides of the higher fatty acids are insoluble in water, while those of the lower are slightly soluble. The triglycerides above those of caprylic acid are lighter than water and all float thereon. They are readily soluble in ether, chloroform, benzene, and other organic solvents in the cold but are much more soluble in these solvents when heated. They are only slightly soluble in ethyl and methyl alcohol and acetone, at ordinary temperatures, but readily soluble when heated. Castor oil is an exception, however, and is readily soluble in ethyl alcohol in the cold.

PERCENTAGE OF THE MORE IMPORTANT FATTY ACIDS COMBINED IN FATS AND OILS

Fat or oil	Lauric	Myristic	Palmitic	Stearic	Oleic	Linolic	Linolenic
Coconut	45	20	5	3	.6		
Palm kernel	55	12	6	4	10		
Olive	..	....	14.6	...	75.4	10	
Peanut	..	....	8.5	6	51.6	26	
Cotton seed	..	....	23.4	...	31.6	45	
Maize	..	....	6.0	2	44.0	48	
Linseed	..	3	....	...	...	77	17.0
Soybean	..	....	11.0	2	20.0	64	3.0
Cantaloup seed oil	..	0.3	10.2	4.5	27.2	56.6	
Sunflower oil	..	....	3.5	2.9	33.4	57.5	
Hubbard squash seed oil	..	....	13.0	6.0	37.0	44.0	

The pure triglycerides are colorless, odorless, and tasteless, the properties of color, odor, and taste, when present, being due entirely to foreign substances mixed with or dissolved in them. The pure triglycerides are for the most part optically inactive. Castor oil is an exception, since it contains an optically active fatty acid. Some of the unpurified triglycerides show optical properties, but these properties are due to such nonfat impurities as resins and sterols.

(*b*) *Chemical Properties.* (1) *Hydrolysis.*—All the fats and fatty oils, under proper conditions, may be hydrolyzed to glycerin and their component fatty acids. Thus, for example, in the case of tripalmitin, hydrolysis proceeds after the following manner:

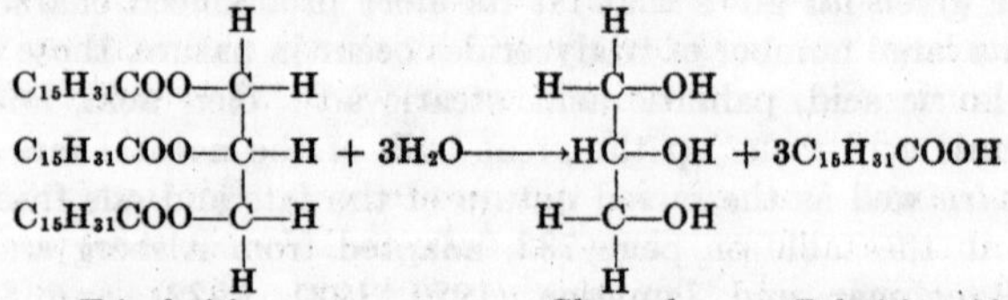

Tripalmitin Glycerol Palmitic acid

The fats may be hydrolyzed: (*a*) By treating them with superheated steam in the presence of a suitable catalytic agent. Four compounds that may be used as catalyzers are sulphuric acid, hydrochloric acid, lime, and magnesia. Sulphuric acid is the most efficient agent since it apparently aids in bringing the fat into a finer emulsion. (*b*) By the action of the enzyme lipase. This enzyme may be isolated from plant tissue and used in the laboratory for hydrolyzing fats. Lipase hydrolyzes the fats in plants under natural conditions as will be described later. The hydrolysis of fats is apparently the first step in their breaking up for utilization in the metabolism of the plant.

(2) *Saponification.*—When fats are boiled with caustic alkali they are hydrolyzed into glycerol and fatty acids, the alkali combining with the fatty acid to form soap, a process termed "saponification." The term saponification literally means soapmaking. The process may be illustrated by using the fat tripalmitin as an example:

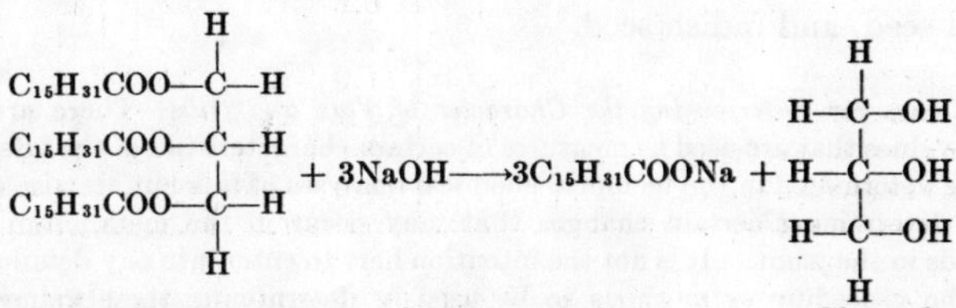

Tripalmitin — Sodium palmitate (a soap) — Glycerol

In the laboratory the saponification of fats is usually carried out by alcoholic alkali solutions, since the reaction is much more rapid with this reagent than with alkali in water. The process is of interest in plant physiology because it is considered to play some part in the translocation and utilization of fats, as will be discussed later.

(3) *Drying of Oils.*—When most of the fatty oils are exposed to the air they tend to thicken or dry. This is due in some cases to polymerization and in others to oxidation. Some oils only thicken, while others become dry and form a more or less hard mass or, if spread out sufficiently, a thin elastic film. The drying process is due primarily to the oxidation of the oils and is characteristic of those oils which contain fatty acids with unsaturated carbon unions; the larger the number of these unsaturated unions the more readily do the oils take up oxygen. According to the degree to which they dry, oils are grouped into three classes (Haas and Hill, 1913):

a) *Nondrying.*—The oils in this group only thicken but do not become hard or form films. They are composed, for the most part, of the triglyceride of oleic acid. To this group belong olive oil, peanut oil, almond oil, rice oil, and the oil from the kernels of cherry, plum, peach, and apricot seeds.

b) Drying.—The oils of this group are composed principally of the triglycerides of the unsaturated fatty acids of the linoleic and linolenic series and contain a relatively small amount of oleic acid. The drying oils absorb oxygen from the air and form an elastic skin or film, a characteristic that is utilized in the manufacture and application of paints. Some of the oils that belong to this group are linseed, hemp seed, sunflower, cedar nut, walnut, and poppy seed.

c) Semidrying.—According to the classification of Haas and Hill (1913), the oils of this group have drying properties lying midway between those of the drying and nondrying oils. They differ from the true drying oils in containing triglycerides of acids of the linoleic series. Some of the oils that fall in this group are cottonseed, pumpkin seed, soybean, sesame and croton, watermelon seed, barley and rye seed, rape, mustard seed, and radish seed.

(4) *Values for Determining the Character of Fats and Oils.*—There are certain chemical values that are used as measures of certain characteristics of the fats. These values are determined in the technical chemical analyses of fats but are also of importance in determining certain changes that may occur in the metabolism of these compounds in the plant. It is not the intention here to enter into any detailed discussion of the procedure or methods to be used in determining these values, but to discuss them only in so far as they will be an aid in understanding the physiological changes that occur in the fat metabolism of the plant. A detailed discussion may be obtained by consulting Haas and Hill (1913), Leathes and Raper (1925), and "The Methods of Analysis of Official Agricultural Chemists" (1925). The chemical values of the fats that will be mentioned here are (*a*) the acid, (*b*) the Hehner, (*c*) the saponification, (*d*) the iodine, and (*e*) the acetyl.

a) Acid Value.—By the acid value of a fat is meant the number of milligrams of potassium hydroxide necessary to neutralize 1 g. of the fat. It is thus a measure of the amount of free fatty acid present in the fat and indicates the degree of hydrolysis it has undergone. The acid value, however, indicates nothing as to the nature of the free acids present in the fat. The acid value of a fat may be obtained by dissolving a measured portion in neutral 95 per cent alcohol, heating to boiling, and titrating with 0.1 *N* alkali, using phenolphthalein as an indicator.

In connection with the acid value of a fat, the total insoluble acids and the total soluble acids should be considered.

b) Hehner Value.—By the Hehner value of a fat is meant the percentage of fatty acids insoluble in water that is yielded on the saponification of the fat. The determination of the insoluble fatty acids of a fat gives some information as to its composition. Thus if the fat contained in a certain plant part shows, during the course of the development of the plant, a decrease in the percentage of insoluble fatty acids, it is an indication that the higher fatty acids are being replaced by those of the lower groups, which are soluble in water. The total soluble acids of a fat represent b th the free and the combined acids of the oil which are soluble in water and represent the fatty acids of lower molecular weight. The determination of the soluble acids supplements the results obtained in the estimation of the total insoluble fatty acids.

c) Saponification Value.—The saponification equivalent or value of a fat is the amount of potassium hydroxide in milligrams that is neutralized during the saponification of 1 g. of the fat by the combined and free fatty acids that it contains. It is in reality an indication of the mean molecular weight of the fatty acids that enter into the composition of the fat. Thus fats that are the glycerides of the higher fatty acids give relatively low saponification values, while those that are glycerides of the lower fatty acids give relatively high saponification values. The saponification values of some of the more common plant fats are as follows:

Fat or oil	Saponification value
Coconut oil	246 to 260
Peanut oil	190 to 196
Cottonseed oil	193 to 195
Linseed oil	192 to 195
Soybean oil	193
Olive oil	185 to 196
Corn oil	188 to 193
Rape-seed oil	170 to 179

d) Iodine Value.—By the iodine value of a fat is meant the amount of iodine, expressed in percentage of the weight of the oil, that the combined and free unsaturated fatty acids of the fat will take up. Thus if the iodine value of the fat content of a plant decreases during any given period, it indicates that the unsaturated fatty acids of the oil are becoming saturated, probably by the addition of oxygen. The iodine value of some of the more common plant fats is shown in the following table:

Iodine Values of Plant Fats
(After Alsberg and Taylor, 1928)

Fat or oil	Iodine value	Fat or oil	Iodine value
Linseed oil	173 to 201	Peanut oil	83 to 100
Soybean oil	137 to 143	Palm oil	51 to 57
Sunflower oil	119 to 135	Cacao butter	32 to 41
Corn oil	111 to 130	Palm kernel oil	13 to 17
Cottonseed oil	108 to 110	Coconut oil	8 to 10
Rape-seed oil	94 to 102		

e) Acetyl Value.—The acetyl value of a fat gives the number of milligrams of potassium hydroxide required to neutralize the acetic acid that is set free when 1 g. of the acetylated fat is saponified. The acetyl value is really a measure of the amount of the hydroxyl groups that a fat contains. The acetyl values of some of the fats are as follows (after Haas and Hill, 1913):

Linseed oil	3.98	Palm oil	18.0
Olive oil	10.64	Grape-seed oil	144.0
Rape-seed oil	14.7	Castor oil	153.0

2. *Waxes.*—The waxes are generally defined as fatty-acid esters of some alcohol other than glycerol, usually a monohydric alcohol such as ceryl alcohol, cetyl alcohol, myricyl alcohol, and phytosterol. The waxes may also contain acids other than those which have been mentioned in considering the fats and oils. According to McNair (1931), plant waxes include as components higher fatty acids, mono- or dihydroxy saturated alcohols of high molecular weight, esters formed from these, ketones, and hydrocarbons. The waxes from the tropics have lower melting points and higher molecular weights than those from the temperate zone. Most of the vegetable waxes are produced by the integuments of the organism and not internally as are the fats. The term "waxes" is used only in the chemical sense and has reference to their composition regardless of their physical condition, so that waxes occur as both solids and liquids. The waxes of the plant kingdom are all solids. Some of the waxes of plant origin are ceryl palmitate in poppy wax and myricyl cerotate and ceryl cerotate in carnauba wax. Some of the waxes of animal origin are beeswax, wool wax, and spermaceti.

Waxes are somewhat less soluble in the ordinary fat solvents than are fats. The waxes, as a general rule, have to be boiled with alcoholic potash much longer than the glycerides in order to be saponified. This is due in part, apparently, to their low solubility even in hot alcohol. Their saponification value is low because the molecular weights of the alcohols as well as the fatty acids that compose them are high. Waxes are commonly found on fruits and leaves and are generally spread over the cuticle as a wax covering. In fruits this covering is termed the "bloom" when it is noticeable. These wax coverings may consist of grains, small rods, or crusts. The greatest thickness of wax deposit that has been observed is on the leaves of some of the palms where in some cases the coverings are more than 5 mm. in thickness. In the waxlike coating of the apple, Sando (1923) obtained from the ether extract triacontane ($C_{30}H_{62}$), melting at 63.5 to 64°C.; heptacosanol ($C_{27}H_{56}O$), melting at 81 to 81.5°; and malol, a crystalline alcohol.

Pollard, Chibnall, and Piper (1931) and Smith and Chibnall (1932) found that *n*-hexacosanol is the chief constituent of the wax of the perennial forage grasses, cocksfoot, and rye grass.

Sahai and Chibnall (1932) identified *n*-nonacosane, cerotic acid, and ceryl alcohol among the constituents of the leaf wax of Brussels sprouts. Chibnall and others (1933) found that a long-chain primary alcohol, *n*-triacontanol, is the principal component of the wax from the leaves of alfalfa, and Pollard, Chibnall, and Piper (1933) reported that *n*-octacosanol, a primary alcohol, is the principal component of the wax from the young blades of wheat. The waxes of the three last mentioned plants contain paraffin of a complex nature, and the wax from the leaves of alfalfa and wheat contains mixed fatty acids of an unknown composition.

Markley and Sando (1931, 1933) noted in the formation of the waxlike coating of the apple that there is an increase in the ursolic acid, the oily fraction, and the total ether extract throughout the growing period and during storage. They considered that the difficulty in removing spray residues cannot be attributed directly to an accumulation of oil of the sprays but rather to an increase of all the ether-soluble, waxlike constituents due to physiological stimulation. The application of a mineral oil may exert a semisolvent action on the natural waxy coating. This would cause the particles of poison to be more easily and firmly embedded. After the disappearance of the dissolving oil, the natural waxy constituent would form again, and this more compact coating would protect the arsenate particles against the cleaning fluid.

b. Compound Lipides.—The term "compound lipides" as defined by Bloor (1925) includes the esters of the fatty-acid-containing groups in addition to an alcohol and a fatty acid. This group of substances has been designated by various authors as "lipins," "lipoids," and "fatlike bodies." MacLean and MacLean (1927) in defining the term "lipins" stated that they are substances of a fatlike nature, yielding upon hydrolysis fatty acids or derivatives thereof and containing either nitrogen or nitrogen and phosphorus. The compound lipides are divided into (1) the phospholipides and (2) the galactolipides.

1. *Phospholipides.*—This group has also been called the "phospholipins," "phosphatides," and sometimes "the lecithins." The phospholipides are substituted fats containing phosphoric acid and nitrogen. They thus contain phosphorus, nitrogen, and fatty acids and on hydrolysis yield glycerophosphoric acid, fatty acids, and basic bodies, such as choline and amino ethyl alcohol. The phospholipides are soluble in the majority of the ordinary fat solvents with the exception of acetone. The phospholipides are precipitated from the crude ether or fat solvent extract by the addition of an excess of acetone (MacLean and MacLean, 1927). The two most abundant phospholipides are lecithin and cephalin.

(*a*) *Lecithin.*—Lecithin is considered the most important plant phospholipide. It may be regarded as a fat in which one of the three fatty acids is replaced by phosphoric acid combined with choline. The type of fatty acids combined in lecithins varies widely. In a lecithin preparation from the soybean, Levene and Rolf (1925) found stearic, palmitic, oleic, linoleic, and linolenic acids. Lecithin is very labile and undergoes changes as the result of oxidation. It combines with acids and bases and acts readily as an adsorbent. The occurrence of lecithin in the plant will be mentioned in a subsequent topic.

(*b*) *Cephalin.*—This compound closely resembles lecithin and is always found closely associated with it. It is distinguished from lecithin by its insolubility in alcohol and is separated in the laboratory from lecithin by the utilization of this property. Cephalin is considered to contain two fatty acids—one of the common fatty-acid series and another peculiar to cephalin, termed "cephalic acid." It also contains three basic bodies, two of choline and one of amino ethyl alcohol. The methods for the separation of cephalin have never been very well defined, and it is probable that pure cephalin has never been prepared.

2. *Galactolipides.*—The galactolipides are compounds of the fatty acids with a carbohydrate and contain nitrogen but no phosphoric acid. They have also been designated as "glycolipins," "cerebrosides," and "galactosides." The galactolipides are bodies of a glucoside nature and upon hydrolysis yield galactose, a fatty acid, and a base.

c. Derived Lipides.—The term "derived lipides" is given those substances which are derived from the simple and compound lipides by hydrolysis and which are soluble in the fat solvents. They include the fatty acids of the various series and the large molecular alcohols which are soluble in the fat solvents and are found in nature combined with the fatty acids. These alcohols include cholesterol, myricyl alcohol, and cetyl alcohol. The derived lipides have been discussed in relation to the compounds of which they are a part and will not be mentioned further here.

3. Distribution in the Plant Cell.—Fatty substances occur apparently in every living plant cell in exceedingly variable quantities. They are present in the cells of the apical meristem and were determined by Priestley (1924) to be for the most part phospholipides. Fats, fatty acids, and soaps can be detected in the walls of plant cells at a very early stage and appear to be present as early as the cellulose and pectic substances. Hansteen-Cranner (1924 to 1926) noted the presence of fats and phospholipides in the cell walls of parenchymatous tissues. He considered these of importance in regard to the permeability of these tissues. Priestley (1924) stated that the cell walls of the phloem tissues are free from fat, although fat is included in the cell content. The external protective coverings of the plant owe their imperviousness to water to various oxidation and condensation products of fatty acids, especially hydroxy-fatty acids, as mentioned in Chap. I. In the photosynthetic tissues, fats and phospholipides are always present, and the pigments of the green leaf are probably dissolved in colloidal solutions of fatty substances. By far the major portion of the fatty substances in plants is found in the protoplasm, but the physical relation between these substances and the protoplasm is, as yet, not clearly understood. Wakker (1886) considered that the oil substances are distributed evenly in very minute drops in the protoplasm, while Tschirch and Kritzler (1900) believed that the fatty substances of oily seeds are not in drops but are homogeneously mixed with the protoplasm. Czapek (1913) stated that fatty substances in seeds are ultramicroscopically divided in the protoplasm and that oil drops cannot be demonstrated. Haberlandt (1914) stated that in oily seeds the greater proportion of the oil is contained in the interstices between the delicate meshwork of the protoplasm, but that when the oil is present in the tissues in small amounts it is suspended in the protoplasm in small drops. Dangeard (1923) by means of intravital staining of living cells of the seeds of *Ricinus* and conifers found the cytoplasm to be alveolar and in the alveoli the aleurone grains and the oil are located. The oil in these alveoli is not a continuous phase but is in the form of spherules, which are thus inclusions in the cytoplasm. The dispersion of fatty substances or lipoids in the cells of the embryo and endosperm was studied by Pack (1925) with especial reference to juniper seeds. As afterripening and germination proceeded at 5°C. the lipoid drops gradually became smaller and increased in number. This dispersion was found to proceed and accompany the appearance of sugar and starch in the hypocotyl region. As germination progresses, the lipoid drops in the root and shoot axil reach a degree of dispersion equal to the limit of the microscope. During germination there is a decrease in the number of these drops because the lipoid material is used in the manufacture of other compounds. The oil reserve observed in the seeds of hawthorn, castor bean, peach, and juniper shows that it is often stored in the form of large drops. At times these drops are collected into masses that fill the meshes of the protoplasm. Resting seeds, with little fatty content, deposit it as fine drops. The lipoids of active cells and tissues are in a very fine state of division. This dispersion of the oily substances increases the oil surface many hundreds of times and is favorable to hydrolysis by enzymes, so that translocation, absorption, and transformation of the oil are favored.

Pack stated that in the deposition of fatty materials in storage organs, one first notices fine oil droplets or bodies in the younger cells. These droplets increase in size with the age of the cells, so that in the old cells large masses or drops of oil can be seen. These changes are the reverse of the dispersion of the lipoids during their digestion in the active tissues. Condensation attends the storage of fats while dispersion accompanies their digestion.

Under certain conditions bodies termed "elaioplasts" are formed in certain cells and have been considered by some to be oil formers. According to Beer (1909), they are formed by the aggregation of plastids and their decomposition products, and, although they frequently contain oil, they are in no sense special oil-forming organs. The oil vacuoles sometimes observed in certain cells originate by the coalescence of numerous minute oil droplets secreted by the protoplasm in a manner similar to that in which the ordinary sap vacuole arises. Although these oil vacuoles may be large and project into the sap vacuole, they continue to be surrounded by a thin film of cytoplasm. The oil vacuoles are in no sense plastids, nor are they formed by elaioplasts but are simply accumulations of fatty substances (Rivett, 1918).

4. Occurrence of Fats and Fatty Oils in the Plant.—The fats and fatty oils make up the greater portion of the fatty substances that are found in plants. Although they are widely distributed in the plant world, the commercial supply of these products is obtained for the most part from a comparatively small number of species (approximately 200). The fats and fatty oils are reserve foods and are utilized by the protoplasm in respiration, growth, and repair after the same manner as carbohydrates. When fats and oils are stored in tissues in relatively large amounts, carbohydrates, as a rule, are present in relatively small amounts. When carbohydrates are present in relatively large amounts, fats and oils generally occur only in limited quantity.

a. In Fruits and Seeds.—The fats and oils are found in the greatest abundance in fruits and seeds. While they occur in the root, stem, branches, and leaves of plants, they are rarely present in these organs in quantities large enough to be of much significance. In some seeds, as the cereals, the fats and oils are confined almost entirely to the embryo. In the oil palm, both the embryo and endosperm contain a large amount of fat. In the olive, a large amount of oil is stored in the pulp surrounding the kernel and a smaller amount is in the kernel itself. The oil or fat in these different parts of the seed may have characteristics that are quite different from each other. The table that follows gives the percentages of oil that may occur in various seeds and plant parts. The percentage of oil varies in the same species under different conditions, so that any data in this regard should be considered as more or less relative. The figures that are commonly given for the fat and oil content mean simply the fat-solvent extract and include, thus, numerous substances other than fats and oils.

THE PERCENTAGES OF FATS AND OILS IN THE DRY MATERIAL OF SEEDS AND OTHER PLANT PARTS

Plant part	Percentage of fat or oil	Plant part	Percentage of fat or oil
Coconut	65	*Madia sativa* seed	32
Brazil nut	70	Olive pulp	50
Castor bean	60	Kafir seed	2.5
Sunflower seed	45–50	Feterita seed	2.4
Flax seed	30–35	Milo seed	2.3
Cotton seed	15–20	Corn seed	5.0
Peanut	40–50	Wheat seed	2.1
Hemp	30–35	Rye seed	1.8
Walnut	50–65	Rice seed	1.9
Cacao bean	40–50	Buckwheat seed	2.5
Poppy seed	40–50	Field pea	1.1
Pumpkin seed	41	Bean	1.5
Almond	40–50	Bluegrass leaves	2.8
Soybean	15–20	Buffalo grass leaves	1.8
Cantaloup seed	30	Orchard grass stem and leaves	2.9
Spurge seed	35–45	Alfalfa stem and leaves	2.3
Rape seed	33–43	Cowpeas stem and leaves	2.6
Sesame seed	50–55	Soybeans stem and leaves	2.5
Colza seed	43–53	Cabbage leaf	1.7

The starch and oil content of the seeds of 216 of the 280 families of angiosperms and gymnosperms was tabulated by McNair (1930). He found that the seeds of 64.3 per cent of these families contain oil but no starch, 24.1 per cent contain both oil and starch, and 7 per cent contain starch but not oil. Sullivan and Near (1933) found that wheat and its products under different storage conditions showed marked variations in the amount of ether extract. The changes apparently correlated with increase of acidity and of content in the sample.

b. In Stem and Leaves.—The fatty components of the leaves had been studied very little until Chibnall and Channon (1927, 1929) and Channon and Chibnall (1927, 1929) examined the leaves of cabbage. They found that the crude lipides of these leaves amounted to about 3.5 per cent of the total solids. Chibnall and Sahai (1931) reported that in the leaves of cocksfoot (*Dactylis glomerata*) the crude lipides amounted to as much as 7 per cent of the dry weight, while the total reducing sugar present amounted to only 3 per cent on the same basis. The relative amounts of some of the various constituents of the crude lipides of the leaves of cabbage have been reported by Chibnall and Sahai (1931) as follows:

Component	Percentage of ether extract
Chlorophyll, carotene, and xanthophyll	10.6
Substances containing phosphorus	23.4
Iron compounds	3.0
Glycerides, waxes, and free acids	17.5
Glycerol	1.3
Unsaponifiable material:	
Saturated fraction	12.3
Unsaturated fraction:	
Sterols	4.5
Unidentified material	13.3

Heyl, Wise, and Speer (1929) and Speer, Wise, and Hart (1929) examined the fatty components of spinach. They found that 53 per cent of the fatty acids were present in the free state and 47 per cent as glycerides. From 550 g. of fatty acids, 26.5 g. of solid acids was obtained. These solid acids consisted chiefly of palmitic, stearic, and cerotic acids. About 145 g. of liquid acids was recovered, and of this amount 12.7 per cent was linolic, 34.7 per cent linoleic, and 26.3 per cent oleic. The volatile acids were present only in traces, if at all.

From the unsaponifiable fraction of the ether extract, they obtained a hydrocarbon of the formula $C_{20}H_{42}$, a common phytosterol with the formula $C_{27}H_{46}O_2$, two alcohols of the formulas $C_{22}H_{46}O$ and $C_{24}H_{50}O_2$, and an unsaturated, oily compound having the formula $C_{27}H_{54}O$.

The crude lipides of the leaves that have been examined contain relatively large amounts of phosphatides, unsaponifiable materials, and unsaturated compounds. The role of lipides in the metabolism of the leaf is impossible of evaluation at the present time because of the occurrence of lipides in relatively small amounts and because of their close association with the pigments of the leaf and other impurities.

c. In Trees and Shrubs.—Fats and oils form a considerable portion of the food reserve in trees and shrubs. Under certain conditions, carbohydrates appear to predominate in amount; and under others, fats and oils. In some plants these two reserves are about equal in amount (Sinnott, 1918). It has been observed for a long time that under certain conditions the carbohydrate reserves are transformed into fats and oils and vice versa. The conditions under which such changes are brought about are still very obscure. In trees growing at Edmonton, Can., a progressive decrease of the sugars from the winter maximum toward the summer was found (Lewis and Tuttle, 1920; Tuttle, 1919, 1921). Oils and fats were present in nearly all cells of the phloem, cortex, and the medullary-ray cells. In a majority of cases, starch disappeared during October and early November, while oils and fats were abundant. In leaves at about the time of leaf fall, 15 species were characterized by the absence of starch, but all showed a relatively high oil and fat content. Sinnott (1918) considered that starch is more common, in the woody plants, in regions remote from the centers of conduction and in cells with well-lignified and small-pitted walls, while fats and oils were more abundant in and near the phloem, close to vessels, and in cells with thin, unlignified walls with large pits. Where movement of liquids apparently is slow and difficult, the reserve food persists as starch, while where such movement is easy, starch disappears at the beginning of winter and fats and oils are produced. The character of the food reserves thus depends primarily upon the ease with which water or substances carried by it have access to the cells.

5. Occurrence of Compound Lipides in the Plant.—Our knowledge of the compound lipides in plants is very limited, and it is doubtful if any of them have yet been obtained in the pure form. The methods used for their isolation from animal tissues are apparently not applicable for their extraction from plant tissues. The chief obstacle in investigating the compound lipides in plants is due, according to MacLean and MacLean (1927), to the presence in the plant of a large amount of carbohydrate material which tends to form physical complexes with the compound lipides. It is not known whether the compound lipides of plants are identical or not with those of animal origin. The occurrence of compound lipides has been reported for a wide range of plants and has been especially studied in seeds and seedlings. These compounds have been variously reported as phospholipins, phosphatides, lecithin, lipoids, and lipins. The compound lipides that have been reported in plants are, for the most part, phospholipides, especially lecithin, but it is probable that cephalin is also present in plants (Levene and Rolf, 1925). According to MacLean and MacLean (1927), the presence of carbohydrates in the compound lipides of plants is almost universal. Although some of this carbohydrate is only in physical association with these substances, there exist bodies of wide occurrence in plants with which the carbohydrates are chemically combined and thus identical with or similar to the galactolipides that are found in animals. The only compound lipides that have been studied to any extent in plants are the phospholipides, and our attention will be devoted entirely to them. The phospholipides are widely distributed in plants and, although occurring in very small amounts, are present in practically every living plant cell (Kossel, 1891).

a. Distribution.—Knop (1859) isolated from plant tissue a fatty extract that contained phosphorus, and thus he was probably the first to observe the presence of phospholipides in plants. Jacobson (1889) showed that one of the decomposition products of the phospholipides occurring in plants is choline, while Schulze and Likiernik (1891) hydrolyzed phospholipides from seeds and obtained fatty acids, glycerophosphoric acid, and choline, thus establishing the similarity of the plant phospholipides to those of animal origin. Winterstein and Hiestand (1908) found phospholipides in the potato and seeds of cereals, vetch, and lupine. Euler and Nordenson (1908) isolated a lecithinlike substance from the carrot, and Winterstein and Stegmann (1909) were able to obtain a phospholipide from the leaves of *Ricinus.* It was determined by Winterstein and Smolenski (1909) that wheat flour contains a mixture of phospholipides that differ in their physical and chemical properties, while Smolenski (1909) obtained a phospholipide from the wheat embryo. Njegovan (1911) obtained three phosphatides from the seeds of *Lupinus albus* differing in their content of phosphorus, nitrogen, and fatty acids. Shorey (1898) found that the raw sap of the sugar cane contained a mixture of several lecithins, as indicated by the different acids and bases obtained upon hydrolysis.

Hansteen-Cranner (1914–1926) made extensive studies of the distribution of the phospholipides in the protoplasmic membrane and in the cell walls. He considered that the cell wall is permeated with phospholipides which are in intimate connection and relation with those of the plasma membrane. His observations were substantiated by Grafe (1925), Grafe and Horvat (1925), and Grafe and Magistris (1925, 1926), who prepared water-soluble phospholipides from beets and carrots among other plant tissues. The methods used by these investigators were considered to extract the phospholipides from the cell wall and the plasma membrane without altering the permeability of the general protoplasmic membrane. Steward (1928), however, by the careful extraction of the tissues of potato and beet concluded that leaching experiments do not yield evidence that phospholipides are present in the surface layer of the protoplasm and diffuse from living tissue into distilled water. In a study of the ether-soluble substances of cabbage leaves, Chibnall and Channon (1927) could not detect any true phospholipides. All the phosphorus present was apparently in combination with calcium, glycerol, and fatty acids, while nitrogen was virtually absent. The substance that was isolated was thus apparently the insoluble calcium salts of glycerophosphoric acids in which the choline was replaced by calcium. The phospholipides that have been extracted from plants are no doubt mixtures of similar compounds and vary widely from different sources in regard to their nitrogen and phosphorus content and in the types of their fatty acids. This is illustrated by the work of Webster (1929), who determined the percentage of nitrogen, phosphorus, and iodine value of the phospholipides secured from the seeds of wheat, corn, sorghums, and oats. The results obtained were as follows:

Source of phospholipides	Percentage of nitrogen	Percentage of phosphorus	Iodine value of the fatty acids
Wheat	0.99	1.26	81.5
Corn	1.14	1.65	65.3
Soybean	0.70	0.50	92.5
Oats	1.61	0.54	88.8

The amount of the phospholipides that occurs in plant tissue apparently varies with the type of tissue, the kind of plant, and the environmental conditions.

Thus Chibnall and Sahai (1931) observed in the leaves of Brussels sprouts that lecithin and cephalin were absent but that calcium phosphatidate was relatively abundant. It appears that in this leaf the synthesis of phospholipides ceases under these conditions and that the formation of an ester with choline to produce lecithin or with amino ethyl alcohol to give cephalin does not occur. In the leaves of cocksfoot (*Dactylis glomerata*), however, Smith and Chibnall (1932) found lecithin and cephalin as well as the magnesium or calcium salt of phosphatidic acid. Jordan and Chibnall (1933) noted that all portions of the seedling of the runner bean contain lecithin and cephalin in progressively smaller amounts from the cotyledons to the pinnate leaves. In the resting seed, a small amount of magnesium phosphatidate is present, and this increases in amount as germination progresses. At the onset of chlorophyll formation, the magnesium in this compound is replaced by calcium, and the chief phospholipide of the mature pinnate leaves is calcium phosphatidate. According to Channon and Foster (1934) lecithin, cephalin, and the calcium, magnesium, and potassium salts of phosphatidic acid are present in the wheat embryo.

b. Relation of the Amount of Phospholipides to the Protein and Oil Content.—It was considered by Stocklasa (1895 to 1898) that lecithins accompany the proteins in plants, while Schulze and Likiernik (1891), and Schulze, Steiger, and Maxwell (1891) considered that the phospholipides vary directly with the protein content. According to Guerrant (1927), it was considered by Parrozzani (1909) that the ratio between the phospholipides and the amides is more definite than that of proteins and phospholipides. The amount of oils, proteins, and phospholipides in various seeds was determined by Guerrant (1927). Some of his results are shown in the table on page 745.

Guerrant (1927) considered that his results indicated a slight correlation between the phospholipide content and the protein, fat, and phosphorus content of the various classes of seeds. In general, the highest percentages of phospholipides are found in the seeds having the highest protein and the highest fat content, but this is not always the case.

c. Phospholipides in Developing and Germinating Seeds.—It was considered by Schulze and Frankfurt (1894) that unripe seeds contain less phospholipides than ripe ones, but M'Clenahan (1909) observed just the opposite in the development of the black walnut. Guerrant (1927) determined the phospholipide content of seven varieties of sorghum seeds at the milk stage, dough stage, and maturity. He obtained an increase in these compounds as maturity was approached, while the percentage of protein, fats, and total phosphorus also increased. Sufficient data, however, were not obtained to show any definite correlation between the rate of formation of any two of these substances.

It was observed by Schulze and Steiger (1889) that phospholipides decreased when seeds were germinated in the dark. Maxwell (1891), Zalenski (1902), and Iwanoff (1902), in the case of the seeds of corn, bean, and cotton, found an increase of these substances when germinated in the light. Guerrant (1927) germinated two samples of grain sorghum

Seed	Number of		Percentage on a dry basis of			
	Samples	Varieties	Protein	Oils	Total phosphorus	Phospholipide phosphorus
Corn	6	6	11.5	4.3	0.196	0.0144
Wheat	5	4	12.5	2.2	0.289	0.0306
Oats	2	2	13.3	4.1	0.262	0.0368
Sorghums	26	12	12.1	2.9	0.245	0.0378
Barley	1	1	13.1	1.8	0.275	0.0442
Clover	1	1	35.2	5.4	0.271	0.0506
Peas	5	5	27.0	1.7	0.292	0.0760
Peanut	1	1	33.9	48.6	0.332	0.0880
Beans	10	8	30.4	12.6	0.387	0.0926
Cotton	1	1	23.5	25.22	0.476	0.1456

seed in both light and darkness and found that the lipoid phosphorus showed a greater increase when germination occurred in the light. Green and Jackson (1905) noted in the germination of the castor bean that the amount of lecithin diminished during the earlier stages of germination, the reserve supply becoming almost exhausted. After the young seedling had begun to develop, there was a gradual increase in the amount, which was maintained during the later stages and remained fairly constant until the endosperm was depleted. They considered that the endosperm of this seed contains the several groups necessary for the formation of lecithin. The decomposition of the oil furnishes the fatty-acid component and the glycerin for the glycerophosphoric acid. The phosphorus is present in the seed, and the nitrogenous body, choline, may arise from the decomposition of the protein.

d. Function of the Compound Lipides.—Since the compound lipides are so widespread in plants and are found especially in those parts of the plant where life activities are very pronounced, it seems evident that they must play an important part in the activities of the protoplasm. In this regard, however, nothing definite is known, and only theories have been proposed. The compound lipides have been considered by some to exercise an influence on the permeability of the protoplasmic membrane, but their influence in this regard is apparently not of the importance that was once thought. It has been considered by some that the compound lipides play a role in the fat metabolism of the plant, but nothing is known concerning their function in this regard. Palladin and Stanewitsch (1910) considered that there is a relationship between the lecithins and respiration, since they found that the respiration intensity of seeds was lower after treatment with those solvents which extracted the most lipides.

Korsakow (1910) considered that the lipides influence the activity of proteolytic enzymes, and Gallagher (1923) believed that the production of peroxidase of potato is intimately associated with the lecithin of the tuber, and that the so-called "oxygenase" is in reality an autooxidizable, lecithinlike substance. It has been pointed out by Bang (1911) that the compound lipides are the most labile of the constituents of the protoplasm and that many of the striking properties of protoplasm may be due to these substances, especially the phospholipides, rather than to the proteins. The compound lipides evidently play an important role in the activities of the living cell, but, in the words of MacLean and MacLean (1927), it is not yet possible to dissociate these compounds from the other cell constituents and attribute to them alone any specific properties associated with the cell. Steward (1929), in a review of the literature concerning the phospholipides of plants, stated that the experimental evidence for the theories concerning the role of phospholipides in plant cells is either lacking or is of a controversial nature.

6. Synthesis of the Lipides.—The study of the synthesis of the lipides in the plant has been confined almost entirely to the changes occurring in the development of oily seeds. The term "lipides" as here used refers almost without exception to the crude lipides, since the quantity of oily matter has been estimated by determining the ether extract.

a. Relation of the Carbohydrates to the Formation of Fats and Oils.—It was first observed by De Luca (1861, 1862) that as the sugar content of the developing olive diminished progressively, the amount of oil correspondingly increased, so that when the oil content had reached its maximum the sugar had disappeared. The same fact was observed by Leclerc du Sablon (1896) in studying the development of the kernels of the walnut and almond. Some of the data obtained by him are shown on page 747.

It was observed by Schwartze and Alsberg (1923), Gallup (1927, 1928), and Caskey and Gallup (1931) that the gossypol content of the cotton seed varied directly with the amount of oil present. They considered that gossypol is associated in some manner with the formation of oil.

It was found by Rushkovskii (1930) that soluble carbohydrates decreased from 37.5 to 4.5 per cent during the ripening of the sunflower seed. Caskey and Gallup (1931) noted that reducing sugars decreased from 2.8 to 0.15 per cent, and total sugars from 4.6 to 0.32 per cent during the period of the formation of oil in the seed of cotton. Sahasrabuddhe and Kale (1933) thought that the oil in the niger seed (*Guizotia abyssinica*) is formed from the carbohydrates that are present in the young seed. Thor and Smith (1935) observed in the formation of the pecan nut that the decrease in the sugar content of the whole fruit during the period of oil synthesis accounted for not more than 5 per cent of the final amount of oil. It appeared that practically all the oil in the kernel of the pecan was formed from materials brought into the fruit from other parts of the tree at the time of oil formation. It was not observed whether the source of this material was reserve carbohydrates in the twigs, trunk, or roots, or whether it was a product of photosynthetic activity during the period of the formation of the oil.

Although the disappearance of carbohydrates and the appearance of fats and oils in a developing organ have been considered as evidence that carbohydrates are transformed into fats and oils, this fact in itself is not conclusive evidence that such is the case. In order to obtain more information on this subject, Gerber (1897) studied the respiratory quotient of the developing olive and the seeds of the almond, castor bean, rape, peach, and others. He found that during the period when

Percentage of Oil, Glucose, Sucrose, Starches, and Dextrins in the Developing Kernel of the Walnut and Almond

Date	Oil	Glucose	Sucrose	Starches and dextrins
Walnut				
July 6	3	7.6	0.0	21.8
Aug. 1	16	2.4	0.5	14.5
Aug. 15	42	0.0	0.6	3.2
Sept. 1	59	0.0	0.8	2.6
Oct. 4	62	0.0	1.6	2.6
Almond				
June 9	2	6.0	6.7	21.6
July 4	10	4.2	4.9	14.1
Aug. 1	37	0.0	2.8	6.2
Sept. 1	44	0.0	2.6	5.4
Oct. 4	46	0.0	2.5	5.3

the sugar content had reached its maximum and before any fats and oils had yet been formed, the respiratory quotient was slightly less than unity. During the period when the sugar content was diminishing and the oil content was increasing, the respiratory quotient was greater than unity, as, for example, in the olive where it ranged from 1 to 1.46. After the sugar had disappeared from the developing seeds and the oil content had reached its maximum, the respiratory quotient again fell to less than unity. Since citric, tartaric, or malic acid, which give rise to a respiratory quotient greater than unity, were not found in these developing seeds, and since there was no production of alcohol, which is also accompanied by a coefficient greater than unity, Gerber concluded that there is a relationship between the disappearance of carbohydrate and the respiratory quotient. He thus considered that the respiratory quotient of these developing organs indicates that the oil is being produced at the expense of the carbohydrate.

b. Changes in the Fats and Oils during Their Formation. 1. *Amount.*—As an oily seed develops, the percentage of oil gradually increases. Except for the period immediately following blooming and directly preceding maturity, there is throughout the development of the seed a gradual and rather uniform gain in the oil content. There is a very sharp increase in the percentage of oil during the first few weeks after blooming and a slow gain until near the end of the ripening period in the case of the soybean (Garner, Allard, and Foubert, 1914). At this time a decrease in the size of the seed and in the oil content occurs, probably due to an intense respiration at that period. The changes in the oil content during the development of the seed may be illustrated by the data obtained by Dillman (1928) for the developing flax seed:

Time of sampling, number days after flowering	Percentage of oil in the developing seed	Time of sampling, number days after flowering	Percentage of oil in the developing seed
8	1.8	24	37.5
9	2.3	27	40.2
12	8.5	30	40.7
15	26.0	33	40.7
18	34.6	36	40.6
21	35.5	39	40.7

Caskey and Gallup (1931) found in the cotton seed that the most rapid increase in oil occurred during the period of 21 to 30 days after flowering. Eyre (1931) noted in flax that there was a rapid formation of oil over a period of 15 days during which time most of the oil was deposited. Thor and Smith (1935) observed in the formation of the pecan nut that 60 to 70 per cent of the final weight of oil was deposited during a period of 4 to 6 weeks.

The factors influencing the percentage of oil in oily seeds have been studied by Garner, Allard, and Foubert (1914) and Stark (1924). By partially defoliating the plants, the number and size of beans produced were decreased, while the percentage of oil was somewhat increased. The general climatic conditions during the growing season seem to have a more marked effect on the oil content than does the length of the season. The difference in the amount of oil per seed may be as much as 100 per cent, while the percentage of oil may vary as much as 7 or 8 per cent. These authors considered that the maximum production of oil in soybeans requires conditions of nutrition favorable to the accumulation of carbohydrates during the vegetative period. Kayser (1925) showed that the application of commercial fertilizers to flax may influence the quantity and quality of the oil of the seeds. Johnson (1932) considered that the date of planting would influence the oil content of the flaxseed in some seasons but not in others. Stark (1924) found that the application of limestone and inorganic matter to the soil decreased the percentage of oil in the soybean, and the addition of rock phosphate to the above fertilizer further decreased the oil content of the seed. He observed that, by varying the soil conditions, greater differences could be obtained within the variety than generally exist between most varieties.

Tottingham (1932) noted that a consistent increase in the lipide content of various plants occurred when they were grown under Vitaglass.

2. *Nature.*—Ivanow (1911) studied the changes that occur in the carbohydrates and oils in the seeds of flax, hemp, rape, and sunflower during their ripening. His observations indicate that there is a connection between the carbohydrates and the higher fatty acids. The first fatty acids that are developed in these seeds from carbohydrates are the saturated ones and evidently belong to the higher series of the fatty acids, since they are not volatile as indicated from their Reichert-Meissl values. It was observed that the acid values of the ether extract decreases sharply with the ripening of the seed. Thus in flax, in one experiment, the acid value decreased from 15.4 to 5.6, in hemp from 5.8 to 2.7, in rape from 74.3 to 9.4, and in sunflower from 46 to 8 during their first ripening period. The evidence seemed to indicate that the unsaturated

Date	Seed and stage of development	Per cent of oil	Acid value	Iodine value
	Flax:			
July 5	Flowering	2.3	15.4	120.6
July 18	Seed soft and green	11.0	3.6	151.0
Aug. 3	Seed unripe	32.5	4.0	168.0
Aug. 25	Seed ripe	35.0	5.6	175.0
	Rape:			
July 7	Seed clear and soft	10.0	74.3	
July 25	Seed green and opaque	37.5	16.0	99.8
Aug. 8	Seed unripe	48.3	13.8	95.3
Aug. 23	Seed ripe	49.9	9.4	97.5
	Hemp:			
Aug. 17	Two weeks after bloom	15.3	5.8	152.1
Aug. 28	Seed unripe	27.0	2.5	155.0
Sept. 13	Seed unripe	33.5	2.7	154.0

acids are derived from the saturated ones, and Ivanow suggested the following scheme to illustrate the procedure in the formation of oil from carbohydrates:

Carbohydrate < glycerin ——————————————————— > oil
Carbohydrate < saturated fatty acids ⟶ unsaturated fatty acids > oil

The data on page 749 taken from his work show the changes that occur in the oil of ripening seeds.

This theory has been further substantiated by Eyre (1931) and Johnson (1932) in the study of the development of oil in flaxseed, and by the work of Sahasrabuddhe and Kale (1933) on the development of the oil in the niger seed. The changes in the nature of the oil during the development of the flaxseed were as follows:

Eyre (1931)		Johnson (1932)	
Days after flowering	Acid value	Days after flowering	Iodine value
14	8.6	5	106
16	8.4	9	116
19	4.8	11	124
25	1.0	13	131
32	0.6	14	148
66	0.5	15	153

Priestley (1924) considered that when the fatty acids are finally deposited in the endodermis, cuticle, or cork layers they undergo oxidation and condensation and in so doing lose, for the most part, their power of dissolving in fat solvents. They are thus changed in the same general way as are certain of the vegetable oils in the drying process that they undergo on exposure to the air.

c. General Observations.—Although the fatty oils are quite different chemically from the carbohydrates, there is an intimate and significant physiological relationship between these two classes of compounds in the plant. There is considerable evidence to indicate that fats and oils are formed from carbohydrates and that in germination of oily seeds, as will be mentioned later, the fats give rise to carbohydrates. The fact that the disappearance of the carbohydrate and the increase in the oil content proceed in unripe seeds detached from the plant is considered as further supporting the evidence that oil is derived from carbohydrate in the plant. Outside the living cell, however, the transformation of carbohydrates into fats and oils or the reverse has been accomplished only in a slight way (Smedley and Lubrzynska, 1913). Smedley (1912) prepared fatty acids from carbohydrates by breaking the hexoses into three carbon compounds and then oxidizing these into pyruvic acid, $CH_3COCOOH$, which was then condensed into acids with longer carbon chains. These reactions are accomplished only with great difficulty in the laboratory, and there is no evidence whatsoever that the formation of oil in the plant follows this procedure.

The particular carbohydrate which is transferred directly into the fats and oils, however, is not known (Vallee, 1903). According to Terroine (1920), saccharose is the last sugar to disappear in the maturation of oily seeds and the first to appear upon their germination. This, however, is not sufficient evidence to state that it is the carbohydrate which is transformed directly into the oil.

Some evidence has been obtained which indicates that fats and oils may be formed in plants from other materials than carbohydrates. Thus M'Clenahan (1909) considered that the tannins might afford the material for the formation of the oil in the developing kernel of the walnut. Scurti and Tommasi (1910-1911) observed that the ether-soluble substance of the green olive fruit consists almost entirely of oleanol, a higher alcohol ($C_{31}H_{50}O_3$), and that later in the process of development it is still present but that, in addition, higher fatty acids both saturated and unsaturated are found. When the ripening of the fruit is progressing, the ether extract consists almost entirely of neutral oil. Oleanol occurs in the leaves of the olive, and it was considered by these investigators that this alcohol is produced in the leaf and is transported to the fruit when it is transformed into neutral oil. They examined other fat-containing seeds and fruits, and in all cases an alcohol closely related to oleanol was found in the leaves and fruits, and, as it diminished in amount, neutral oil increased. If a procedure like that above occurs, it is not in accord with the high respiratory quotients reported by Gerber (1897) during the ripening process, since the conversion of oleanol into fatty acids would be accompanied by a respiratory quotient less than unity.

Although oily seeds are generally rich in protein and the accumulation of oil proceeds simultaneously with protein, there is no evidence of any relationship between the two processes. In the case of the soybean, however, Stark (1924) noted that the conditions which produce an increase in the percentage of protein result in a decrease in the oil content, and vice versa.

It is not known whether the formation of oil is brought about by the protoplasm itself or results from a set of reactions catalyzed by the plant enzymes, but which could also be performed by the extracted catalysts. The synthesis of fats from fatty acids and glycerol in the presence of oil-free material from oily seeds was undertaken by Dunlap and Gilbert (1911). They found that flaxseed is a good emulsifying agent, so that, when glycerol, oleic acid, and oil-free castor-bean powder are mixed with it and thoroughly ground together, an emulsion is formed which persists for many days, and as a result of such a mixture they obtained evidence of the synthesis of oil. The method used for detecting the synthesis of oil in such a mixture was as follows: Equal portions of the mixture were placed in a series of flasks, with the exception that in the control flask the oil-free castor-bean material was replaced by an equal amount of flaxseed. The acid content of the flasks was determined at successive periods with the following results:

Period	Milligrams of oleic acid in one gram of the mixture	
	Control, without castor-bean powder	Experiment, with castor-bean powder
At once	315.5	337.3
After 2 days	319.0	322.0
After 6 days	314.8	311.0
After 11 days	314.9	248.6

The decrease in the amount of acid present could be accounted for only by the esterification of the oleic acid. The results, however, do not show whether the combination of the oleic acid and the glycerol produces a mon- or diglyceride before the triglyceride is produced.

An interesting observation was made by Abegg (1929) on the effects of the waxy gene in maize on fat metabolism. He noted that the average acid value of the ether-soluble crude oil from nonwaxy maize was 13, while that of the waxy was 34. The average saponification number of the crude fats from the nonwaxy endosperm was 177 and that from the waxy 200. These marked differences between the nonwaxy and waxy types of grain are restricted to the endosperm tissue. The evidence indicates that the waxy gene in maize produces marked effects upon the fat metabolism of the endosperm tissue. It is considered that the activities of this gene are connected with the synthetic and hydrolytic powers of maize endosperm lipase. It appears that the waxy-type lipase does not affect a condensation of fatty acids with glycerol to the same degree as does the nonwaxy, hence the waxy endosperm contains a crude fat the acid value of which is higher than that from the nonwaxy type.

7. Changes in the Fats and Fatty Oils during Germination. *a. Changes in the Amount of Oil.*—In 1842 it was observed by De Saussure that as the germination of rape and hemp seeds progressed, the amount of oil in the seeds diminished. He undertook this work in order to test the suggestion that the oil in seeds might subserve the same purpose during germination as the starch in the cereal grains. It is now known that the fats and oils are reserve foods, and all the numerous investigators who have studied oily seeds, since the time of De Saussure, agree that the oils in seed disappear during the course of germination. This behavior of the oily matter in seeds may be illustrated by the data obtained by Miller (1910, 1912) in the case of sunflower seeds and seedlings, as shown in the following table:

Parts of seeds or seedlings	Seeds	Seedlings				
		4 days	5 days	7 days	10 days	14 days
Percentage of ether extract on dry basis						
Cotyledons	55.6	55.9	51.2	33.9	16.7	13.5
Hypocotyls and roots	47.4	24.2	9.3	9.7	9.8	11.4
Grams of ether extract per 100 seeds and seedlings						
Cotyledons	3.786	3.00	2.53	1.298	0.501	0.317
Hypocotyls and roots	0.219	0.188	0.123	0.214	0.273	0.238

It is noted from the above data that after 4 days the percentage of oil in the cotyledons is the same as or somewhat higher than that in the cotyledons of the seed, while the actual amount of oil has markedly diminished. This fact has been frequently observed in the germination of oily seeds and may be attributed to one or two causes. In the first place, it may be due to the depletion of the protein and carbohydrate reserve in a relatively greater amount than the oily reserve during that period. On the other hand, it may be due to the combining of oxygen with the unsaturated oils, thus increasing their weight to the same extent as or a greater extent than it has been diminished by depletion during the period under consideration. In most oily seeds, the oily reserve begins to disappear at a very early stage. In the case of the sunflower seed 4 days after planting, when the hypocotyls and roots have a length of only 2.5 to 3.5 cm., over one-fifth of the oil has already disappeared.

It was observed by Von Ohlen (1930, 1931) and MacLachlan (1936) that the total oil content of the cotyledons of soybeans diminished markedly as germination proceeded. According to the former investigator the depletion of oil began at the base of the cotyledon and progressed toward the apex. The palisade tissue of the cotyledons was depleted of oil much more slowly than were the other tissues. According to Peters (1861), Schmidt (1891), and Miller (1910, 1912) the actual amount of ether extract in the roots and hypocotyls remains practically constant during germination.

b. Chemical Changes in the Oily Reserve.—The changes in the chemical nature of the oily reserve in seeds during germination have been studied for many seeds by numerous investigators. Miller (1912) studied in considerable detail the changes in the oily reserve of the sunflower seed during its germination, and his work is summarized in tabular form as an example of the general changes that the oily reserve undergoes during germination.

Chemical Nature of the Ether Extract of the Cotyledons, Hypocotyls, and Roots of the Sunflower Seeds and Seedlings

Items considered	Seeds	Stage I 3½ days	Stage II 5 days	Stage III 7 days	Stage IV 10 days	Stage V 14 days
Cotyledons						
Dry weight of the cotyledons of 100 seedlings	4.884	3.153	2.785	2.319	2.021	1.621
Ether extract (percentage of dry material)	54.1	52.6	49.2	36.0	16.8	8.7
Grams of ether extract per 100 cotyledons	2.642	1.658	1.370	0.834	0.339	0.141
Percentage of the original oil present	....	62.7	51.8	31.8	12.8	5.3
Acid value of the ether extract	1.6	1.7	1.5	4.6	27.5	66.8
Percentage of free fatty acid in ether extract[1]	0.008	0.009	0.009	2.3	13.8	33.5
Saponification value of ether extract	189.3	190.9	192.1	184.3	186.1	204.2
Saponification value of the neutral oil	188.4	189.1	190.6	188.2	184.4	226.1
Total insoluble acids of ether extract	95.4	96.0	95.7	93.6	87.6	84.8
Total insoluble acids of the neutral oil	94.6	95.2	94.7	95.9	88.9	
Total soluble acids of ether extract[2]	0.005	0.005	0.007	0.005	0.008	4.5
Total soluble acids of the neutral oil[2]	0.005	0.003	0.006	0.003	0.002	3.0
Iodine number of the ether extract	125.5	126.4	124.5	125.8	120.1	111.7
Iodine number of the neutral oil	124.9	126.0	124.1	126.0	119.9	111.9
Acetyl saponification value of ether extract	222.7	225.0	225.1	215.0	236.3	263.6
Acetyl value of ether extract	40.1	39.0	40.6	38.2	36.5	37.5
Hypocotyls and roots						
Dry weight of the hypocotyls of 100 seedlings	....	0.605	0.885	1.21	1.52	2.17
Ether extract (percentage of dry material)	....	9.9	7.4	3.8	3.1	1.8
Grams of ether extract per 100 hypocotyls	....	0.060	0.065	0.046	0.047	0.040
Acid value of ether extract	....	18.2	24.0	27.1	58.3	97.8
Percentage of free fatty acid in ether extract[1]	....	9.1	12.0	13.4	26.4	49.1
Saponification value of ether extract	....	190.3	189.2	198.4	236.9	238.3
Total insoluble acids in ether extracts	....	89.6	85.6	86.5	67.1	57.2
Total soluble acids in ether extract[2]	....	1.0	1.6	1.8	16.1	18.5
Iodine number of ether extract	....	117.7	118.8	96.1	72.6	48.3
Acetyl saponification value of ether extract	....	251.4	300.0	274.8		
Acetyl value of ether extract	....	71.2	114.0	95.1		

[1] Estimated as oleic acid.
[2] Estimated as butyric acid.

1. *Fatty Acids of the Oil.*—It was first observed by Fleury (1865) that nonvolatile acids appeared during the germination of oily seeds. Müntz

(1871) in the study of the seeds of the rape, poppy, and radish observed for the first time that during germination the oil in the seeds gives rise to free fatty acids. In the case of these particular seeds, the amount of free fatty acids in the oil increased from 10 per cent in the resting seed to as much as 98 per cent in the 10-day seedlings. The increase in the amount of free fatty acid in the germination of oily seeds has since that time been observed by Leclerc du Sablon (1895, 1897), Miller (1910, 1912), Ivanow (1912) and others.

It was suggested by Müntz (1871) that the oil during germination is split up into glycerin and fatty acids. In 1890 Green discovered the enzyme lipase in the castor-bean seedling and showed that the fats and oils are hydrolyzed into fatty acids and glycerin by its action. Although glycerin is easily obtained by the hydrolysis of fats and oils under artificial conditions, no one has as yet been able to detect it in the germinating seeds and seedlings. The changes that occur in the fatty acids of the oil of seeds and seedlings have for the most part been observed in the ether extract of the entire seedling. In order, however, to understand the significance of the changes in the oily reserve in the metabolism of the seedling, the changes in the oil in the cotyledons or in the endosperm must be considered separately from the oily material of the roots and hypocotyls.

(a) *Fatty Acids of the Cotyledons.*—The changes in the fatty acids of the oil of the sunflower seed during its germination were studied in considerable detail by Miller (1912). In this seed the oily reserve is stored in the cotyledons and amounts to approximately 50 per cent of their dry weight. Miller observed that the ether extract of the cotyledons has an acid value of 1.6 in the resting seed and that this remains constant until one-half of the oil has disappeared. In the 7-day seedlings when the cotyledons are above ground and are spread out perpendicular to the hypocotyl and when the oily reserve has decreased to one-third its original amount, the acid value rises to 4.6. The acid value continues to increase so that when only 5.3 per cent of the original amount of oil remains the acid value amounts to 66.8. The free fatty acids, estimated as oleic, constitute less than 1 per cent of the ether extract of the seed. This remains constant until over two-thirds of the oil has disappeared, after which it increases to 2.3 per cent of the ether extract. This percentage continues to increase until at the end of 2 weeks the free fatty acids constitute 33.5 per cent of the oily material in the seed. Some of the free fatty acids present in the cotyledons are those of low molecular weight and are soluble in water, but most of them are of higher molecular weight and are insoluble in water.

The iodine value of the oils of seeds at different stages of germination has been studied by Ivanow (1912), Jegorow (1904), and Miller (1912).

It has been observed that as the germination of flax, hemp, and rape progressed, the iodine value of the oil decreased. In the sunflower seed, the iodine value of the ether extract is 125. This value remains constant for a considerable period of time and drops to only 120 when the seedlings are 7 days old. After 14 days, when only 5.3 per cent of the original oil remains in the cotyledons, the iodine value falls to 111.8. Miller (1912) considered that this decrease in the iodine value of the oil of the seed during germination indicates that unsaturated fatty acids are becoming saturated. Ivanow (1912), however, considered that this conclusion is erroneous and that the decrease in the iodine value indicates that the unsaturated fatty acids are being utilized. He noted that the unsaturated fatty acids are the first to disappear during germination. Thus in the flax and hemp seedlings the linolenic acids first disappeared, then the linoleic, and finally the oleic series. In the germination of soybeans, MacLachlan (1936) observed that so far as the degree of saturation was concerned the fatty acids of the cotyledons were no different from those of the ungerminated seeds.

The saponification value of the oil in the cotyledons of the sunflower seed does not change until the oily reserve has been depleted to 5.3 per cent of the original amount. There is a marked increase in the saponification value at this period, which indicates the presence of glycerides or free fatty acids of lower molecular value than those originally contained in the cotyledons of the seed.

The acetyl value of the ether extract of the sunflower seed is 40.1, a value that remains practically constant during all stages of the germination. There is thus apparently no increase in the number of the hydroxyl groups of the oil during any stage of germination. These observations are in accord with those of Von Fürth (1904) for the sunflower and castor bean.

(b) *Fatty Acids of the Roots and Hypocotyls.*—Miller (1912) observed in the roots and hypocotyls of the sunflower seedlings that the saponification value of the ether extract remained practically constant at 190 until the seventh day when it increased to 198. After that it increased rapidly until at the end of 2 weeks it had risen to 238.

The amount of insoluble fatty acids remains constant during the 7-day period and is about 10 per cent less than the amount of insoluble acid present in the ether extract of the cotyledons at the same stages. After the first week the amount of insoluble acid falls rapidly and amounts to only 57.2 per cent of the oily material present at the end of 14 days, as compared to 90 per cent at the beginning of germination. The amount of soluble fatty acids during the first 7 days of germination changes but little, being about 2 per cent, the amount being somewhat higher than that contained in the oily matter of the cotyledons at these stages. During the second week of germination the amount of soluble fatty acids increases rapidly and amounts to 18.5 per cent of the oily matter present at the end of 14 days. The acid value increases from 18.2 at the first stage of the seedling to 97.8 at the last stage examined. During the first week of germination there is evidence that a considerable portion of the free acid is composed of acids of higher molecular weight, which are insoluble in water. During the last week of germination, however, the free acids present seem to be composed entirely of those of low molecular weight, which are soluble in water.

The iodine value of the ether extract of the cotyledons and roots remains at 118 until the end of 7 days when it falls to 96 and finally to 48.3 at the end of 2 weeks. The iodine value is thus considerably lower at the earlier stages of germination than it is in the oily material of the cotyledons.

The acetyl value of the ether extract of the hypocotyls and roots is approximately twice as great as that of the ether extract of the cotyledons and increases in value as germination progresses.

The properties of the ether extract of the hypocotyls and roots during the first 7 days of germination bear a striking resemblance to those of the ether extract of the cotyledons during that time. Observations, however, indicate that the changes in the oily material of the hypocotyls and roots during the earlier stages of germination consist in a gradual but evident breaking down of the higher free fatty acids and glycerides into those of lower molecular weight, the saturation of the fatty acids, or the utilization of the unsaturated ones and an increase in the amount of hydroxyl groups present. During the later stages of germination, however, these changes are rapid and very marked, as indicated by the different values determined.

MacLachlan (1936) found during the germination of the soybean that the newly formed fatty acids of the roots, stem, and leaves were considerably more saturated than those of the cotyledons. A marked increase in the amount of sterols occurred in the roots, stem, and leaves of the young plants. The results indicate that a close relationship exists between the metabolism of the sterol and the utilization of oil in the cotyledon, and that the sterol is a vital constituent of the plant and not a waste product. It was also noted by Beumer (1933) in peas and beans that a marked synthesis of sterol occurred during germination in both light and darkness. Kao (1936) in the germinating mung bean noted that there was an increase in the sterol fraction and a decrease in the crude phospholipides. The fatty-acid content greatly increased in the growing portion of the plant while that of the cotyledons remained practically constant.

2. *Relation of Carbohydrates to the Disappearance of the Fats and Oils.*—It was first observed by De Saussure (1842) that as the oily reserve disappeared in the germination of oily seeds, the carbohydrate content

of the seeds and seedlings increased. Hellriegel (1855) examined the seedlings of rape at five different stages of growth. He found that the oil decreased from 47 per cent in the seed to 36 per cent in the oldest seedlings, and that the sum of the sugar, organic acids, and tannin increased at the same time from 7.7 to 15.4 per cent. He also observed that the seeds contained 3.4 per cent cane sugar and that during the early stages of germination it disappeared. This fact has been noted by other investigators since that time, and it is inferred that the sugar is utilized directly at the beginning of germination before the oily reserve has been transformed or before it has become available.

Sachs (1859, 1863) concluded that the oil in seeds is transformed during germination into starch or sugar, but he did not consider that starch is a transition between oil and sugar or sugar between oil and starch. The fact that sugar increases in the germination of oily seeds as the oily reserve decreases has also been observed by Peters (1861), Laskovsky (1874), Detmer (1875), Green (1890), Leclerc du Sablon (1893 to 1897), Maquenne (1898), Mazé (1900), Kirkwood and Gies (1902), Miller (1910), Von Ohlen (1930, 1931), and others. The changes in the amounts of oil, protein, and carbohydrate in the seedlings of the sunflower as found by Miller (1910) are shown in the following table.

Constituents	Seed		4 days		5 days		7 days		10 days		14 days	
	Cot.	Hyp. and roots	Cot.	Hyp. and roots	Cot.	Hyp. and roots	Cot.	Hyp. and roots	Cot.	Hyp. and roots	Cot.	Hyp. and roots
Average percentage of constituents												
Ether extract	55.6	47.4	55.9	24.2	51.2	9.3	33.9	9.7	16.7	9.8	13.5	11.4
Total sugars	4.1	4.1	1.1	9.2	1.8	22.5	3.1	18.6	3.1	12.6	2.1	7.7
Reducing sugar	Tr.	Tr.	None	8.7	None	20.5	1.4	17.3	3.1	12.6	1.1	7.7
Protein	24.4	25.3	22.0	14.2	21.0	9.4	19.8	9.3	21.0	7.0	20.4	6.5
Grams of constituents per 100 seeds and seedlings												
Ether extract	3.786	0.219	3.00	0.188	2.53	0.123	1.298	0.214	0.501	0.273	0.317	0.238
Total sugars	0.279	0.019	0.06	0.071	0.09	0.298	0.12	0.431	0.09	0.351	0.05	0.161
Reducing sugar	Tr.	Tr.	None	0.068	None	0.271	0.054	0.382	0.09	0.351	0.025	0.161
Protein	1.66	0.117	1.18	0.110	1.03	0.125	0.76	0.205	0.63	0.195	0.48	0.135

Thus in the case of the sunflower the amount of sugar in the resting seed amounts to 4.1 per cent. Of this amount all but a trace is nonreducing sugar and has been identified as cane sugar. The total weight of sugar in the cotyledons of the seedlings at all stages is comparatively small. At the beginning of germination the nonreducing sugar falls rapidly until the 4-day stage, after which it gradually increases until the cotyledons begin to unfold. Up until that time the only sugar present in the cotyledons is of the nonreducing type, but, when the cotyledons assume the foliage functions, reducing sugars begin to make their appearance, and in the 10-day seedlings it is the only sugar present.

The percentage of total sugar rapidly rises in the hypocotyls and roots, and when they have reached a length of 3 to 4½ in. it amounts to 20 per cent of their dry weight. After that period it increases, and in the 10-day seedling it amounts to 12.6 per cent. The actual amount of sugar, however, reaches its maximum at the end of the 7-day period when the cotyledons have just spread out, and from that time on it gradually decreases. A small amount of starch appears in the starch sheath of the hypocotyls and roots and in the parenchyma cells of the vascular bundles of the cotyledons during the process of germination.

Pierce, Sheldon, and Murlin (1933) found in germinating castor beans that there was a continual decrease in the amount of oil present in the entire seedling and that there was a continual increase in the amount of sugar to 40 per cent of the dry weight when the hypocotyls had attained a length of 80 to 140 mm. The carbon balance between fat loss and carbohydrate gain, including the crude fiber, was not close except at the beginning of germination. An undetermined residue, which increased steadily with the increase in total carbohydrate, accounted for more and more of the carbon as time progressed.

Murlin (1933) studied the respiration of single castor beans at various stages of germination. He found that the respiratory quotients had a value of 0.30 to 0.58, indicating the conversion of oil to carbohydrates. Daggs and Harco-Wardlaw (1933) by the use of a modified oxycalorimeter found that the respiratory quotient of the germinated seed increased as the stage of germination increased. This indicates a change from an oxygen-poor to an oxygen-rich substance, which change is probably the transformation of oil to sugar.

The marked increase in the amount of carbohydrate in the seedlings of oily seeds raises the question as to its origin. Miller (1910) has shown that in the sunflower the changes in the protein reserve could not account for the increase in carbohydrate. The only other possible source of the sugar, then, is the oil, but how sugar is formed from this is not known. Detmer (1875) considered that when oil is hydrolyzed in the seedling the glycerin formed is changed into unknown bodies, and the free fatty acids might be the source of the carbohydrates. Green (1890) considered that the glycerin formed gives rise directly to sugar and that the free fatty acids give rise to vegetable acids. Leclerc du Sablon (1895) thought that the glycerin with the acids still combined with it goes directly to form carbohydrate, since he found that the amount of free fatty acids, as well as sugar, increased during the process of germination, and since glycerin could not be detected. He thus considered that fatty acids were liberated in such a way that glycerin is not set free. Maquenne (1898) and Ivanow (1912) considered that the unsaturated fatty acids contribute to the formation of sugar. Pirschle (1926) found considerable amounts of acetaldehyde in germinating fatty seeds of several different genera and families and considered that it might possibly be the compound through which the fatty acids pass in being transformed to carbohydrates. It was observed by Matthes (1927) that, in the germinating seeds of sunflower, the oil was saponified and the fatty acids were broken into shorter and shorter chains, and eventually became oxy-acids and oxaldehydes, which were later on built up into sugars.

A study of the fatty-acid-to-sugar process was made by Rhine (1926). He extracted enzymes from germinating fatty seeds by the methods used in extracting lipase. One part of fatty acid to 10 parts of enzyme extract was placed in small flasks and slightly acidified with HCl and kept at 40°C. with frequent agitation for varying periods of time. The results of this simple experiment indicated that a slight decomposition of fatty acids occurred, and that a small amount of a water-soluble reducing substance was produced.

In later and more elaborate experiments, higher temperatures, increased acidity, and an abundance of oxygen were substituted for enzyme action upon the mixture of fatty acids and water. In an 800-cc. Kjeldahl flask fitted with a reflux condenser and heated at temperatures varying from 75 to 95°C. were placed 100 cc. of fatty acid and 200 cc. of water. Air from a pressure tank was allowed to bubble through the mixture and served to keep a good emulsion and to furnish an oxygen supply. After varying periods of such treatment, it was found that water-soluble, ether-soluble, and nonvolatile aldehydes were produced. These aldehydes had more oxygen than that of the ordinary aldehyde or carbonyl group. The actual structure of these substances, however, is not known, but Rhine considered that they approached more nearly the sugars in structure than any products yet reported in the literature. Also produced were short-chain acids which were ether-, water-, and alcohol-soluble and which were fermentable by bread yeast, yielding carbon dioxide and fermenting in about the same time as glucose with the same yeast.

B. Fatty Substances Not Compounds of Fatty Acids

Two of the more important groups of substances, not compounds of fatty acids that may be found in the crude lipides, are the essential oils and resins. These substances, according to Thatcher (1921), include those compounds to which the characteristic odors of plants are due, along with others similar in structure and possessing characteristic uniformity in composition, and belong to several widely different chemical groups. The essential oils may be divided into two major groups: (1) the hydrocarbon oils or terpenes, some forms of which constitute the main proportions of the oils of turpentine, bergamot, lemon, eucalyptus, fennel, and pennyroyal; (2) the oxygenated and sulphuretted oils. The oxygenated essential oils include alcohols, aldehydes, ketones, acids, and phenols derived from either five-membered or six-membered closed-ring hydrocarbons. These compounds include, among others, menthol, oil of bitter almonds, oil of cinnamon, camphor, and thymol. The two most common sulphuretted oils are oil of mustard and oil of garlic. The latter is present in onions, garlic, radishes, and many other plants. The difference in flavor of these plants is due to the fact that the allyl sulphide is united with other different groups in the glucoside arrangement.

The resins are the oxidation products of the terpenes, but their exact structure is little understood. They are divided into two classes, the balsams and the solid or hard resins. Canada balsam and crude turpentine are examples of the first class and consist of resinous substances dissolved with fluid terpenes. Asafoetida and myrrh are resinous substances that are mixtures of gums and true resins.

McNair (1932) reported that 29 per cent of the families of higher plants contain volatile oils. Approximately 28 per cent of the families that contain essential oils have resin in appreciable quantities, while 100 per cent of the resin families possess essential oils. Both these substances are located in the same anatomical structures. Apparently, essential oils contain substances from which resins may be formed by either condensation or polymerization, or by a combination of these two processes.

The use of the essential oils and resins to the plant is not known. They are formed sometimes normally in healthy tissue and at other times they are the result of injury or disease. They are frequently classed as excretions, since aside from possible protective influences to the plant no biological use of these substances is known.

Bibliography

Abegg, F. A., 1929: Some effects of the waxy gene in maize on fat metabolism, *J. Agr. Res.*, **38**: 183–193.

Alsberg, C. L., and A. E. Taylor, 1928: The fats and oils, *Leland Stanford Junior Univ., Food Res. Inst.*, 1.

Anderson, R. J., and M. G. Moore, 1923: A study of the phytosterols of corn oil, cotton seed oil and linseed oil, *J. Am. Chem. Soc.*, **45**: 1944–1953.

———, 1923: Composition of corn pollen. II, Concerning certain lipoids, a hydrocarbon and photosterol occurring in the pollen of white flint corn, *J. Biol. Chem.*, **55**: 611–628.

———, 1924: The phytosterols of the endosperm of corn, *J. Am. Chem. Soc.*, **46**: 1450–1460.

——— and R. L. Shriner, 1926: The phytosterols of corn oil, *N. Y. Sta.* (*Geneva*) *Tech. Bull.*, **124**: 10–25.

———, ———, and G. O. Burr, 1926: The phytosterols of wheat germ oil, *N. Y. Sta.* (*Geneva*) *Tech. Bull.*, **124**: 26–41.

———, F. P. Nabenhauer, and R. L. Shriner, 1926: The distribution of dihydrositosterol in plant fats, *N. Y. Sta. (Geneva) Tech. Bull.*, **124**: 42–51.

———, 1926: Properties of cholesterol obtained from different sources, *N. Y. Sta. (Geneva) Tech. Bull.*, **124**: 57–67.

Bang, I., 1911: "Chemie und Biochemie der Lipoide," J. F. Bergman, Wiesbaden. 187 pp.

Baughman, W. F., and G. S. Jamieson, 1920: The composition of Hubbard squash seed oil, *J. Am. Chem. Soc.*, **42**: 152–157.

———, D. Brauns and G. S. Jamieson, 1920: Cantaloup seed oil, *J. Am. Chem. Soc.*, **42**: 2398–2402.

——— and G. S. Jamieson, 1921: The chemical composition of corn oil, *J. Am. Chem. Soc.*, **43**: 2696–2702.

——— and ———, 1922: The chemical composition of soy-bean oil, *J. Am. Chem. Soc.*, **44**: 2947–2952.

Beer, R., 1909: On elàioplasts, *Ann. Bot.*, **23**: 63–72.

Bengis, R. O., and R. J. Anderson, 1934: The chemistry of the coffee bean. II, The composition of the glycerides of the coffee bean oil, *J. Biol. Chem.*, **105**: 139–151.

Beumer, H., 1933: Über die Sterinbildung bei der Keimung, *Biochem. Z.*, **259**: 469–470.

Bloor, W. R., 1925: Biochemistry of the fats, *Chem. Rev.*, **2**: 243–300.

Bull, H. B., 1936: "The Biochemistry of the Lipids," Burgess Pub. Co., Minneapolis, Minn., 135 pp.

Caskey, C., and W. D. Gallup, 1931: Changes in the sugar, oil, and gossypol content of the developing cotton boll, *J. Agr. Res.*, **42**: 671–673.

Channon, H. J., and A. C. Chibnall, 1927: The ether-soluble substances of cabbage leaf cytoplasm. IV, Further observations on diglyceridephosphoric acid, *Biochem. J.*, **21**: 1112–1120.

——— and ———, 1929: The ether-soluble substances of cabbage leaf cytoplasm. V, The isolation of n-nonacosane and di-n-tetradecyl ketone, *Biochem. J.*, **23**: 168–175.

——— and C. A. M. Foster, 1934: The phosphatides of the wheat germ, *Biochem. J.*, **28**: 853–864.

Chibnall, A. C., and H. J. Channon, 1927: The ether-soluble substances of cabbage leaf cytoplasm. I, Preparation and general characters, *Biochem. J.*, **21**: 225–232.

——— and ———, 1927: The ether-soluble substances of cabbage leaf cytoplasm. II, Calcium salts of glyceridephosphoric acids, *Biochem. J.* **21**: 233–246.

———, E. F. Williams, A. L. Latner, and S. H. Piper, 1933: The isolation of n-triacontanol from lucerne wax, *Biochem. J.*, **27**: 1885–1888.

——— and H. J. Channon, 1929: The ether-soluble substances of cabbage leaf cytoplasm. VI, Summary and general conclusions, *Biochem. J.*, **23**: 176–184.

——— and P. N. Sahai, 1931: Observations on the fat metabolism of leaves. I, Detached and starved mature leaves of Brussels sprout (*Brassica oleracea*), *Ann. Bot.*, **45**: 489–502.

Collin, G., and T. P. Hilditch, 1929: Regularities in the glyceride structure of vegetable seed fats, *Biochem. J.*, **23**: 1273–1289.

———, 1933: The kernel-fats of some members of the *Palmae*, *Biochem. J.*, **27**: 1366–1372.

Cruz, A. O., and A. P. West, 1932: Composition of Philippine rice oil (Ramai variety), *Philippine J. Sci.*, **48**: 5–12.

——— and ———, 1932: Composition of Philippine soybeans and soybean oil, *Philippine J. Sci.*, **48**: 77–89.

Czapek, F., 1913: "Biochemie der Pflanzen," **1**: 710–733, Gustav Fischer.

Daggs, R. G., and H. S. Halcro-Wardlaw, 1933: The conversion of fat to carbohydrate in the germinating castor bean, *J. Gen. Physiol.*, **17**: 303–309.

Dangeard, P., 1923: Remarques sur l'état de l'huile à l'intérieur des graines oléagineuses, *C. R. Acad. Sci. Paris*, **177**: 67–69; *Bot. Abst.*, **13**: 487.

Deleano, N. T., 1909, 1910: Recherche chimique sur la germination, *Cent. Bakt.* II, **24**: 130–146; *Arch. Sci. Biol.* (St. Petersburg), **15**: 1–24.

DeLuca, S., 1861, 1862: Recherches sur la formation de la matière grasse dans les olives, *C. R. Acad. Sci. Paris*, **53**: 380–384; **55**: 470–473, 506–510.

De Saussure, T., 1842: Ueber das Keimen der Oelsamereien, *Froriep's Notizen*, **24**: 24.

Detmer, W., 1875: "Phys.-chem. Untersuchung über die Keimung ölhaltiger Samen," Gustav Fischer, Leipzig.

———, 1880: "Vergleichende Physiologie des Keimungsprocesses," pp. 336–338, Jena.

Dillman, A. C., 1928: Daily growth and oil content of flaxseeds, *J. Agr. Res.*, **37**: 357–377.

Dunlap, F. L., and L. O. Gilbert, 1911: The synthesis of fats by the action of enzymes, *J. Am. Chem. Soc.*, **33**: 1787–1791.

Euler, H., and E. Nordenson, 1908: Zur Kenntnis des Möhrencarotens und seiner Begleitsubstanzen, *Z. physiol. Chem.*, **56**: 223–235.

Evans, E. I., 1935: Antioxidant properties of vegetable lecithin, *Ind. and Eng. Chem.*, **27**: 329–331.

Eyre, J. V., 1931: Notes on oil development in the seed of a growing plant, *Biochem. J.*, **25**: 1902–1908.

Fleury, M., 1865: Recherches chimiques sur la germination, *Ann. Chim. et Phys.*, 4e série, **4**: 38.

Francis, C. K., and W. G. Friedemann, 1917: The fats and fatty acids of the grain sorghums, *Okla. Sta. Bull.*, **117**: 3–14.

Gallagher, P. H., 1923: Mechanism of oxidation in the plant. I, The oxygenase of Bach and Chodat: function of lecithins in respiration. *Biochem. J.*, **17**: 515–529.

Gallup, W. D., 1927: The gossypol content and chemical composition of cotton seeds during certain periods of development, *J. Agr. Res.*, **34**: 987–992.

———, 1928: A chemical study of the development of cotton bolls and the rate of formation of gossypol in the cotton seed, *J. Agr. Res.*, **36**: 471–480.

Garner, W. W., H. A. Allard and C. L. Foubert, 1914: Oil content of seeds as affected by nutrition of the plant, *J. Agr. Res.*, **3**: 227–249.

Gerber, C., 1897: Étude de la transformation des matières sucrées en huile dans les olives, *C. R. Acad. Sci. Paris*, **125**: 658–661.

———, 1897: Recherches sur la formation des réserves oléagineuses des graines et des fruits, *C. R. Acad. Sci. Paris*, **125**: 732–735.

———, 1901: Recherches sur la respiration des olives et sur les relations existant entres les valeurs du quotient respiratoire observé et la formation de l'huile, *J. Bot. Année*, **15**: 9, 88, 121; *Bot. Cent.*, **89**: 622.

Grafe, V., 1925: Zur Physiologie und Chemie der Pflanzenphosphatide, *Biochem. Z.*, **159**: 444–448.

——— and V. Horvat, 1925: Die wasserlöslichen Phosphatide aus der Wurzel der Zuckerrübe. I, *Biochem. Z.*, **159**: 449–467.

——— and H. Magistris, 1925: Zur Chemie und Physiologie der Pflanzenphosphatide. II, Die wasserlöslichen Phosphatide aus *Aspergillus oryzae*, *Biochem. Z.*, **162**: 366–398.

——— and ———, 1926: Über die Phosphatide aus *Daucus carota*, *Z. wiss. Biol. Abt. E. Planta*, **2**: 429–437.

———, 1933: Die Phosphatide der Pflanzenzelle, *Protoplasma*, **17**: 602–609.

Green, J. R., 1890: On the germination of the seed of the castor oil plant (*Ricinus communis*), *Proc. Roy. Soc.*, **48**: 370–392.

——— and H. Jackson, 1905: Further observations on the germination of the seeds of the castor oil plant, *Proc. Roy. Soc.*, B, **77**: 69–85.

Guerrant, N. B., 1927: Some relations of the phospholipins in seeds to other constituents, *J. Agr. Res.*, **35**: 1001–1021.

Haberlandt, G., 1914: "Physiological Plant Anatomy," English translation. The Macmillan Company, New York.

Hanriot, M., 1898: Sur la transformation de la graisse par oxydation directe, *C. R. Acad. Sci. Paris.*, **127**: 561–563.

Hansteen-Cranner, B., 1914: Über das Verhalten der Kulturpflanzen zu den Bodensalzen. II, Beiträge zur Biochemie und Physiologie der Zellwand lebender Zellen, *Jahrb. wiss. Bot.*, **53**: 536–598.

———, 1919: Beiträge zur Biochemie und Physiologie der Zellwand und der plasmatischen Grenzschichten, *Ber. bot. Ges.*, **37**: 380–391.

———, 1926: Untersuchungen über die Frage ob in der Zellwand lösliche Phosphatide vorkommen, *Planta Archiv. wiss. Bot.*, **2**: 438–445.

———, 1926: Untersuchungen über die Frage, ob in der Zellwand lösliche Phosphatide vorkommen, *Planta*, **2**: 438–445; *Bot. Abst.*, **1**: 610, 1927.

Hellriegel, H., 1855: Beitrag zur Keimungsgeschichte der ölgebenden Samen, *J. prakt. Chemie*, **64**: 94.

Heyl, F. W., E. C. Wise, and J. H. Speer, 1929: The unsaponifiable fraction from spinach fat, *J. Biol. Chem.*, **82**: 111–116.

Hicks, G., 1895: Oil producing seeds, *U. S. Dept. Agr. Year Book*, pp. 185–204.

Hilditch, T. P., 1928: The chemical composition of vegetable seed fats in relation to the natural orders of plants, *Proc. Roy. Soc.*, B, **103**: 111–117.

———, 1935: The fats: new lines in an old chapter of organic chemistry, *J. Soc. Chem. Ind.*, **54**: 139–145.

Ivanow, S., 1911: Ueber Oelsynthese unter Vermittlung der pflanzlichen Lipase, *Ber. bot. Ges.*, **29**: 595–602.

———, 1912: Über die Verwandlung des Öls in der Pflanze, *Jahrb. wiss. Bot.*, **50**: 375–386.

———, 1912: Über den Stoffwechsel beim Reifen ölhaltiger Samen mit besonderer Berücksichtigung der Ölbildungsprozesse, *Beih. bot. Cent.*, I, **28**: 159–191.

Iwanoff, L., 1902: Ueber die Umwandlungen des Phosphors beim Keimen der Wicke, *Ber. bot. Ges.*, **20**: 366–372.

Jacobson, H., 1889: Ueber einige Pflanzenfett, *Z. physiol. Chem.*, **13**: 32–65.

Jamieson, G. S., W. F. Baughman, and D. H. Brauns, 1921: The chemical composition of peanut oil, *J. Am. Chem. Soc.*, **43**: 1372–1382.

——— and ———, 1922: The chemical composition of sunflower-seed oil, *J. Am. Chem. Soc.*, **44**: 2952–2957.

Jegorow, M., 1904: Ueber Stoffmetamorphose bei der Samenkeimung von *Cucurbita maxima*, *Bot. Cent.*, **101**: 597–599.

Johnson, I. J., 1932: The relation of agronomic practice to the quantity and quality of the oil in flax seed, *J. Agr. Res.*, **45**: 239–255.

Jordan, R. C., and A. C. Chibnall, 1933: Observations on the fat metabolism of leaves. II, Fats and phosphatides of the runner bean (*Phaseolus multiflorus*), *Ann. Bot.*, **47**: 163–186.

Kao, H. C., 1936: Lipoid metabolism in the mung bean during germination, *Biochem, J.*, **30**: 202–207.

KAYSER, R., 1925: Hat eine Mineraldüngung Einfluss auf die Eigenschaften von Oelpflanzen und ändert sich durch die Düngung das Oel in seiner Zusammensetzung? *Bot. Arch.*, **10**: 349–386.

KIRKWOOD, J. E., and W. J. GIES, 1902: Chemical studies of the cocoanut with some notes on the changes during germination, *Bull. Torrey Bot. Club.*, **29**: 321–359.

KNOP, W., 1859: Ueber ein phosphorhaltiges Oel der Erbsen, *Landw. Versuchs-Stat.*, **1**: 26–30.

KORSAKOW, M., 1910: Ueber den Einfluss der Zellipoide auf die Autolyse der Weizenkeime, *Biochem. Z.*, **28**: 121–126.

KOSSEL, A., 1891: Chemische Zusammensetzung der Zelle, *Arch. Physiol.*, **1891**: 181–186.

LASKOVSKY, N., 1874: Ueber einige chemische Vorgänge bei der Keimung der Kürbissamen, *Landw. Versuchs-Stat.*, **17**: 219–244.

LEATHES, J. B., and H. S. RAPER, 1925: "The Fats," a mon., Longmans, Green and Company, New York, 243 pp.

LECLERC DU SABLON, M. 1893: Sur la germination du *Ricin*, *C. R. Acad. Sci. Paris*, **117**: 524–527.

———, 1894: Sur la germination des graines oléagineuses, *C. R. Acad. Sci. Paris*, **119**: 610–612.

———, 1895: Recherches sur la germination des graines oléagineuses, *Rev. Gén. Bot.*, **7**: 145–165, 205–215, 258–269.

———, 1896: Sur la formation des réserves non azotées de la noix et de l'amande, *C. R. Acad. Sci. Paris*, **123**: 1084–1086.

———, 1897: Sur la germination des amandes, *Rev. Gén. Bot.*, **9**: 5–16.

———, 1897: Sur les réserves oléagineuses de la noix, *Rev. Gén. Bot.*, **9**: 313–317.

LEVENE, P. A., and I. P. ROLF, 1925: Plant phosphatides. I, Lecithin and cephalin of the soybean, *J. Biol. Chem.*, **62**: 759–766.

———, 1926: Plant phosphatides. II, Lecithin, cephalin and so-called cuorin of the soybean, *J. Biol. Chem.*, **68**: 285–293.

LEWIS, F. J., and G. M. TUTTLE, 1920: Osmotic properties of some plant cells at low temperatures, *Ann. Bot.*, **34**: 405–416.

MACDOUGAL, D. T., 1922: The probable action of lipoids in growth, *Proc. Am. Phil. Soc.*, **61**: 33–53; *Sci.*, **55**: 653–654.

MACLEAN, H., and I. MACLEAN, 1927: "Lecithin and Allied Substances," mon., Longmans, Green, and Company, New York, 220 pp.

MAQUENNE, L., 1898: Sur les changements de composition qu' éprouvent les graines oléagineuses au cours de la germination, *C. R. Acad. Sci. Paris*, **127**: 625–628.

MARKLEY, K. S., and C. E. SANDO, 1931: Progressive changes in the waxlike coating on the surface of the apple during growth and storage, *J. Agr. Res.*, **42**: 705–723.

———, S. B. HENDRICKS, and C. E. SANDO, 1932: Further studies on the waxlike coating of apples, *J. Biol. Chem.*, **98**: 103–107.

——— and C. E. SANDO, 1933: Possible changes in the waxlike coating of apples caused by certain spray and other treatments, *Plant Physiol.*, **8**: 475–478.

——— and ———, 1933: Progressive changes in the cuticle of apples during growth and storage, *J. Agr. Res.*, **46**: 403–412.

MATLACK, M. B., 1935: A phytosterol and phytosterolin from the sweet potato, *Sci.*, **81**: 536.

MATTHES, E., 1927: Physiologische Untersuchungen über Umwandlungen des Oeles im keimenden Sonnenblumensamen, *Bot. Arch.*, **19**: 79–135; *Biol. Abst.*, **2**: 872.

MAXWELL, W., 1891: On the behavior of the fatty bodies and the role of the lecithins during normal germination, *Am. Chem. J.*, **13**: 16–24.

MAZÉ, M., 1900: Recherches sur la digestion des réserves dans les graines, en voie de germination et leur assimilation par les plantules, *C. R. Acad. Sci. Paris.*, **130**: 424–427.

M'CLENAHAN, F. M., 1909–1913: The development of fat in the black walnut. I, II, *J. Am. Chem. Soc.*, **31**: 1093–1098; **35**: 485–493.

MCNAIR, J. B., 1930: The taxonomic and climatic distribution of oil and starch in seeds in relation to the physical and chemical properties of both substances, *Am. J. Bot.*, **17**: 662–669.

———, 1931: Some properties of plant waxes in relation to climate of habitat, *Am. J. Bot.*, **18**: 518–526.

———, 1932: The interrelation between substances in plants: essential oils and resins, cyanogen and oxalate, *Am. J. Bot.*, **19**: 255–272.

MILLER, E. C., 1910: A physiological study of the germination of *Helianthus annuus*, *Ann. Bot.*, **24**: 693–726.

———, 1912: A physiological study of the germination of *Helianthus annuus*. II, The oily reserve, *Ann. Bot.*, **26**: 889–901.

MOYER, L. S., 1935: Electrophoresis of sterols. II, Ergosterol, *J. Gen. Physiol.*, **18**: 749–753.

MÜNTZ, M., 1871: Sur la germination des graines oléagineuses, *Ann. Chim. et Phys.*, 4e série, **22**: 472.

MURLIN, J. R., 1933: The conversion of fat to carbohydrate in the germinating castor bean. I, The respiratory metabolism, *J. Gen. Physiol.*, **17**: 283–301.

NJEGOVAN, V., 1911: Beiträge zur Kenntnis der pflanzlichen Phosphatide, *Z. physiol. Chem.*, **76**: 1–26.

NOLLER, C. R., I. J. MILLNER, and J. J.GORDON, 1933: Capric acid from the seed fat of the California bay tree, *J. Am. Chem. Soc.*, **55**: 1227–1228.

PACK, D. A., 1925: Dispersion of lipoids, *Bot. Gaz.*, **79**: 334–338.

PALLADIN, W., and E. STANEWITSCH, 1910: Die Abhängigkeit der Pflanzenatmung von den Lipoiden, *Biochem. Z.*, **22**: 351–369.

PARROZZANI, A., 1909: Il fosforo organico ed il rapporto fra l'azoto amidico e quello delle altre combinazioni azotate non proteiche nei semi maturi, *Staz. Sper. Agr. Ital.*, **42**: 890–901.

PETERS, E., 1861: Zur Keimungsgeschichte des Kurbissamens, *Landw. Versuchs-Stat.*, **3**: 1–18.

PIERCE, H. B., D. E. SHELDON, and J. R. MURLIN, 1933: The conversion of fat to carbohydrate in the germinating castor bean. III, The chemical analysis and correlation with respiratory exchange, *J. Gen. Physiol.*, **17**: 311–325.

PIRSCHLE, K., 1926: Acetaldehyd als Zwischenprodukt bei der Keimung fetthaltiger Samen, *Biochem. Z.*, **169**: 482–489; *Biol. Abst.*, **2**: 463.

POLICARD, A., and G. MANGENOT, 1923: Recherches cytologiques sur l'état de l'huile dans les graines oléagineuses. La graine mure, *C. R. Acad. Sci. Paris*, **176**: 1841–1844.

——— and ———, 1923. Sur l'état de l'huile dans la cellule de réserve des graines oléagineuses. La graine en germination, *C. R. Acad. Sci. Paris*, **177**: 346–348.

POLLARD, A., A. C. CHIBNALL, and S. H. PIPER, 1931: The wax constituents of forage grasses. I, Cocksfoot and perennial rye grass, *Biochem. J.*, **25**: 2111–2122.

———, ———, and ———, 1933: The isolation of *n*-octacosanol from wheat wax, *Biochem. J.*, **27**: 1889–1893.

PRIESTLEY, J. H., 1924: The fundamental fat metabolism of the plant, *New Phytol.*, **23**: 1–20.

RHINE, J. B., 1926: Studies on the oxidation of certain fatty acids, *Plant Physiol.*, **1**: 349–361.

Riebsomer, J. L., and G. A. Nesty, 1934: An examination of the fatty oil from pumpkin seed. The constitution of linoleic acid, *J. Am. Chem. Soc.*, **56**: 1784–1785.

Rivett, M. F., 1918: The structure of the cytoplasm in the cells of *Alicularia scolaris*, *Ann. Bot.*, **32**: 207–214.

Rohrabaugh, P. W., 1934: Penetration and accumulation of petroleum spray oils in the leaves, twigs and fruit of citrus trees, *Plant Physiol.*, **9**: 699–730.

Rushkovskii, S., 1930: Changes in the chemical composition of sunflower seeds with the sowing time, *Masloboino Delo*, **1930**: 43–56; *Chem. Abst.*, **26**: 4356.

Sachs, J., 1859: Ueber das Auftreten der Stärke bei der Keimung ölhaltiger Samen, *Bot. Ztg.*, **17**: 177–183, 185–188.

———, 1863: Ueber die Keimung des Samens von *Allium Cepa*, *Bot. Ztg.*, **21**: 57–65.

Sahai, P. N., and A. C. Chibnall, 1932: Wax metabolism in the leaves of Brussels sprout, *Biochem. J.* **26**: 403–412.

Sahasrabuddhe, D. L., and N. P. Kale, 1933: A biochemical study of the formation of oil in niger seed (*Guizotia abyssinica*), *Indian J. Agr. Sci.*, **3**: 57–88; *Biol. Abst.*, **9**: 750.

Sando, C. E., 1923: Constituents of the wax-like coating on the surface of the apple, *J. Biol. Chem.*, **56**: 457–468.

———, 1928: Lipides and their estimation in vegetable tissues, *Plant Physiol.*, **3**: 155–184.

Schmidt, R. H., 1891: Ueber Aufnahme und Verarbeitung von fetten Oelenpflanzen, *Flora*, **74**: 300–371.

Schulze, E., and E. Steiger, 1889: Ueber den Lecithingehalt der Pflanzensamen, *Z. physiol. Chem.*, **13**: 365–384.

———, ———, and W. Maxwell, 1891: Untersuchungen über die chemische Zusammensetzung einiger Leguminosensamen, *Landw. Versuchs-Stat.*, **39**: 269–326.

——— and A. Likiernik, 1891: Ueber das Lecithin der Pflanzensamen, *Z. physiol. Chem.*, **15**: 405–414.

——— and S. Frankfurt, 1894: Über den Lecithingehalt einiger vegetabilischer Substanzen, *Landw. Versuchs-Stat.*, **43**: 307–318.

Schwartze, E. W., and C. L. Alsberg, 1923: Quantitative variation of gossypol and its relation to the oil content of cotton seed, *J. Agr. Res.*, **25**: 285–295.

Scurti, F., and G. Tommasi, 1909–1910: Sulla formazione del grasso nei frutti oleaginosi; 1910–1911: *Ann. della R. Staz. Chim. Agrar. Sperim. di Roma*, **4**: 253–286; **5**: 103.

——— and ———, 1911: Sulla formazione del grasso nei frutti oleaginosi, *Ann. della R. Staz. Chim. Agrar. Sperim. di Roma*, **5**: 223.

——— and ———, 1912: In regard to the formation of fatty acid in oleaginous fruits. *R. Soc. Chim. Ital.*, **3**: 358–363; *Exp. Sta. Rec.*, **26**: 801.

Shorey, E. C., 1898: The lecithins of sugar cane, *J. Am. Chem. Soc.*, **20**: 113–118.

Sinnott, E. W., 1918: Factors determining character and distribution of food reserve in woody plants, *Bot. Gaz.*, **66**: 162–175.

Smedley, I., 1912: The biochemical synthesis of fatty acids from carbohydrates, *J. Physiol.*, **45**: 25–27.

——— and E. Lubrzynska, 1913: The biochemical synthesis of the fatty acids, *Biochem. J.*, **7**: 364–374.

Smith, J. A. B., and A. C. Chibnall, 1932: The glyceride fatty acids of forage grasses. I, Cocksfoot and perennial rye grass, *Biochem. J.*, **26**: 218–234.

——— and ———, 1932: The phosphatides of forage grasses. I, Cocksfoot, *Biochem. J.*, **26**: 1345–1359.

Smolenski, K., 1909: Zur Kenntniss der aus Weizenkeimen darstellbaren Phosphatide, *Z. physiol. Chem.*, **58**: 522–526.

SPEER, J. H., E. C. WISE, and M. C. HART, 1929: The composition of spinach fat, *J. Biol. Chem.*, **28**: 105–110.

STANLEY, O. B., 1931: Fat deposits in certain *Ericaceae*, *Buller Univ. Bot. Studies*, **2**: 33–41.

STARK, R. W., 1924: Environmental factors affecting the protein and oil content of soybeans and the iodine number of soybean oil, *J. Am. Soc. Agron.*, **16**: 636–646.

STEWARD, F. C., 1928: An experimental examination of the evidence for the presence of phosphatides in the limiting surface of the living protoplast, *British J. Exper. Biol.*, **6**: 32–41.

———, 1928: On the evidence for phosphatides in the external surface of the plant protoplast, *Biochem. J.*, **22**: 268–275.

———, 1929: Phosphatides in the limiting protoplasmic surface. I, A review with special reference to the plant protoplast, *Protoplasma*, **7**: 602–621.

STOCKLASA, J., 1895: Die Assimilation des Lecithins durch die Pflanze, *Sitzungsber.* (*Math. Naturw., Kl.*) *K. Akad. Wiss. Wien.*, **104**: 712–722.

———, 1898: Ueber die Entstehung und Unwandlung des Lecithins in der Pflanze, *Z. physiol Chem.*, **25**: 398–405.

STRASBURGER, E., F. NOLL, H. SCHENCK, and G. KARSTEN, 1908: "Textbook of Botany," English translation. The Macmillan Company, New York.

SULLIVAN, B., and C. NEAR, 1933: Change of crude lipides of wheat on storage, *Ind. and Eng. Chem.*, **25**: 100–103.

TERROINE, E. F., 1920: État actuelle de nos connaissances sur la formation des graisses au cours de la maturation des graines et fruits oléagineux et sur l'utilisation des graisses au cours de la germination, *Ann. Sci. Nat.* 10, **26**: 1–63; *Bot. Gaz.*, **75**: 224.

———, R. BONNET, G. KOPP, and J. VECHOT, 1927: La formation des stérols est-elle liée au métabolisme des matières graisses? *Bull. Soc. Chim. Biol.*, **9**: 678–691: *Biol. Abst.*, **2**: 1506.

THATCHER, R. W., 1921: "The Chemistry of Plant Life," McGraw-Hill Book Company, Inc., New York.

THOR, C. J. B., and C. L. SMITH, 1935: A physiological study of seasonal changes in the composition of the pecan during fruit development, *J. Agr. Res.*, **50**: 97–122.

TOTTINGHAM, W. E., 1932: Are leaf lipides responsive to solar radiation? *Sci.*, **75**: 223–224.

TSCHIRCH, A., and H. KRITZLER, 1900: Microchemische Untersuchungen über die Aleuronekörner, *Ber. Pharm.*, **10**: 214–223.

TUTTLE, G. M., 1919: Induced changes in reserve materials in evergreen herbaceous leaves, *Ann. Bot.*, **33**: 201–210.

———, 1921: Reserve food materials in vegetative tissue, *Bot. Gaz.*, **71**: 146–151.

VALLEE, C., 1903: Sur la présence du saccharose dans les amandes et sur son rôle dans la formation de l'huile, *C. R. Acad. Sci. Paris.*, **136**: 114–117.

VON FÜRTH, O., 1904: Ueber das Verhalten des Fettes bei der Keimung ölhaltiger Samen, *Hofmeisters Beiträge zur chem. Physiol. u. Path.*, **4**: 430.

VON OHLEN, F. W., 1930, 1931: A microchemical study of soybeans during germination, *Am. J. Bot.*, **17**: 1046; **18**: 30–49.

WAKKER, J. H., 1886: Studien über die Inhaltskörper der Pflanzenzelle, *Jahrb. wiss. Bot.*, **19**: 423–496.

WEBSTER, J. E., 1929: Iodine value of fatty acids from plant phosphatides, *Ohio J. Sci.*, **29**: 39–42.

WINTERSTEIN, E., and O. HIESTAND, 1908: Beiträge zur Kenntniss der pflanzlichen Phosphatide. II, *Z. physiol. Chem.*, **54**: 288–330.

——— and K. SMOLENSKI, 1909: Beiträge zur Kenntnis der aus Cerealien darstellbaren Phosphatide, *Z. physiol. Chem.*, **58**: 506–521.
——— and L. STEGMANN, 1909: Ueber einen eigenartigen phosphorhaltigen Bestandteil der Blätter von *Ricinus*, *Z. physiol. Chem.*, **58**: 527–528.
ZALENSKI, W., 1902: Beiträge zur Verwandlung des Eiweissphosphors in den Pflanzen, *Ber. bot. Ges.*, **20**: 426–433.

CHAPTER XI

THE PROCESS OF DIGESTION IN THE GREEN PLANT

I. FOODS OF THE GREEN PLANT

Before considering the process of digestion it will be necessary to discuss the foods of plants in order to understand the significance of this process in their life functions. A food may be defined as any substance that may be used directly, or after hydrolysis, by the protoplasm for growth and repair or as a source of energy. Since this definition applies to animals as well as to plants, it raises the question whether plants and animals use the same kind of foods in their life functions. It is common knowledge that animals are nourished with carbohydrates, fats, and proteins, but the fact that the protoplasm of plants requires for its nourishment and energy the same foods as are used by animals is not so well known. Such, however, is the case, as will be proved in the subsequent discussion.

A. Plant Sources of Animal Foods

It is well known that animals obtain their food supply either directly or indirectly from plants, since they live entirely upon plants or prey upon other animals that are dependent upon plants for their food supply. Animals obtain this food supply from the seeds and grains, fruit, stems, roots, and leaves of plants. Seeds and grains are one of the main sources of food for animals, including man. Some of the more important seeds and grains that are a source of food for animals are wheat, corn, rye, oats, barley, rice, peas, beans, sorghum grains, nuts, cotton seed, sunflower seed, buckwheat, millet, and peanuts. Some of the stems that are a source of food to animals are the stems of the grains, grasses, and legumes, Irish potatoes, artichokes, asparagus, sugar cane, and young bamboo, while some of the roots that furnish food are sweet potato, yams, beets, carrots, parsnips, salsify, turnips, rutabagas, and cassava. Some of the leaves that furnish food to animals are those of the grains, grasses and legumes, celery, rhubarb, onion, spinach, lettuce, cabbage, Swiss chard, kale, and rape. The foods that are stored in these plant parts are the proteins, carbohydrates, and fats together with certain minerals and vitamins. These can satisfy all the needs of the animals that feed upon them, in so far as their food supply is concerned. The question then naturally arises concerning the benefits of the foods stored in plants to the plants themselves. Are these foods stored in the organs just mentioned of use to the plant or are they beneficial only to the animal kingdom?

B. Value to the Plant of Its Stored Foods

Let us first consider the function of the foods stored in seeds. A normal seed contains a young plant which will, if the proper conditions are supplied, begin to grow and develop. The young seedling uses the foods stored in the seed to form new protoplasm and new tissues and from them it also derives the energy to push the stem out of the soil and the roots downward. As the young plant increases in size, the amount of food in the seed continues to decrease until it all disappears. This fact may be illustrated by considering the germination of the sunflower seed. This seed contains protein and oil as stored foods, the former making up 26 per cent and the latter about 50 per cent or more of the dry weight of this seed. This seed does not have an endosperm and these foods are stored in the cotyledons of the embryo. The depletion of these foods as germination progresses is shown in the following table:

Grams of Oil and Protein in the Cotyledons of 100 Seeds and Seedlings of the Sunflower Seed at 2, 4, 7, and 10 days, Respectively

Substance	Stage				
	Seed	2 days	4 days	7 days	10 days
Protein	1.7	1.2	1.0	0.8	0.6
Oil	4.0	3.0	2.5	1.3	0.5

A plant can thus grow to a considerable size without any food except that which is contained in the seed. These foods are transferred to the young plant parts and built into new tissue in much the same manner as this process occurs in animals.

In the aerial stems and branches of plants there is found in the region of the buds a large amount of protein, oil, or carbohydrates stored in the cells. As the buds develop into the new branches and leaves, this stored food is rapidly depleted and used in the formation of these new plant organs. In modified stems like the Irish potato and artichoke, the young sprouts that grow from them when they are planted are nourished until they are above ground and sometime thereafter from the food supply in the old tuber beneath the soil.

The three types of foods are stored in all roots of plants but in especially large quantities in roots of the fleshy type. The use to which the stored foods are put can be best illustrated by considering beets, carrots, parsnips, and other biennial plants. These plants during their first season's growth store up food in the roots, and during the second season develop a new stem that produces a crop of seed. The foods stored in these roots during the first year furnish the food necessary for this development of stem and seeds so that when the seed has matured the roots have been depleted of their stored food and during that time little or no material has been absorbed by the roots or manufactured by the aerial parts. In the majority of cases, the foods that are found in leaves have been manufactured there and are only awaiting transportation to the roots, stem, or seeds of the plant. Certain fleshy leaves, however, as the cabbage and onion, are real storage organs where the foods are stored permanently.

From what has been mentioned above, it is seen that the proteins and carbohydrates, or fats, are stored in all parts of the plant where growth is taking place or is going to take place. When the new organs or parts of the plant are formed, they draw upon these foods and form their tissues from them. We know this to be the case because these parts have no access to any food except that which is stored and also because the translocation of this food from its place of storage to the new parts can readily be detected. Plants thus use for their growth and development the same three types of foods as are used by animals in their growth and development. They differ in regard to the food proposition in that plants can manufacture the proteins, fats, and carbohydrates that they use as foods from the simple materials which they obtain from the air and the soil, while animals have no power to do this but have to depend entirely upon plants to furnish these foods already prepared for them. Thus it may be stated that plants are independent, while animals are dependent in regard to their food supply.

The simple inorganic compounds that plants obtain from the air and soil and from which they manufacture the three types of foods are frequently termed "plant foods." These compounds, however, are not foods in the strict sense of the word, since they cannot be used directly by the protoplasm. They are the crude materials from which foods are formed, in the same fashion as finished walls are formed from bricks, sand, and cement or finished cloth is made from the crude cotton or woolen fibers. The question now arises as to what changes if any the foods found in plants must undergo before they can be utilized by the protoplasm of the plant.

II. NATURE OF DIGESTION

The greater portion of the carbohydrates, proteins, fats, and oils of plants is stored in plants in forms that are insoluble in water. The storage of foods in an insoluble form in the plant cells has several advantages. In the first place, more food can be stored in a given space in the insoluble than in the soluble form. In the second place, foods are more stable in the insoluble form than in the soluble form and are less liable to be destroyed by decay. In the third place, the conversion of soluble foods to the insoluble form keeps the osmotic value of the cell sap at a level that is not injurious to the cell.

The foods in the insoluble form, however, cannot leave the cells in which they are stored until they are changed to a form that is soluble in water. They must therefore be changed to a soluble form before they can be translocated. Furthermore, all foods must be in a soluble form before they can be utilized for growth or as a source of energy. Even if a food is soluble in water it must in some cases be reduced to a more simple form before the protoplasm can utilize it in its metabolism. With these general facts concerning the foods of plants, we can now understand better what is meant by digestion.

Digestion may be defined as the processes whereby the foods of plants and animals are changed from an insoluble to a soluble form or from a complex to a more simple form. In nearly every case the action on foods in digestion is one of hydrolysis. The food is made to take up water and is then broken down, a fact that will be considered in the discussion of the action of digestive enzymes. As a result of this change, insoluble foods are rendered translocatable and changed to a form that is usable by the protoplasm in growth and development. An example of digestion in which the food is changed from an insoluble to a soluble form is the transformation of starch to sugar. Starch is an insoluble compound and cannot be transferred through the walls of the cells in which it is stored or be directly utilized by the protoplasm. When starch by the process of digestion is changed to maltose or eventually to glucose, we have a carbohydrate that is soluble in water, that can readily move from cell to cell, and that can be utilized by the protoplasm. Cane sugar is an example of a food that is soluble in water and easily translocated, but which must be digested into the more simple sugars glucose and fructose before it can be assimilated by the protoplasm of plants and animals.

III. ENZYMES

One of the most striking characteristics of living organisms is the ease with which they are able to split up compounds of a highly stable nature. The oxidation and hydrolysis of compounds in plants and animals occur at ordinary temperatures very rapidly, while in the laboratory these changes are effected in many cases only at higher temperatures and by the use of strong reagents. Little is known, however, concerning the manner in which these reactions are carried out by living organisms. It is well established, however, that the process of digestion in both plants and animals is not brought about directly by the protoplasm itself but by substances secreted by it. These substances behave as catalysts and are called "enzymes." This leads us to a discussion of catalysts in general and of the nature of enzymes in particular.

A. General Nature of Catalysts

In regard to the speed with which they are completed, chemical reactions may be placed in two main groups: (1) those reactions that are completed practically instantaneously, *e.g.*, the neutralization of a base by an acid or the precipitation of copper hydroxide by the addition of a solution of potassium hydroxide to a solution of copper sulphate; (2) those which require a measurable time for their completion, *e.g.*, the hydrolysis of cane sugar to glucose and fructose by a mineral acid or the saponification of a fat or oil by sodium hydroxide. It is with this latter type of reaction that catalysts are primarily concerned. A catalyst may be defined as a body which alters the speed of a chemical reaction that requires a measurable time to arrive at its final state. This alteration in the speed of a reaction may be either an acceleration or a retardation. Catalysts, however, are generally considered in regard to their acceleration of reactions, and the process of catalysis has been defined as "the acceleration of a chemical change by the presence of some foreign substance" (Bayliss, 1925). It is almost a universal opinion that catalysts cannot in themselves initiate reactions but that they only accelerate or retard reactions that are proceeding in their absence. Some of the general properties of catalysts are: (1) They are not chemically combined with the final products of the reaction but may be recovered at the end of the reaction measurably unchanged in quantity and quality, except where they may be destroyed by subsidiary reactions. (2) A relatively small amount of catalysts produces very large results in the reacting mixture. (3) The effect of a small amount of catalyst is in the end the same as that of a larger quantity if sufficient time is allowed, the only difference being the rate at which the new products appear.

B. General Nature of Enzymes

In beginning a discussion of this topic, the first step should be to give a definition of the term "enzyme." A definition, however, is difficult of formulation, since so little is known concerning the nature of enzymes. In the light of our present knowledge, perhaps as exact and inclusive a definition as can be formulated is that of Bayliss (1925) who defined an enzyme as "a catalyst produced by living organisms."

These biochemical catalysts, however, differ widely in their reaction towards the environment. According to Tauber (1936) some of these, as pepsin, trypsin, maltase, lipase, and others, can act independently of the living cell and are destroyed by heat. Others, however, as for example the catalyst affecting the synthesis of urea in the liver act only in the unimpaired cell and are destroyed by heat. There are certain other nonspecific biochemical catalysts, as glutathione and ascorbic acid, which although elaborated by the living cell can act independently of the living cell and are not destroyed by heat.

Enzymes are colloidal substances and do not readily diffuse through artificial membranes. The rate at which they diffuse through membranes is largely dependent upon the nature of the membrane, but as a rule they will not pass through parchment membranes. This is one important characteristic that distinguishes enzymes from other organic catalysts. Most enzymes, however, will pass through a porcelain filter, and this characteristic is utilized for their separation from the materials with which they are associated. Since enzymes are colloids, they have the property of carrying down with them by adsorption some of the constituents of the solutions from which they are precipitated. The methods used for the precipitation of enzymes also precipitate most proteins, so that proteins are generally present in an ordinary enzyme preparation. On that account it is difficult to determine the chemical composition of enzymes with any degree of certainty, and so far all attempts to isolate an enzyme as a pure substance of definite chemical composition have been without satisfactory results. In general, the more the enzymes are purified the fewer characteristic reactions do they show, although in some cases their activity, weight for weight, can be greatly increased. On the other hand, in many cases the attempts to purify enzyme preparations by the means at present at our disposal greatly decrease the activity of the enzyme. Since, as will be mentioned later, enzymes are specific in their action, it would seem probable that they differ in their chemical structure. On that account the chemical reactions of the different enzymes will be considered under their individual headings. According to Waldschmidt-Leitz (1933), it was considered by Willstätter (1922) that enzymes consist of a carrier that is colloidal in nature, and of one or several chemically active groups. This hypothesis accounts for the physico-chemical and chemical behavior of enzymes and has been widely accepted. The colloidal carrier is considered to determine the stability and the magnitude of catalytic activity of the active groups, while the nature of the active groups is responsible for the specificity of the enzymes. Willstätter, Graser, and Kuhn (1922) believed that the colloidal carrier of an enzyme can be varied by changing the procedure of purification, and that a small change in the nature of the active group, such as the introduction of two hydrogen atoms, produces great changes in the specificity of enzymes.

Hogounenq and Loiseleur (1925) considered that an enzyme consists of a colloidal organic complex and a mineral element. The organic complex constitutes a colloidal support upon which the electrolyte is held by adsorption, retaining its crystalloid properties and specific chemical activity. The electrolyte is considered specific for a given enzyme, *e.g.*, chlorine for pepsin and manganese for oxidases. The adsorption of the electrolyte is determined by the electrical sign of the protein micelles, and the sign is determined by the functional grouping in the molecule. Thus pepsin is supposed to consist of a colloidal protein support having predominantly acid groups that determine its negative sign. It absorbs such cations as sodium, setting free chlorine, which attacks the NH_2 groups of the proteins digested. Trypsin is a similar colloidal complex in which amidogenic groups predominate, giving the micelles a positive charge. Zeile and Hellström (1930) and Zeile (1931) found by photospectrometric measurements that an iron-porphyrin complex is the active group of the catalase of the pumpkin. Kuhn, Hand, and Florkin (1931) considered that this complex is also the active component in certain peroxidases. According to Balls (1931), Sumner (1933), and Falk (1935), it is generally agreed that practically all enzymes are of a protein nature, and the fact that many enzymes are digested and inactivated by proteases lends support to that general belief (Glick and King, 1933; Falk, 1935; and Tauber, 1936). The active substance of an enzyme cannot exist alone in solution but apparently must always be accompanied by some protective colloid with which it is in some sort of combination. The active principle of an enzyme, however, has never been isolated. There are, however, some observations which indicate that the enzyme is not of a colloidal nature. Thus, Miller (1929) reported that a very active soluble tyrosinase obtained from a mushroom was not colloidal in nature since it dialyzed through a cellophane tube. He considered that this observation invalidates the general application of the theory of Willstätter that enzymes exist in a particular, colloidal state.

Enzymes are sensitive to heat. The optimum temperature for most plant enzymes is between 37 and 55°C. In most cases, enzymes are injured at a temperature above 60°C. and all are completely destroyed at a temperature of 100°C. Their resistance to heat differs with different types of enzymes, with the kind of material associated with them, and with the amount of water present, as will be mentioned when the different types of enzymes are considered. The destruction of enzymes by heat is attributed to the alteration of their colloidal nature probably by coagulation. In general, the activity of enzymes is doubled for every rise of 10°C., but this effect is diminished at higher temperatures because of the destruction of the enzymes by heat. The relation of the increased activity of an enzyme to temperature, the effects of the increased temperature on the destruction of the enzyme, and the resultant activity of increases in temperature are shown in Fig. 27. Enzymes are inactivated at lower temperatures but again regain their activity when the temperature is again raised.

It has generally been considered that enzymes are sensitive to light, especially ultraviolet and polarized light. On that account experiments with the activity of enzymes have generally been conducted in the dark. Recently, however, Fuller (1931, 1932) found that when tomato and bean plants were severely injured by ultraviolet rays the activity of their amylase, invertase, peptase, and catalase was significantly increased. When solutions of taka-diastase and commercial invertase were irradiated *in vitro* by a quartz mercury lamp, they underwent a partial inactivation, but this was partially due to the infrared radiations.

In the study of the action of enzymes, an antiseptic must be employed to prevent the hydrolytic action of bacteria. The most commonly used antiseptics are toluene, chloroform, sodium fluoride, phenol, thymol, and formaldehyde. Practically all these compounds exert more or less of an inhibiting influence on enzymic action, depending upon the enzyme under observation. Of these, toluene is the most suitable and is the most commonly employed antiseptic in the study of enzymes.

C. General Nature of Enzyme Action

Enzymes have two properties that are common to all catalysts in that they are not capable of initiating a new reaction, but merely of changing the rate of one already in progress, and in that they do not appear combined with the final products of the reactions that they influence. Enzymes differ from catalysts in that they are more specific in their reactions. Thus a catalyst, as the hydrogen ions of mineral acids, will hydrolyze proteins, carbohydrates, fats, and other esters, while a given enzyme will act on only one of these compounds. They also differ from catalysts in that they do not always carry the process to the same state of completeness as does an inorganic catalyst that influences the same reaction. Thus the enzyme diastase hydrolyzes starch to malt sugar, while a mineral acid hydrolyzes the starch to glucose. Certain of the proteolytic enzymes also do not carry the digestive process so far as do acids. Thus an acid hydrolyzes the protein to amino acids, while the enzymes frequently leave complex polypeptides that are unattacked. Thus an enzyme catalyzes only a single reaction as the hydrolysis of starch to maltose or of maltose to glucose, while the acid catalyzes both reactions. This difference between enzymes and the inorganic catalysts may be more apparent than real, since the reactions that occur under the influence of enzymes might proceed to complete hydrolysis if the appropriate conditions were present. Thus it has been observed, for example, that if malt extract is allowed to act for a long time on starch, the hydrolysis proceeds beyond malt sugar, and glucose is formed. Enzyme action in many cases apparently comes to an end or equilibrium point, owing to the accumulation of the products of the reaction, so that by the dilution or removal of products the reaction can proceed farther.

The mechanism by which an enzyme accomplishes its catalytic effects is not definitely known. Two general theories concerning the mode of this catalytic action have been advanced and will be briefly mentioned here, since a full discussion of the nature of enzyme action belongs to the province of advanced biochemistry rather than to the field of plant physiology. The few statements in regard to enzyme action that are given herein are made in order that the student may be familiar with the complexity of the problem and with the meager knowledge available on the subject. The following presentation is based primarily on the discussion by Thatcher (1921).

The earliest and simplest theory of enzyme action that was proposed was that the enzyme simply creates an environment favorable for the particular chemical reaction to take place and does not enter into the combination with the substrate at all. The favorable environment was considered to be brought about by the exposure of large surfaces of the substance under consideration to the action of the active agent of the enzyme by the means of surface adsorption of this substrate on the colloidal material of the enzyme. According to Alexander (1934), high efficiency for an enzyme demands an intermediate degree of dispersion, which involves a large exposure of active interfacial surface coupled with a high kinetic activity.

The theory that is now most generally accepted is that there is an actual combination between the substrate and the enzyme. This combination is only temporary and breaks down with a resultant change in the substrate and the freeing of the enzyme for recombination with additional substrate. The theory of this mode of enzyme reaction is based on the following: (1) the fact that if an enzyme and its substrate, each of which is filterable through a given filter, are mixed; the active material in the combined solution will not pass through the filter; (2) the interpretation of the curves representing the reaction velocities of typical reactions that are proceeding under the influence of an enzyme; and (3) the fact that the limitation of a given enzyme to a specific substrate is definitely related to the molecular configuration of the molecules of the substrate.

There are two general theories in regard to the nature of the supposed combination of the enzyme and substrate. One is that the combination is molecular, and that a definite chemical compound is formed. The other is that the result of the union is purely a physical or colloidal complex. The latter theory is substantiated by the effects of electrolytes and heat on enzyme action and by the appearance of the reacting substances under the microscope.

According to Falk (1935) the only conclusion that appears justified at present is that addition compounds of enzyme and substrate are formed, which then break down to form the products of the enzymatic action. Such addition compounds, however, have not been isolated, and the evidence for their presence is wholly indirect.

In many cases the chemical action brought about by enzymes never goes to completion, so that there is some of the substrate remaining intact. This is explained by saying that the action of enzymes is reversible and that the same enzyme will accelerate the velocity of the reaction in either direction, depending upon the environmental conditions of the reacting materials. The synthesis of fats and oils from fatty acids and glycerin in the presence of lipase, as mentioned in Chap. X, is an example of the synthetic action of an enzyme. The synthesis of isomaltose from glucose by maltase is another example of the reversible action of enzymes. It is considered that the synthesis of the various plant products is brought about by enzyme action, although the experimental evidence in this regard is very meager. Enzyme action under artificial conditions is distinguished from direct protoplasmic action in that it occurs in the presence of an amount of antiseptic that is destructive to the life of protoplasm. Some enzymes, however, are very sensitive to certain antiseptics, as will later be mentioned.

D. Nomenclature

The substance whose chemical change is catalytically affected by an enzyme is termed the "substrate." The substrate is generally defined as the substance upon which the enzyme acts.

The activity of enzymes is greatly influenced by the presence in the solution of other bodies. Any substance that increases the catalytic activity of an enzyme is termed an "accelerator" or "activator," while one that inhibits or destroys its action is called an "inhibitor" or "paralyzer." The substances that thus influence the rate of enzyme action are generally electrolytes, such as mineral acids, alkalies, and salts, although this is not always the case. The accelerating action of the amino acids on the activity of certain enzymes is an example of these exceptions. All enzymes, however, do not respond alike to the same substance. Thus the activity of some enzymes is greatly increased by the presence of a small amount of mineral acid, while the action of another may be partially or completely inhibited by the same acid in the same concentration. Some of the substances that almost always exercise an inhibitive or toxic action on enzyme activity are hydrogen sulphide, formaldehyde, hydrocyanic acid, chloroform, and the salts of mercury, silver, and copper.

It has been found that many enzymes are inactive unless accompanied by some other substance which is normally present in the protoplasm that produces them. Such substances have been named "coenzymes." This accompanying substance can usually be separated from the enzyme by dialysis, the coenzyme passing through the parchment membrane. After the coenzyme is thus separated, it is not injured by boiling, and the activity of the enzyme may be restored by adding the boiled substance to the liquid that remains behind in the dialyzer. Coenzymes have been studied in connection with the enzymes of animals and in connection with the activity of zymase of yeast cells, but few observations have been made in this regard with the enzyme studies of green plants.

The term "antienzyme" has been applied to a substance occurring naturally in a living organism, or which is produced after the injection of an enzyme, that prevents the action of the specific enzyme upon the tissues. Antienzymes have been considered more particularly in the physiology of animals, but in many cases the evidence of the existence of such substances and their action rests upon theory rather than experimental evidence. The evidence of antienzymes in the green plants is extremely meager. The only work in this regard that is known to the author is that of Czapek (1905), who considered that he obtained evidence of antioxidases in his studies of the reactions occurring during the tropistic movements of plants.

Since enzymes are produced by the protoplasm, it is apparent that, at a given stage in their synthesis, they have not yet acquired their catalytic powers, although possessing, in general, the other properties of enzymes. An enzyme that has reached this stage of its formation is termed a "proenzyme" or "zymogen." These terms are used, however, only when the substance can be obtained free from the cells in which it is formed and can be converted after its extraction into the active enzyme by purely chemical means (Bayliss, 1925). When such a substance has once been activated, it cannot, according to present knowledge, be converted again to the proenzyme or zymogen state. Calcium salts and dilute acids are considered to be the most energetic activators of proenzymes. The activator of a proenzyme has also been termed a "kinase." According to Thatcher (1921), proenzymes are believed to be present in plant cells in the form of definite characteristic granules which may be observed under the microscope but which disappear when the enzyme becomes active. According to him, proinulase has been reported as occurring in artichoke tubers, prolipase in castor beans (Tanka, 1910), and prooxidase in tobacco leaves.

When organic catalysts were first isolated from plant and animal tissues, they were termed "ferments" because of the resemblance of the changes produced to alcoholic fermentation. After it was found that fermentation was due to the presence of living organisms as yeast, these organic catalysts were termed "soluble" or "unorganized ferments" to distinguish them from living organisms producing similar changes, which were termed "insoluble" or "organized ferments." The double use of the word ferment caused much confusion and induced Kühne (1878) to suggest that the name "enzymes" be given to those substances which were then designated as unorganized ferments. The name enzyme comes from the Greek words *en zymos* and literally means "in yeast." Kühne stated that the term was meant to include those unorganized ferments which behave in a manner similar to those substances which occur in yeast. When it was shown in 1897 by Büchner that if yeast cells are crushed and filtered the filtrate is just as active in fermentation as the intact yeast cells, the difference between organized and unorganized ferments disappeared and the term enzyme came into general use.

E. Classification

Enzymes are specific in their action, each one activating a particular chemical change upon one substance, so that there are as many enzymes as there are substances upon which they act. On this account, a system of nomenclature has been adopted which assigns to each enzyme the name

Enzymes that function in the process of digestion in plants
- Hydrolases
  - Carbohydrases
    - Invertins, invertases, saccharases, or sucrases
    - Diastases or amylases
    - Dextrinases
    - Inulases
    - Glucases or maltases
    - Cellulases or cytases
    - Pectinases
    - Melibiase
    - Gentianase
  - Glucosidases
    - Emulsin
    - (Maltase)
    - Phytase
    - Rhamninase
    - Myrosin
  - Esterases and Lipases
  - Proteases
    - Pepsins or peptases
    - Trypsins or tryptases
      - Papaïn
      - Bromelin
      - Cradina
      - Other trypsins
    - Erepsins or ereptases
- Coagulases
  - Rennins or rennets
  - Pectases

of the material upon which it acts, followed by the suffix *-ase*. Thus sucrase is the enzyme acting upon sucrose, amylase the enzyme acting upon amylum (starch), and cellulase the enzyme acting upon cellulose. This system of nomenclature is now generally followed, although in some cases, where the original name of the enzyme has long been in use, the older terminology is used, *e.g.*, pepsin, trypsin, diastase, invertase, and so on. The enzymes that have been the most studied and the ones with which we are primarily concerned in the study of digestion accelerate hydrolytic reactions and may be termed "hydrolases." Certain enzymes that cause coagulation are termed "coagulases" and in some cases apparently play a role in the digestive process. The enzymes that are concerned in digestion may be classified after the manner as shown at the bottom of page 781.

F. Occurrence

Digestive enzymes of one type or another are found in all living plant tissue. A few examples will suffice to illustrate this point. Robertson, Irvine, and Dobson (1909) found diastase, invertase, maltase, inulase, and emulsin in the stem and leaves of the beet. Bailey (1912) found invertase, diastase, proteases, and lipase in the banana, and in the stem, leaves, roots, and seeds of alfalfa, Jacobson and Holmes (1914) detected lipase, diastase, coagulases, emulsin, invertase, pectinase, and certain proteases. The fungi are especially rich in digestive enzymes and are the sources of many of the commercial enzyme preparations. Thus in *Echinodontium tinctorium,* Schmitz (1920) demonstrated the presence of esterase, maltase, lactase, invertase, diastase, inulase, cellulase, rennet, and others. Thatcher (1915) found oxidases, esterases, and proteases in ripening apples but could not detect any of the carbohydrate-splitting enzymes. Paton (1921) found catalase, diastase, invertase, reductase, and pectinase in the pollen of 18 species of plants. Pepsin, trypsin, erepsin, and lipase were in the pollen from some plants but not in that of others.

The abundance of enzymes in a given part of a plant depends apparently on the conditions under which it is placed. There is some evidence that fungi in some cases may secrete an enzyme corresponding to the kind of substrate that is supplied, but no observations in that regard have been made upon green plants (Kertesz, 1931). After enzymes are formed in the plant they may remain active for a long period of time. Thus White (1909) found that the seeds of wheat, oats, corn, barley, and rye which had been stored for 20 years and which had lost their germinating power, contained diastase and erepsins that had retained their activity apparently unimpaired. Miehe (1923) examined rye seeds that were at least 112 and probably 280 years old. Although the embryos were disintegrated, the endosperms were intact and the starch contained in them reacted to the iodine test. Enzymes were obtained from these seeds by water extractions and changed starch to sugar and differed from those of fresh rye-seed extracts only in acting more slowly. Maestrini (1923) studied acidulated aqueous extracts of germinating barley that had been kept for 3 or 4 years. Diastase did not appear to be perceptibly modified in its enzymic action by this treatment. The proteases, however, showed a marked reduced hydrolytic capacity, and lipase and emulsin were destroyed in less than 2 years (Longenecker and Haley, 1935).

We shall now discuss the distribution, general properties, reactions, and methods of preparation of the various digestive enzymes found in the green plant.

1. The Carbohydrases of Plants. *a. The Invertases, Invertins, Saccharases, or Sucrases.*—The enzyme that hydrolyzes sucrose to glucose and levulose has been variously named "invertase," "invertin," "saccharase," or "sucrase." This hydrolysis is one of the most simple of the enzymic reactions and proceeds after the following manner:

$$\underset{\text{Sucrose}}{C_{12}H_{22}O_{11}} + \underset{\substack{\text{In presence}\\\text{of invertase}}}{H_2O} \longrightarrow \underset{\text{Glucose}}{C_6H_{12}O_6} + \underset{\text{Levulose}}{C_6H_{12}O_6}$$

The occurrence of invertase in green plants has been reported by Brown and Morris (1893); Kastle and Clark (1903); Martinand (1907); Vinson (1907); Robertson, Irvine, and Dobson (1909); Colin (1915); McGuire and Falk (1919, 1923); and others. Invertase has been found in the roots and leaves of the radish; in the leaves and tubers of the artichoke; in the leaves, tubers, and sprouts of the potato; in the leaves of the dahlia; in the leaves and roots of the dandelion; in the entire plant of corn and *Sorghum saccharatum;* in the leaf lamina, petioles, and collar of the sugar beet; in all parts of the leaves, stem, and fruit of the grape; in the leaves, stem, and pods of the soybean; in the leaves and roots of the sweet potato; in the fig; in the banana fruit; and in many other plants and plant parts. Invertase is thus apparently of almost universal occurrence in green plants. It has not, however, been definitely established whether the invertases from different sources are identical substances (Doby, 1915). Invertase occurs in great abundance in yeast, and it is from this source that the invertase of commerce is mostly obtained. It may also be prepared from cultures of *Aspergillus niger* (Stoward, 1912). Most of the studies on the nature and action of invertase have been made on the invertase of yeast. Invertase is now used rather extensively in the industries. In the hydrolysis of a number of commercial products in which sucrose is the principal saccharine constituent, this enzyme has been found more suitable than an acid as a catalyst. It is used in products which exhibit a marked buffer effect toward added acid and which possess a flavor adversely influenced by the concentration of acid required to effect hydrolysis (Paine, Walton, and Badollet, 1925). According to Paine and Balch (1925), an analytical procedure involving the use of the enzymes invertase and melibiase has been adapted to practical use for the precise determination of the sugars sucrose and raffinose in the chemical control of beet-sugar factories.

1. *Preparation and Study of Invertase.* (*a*) *Preparation from Yeast.*—Although this text deals only with the physiology of the green plant, the preparation of invertase from yeast is here discussed, since much of our knowledge of the action of invertase has been learned from enzyme preparations obtained from yeast. Methods for the preparation of invertase from yeast have been given by O'Sullivan and Tompson (1890), Hudson (1910, 1914), and Nelson and Born (1914). The modified method of Nelson and Born as used by Hudson (1914) is as follows: Equal amounts of water and yeast are autolyzed at room temperature for 5 days with toluene as an antiseptic. The material is then filtered, and 95 per cent alcohol is added in equal volume. After the precipitate settles, the alcohol is decanted and the residue dissolved in water. Alcohol is again added as before and again decanted. After the precipitate is again dissolved in water, a concentrated solution of lead acetate is added until no more precipitate is formed. After filtering off the precipitate, potassium oxalate is added to throw down the excess lead, and the precipitate is filtered off. The filtrate is then treated with kaolin and stirred constantly for 1 hr., the treatment being repeated several times. The resulting liquid is then placed in collodion bags with toluene and dialyzed in running water from 3 to 20 days. After this dialysis, a precipitate cannot be obtained by the addition of alcohol until some sodium chloride, potassium acetate, or acetic acid is added to alter the colloidal nature of the solution. If a precipitate is thus obtained, it is washed with absolute alcohol and dried over sulphuric acid. The purest preparation of invertase obtained after this manner will give a faint biuret and strong Millon and xanthoproteic reactions as long as the enzyme remains active, and there is a rough parallelism between the nitrogen content and activity when the preparation is fairly pure. An active preparation of invertase has a nitrogen content of 2.2 per cent, but when the nitrogen content falls below 1 per cent the enzyme is no longer active (Mathew and Glenn, 1911). The invertase of yeast as ordinarily prepared is considered to be a union of protein with a carbohydrate gum, the protein constituent being the active part of the preparation. Nelson and Born (1914) noted that a 10 per cent solution of invertase prepared from yeast after the above method was not precipitated by any of the ordinary protein precipitants. After the hydrolysis of this solution with 2.5 per cent sulphuric acid and neutralization with barium carbonate, copious precipitates were obtained with mercuric chloride, mercuric acetate, phosphomolybdic acid, and phosphotungstic acids. This indicates that in the original invertase preparation either the protein part is combined with the carbohydrate or the latter acts as a protective colloid.

(*b*) *Preparation from Green Plants.*—Falk and McGuire (1921) used the following method for the preparation of invertase from bananas: The pulp is ground finely in a food chopper and then mixed in a porcelain mortar with normal sodium chloride, 100 cc. to each 400 g. of pulp, toluene is added, and the mixture is filtered through paper. The filtrate is then dialyzed in collodion bags for 18 to 24 hr. against running water to remove salts, carbohydrates, and other products. The resulting solution will keep for a considerable period of time under toluene and is used for invertase experiments. Invertase in leaves has been studied, for the most part, by drying the leaves at air temperature, pulverizing the dried material to a fine powder, and taking a weighed portion for the study of enzyme action. It should always be remembered that the manner in which an enzyme is obtained may affect not only its activity but its physical properties as well. Thus Falk and McGuire in studying invertase in the banana found a water-soluble, a sodium chloride-soluble, and another invertase in the extracted residue of the fruit pulp. All three preparations were identical, as far as could be observed in their action on cane sugar, but were entirely different in their physical behavior.

The general method for the study of the action of invertase is to add 10 to 15 cc. of an invertase solution to 10 to 25 cc. of a 1 to 20 per cent sucrose solution together with sufficient toluene to act as an antiseptic. This mixture is incubated at 35 to 38°C. for varying periods of time, depending upon the activity of the invertase preparation. The periods of incubation vary from 2 to 24 hr. As a rule, the invertase preparations from leaves and fruits are relatively slow in their action as compared to the preparations from yeast. After the incubation, a portion of the mixture is treated with Fehling's solution, heated, and the degree of invertase action determined in terms of the number of milligrams of copper oxide produced by the action of 1 cc. of the original enzyme solution, correction always being made for the controls. The rate of invertase action may be obtained qualitatively by estimating the amount of reduction of Fehling's solution by the color of the solution or by the relative amount of the precipitate produced.

2. *Nature of the Action of Invertase.*—Invertase has been the best studied of any of the plant enzymes. Since the action of this enzyme is relatively simple, starting with a well-known substance and producing well-known end products, the hydrolysis of cane sugar by it has been chosen by many investigators as the best process with which to study the velocity of enzyme action in relation to different factors.

Invertase is not destroyed or injured by its action on sucrose. O'Sullivan and Tompson (1890) found that a sample of invertase which had induced inversion of 100,000 times its own weight of cane sugar was still active, so there is apparently no limit to the amount of sugar that may be hydrolyzed by a given amount of this enzyme, provided that the proper conditions are maintained for its action.

It should be mentioned here that there is apparently a difference between the action of acids and invertase on cane sugar, although both substances are catalysts and both produce the same end products in the hydrolysis of this sugar. Thus in different concentrations of cane sugar, the same amount of acid gives the same velocity constant. For example, a 5, 10, or 15 per cent sucrose solution will be inverted by a 1 per cent acid solution in the same time to the same extent, say halfway. In the case of invertase, however, the same quantity of enzyme in the different concentrations of sucrose invert in the same time, not the same fractions of each solution, but the same absolute amounts.

The velocity of the inversion of cane sugar is directly proportional to the concentration of invertase. The velocity of reaction is nearly independent of the concentration of the sucrose in the more concentrated solutions, while in very dilute sugar solutions, the velocity increases with the increase of concentration of the substrate and finally reaches a maximum (Nelson and Vosburgh, 1917). It was shown by Nelson and Bodansky (1925) that the invert sugar formed in hydrolysis exerts a retarding influence on the velocity of the reaction of invertase. This is due to the fact that invert sugar has a different retarding effect upon hydrolysis according to whether it is in a freshly liberated or in a final mutarotated form. If the invert sugar were mutarotated immediately upon its liberation, the course of reaction would be different from the ordinary observed course of the reaction.

According to Nelson and Griffin (1916), invertase is of a colloidal nature and the reaction between the enzyme and a cane-sugar solution depends on the contact of two phases. They found that the activity of invertase is not affected when it is adsorbed to a solid like charcoal or to a colloid like saponin, serum, or egg albumin distributed uniformly throughout the substrate (Nelson and Hitchcock, 1921). Nelson and Vosburgh (1917) considered that adsorption is one of the controlling factors in the kinetics of invertase action, since the velocity of the inversion curve, where the concentration of the cane sugar is used as the abscissas, has the same general shape as adsorption curves. There are yet considerable contradiction and uncertainty, however, concerning the nature of the reaction involved in the hydrolysis of cane sugar by invertase. The results obtained by Nelson and Vosburgh (1917) and others indicate that it is a heterogeneous reaction and not a unimolecular homogeneous one.

It was observed by Nelson and Hitchcock (1921) that not all the preparations of yeast invertase are alike in their action, but that some are abnormal in allowing the hydrolysis of cane sugar to slow up more than others after the first 20 per cent of the inversion. This abnormality could be rendered normal by the addition of boiled normal invertase or 0.1 *N* sodium chloride in some cases, while in others it was not affected by either of these additions. The cause of this abnormal behavior is not known.

It is generally considered that invertase exerts a reversible reaction, and Kohl (1908) stated that inversion gives place to the opposite process sooner in darkness than in light. Hudson and Paine (1914), however, concluded that invertase from yeast accomplishes a complete hydrolysis of sucrose to yield invert sugar and that the reaction does not establish mobile equilibrium and is not a reversible or balanced reaction within the limits of detection.

3. *Factors Influencing the Action.*—The method by which invertase is prepared, the age of the preparation, the dilution of the preparation, and the general treatment of the preparation must all be taken into consideration in discussing the influence of various factors on the activity of

invertase. Thus Hudson and Paine (1910) noted that alcohol reduces the activity of invertase. This reduction is not noticeable below 20 per cent alcohol at 30°C., is almost instantaneous at 50 per cent, and decreases to zero at 80 per cent. Cane sugar in alcohol has a protective value on the enzyme. Invertase may be precipitated with alcohol without much destruction, provided the strength of the alcohol is approximately 90 per cent. A solid preparation obtained in this manner was 78 per cent as active as the original solution. If cane sugar is present, the invertase may be precipitated with 70 per cent alcohol, and the resulting precipitate give 94 to 96 per cent of the original reaction. Vosburgh (1921) found that invertase solutions are subject to loss in activity when diluted, the loss varying with the substances present in the water with which the invertase is diluted. Dilution with distilled water is attended by less loss than is dilution with weak acids. When an invertase solution is added to a solution containing sucrcse, the losses in activity due to dilution are less than when the invertase is diluted by similar solutions not containing sucrose. Different preparations of invertase differ in this regard. In studying the action of invertase of banana extracts, McGuire and Falk (1923) showed that under certain conditions this enzyme exhibited apparently spontaneous increases of activity of considerable magnitude. In some cases the original activity was almost doubled, the activity increasing with the aging of the extract. After reaching a maximum value in a certain number of days, the invertase activity decreased. This increase of invertase activity was independent of the composition of the solution used for extraction and was not due to bacterial growth or cell decomposition accompanied by enzyme liberation. The behavior observed might be due to the fact that the extract contained materials that in the absence of life processes form new enzyme. The invertase in the extract may lose its activity steadily and the formation of new enzyme may be at first greater than the destruction and then become less. This theory would account for the increase and subsequent decrease in the activity of the enzyme.

In their classical paper on invertase, O'Sullivan and Tompson (1890) stated that small amounts of acid are favorable to the action of this enzyme but that alkalies even in small amounts are very destructive to its action. These observations, in general, have been substantiated by the work of later investigators. Hudson and Paine (1910) found that acids and alkalies in small concentrations influence the activity of the enzyme but do not permanently destroy it. The destruction by acids at 30°C. reaches a barely noticeable rate at a concentration of one-hundredth normal and increases with the acidity until it becomes almost instantaneous at a one-twentieth normal concentration. The alkaline destruction of invertase is almost instantaneous at a concentration of 0.045 *N*:

The activity of invertase in weak alkaline solutions is zero, rises to a maximum in very weakly acid ones, and decreases with stronger acid solutions. The activity of the enzyme in weak solutions of hydrochloric, nitric, sulphuric, phosphoric, boric, oxalic, tartaric, citric, and acetic acids depends almost entirely on the concentration of the hydrogen ions, and the acids thus show typical differences that correspond to their degree of dissociation. The optimum activity of invertase, according to Nelson and Bloomfield (1924), at 25, 30, and 35°C. is between pH 4.5 and 5.0. They found that the effect of temperature and hydrogen-ion concentration is independent of the concentration of sucrose, and the sucrose concentration, at which the hydrolysis in the presence of invertase attains a maximum velocity, is independent of temperature and hydrogen-ion concentration. They considered that the hydrolysis of cane sugar in the presence of invertase involves at least two distinct stages. One of these stages is influenced by the concentration of the sucrose but is independent of the temperature and hydrogen-ion concentration, while the other is influenced by both these factors (Compton, 1921).

O'Sullivan and Tompson (1890) stated that the speed of inversion by invertase increases with the temperature until 55 to 60°C. is reached, and that at 65°C. the enzyme is slowly destroyed. The optimum temperature noted by them was about 54°C. Hudson and Paine (1910) found that at 60 to 65°C. the destruction of invertase with hot water was rapid. A dry sample of the enzyme, however, may be heated for some time at 100°C. without any appreciable deterioration. As the temperature is raised, acids and alkalies react more readily on invertase. Hudson and Paine considered that the destruction of this enzyme by acids, alkalies, and hot water is caused by the hydrolysis of the enzyme molecule. The presence of fructose and sucrose protects the destruction of invertase, and O'Sullivan and Tompson stated that a solution of invertase in the presence of cane sugar will withstand a temperature 25°C. higher than in the absence of the sugar. It is assumed that the enzyme forms a combination with the sugar which is more resistant to the destructive action of acids, alkalies, hot water, and alcohol than invertase itself.

It was observed by Joslyn and Sherrill (1933) that sucrose was inverted by invertase at temperatures as low as −12 to −16°C., but that this enzyme was completely inactivated at −40°C.

The effect of tannin on the solubility of the invertase of the date was noted by Vinson (1908). The invertase of the date remains insoluble in all ordinary solvents throughout its green stages but becomes readily soluble on ripening. This change of the invertase toward solvents coincides very closely in point of time with the passage of the tannin of the date into the insoluble form. Vinson showed experimentally that, although soluble tannin hinders the solubility of date invertase in water, it may be extracted with glycerol, provided the glycerol is added at the same time as the tannin.

b. The Diastases or Amylases.—The enzyme or aggregate of enzymes that hydrolyze starch to malt sugar is termed "diastase" or "amylase." The general reaction of this hydrolysis may be represented by the following equation:

$$\underset{\text{Starch}}{(C_6H_{10}O_5)_n} + \tfrac{1}{2}nH_2O \xrightarrow[\text{of diastase}]{\text{In presence}} \underset{\text{Maltose}}{\tfrac{1}{2}nC_{12}H_{22}O_{11}}$$

This process of digestion proceeds from starch to amylodextrin, to erythrodextrin, to achrodextrin, to maltose. The substance designated as diastase is thus not composed of a single enzyme but of a series of amylases and dextrinases, none of which, however, has been isolated in a pure condition.

According to Bayliss (1925), Dubrunfaut (1830) prepared an extract of malt which converted starch into sugar just as strong acids were known to do. This, according to Bayliss, was the first account of an enzyme in solution. Three years later Payen and Persoz precipitated from malt extract by alcohol a substance which could be dried and preserved and which had a hydrolytic action on starch. To this preparation they gave the name "diastase." Diastase thus was the first plant enzyme to be reported, and due primarily to its importance in the brewing industry, it has been the most extensively studied enzyme in the plant kingdom. Its presence in leaves was first proved by Kosmann (1877), and since then (Baranetzky, 1878; Krauch, 1879; and Brasse, 1884) it has been found in all green plants or parts thereof that have been examined, so that apparently it is one of the most widespread as well as abundant enzymes of plants. Diastase occurs in many fungi, and the commercial taka-diastase, which is used in medicine and in digestion experiments in the laboratory, is derived from the fungus *Aspergillus oryzae.* The diastase produced by this fungus has been known to science since about 1875 but has been in use in Japan empirically for centuries. Commercial taka-diastase was introduced by Takamine in 1898 and is prepared by growing the fungus on wheat bran, extracting it with water, and precipitating the enzyme and other substances by the addition of alcohol in such quantity as to give a concentration of 70 per cent (Sherman and Tanberg, 1916).

Otis (1930) reported that a digestive ferment with the trade name of "Pangestion" is capable of converting 80 parts of potato starch into water-soluble substances in 5 min., and that the treated starch solution produces positive tests with Fehling's solution after 10 min. at room temperature. It is not a pure preparation of diastase, for it also contains active proteolytic and lipolytic enzymes.

Lothrop and Paine (1931) found that all American honeys contain diastase. Those darker in color usually show a high diastatic value, while honey from alfalfa and orange bloom shows low values. Moderate heating lowers the diastatic value of honey. Europeans object to American honey because its naturally low diastatic activity leads them to believe that it has been heated.

McGinty (1919) noted that the diastatic activity of the potato increased as the tuber developed. Tysdal (1934) studied the relation of the protected diastatic activity to winter hardiness in alfalfa. The protected diastatic activity is the diastatic activity observed after the extract has been subjected to a temperature of 70°C. for 10 min. He found that the hardier a variety of alfalfa, the greater was its protected diastatic activity. The concentration of sugar and the concentration of amino acids influenced the protected diastatic activity. Since an increase in some of these substances occurs during hardening, and since these substances increase the resistance of diastatic enzymes to heat, Tysdal suggested a relationship between winter hardiness and protected diastatic activity.

Bradley and Kellersberger (1912) could detect no starch in the radish, although it showed the highest diastatic activity of any of the tissues studied. The potato tuber that was rich in starch was low in diastase. This enzyme appeared the most abundant in the leaves where starch is never stored permanently. From these observations, these investigators concluded that the diastase in plants exercises little or no synthetic activity.

1. *Types.*—The diastatic enzymes of plants are classified according to their origin, general action, and the nature of the products formed.

(*a*) *Origin and Action.*—There are apparently two well-defined types of diastase that have been termed by Brown and Morris (1890) "diastase of secretion" and "diastase of translocation." The former receives its name because it is secreted by specialized cells, as will be described in a subsequent paragraph. Its distribution is rather limited, being confined for the most part to the germinating seeds of the grains and grasses. Diastase of translocation is so named because it is the type of this enzyme that digests starch for translocation to various parts of the plant. It is widely distributed and is found in practically all living parenchymatous tissues of green plants and is probably the product of the protoplasm of the cells in which it occurs. In this regard, Neidig (1914) found in alfalfa hay, clover hay, and corn stover that the activity of the diastase therein was roughly proportional to the number of living cells in the parts at the time of cutting. Diastase of translocation is always found in the greatest quantity in the actively growing regions of the plant

(Prunet, 1892; Green, 1894; and Sjöberg, 1922, 1923). Diastase of secretion has the power actively to liquefy and saccharify starch paste, while diastase of translocation does not have the power to liquefy starch paste but has the power to saccharify solutions of soluble starch. Diastase of secretion etches and corrodes the starch grains, giving them the notched and irregular markings that are easily observed in the germinating seeds of grains and grasses (Fig. 30). Diastase of translocation dissolves the starch grains gradually over the whole surface so that no markings can be observed. Diastase of secretion is much more rapid in its action on starch than is diastase of translocation. According to Brown and Morris (1893), diastase of secretion is from two to three times more active than the diastase of translocation obtained from the leaves of various plants. The amount of diastase in leaves, however, is ample to transform all the starch in them to maltose, and Brown and Morris estimated that the quantity of diastase in the leaves of *Pisum sativum* examined by them was sufficient to hydrolyze twenty-four times their own dry weight of starch in 24 hr.

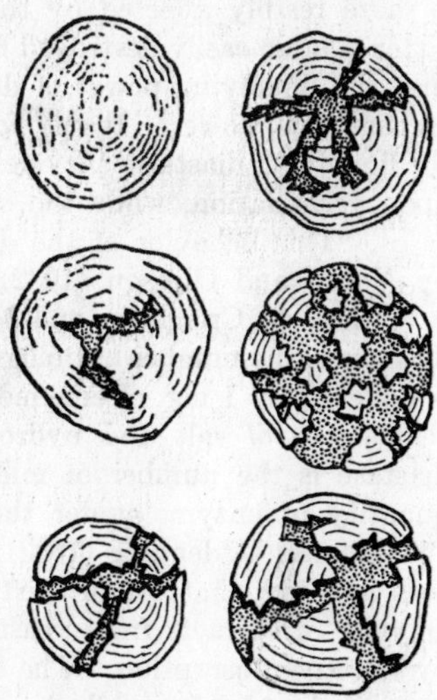

FIG. 30.—Starch grains of the endosperm of the corn kernel showing different stages of digestion by diastase of secretion.

The diastases obtained from different plants are similar in many respects but are not identical (Effront, 1922). They all digest starch, but the conditions under which their optimum activity occurs vary widely, as will be discussed in detail under another heading. Sherman, Walker, and Caldwell (1919) noted that when similarly purified by washing with very dilute alkali, wheat, corn, and rice starches showed the same digestibility in the sense that under the action of the same amount and kind of diastase they were all transformed into sugar at the same rate. Their observations were made with malt diastase and taka-diastase. Stone (1896) found that the starches of potato, sweet potato, maize, rice, and wheat varied greatly in their susceptibility to the action of diastase, so that under precisely the same conditions certain of the starches required eighty times as long as others for saccharification. It was found that the order in which the starches were the most easily digested, beginning with the one that was the most readily changed was as follows: for malt extract, the starch of sweet potato, potato, wheat, and corn; for saliva, the starch of potato, sweet potato, corn, rice, and wheat; for pancreatic diastase, the starch of potato, sweet potato, and corn; while for taka-diastase, the potato was more quickly changed than any other.

(*b*) *Products.*—The plant diastases are apparently capable of two types of activity. They possess liquefying power, which is the ability to destroy the viscosity of starch paste, and saccharifying power, which is the ability to produce maltose from liquid starch. It is therefore considered that amylase consists of an amyloclastic enzyme and a saccharogenic enzyme. Ohlsson (1922, 1926, 1930) believed that the former is more readily affected by the hydrogen-ion concentration, while the latter is more easily destroyed by heat. Gore and Józsa (1932) reported that the liquefying power of diastase is much more prominent than its saccharifying power. It was claimed by Chrzaszcz and Joscht (1917) that the liquefying diastatic enzyme is lacking in resting seeds but is developed upon germination, while the saccharogenic enzyme is present in both cases. This behavior of the diastatic enzymes has been substantiated by Nordh and Ohlsson (1932) and by Freeman and Hopkins (1936). According to Creighton and Naylor (1933) the amyloclastic power of diastase is the number of milligrams of a 1 per cent starch dispersion that is liquefied by 1 mg. of enzyme in 30 min. at 40°C. under optimum concentrations of salt and hydrogen ions. The saccharogenic power of diastase is the number of milligrams of maltose formed by the same quantity of enzyme under the same conditions as above mentioned. Ohlsson and Uddenberg (1933) and Ohlsson and Edfeldt (1933) found for oats and rye that α-, or dextrinogenic, and the β-, or saccharogenic, amylase of extracts from yeasts may be obtained free from each other by selective absorption. The former is obtained by heating the extract at 70°C. for 15 min., while β-amylase is obtained by treating the mixture with 0.1 *N* hydrochloric acid. According to Freeman and Hopkins (1936), α-malt diastase splits starch initially into dextrin. A mixture of the α- and β- amylases in low concentration functions additively in hydrolyzing starch.

2. *Comparison with Animals.*—The diastases from animal sources are, as a rule, more active than those of vegetable origin. Sherman and Schlesinger (1915) made a comparative study of the composition and activity of pancreatic and malt diastase preparations. They found that both preparations were amorphous nitrogenous compounds soluble in water or 50 per cent alcohol but insoluble in concentrated alcohol or acetone. Both showed typical protein reactions with Millon's, xanthoproteic, tryptophane, and biuret tests. Both contained 15 to 16 per cent nitrogen with the amino acids in proportion and within the range of variation shown by casein, edestin, and hemoglobin. When allowed to

act on soluble starch for 30 min. at 40°C. under optimum conditions of reaction and salt concentration, the pancreatic diastase showed a much higher activity than any yet obtained from malt. Under such conditions the pancreatic diastase formed 10,000 times its weight of maltose, while malt diastase formed about 4,000 times its weight of maltose. For long digestion experiments at 40°C. the malt diastase was observed to form a total of 9,300 times its weight of maltose, whereas the pancreatic diastase had formed 1,200,000 times its weight of maltose. Sherman, Caldwell, and Doebbeling (1934) obtained a malt amylase, by repeated precipitations with ammonium sulphate and subsequent dialyses, which formed approximately 10,000 times its weight of maltose in a 2 per cent starch solution in 30 min. at 40°C. in a dilution of ⅙ p.p.m. of the enzyme. This preparation shows as high a sugar-forming activity as the most active preparation of pancreatic amylases that has so far been obtained. Malt diastase is always more stable than pancreatic diastase on standing in water, but both deteriorate on dialysis. Koga (1923) was able to show by means of serological reactions the difference between animal and plant diastases.

3. *Preparation of Plant Diastase.*—Plant diastase has been prepared, for the most part, from the germinating seeds of the cereals, especially barley (Osborne, 1895; Thatcher and Koch, 1914; Sherman and Schlesinger, 1913, 1915; Glimm and Sommer, 1927). Numerous methods for its preparation have been reported, but those used by Sherman and Schlesinger (1915) and Naylor, Spencer, and House (1925) represent the most improved technique for the preparation of diastase from germinating grains. The general procedure is as follows:

A definite weight of the air-dry germinated grain is ground and soaked for 3 hr. in 2.5 times its weight of cold distilled water. The entire mass is then placed in collodion bags and dialyzed against running tap water for 24 hr. at as nearly icebox temperature as possible and then filtered. The filtrate is then treated with solid ammonium sulphate (42 g. to 100 cc. of filtrate) and the precipitate that contains the active diastase is separated by means of a centrifuge, dissolved in a small quantity of water, and dialyzed in collodion bags against running tap water and finally against distilled water until free from sulphates. At the end of this dialysis the sacks may contain a deposit of material which has precipitated with the removal of the dialyzable substances from the solution. This insoluble material, which is without diastatic power, is removed from the solution by centrifuging. The solution is placed in fresh collodion bags and concentrated by evaporation through these bags until the volume is reduced one-half. (This evaporation in the case of rye lowers the activity of diastase and consequently is omitted.)

The solution is then treated with an equal volume of cold alcohol, keeping the temperature below 15°C. The material precipitated by this amount of alcohol is separated by means of the centrifuge and rejected. To the liquid, sufficient cold alcohol is added to make the alcohol content 70 to 80 per cent by volume. The precipitate thus obtained is separated by means of the centrifuge and dried in a partial vacuum over sulphuric acid in the dark, at a temperature not exceeding 15°C. The end product that is obtained from the above procedure is considered to be as nearly pure diastase as any preparation that has so far been made.

In the preparation of diastase after the above manner the greatest destruction of enzyme usually occurs in the first precipitation with alcohol. The losses in the final precipitation and in drying are less serious. In general, considerable losses of diastatic power also occur during dialysis, but in order to eliminate impurities it has not been possible to omit this part of the preparation. The loss of activity is not due in any large measure to the passage of the enzyme as such through the dialyzing membrane, as shown by the tests of the dialysate. Sherman and Schlesinger (1915) considered that this behavior indicates that the diastase is a compound composed of an albumin with a proteose or peptone, as suggested by Osborne (1895). Since this compound is destroyed apparently through hydrolysis on heating in water, it seems probable that a fraction of the enzyme would be hydrolyzed in water solution even at low temperatures. The removal of the products of hydrolysis by dialysis would result in a further hydrolysis of the enzyme and loss of diastatic power without any accumulation of enzyme in the dialysate. If carried out at icebox temperature, the loss of diastatic power is much diminished, and the removal of impurities is little retarded.

Hanes (1932) used the following method for the preparation of diastase from barley. Two hundred grams of barley are washed thoroughly and allowed to soak in distilled water 10 hr. The grain is then spread on filter paper to germinate in a dark chamber. When the plumules have grown to 0.5 to 0.75 of the length of the seed, the grains are placed in a beaker and killed by stirring with a little toluene. They are then ground to a paste. The paste is extracted with 0.1 per cent acetic acid for 6 to 24 hr. with occasional stirring. The coarser material is removed either by squeezing through a fine cloth in a press or by centrifuging. The turbid liquid is filtered until it is almost clear, and the enzyme is precipitated by adding 95 per cent alcohol to make a final concentration of 70 per cent by volume. The liquid is set aside in the icebox for 12 to 24 hr. during which time the precipitate settles. The bulk of the liquid is decanted and the residue filtered on a Büchner funnel through filter paper. The paper bearing the precipitate is ground in a mortar with distilled water, and the paper is removed by filtration. The filtrate containing the enzyme is then made up to a definite volume and toluene is added as a preservative.

Work by McGinty (1919), Baker and Hulton (1929), Schultz and Landis (1932), and Oparin and Risskina (1932) gives special information concerning the preparation of diastase.

Diastase may be prepared from leaves or any other plant parts that contain a relatively small amount of diastase after the following method, which was used by Bartholomew (1914) in his study of the diastase of red algae:

The fresh material to be studied is immersed in 95 per cent alcohol for 20 min. and after freezing from alcohol is plunged into acetone for 10 min. It is then partially dried *in vacuo* and placed in an oven at 35 to 40°C. until dry. The material is then pulverized and placed in three times its volume of 20 per cent alcohol and left standing 18 to 20 hr. and then filtered through cheesecloth and filter paper if possible. To the filtrate is added two and one-half times its volume of 95 per cent alcohol. The precipitate is then filtered off and washed with equal parts ether and alcohol, dried in a desiccator, and pulverized for use. The amount of diastase material obtained in this manner from ordinary vegetative tissue is very small. Thus, for example, Bartholomew from 51 g. of dried algal material obtained only 0.15 g. of diastase preparation.

The presence of diastase in leaves or other plant parts may be demonstrated by using a water extract of the finely macerated tissues. This water extract should be filtered through cheesecloth or other porous cloth but not through filter paper, since it has been found that if the extract is filtered clear it loses much of its diastatic power

(Vines, 1891). Apparently the diastase of the leaves is closely held in the protoplasm (Palladin and Popoff, 1922; Palladin and Popova, 1924) and when freed is adsorbed to a considerable extent by the fine particles of tissue that do not pass through filter paper. The activity of such adsorbed diastase, however, is not impaired by being adsorbed and exerts its full power when in contact with the substrate. In regard to the adsorption of diastase, the work of Ambard (1920, 1921) is worthy of note. He found that it is possible to adsorb, quantitatively, the amylase present in dilute solutions upon raw commercial rice starch and to remove foreign substances without the loss of enzyme. The adsorption by the raw starch is specific, since it has no power to adsorb invertase. When diastase has been adsorbed by starch after this manner, repeated washings with various solutions do not remove the enzyme. Upon the addition of a neutral salt as sodium chloride the enzyme is released by the starch and again goes into solution without any loss of activity.

4. *Study of Diastatic Activity.*—Two methods have been used to determine the activity of diastase: (*a*) Liquefaction. This method measures the power of the enzyme to convert completely a known amount of starch paste into products that no longer give the color reaction with iodine. (*b*) Saccharification. By this method is measured by means of Fehling's solution the amount of reducing sugar produced by the enzyme in a given period of time. These two steps in the action of diastase upon starch are more or less independent of each other, since the conditions for their optimum activity are not the same. For quantitative work the saccharification method is now considered the more reliable.

Various methods have been used for preparing starch for the substrate in the study of diastatic activity, but for the most part they may be grouped under two headings: (*a*) The dispersion of starch in water under different conditions of time, temperature, and pressure but without chemical treatment. A substrate prepared in this manner is commonly called "starch paste." The concentrations that have been used vary from 0.25 to 2 per cent. A common method for the preparation of such a paste is to heat the desired amount of water to boiling and then add the desired amount of starch, thoroughly pulverized and suspended in as small an amount of cold water as possible, to the boiling water and continue to boil for 2 to 5 min. with constant stirring. After cooling, the paste is ready for use. Some investigators discard the starch sediment, which settles out when such a paste is allowed to stand, and use for experimental purposes the more or less clear supernatant liquid. (*b*) Starch that has been subjected to acids or other chemical treatment to render it soluble so that when mixed with water a more or less clear suspension results. Starch treated in this manner may be obtained commercially and is commonly called "soluble starch." The degree of treatment with acids varies greatly, so that while some of the soluble starches react readily with iodine some no longer give that test.

The methods used in determining the activity of diastase are based primarily upon a method devised by Lintner (1885). These methods in general consist in using a series of test tubes each containing from 2 to 10 cc. of a given concentration of raw or soluble starch. To each of the test tubes is added a different amount of diastase extract, generally in a series of 0.1, 0.2, 0.3, 0.4 cc., and so on. After standing under toluene for periods of time ranging from 2 to 48 hr. at 37 to 40°C., 5 cc. of Fehling's solution is added to each tube. The tubes are then placed in boiling water for 10 min. and examined at the end of that time to determine the lowest concentration of diastase in which the copper is all reduced. This may be determined qualitatively by noting the absence of blue color or quantitatively by the usual weighing method. The sample of diastase that produces this degree of conversion into maltose under a given set of conditions is taken as the standard and rated as having an activity of

100. To this standard the activity of diastase under different conditions or from different sources is compared.

The method for determining the degree of diastatic activity by means of iodine may be illustrated by the procedure used by Appleman (1911) in his work with the potato. One cubic centimeter of a 1 per cent soluble starch solution was placed in each of 10 test tubes surrounded by ice. Increasing amounts of the diastase extract were added to the tubes beginning with 1 cc. and increasing the amount 0.1 cc. for each succeeding tube, using toluene as a preservative. The tubes were then incubated at 40°C. for 48 hr., placed again in ice water, and filled nearly full with water, and 3 drops of iodine solution added to each tube. The first tube in the descending series which showed a blue or violet color was considered the index for comparing diastatic activity.

5. *Factors Influencing the Action.*—The literature in regard to the action of the medium upon the activity of diastase is very confusing, and there are almost as many contradictory results as there are investigators. This confusion is doubtless due to two main causes. In the first place, the method by which the diastase is obtained greatly influences its response to its environment (Osborne and Campbell, 1896); and, in the second place, the methods for the determination of the diastatic activity also influence the response of the enzyme to its environment. The nature of the antiseptic used also has an influence upon the activity of the enzyme. Thus Sherman and Wayman (1921) found in low concentrations that chloroform did not affect commercial malt extract, but, when the enzymes were purified, chloroform diminished their action. Toluene had no appreciable effect on either pure or impure diastase preparation, while formaldehyde with a concentration of 0.0000116 *M* gave a 3 per cent reduction of enzymic activity. All diastases studied were retarded in their action by copper sulphate. It is the intention to discuss here only briefly some of the observations that have been made. A detailed account of the work pertaining to this topic may be found in the literature cited at the end of this chapter.

(*a*) *Chemicals.*—Much study has been devoted to the effect of chemicals upon the behavior of plant diastase. In the following discussion, mention is made only of a sufficient number of cases to indicate the general enzymic behavior under various chemical treatments.

(1) *Inorganic Salts.*—Sherman and Thomas (1915) studied extensively the effect of the chlorides, nitrates and sulphates, and primary phosphates of sodium and potassium with reference to the concentrations favoring optimum activity of malt diastase. All the electrolytes mentioned above increased the activity of this enzyme. The activities observed at the optimum concentrations of these activating compounds varied, depending upon the purity of the enzyme preparation and of the starch used, from less than two- to more than thirty-fold the corresponding activities in the absence of the electrolyte. Berczeller and Freud (1922) found that malt diastase was permanently inactivated by iodine, chlorine and bromine, and that starch exercised a protective action against this inactivation, although the enzyme eventually lost its digestive power. According to Haehn and Schweigart (1923), the chlorides of potassium, calcium, sodium, barium, and magnesium activated potato diastase under the conditions of their experiment, while diastatic hydrolysis was delayed by salts of zinc, cadmium, lead, and copper. Salt-free diastase prepared by dialysis and ultrafiltration was entirely inactive, no change occurring during 24 hr. The preparation could be rendered active by the addition of sodium chloride. Ambard (1923) considered that neutral salts in some way act upon the substrate. The most widely accepted hypothesis is that they accelerate the enzymic activity by increasing the colloidal dispersion of the enzyme.

Englis and Lunt (1925) found that diastatic activity in the leaves of nasturtium decreased with increased rates of application of potassium to sand cultures, while an intermediate rate of application of potassium to peat cultures gave the highest activity of diastase. Apparently there was a correlation of diastatic activity with favorable growing conditions rather than with the presence or absence of any element. Doby and Hibbard (1927) found that amylase is strongly activated by the chloride ion and slightly activated by the potassium, nitrate, and fluoride ions. Englis and Gerber (1929) obtained only slight response of diastatic action to the application of acid phosphates to soybeans in pot cultures. Józsa and Gore (1932) noted that sodium chloride and other salts, when added to flour suspensions, greatly increased the solubility of the diastatic, liquefying, and saccharifying enzymes of flour. James and Cattle (1933) observed that the breakdown of starch by potato diastase was accelerated by the application of potassium chloride, while the formation of sugar was not affected.

(2) *Acidity.*—In studying the effects of various acids upon the action of diastase, Sherman and Thomas (1915) found that the acids showed a greater activating influence than the neutral salts, while the acid phosphates of sodium and potassium gave as high activation as free acids. The acids all showed optimum activation in those concentrations which had essentially the same actual acidity. This optimum hydrogen-ion concentration was in each case between pH 4.2 and 4.6. Acetic and propionic acids, in quantity ten times the optimum, decreased the activity about one-half, while hydrochloric, nitric, and sulphuric acids reduced the activity more than one-half when present in concentrations 2½ times the optimum.

Harley, Fisher, and Masure (1931) showed that the juice of the apple contains an effective inhibitor of diastase. This inhibiting substance is soluble in water and alcohol, is acid in reaction, and can be separated from the enzyme by dialysis or by precipitation of the diastase by neutral alcohol.

A large amount of work has been done to determine the optimum hydrogen-ion concentration for diastatic activity. It should be remembered that the apparent optimum reaction may vary to a considerable degree depending upon the temperature (Chrzaszcz, Bidzinski, and Krause, 1925), the buffer used, the accumulation of products formed, and the source of the enzyme. Sherman and Thomas (1915) found that the optimum hydrogen-ion concentration for malt diastase was pH 4.2 to 4.6. Sjöberg (1922) found the optimum acidity for a series of plant diastases to be between pH 5.0 and 5.4. Sherman, Thomas, and Baldwin (1919) found that the optimum pH value for malt diastase was 4.4 to 4.5, taka-diastase 4.8, and pancreatic diastase 7.0. Sherman, Thomas, and Caldwell (1924) found that the isoelectric point of a malt-diastase preparation was pH 4.3 to 4.5, which coincides with that of its optimum enzymic action upon starch. Maslow and Davidson (1926) found that the optimum reaction for the dextrin-liquefying activity of the dextrinase of taka-diastase was pH 4.0 at 34°C. According to Polak and Tychowski (1928), there are present in malt extract two diastases whose optimum pH values are different. α-Diastase works best at pH 5.1, while β-diastase reacts best at pH 4.3. Sjöberg (1922) noted that the optimum pH for sugar formation by diastase was 5.0 to 5.5, while that for the disappearance of starch was 4.0 to 6.0.

Doby and Burger (1932) found in the potato tuber that the optimum pH value for β-amylase was approximately 7.0 under varied conditions. Amylase activity increased during the resting period of 2 months to approximately five times the initial activity. This was partially due to the alteration of the pH value of the tuber and partially because of the formation of new enzyme. The optimum reaction of the medium for the saccharogenic amylase of the leaves of the sugar beet was pH 6.0.

Hopkins, Cole, and Green (1933) found that the optimum pH for the saccharifying action of barley diastase was 4.5 to 4.7. Ohlsson and Uddenberg (1933), and Ohlsson and Edfeldt (1933) found that the β-amylase of oats and rye had an optimum activity at pH 4.3, while the α-amylase had its optimum action at pH 5.5. Tysdal (1934) noted that the hydrogen-ion concentration influenced the protected activity of diastase in alfalfa. This activity increased from 4 mg. of maltase, produced at pH 5.2, to 11 mg. at a pH of 6.7.

(3) *Organic Materials.*—It was found by Brown and Morris (1893) that tannin exercised an inhibiting action on the diastase of leaves and that when it was present in considerable amounts it was difficult to obtain an extract of the leaf with any marked degree of hydrolyzing power. They demonstrated that tannin prevented the diastase from going into solution.

It was discovered by Sherman and his workers (1919 to 1922) that numerous amino acids including glycine, aspartic acid, arginine, tyrosine, cystine, and lysine increased the activity of certain animal diastases. These amino acids also had the power to restore to full activity diastase that had been partially inactivated by copper sulphate and to prevent the deterioration of this enzyme in water. Haehn and Schweigart (1923) noted that glycine, alanine, and leucine activated the diastase of the potato.

Filipowicz (1931) found that ovalbumin, gelatin, peptone, glycine, and aspartic acid retarded the action of malt diastase upon starch at pH values below 4.5 and accelerated it at values above that figure. He attributed these effects to the amino acid units.

Denny (1930) reported that potassium cyanide added to a mixture of potato juice and soluble starch markedly increased the activity of amylase as measured by the gain in reducing sugar.

The mechanism whereby ethylene, thiocyanates, and ethylene chlorhydrin produce artificial ripening or break the dormancy of plants has been sought in the action of these compounds on diastatic activity. Englis and Zannis (1930) found that ethylene had no effect upon the action of corn-meal diastase upon corn starch. They concluded that the effects of ethylene in ripening fruits and vegetables is primarily concerned with color changes rather than with a true ripening process involving marked changes in certain of the food reserves. Denny (1931, 1932, 1933) could find no simple relation between the effects of potassium thiocyanate and ethylene chlorhydrin upon the amylase activity of taka-diastase, malt diastase, pancreatin, pangestion, and of an extract from germinating barley seeds. Since these two chemicals produce almost identical results in the initiation of sprouting of dormant potatoes, the indications are that the changes which occur are not due to their direct effect upon diastase. Clark, Fowler, and Black (1931), however, reported that the hydrolysis of soluble starch by diastase was increased in the presence of ethylene chlorhydrin, potassium thiocyanate, or thiourea.

(*b*) *Temperature.*—The maximal and optimum temperatures for diastatic action will depend upon the source of the enzyme and the nature of and amount of the substrate as well as the presence of the end products. Chrzaszcz (1923) by the use of watery extracts of rye, wheat, oats, corn, buckwheat, barley, broom corn, and millet found that diastases from different sources did not respond to temperature in the same manner at the supposedly optimum hydrogen-ion concentration, *i.e.*, pH 4.9. The optimum temperatures for barley diastase were 49 to 54°C.; for wheat and rye, 49 to 55°; for oats, 51 to 53°; for buckwheat, 50 to 55°; for corn, 56 to 57°; and for millet, 58 to 59°. Barley diastase was completely destroyed at 61 to 62°C., wheat at 63 to 64°, and others at 65 to 66°. Sjöberg (1922) found that the temperature coefficient for sugar formation by diastase decreases between 20 and 40°C., while the temperature coefficient for starch disappearance is constant between those two points.

Fisher, Harley, and Brooks (1930) considered that "water core" is a result of the nonuniform conversion of starch induced by relatively high atmospheric temperatures.

(c) *Light.*—It was observed by Brown and Morris (1893) that the amount of diastase in leaves increased when they were placed in the dark. They considered that the secretion of diastase is stimulated by the absence of soluble carbohydrates. Sjöberg (1923), however, in experiments with the leaves and blossoms of the tulip, concluded that the formation of diastase is independent of light. Pincussen (1923) found that the reaction of light from a quartz lamp on malt diastase depended on the concentration of the enzymes, on accompanying compounds, and on the reaction of the medium. The greatest injury from light occurred at the optimum reaction for enzyme activity. Green (1894) exposed portions of a preparation of malt diastase to light for periods varying from 2 to 10 days and tested the action of these exposed preparations upon starch paste. He concluded that light, both solar and electric, exercises a destructive influence upon diastase, the deleterious influence being confined to the rays of the violet end of the spectrum, the other rays being slightly favorable instead of destructive. He considered also that the coloring matter of the barley husk acts as a screen in preserving the diastase in that grain from the destructive effects of light. The destruction by light of diastase in the leaves is only 15 to 20 per cent as compared with 68 per cent for malt diastase under the same conditions. Green (1897) considered that either the diastase is more resistant in the leaves or there is some constituent that has the power of screening the enzyme from the deleterious rays. Chlorophyll might serve this purpose, and protein is known to protect the enzyme in this regard. Green considered that when a leaf is illuminated by the whole spectrum, the beneficial rays convert the zymogen into diastase and the latter is speedily destroyed by the deleterious rays. The latter action is the more rapid so that the effect of the whole spectrum is to diminish the amount of diastase in solution.

Baly and Semmens (1924) in experiments with the action of diastase upon the starch of potato, wheat, and corn obtained results which indicate that plane-polarized light exercises a powerful acceleration on the hydrolysis of starch by weak solutions of diastase. Later (1925, 1926) they claimed that starch grains in pure distilled water may be hydrolyzed by a beam of polarized light and that after 2 to 4 days' exposure the etching on the starch grains may be observed. Macht (1928) substantiated their results when he found that polarized light hastened the conversion of starch into sugar in the presence of diastase. Macht and Hill (1925) noted also that when a suspension of *Saccharomyces cerevisiae* was added to solutions of sucrose the fermentation of sugar proceeded much more rapidly in polarized than in nonpolarized light. The work of Baly and Semmens (1924), however, has been adversely criticized by Jones (1925), who considered that the results reported for the action of polarized light on starch grains are doubtful.

The effects of polarized light and ordinary light upon the action of diastase have been studied by Navez and Rubenstein (1928, 1932), and Navez (1930). They reported that there is present in a mixture of starch and diastase a substance that partially inhibits hydrolysis. This substance is equally sensitive to ordinary and to plane-polarized light. The addition of light during hydrolysis increases the rate of liberation of reducing substances over that of the same reaction in the dark. This inhibitor is linked to the diastatic complex, as is evidenced by the fact that irradiation of starch alone does not produce the same effects as irradiation of the total mixture.

Bunker and Anderson (1928) studied the effects of polarized light on the hydrolysis of starch by taka-diastase, using intact starch grains, swollen starch grains, broken grains, and soluble starch from numerous sources. In all these cases, they obtained negative results. Semmens (1932) found in a vine leaf that the starch disappeared from that portion which was exposed to moonlight, while it remained intact in the protected part. He considered that the depletion of the starch in the exposed portion was due to the influence of polarized light of the moon on diastatic activity.

Hutchinson and Ashton (1933) found that full irradiation from a mercury-arc light retarded the dextrinogenic and saccharogenic activity of diastase directly with the intensity. The monochromatic effects on malt diastase were generally inhibitory for the dextrinogenic phase and stimulatory for the saccharogenic phase of diastatic activity.

c. The Inulases.—Inulase is an enzyme that hydrolyzes inulin to levulose or fruit sugar. It was named by Green (1887), who first observed it in the germinating tubers of the Jerusalem artichoke (*Helianthus tuberosus*) and later (1899) found it in the bulbs of *Leucocrium* and *Scilla*. Green could not find inulase in the resting stage of the tubers and bulbs, but if the macerated tissue was kept at 35°C. for a time, the enzyme was found to be present. It thus appears to occur in the resting tissues in the zymogen form. Inulase may occur with diastase but has no action whatsoever upon starch. Green found that inulase works most advantageously in a neutral or very faintly acid medium, 0.001 per cent hydrochloric acid being very favorable, but higher concentrations than this were very destructive. An alkali medium was extremely deleterious. These observations in regard to the medium have been confirmed by Kizel (1915). The optimum activity of inulase occurs at 50 to 55°C. but loses its activity when heated to 70 to 75°. Wolff (1916) found in the roots of *Dahlia variabilis* and *Cichorium intybus* a substance that coagulates very actively the juices extracted from these plants and precipitates inulin from the solution.

In 1893 Bourquelot found inulase in the fungi *Aspergillus niger* and *Penicillium glaucum.* It has since been studied in these plants by Dean (1903) and Young (1918). It occurs in abundance in these fungi and most of our knowledge concerning inulase has been derived from these sources. Dean (1903) verified the work of Bourquelot (1893) and found that the enzyme from these fungi reacted in much the same manner as the inulase of the Jerusalem artichoke described by Green (1887).

d. The Glucases or Maltases.—The enzyme that hydrolyzes maltose to glucose has been termed "glucase" or "maltase." The reaction occurs after the following manner:

$$\underset{\text{Maltose}}{C_{12}H_{22}O_{11}} + H_2O \xrightarrow[\text{of maltase}]{\text{In presence}} \underset{\text{Glucose}}{2C_6H_{12}O_6}$$

The occurrence of a maltose-splitting enzyme in plants was first suggested by the work of Brasse (1885). He noted that, when a preparation of malt diastase was allowed to act on starch at 32 to 42°C., glucose was formed, but that, when the action occurred at 50 to 57°, only maltose was formed. Brasse, however, did not realize that he was working with a special enzyme capable of digesting maltose. According to Daish (1916), maltase was first observed in corn seeds and seedlings by Cuisinier (1885), who termed it "glucase" and patented a process of converting starch into glucose based on its use. He stated that this enzyme is present in the organs and seeds of a large number of plants, a statement which is now known to be correct but which could not be substantiated by many subsequent workers for reasons that will be mentioned later in this discussion. Observations by Beyerinck (1895), Huerre (1909), Wierzchowski (1913), and Daish (1916) have substantiated the statement of Cuisinier that maltase is widely distributed in plants. It has been demonstrated in the leaves of a large number of plants and in the resting seeds and seedlings of corn, rice, millet, oats, wheat, barley, rye, buckwheat, and others. Maltase is also present in many of the fungi, and the commercial taka-diastase contains this enzyme in larger amounts than does germinating barley.

Maltase has three or four characteristics that are considerably different from other carbohydrate-splitting enzymes, and it is due to these characteristics that many investigators failed to detect maltase in the plant material with which they worked. The optimum temperature for activity is from 38 to 40°C., but above that temperature the maltase is rapidly destroyed. Much of the plant material that has been examined for maltase was dried at a temperature of from 40 to 50°C. so that the enzyme was completely inactivated in the preparation. This also explains the reason for the observation of Brasse (1885) that a malt-diastase preparation at 32 to 42°C. formed glucose when acting on starch, while at 50 to 57°C. only maltose was formed. The maltase obtained from different sources varies widely in its temperature range, which indicates that there are several varieties of the enzyme (Huerre, 1909). Maltase is practically all destroyed by precipitation by alcohol, a treatment that injures only to a limited degree most of the enzymes. It is very difficult to obtain this enzyme from plant tissue by extraction with water. The enzyme is an endocellular one, and unless the material is extremely well pulverized very little of the enzyme is released. The best action of maltase has been obtained by using the pulverized powder of the seeds or the crushed pulp of the vegetative portions of the plant. It is very sensitive to chloroform and shows only a slight action in the presence of that antiseptic. Toluene has been found to be very satisfactory as a preservative in studying this enzyme.

e. The Cellulases or Cytases.—The enzymes that are capable of dissolving the cellulose walls of plants have been termed "cytases," "cellulases," or "cytohydrolytic enzymes." The existence of cytase was first noted by DeBary in 1886 when he observed that the hyphae of the fungus *Peziza sclerotiorum* were able to penetrate the cell walls of plants. In 1888 a similar enzyme was reported by Ward for a fungus belonging to the genus *Botrytis.* Since then similar enzymes have been found in numerous green plants and in other fungi. The action of cytase is relatively slow and is confined entirely to normal cellulose and to hemicelluloses. In all the cases that have been observed the cell wall at first becomes hyaline, then gradually becomes more and more transparent, and finally fades away into solution. The cytases are destroyed at a temperature of 60°C. or above.

Brown and Morris (1890, 1898) noted in the early stages of the germination of barley that the parenchymatous cell walls of the endosperm directly under the epithelium cells of the scutellum and the cells of the aleurone layer are disintegrated and ultimately dissolved. This dissolution of the cell walls always precedes any visible action upon the starch grains contained within these cells. This dissolving action they attributed to cytase secreted by the epithelial cells of the scutellum and aleurone layer. They were, however, unable to obtain any action of this enzyme upon the cellulose of the date, asparagus, coffee, or onion seeds, but in the case of the Jerusalem artichoke, potato, carrot, and turnip this enzyme preparation from malt dissolved cell walls. The most thorough work that so far has been done on cytase is that of Newcombe (1899). He prepared a water extract of the seedlings of barley and *Lupinus albus* and the embryos and endosperm of the date seed and prepared cytase by precipitation from the extract after the manner used in the preparation of diastase. He used the following method to determine the action of cytase: Sections were made of the tissues to be examined and were freed from starch if present by treating for 24 hr. with saliva or a pancreatic preparation. The sections were then placed in a solution containing 150 mg. of the enzyme preparation to 10 cc. of water with chloroform as an antiseptic and allowed to stand at 32 to 34°C. The action of the cytase was determined by microscopical examination. In the cell walls of the endosperm of barley, the cytase from various sources dissolved them down to the middle lamella in from 5 to 10 hr., but the cell walls of the aleurone layer were more resistant. In the cell walls of the white lupine, 9 days were required to reduce the cell walls to a hyaline condition, while complete dissolution was not effected even in thin sections until 3 or 4 weeks and then only at the edges of the sections. The enzyme prepared from the embryo and endosperm of the date was capable of digesting the heavy cell walls of the endosperm cells of that seed. After 30 days the whole surface of the section was corroded and the exposed walls frayed out. All the walls became hyaline and the whole section became smaller owing to the gradual dissolving action. Newcombe found that the cytase preparations obtained from the seedlings of the date, white lupine, barley, and *Aspergillus oryzae* were apparently not specific so far as could be observed.

f. Other Carbohydrases.—Some of the carbohydrases that have been found in plants, though in most cases playing an unimportant role in the life of the green plant, are (1) melibiase, which hydrolyzes melibiose to glucose and galactose; (2) gentianase, which hydrolyzes gentiobiose to glucose; and (3) pectinase, an enzyme capable of hydrolyzing pectose to arabinose.

2. The Glucosidases of Plants.—Before discussing the action of the enzymes of this group, a few statements should be made concerning the compounds upon which they act. The glucosides for the most part are compounds that contain glucose as the characteristic basic group. Upon hydrolysis the glucosides yield glucose, together with one or more other substances, usually of an aromatic nature. Some of the organic constituents that may be combined with sugar to form glucosides are phenols, alcohols, aldehydes, acids, and mustard oils. Most of the common glucosides are derived from *d*-glucose. Some, however, are derivatives of galactose or rhamnose, but in others the exact sugar that is combined in the glucoside is not known. Some of the glucosides are amygdalin found in the almond and other plants of the *Rosaceae;* sinigrin in the *Cruciferae;* salicin in the willow; arbutin in the leaves of bearberry; phlorizin in the bark of apple, pear, cherry, and plum; populin in the bark of the poplar tree; esculin in the bark of horse-chestnut; phytin in the coats of seeds; and saponins, which occur in more than 400 species of plants.

In this connection some mention should be made of the tannins, although they are not at present classified as glucosides. Tannins are a group of substances that are almost universally distributed in plants. They occur in leaves, wood, bark, unripe fruits, walnut hulls, and many other plant parts. They are especially abundant in the pathological plant growths known as "galls" and their dry weight may be composed of from 40 to 75 per cent of this group of substances. Tannins make up about 15 per cent of the dry weight of tea leaves and about 40 per cent of the dry weight of oak bark.

The tannins are amorphous, have an astringent taste, give ink colors with ferric salts, precipitate gelatine from solution, and form insoluble compounds with it and are precipitated from solution by copper or lead acetate, stannous chloride, and other metallic salts and by a strong aqueous solution of potassium bichromate. They are readily soluble in hot water and form solutions that are in reality colloidal gels.

Tannins are usually hydrolyzed by acids into a variety of products, one being nearly always *d*-glucose and the other a hydroxy derivative of the aromatic series. Although they usually contain sugar, they do not show the characteristic properties of the true glucosides and are considered as a separate class of substances.

The tannins are generally considered as waste products, rather than as substances that can be utilized in the nutrition of the plant, for the following reasons: (*a*) The known uses of tannin in the life of the plant are very few and limited as compared with its abundance and almost universal occurrence. (*b*) It is present in great abundance in the bark, which will be eventually lost from the plant. (*c*) It is produced in large amounts in unfolding leaves, in germinating seeds, in the growth of galls, and in fruit development where intense metabolism is going on. It seems certain that in these cases tannins are the result and not the causative agents of the very rapid growth and changes that take place in these regions.

Tannins are of frequent occurrence in the green fruits and give to them their characteristic puckery taste. As the fruit ripens, the tannins may disappear or, as in the persimmon, remain in the ripe fruit encased in special large cells or sacks with impermeable membranes so that when the fruit is eaten by animals the tannins do not affect the organs of taste and thus cause no disagreeable effects.

Michel-Durand (1928 to 1932) concluded that the free tannins may be utilized by the plant, but that the great variation in their structure and composition precludes the possibility that all members of the group serve the same purpose. In the young etiolated plants of *Castanea*, the tannins arise from carbohydrates stored in the seed, while the tannins in the leaves and branches of *Aesculus* come from the disintegration of proteins. Hence, no single explanation of the origin of tannins can be given. Light in general favors their formation and may influence not only the quantity but the nature of the tannins that are produced. Baens, Yenko, West, and Curran (1934) noted that the tannin content of the bark of trees varied from 5 to 45 per cent, and that there were marked variations in the amount of tannin in the same species grown under different conditions.

a. Emulsin.—The name "emulsin" was first given to the enzyme that hydrolyzes amygdalin to benzoic aldehyde, hydrocyanic acid, and glucose. This reaction proceeds after the following manner:

$$\underset{\text{Amygdalin}}{C_{20}H_{27}NO_{11}} + 2H_2O \xrightarrow[\text{of emulsin}]{\text{In presence}} \underset{\substack{\text{Benzoic}\\\text{aldehyde}}}{C_7H_6O} + \underset{\substack{\text{Hydrocyanic}\\\text{acid}}}{HCN} + \underset{\text{Glucose}}{2(C_6H_{12}O_6)}$$

This enzyme has been the most thoroughly studied of any of the glucosidases. It has been found that it will also hydrolyze phlorizin, salicin, arbutin, or any of the β-glucosides. Emulsin has been found in the almond, cherry laurel, in certain of the *Euphorbiaceae*, in certain lichens, and in the fungi *Aspergillus niger* and *Penicillium glaucum*. According to Green (1899), the enzyme is most active at a temperature of 30 to 40°C., but its power gradually declines above that and is entirely destroyed at 80°C.

According to Robinson (1930) hydrocyanic acid is known to occur in about 50 natural orders of plants. McNair (1932) stated that cyanogenetic glucosides are found in 13 per cent of the plant families of the gymnosperms and angiosperms. It is generally considered to exist exclusively in glucosidal combination in the living plant, although some workers have postulated the existence of free cyanide in plant tissues. Ten cyanophoric glucosides have been isolated in crystalline form from plants and of these seven are derivatives of benzaldehyde cyanhydrin.

In plants, the cyanophoric glucosides are, with few exceptions, accompanied by active hydrolytic enzymes capable of liberating cyanide. In general, the concentration of these glucosides is highest in the young growing organs, but in some instances it is highest in the bark.

In the *Rosaceae*, the cyanophoric glucosides seem to be constant constituents of the plant throughout its life cycle, while in the grass family they disappear as maturity approaches and are not found in the seed. In *Amygdalus communis*, *Vicia angustifolia*, and *Phaseolus lunatus* the concentration of hydrocyanic acid in the plant has been diminished by cultivation. Climatic conditions, especially drought, cause variations in the content of *d*-hurrin in *Sorghum vulgare* and of the cyanophoric glucoside of *Lotus corniculatus*. Temperatures below freezing cause a rapid increase in the amount of cyanophoric glucosides in *Sorghum vulgare* and *Prunus laurocerasus*. The function of hydrocyanic acid in the plant is unknown. Its rapid disappearance under conditions of starvation in some plants lends support to the view that such nitrogen is readily utilizable by the plant. In some cases, the cyanophoric glucosides are apparently excretory products and may serve as protective substances.

It is common knowledge that the ordinary sorghums and other species of *Andropogon* form hydrocyanic acid in their tissues following the breakdown of glucosides that apparently occurs under unfavorable conditions of growth. *d*-Hurrin ($C_{14}H_{17}O_7N$) is the cyanophoric glucoside in sorghums and on hydrolysis yields hydrocyanic acid and *p*-oxybenzaldehyde (Harris and Goss, 1934). The stem and leaves contain this glucoside, but none is present in the roots. Slade (1903) found most of it in the stems, while Acharya (1933) in India found most of it in the leaves. Apparently the conditions under which the plants are grown determine the location of the major portion of this glucoside. The hydrocyanic acid content decreases from the early stages of growth to maturity. In sorghums, the seedlings up to 40 days of age, plants stunted by drought, second-growth tissues, and plants directly after being frozen (Swanson, 1921) have the highest content of hydrocyanic acid. The largest amounts may be from 0.1 per cent to 0.2 per cent of the dry matter of the plants. The content of hydrocyanic acid appears to be the lowest in the morning and to increase to a maximum in midafternoon. The hydrocyanic acid rapidly disappears from the sorghum plants after they are harvested and cured.

b. Maltase, Phytase, and Rhamninase. 1. *Maltase.*—According to Thatcher (1921), maltase acts on all α-glucosides but does not produce the slightest effect upon β-glucosides.

2. *Phytase.*—The glucoside phytin is decomposed into phosphoric acid and inosite ($C_6H_{12}O_6$), by the action of the enzyme phytase.

3. *Rhamninase.*—According to Green (1899), the glucoside xanthorhamnin, which is found in the seeds of *Rhamnus infectorius* (Persian berry), is hydrolyzed into rhamnin and glucose by an enzyme that has been termed "rhamninase."

c. Myrosin.—This name has been given to the enzyme that acts upon the glucoside, sinigrin, or myronate of potassium, decomposing it into sulphocyanate of allyl or mustard oil, glucose, and potassium hydrogen phosphate. The reaction occurs after the following manner:

$$\underset{\text{Sinigrin}}{C_{10}H_{18}NKS_2O_{10}} \longrightarrow \underset{\text{Sulphocyanate}}{C_3H_5CNS} + \underset{\text{Glucose}}{C_6H_{12}O_6} + \underset{\text{Potassium hydrogen sulphate}}{KHSO_4}$$

Myrosin not only acts on sinigrin but has the power to decompose practically all sulphur-containing glucosides that have been examined.

According to Sandberg and Holly (1932), myrosin consists of two components, a glucosidase and thiosulfase.

3. The Esterases or Lipases of Plants.—The enzymes of this group accelerate the cleavage of all the simple esters of the trihydroxy alcohols and fatty acids as well as many synthetic esters. These enzymes are frequently called "fat splitting" because they hydrolyze the fats and oils to glycerin and fatty acids. The term "lipase" has been almost universally used in a collective sense in speaking of the enzymes of this group. Recent work, however, has shown that the ordinary preparations of lipase contain at least two fat-splitting enzymes, which differ in their solubilities and rate of action. It has also been observed that, although lipases from different sources show striking similarities in their behavior (Barton, 1920), they at the same time show minor differences which indicate that they are not identical enzymes. Thus, Longenecker and Haley (1935) noted that the lipase of the castor bean exhibited a differential rate of digestion of various oils, the decreasing rates of hydrolysis being in the following order: peanut, castor bean, corn, cotton seed, soybean, rape, olive, and linseed oils.

The presence of a fat-splitting enzyme in plants was suggested by the observations of Pelouze (1855) on the seeds of flax, mustard, and rape. Lipase, however, was first proved to exist in plants by Green (1890) in working with the germinating castor bean. Sometime later Sigmund (1890, 1892) found it in both the resting and germinating seeds of the rape, opium, poppy, hemp, flax, and corn. These observations were later confirmed and extended by Connstein, Hoyer, and Wartenberg (1902) and Hoyer (1904) who found that some oily seeds, at least, contain the enzyme whether germinating or not, and that an enzyme obtained from a given seed is capable of hydrolyzing fats and oils from other sources. Theis, Long, and Brown (1929) found lipase in the developing seed of flax and noted that its activity decreased as the seed matured. Sullivan and Howe (1933) obtained this enzyme from the wheat grain and its various products.

a. Preparation and Study of Lipase.—Numerous studies have been made concerning the preparation and action of this enzyme, but they have been confined almost entirely to the lipase of the castor bean (*Ricinus communis*). This is probably due to the fact that the enzyme from this source is easily prepared, very stable, and relatively very active. To understand the methods used in the preparation of lipase, a few facts concerning the nature of the enzyme should be considered. Lipase in the castor bean occurs apparently in the zymogen stage. This zymogen appears to be somewhat soluble in fats or in a mixture of fat and ethyl ether but is insoluble in ether alone (Taylor, 1906). The lipase zymogen is activated by acids. According to Haley and Lyman (1921), the active enzyme is unstable and is rapidly destroyed in an acid medium in the absence of fats. In the presence of fats, however, the enzyme shows much greater stability. The lipase found in the seeds of *Chelidonium majus* does not exist in the zymogen state, so that it is not necessary to treat with an acid in order to activate it. The method used by Haley and Lyman (1921) in preparation of the lipase of the castor bean may be taken as an example of the procedure generally followed in the preparation of the enzymes of this group. Fifty grams of hulled castor-bean kernels are ground as finely as possible, mixed with 150 cc. of 1 per cent acetic acid, and allowed to stand for 3 days at room temperature (the acid treatment varying from 15 min. to several days with other investigators, depending on the concentration and types of acid used). The mixture is then filtered, washed with water, and dried at room temperature, after which it is extracted in a Soxhlet apparatus with petroleum ether of a low boiling point. The extracted material is passed through a 40-mesh sieve and again extracted if necessary to completely free it from oil. The extracted material may then be dried in vacuum or over any drying agent in a desiccator, and the light fluffy powder thus obtained may be kept indefinitely in the dry state.

Longenecker and Haley (1935) prepared lipase from the castor bean in the following manner: The beans were hulled, macerated, and the oil removed by extraction with petroleum ether having a boiling point between 20 and 40°C. The residue that remained after the extraction was pulverized sufficiently to pass through a 60-mesh sieve.

It has been observed by Falk (1913, 1917) and Falk and Sugiura (1915) that two lipases are present in a lipase preparation that has been obtained after the manner mentioned above. One of these is soluble in water and the other insoluble. The former has, comparatively, a greater action toward ethyl butyrate than toward triacetin, while the latter has a greater action toward triacetin than toward ethyl butyrate. The water-soluble portion of such a lipase preparation has been termed "esterase" by Falk, and the other portion has been termed "lipase." He obtained the esterase from a dialyzed and filtered water extract of oil-free castor-bean powder, 0.5 g. to 60 cc. of water. The lipase preparation was obtained by extracting the water-extracted castor-bean powder with a 1.5 N sodium chloride solution, 1.0 g. of material to 100 cc. of solution, and dialyzing until salt free. After such dialysis the lipase is in a suspension in the water. Both the "esterase" and "lipase" preparations act on the higher glycerides, but the latter is somewhat more active than the former. Falk (1915) found that soybeans contain apparently the same lipases as castor beans, the only difference being that the reaction of the castor-bean lipase was somewhat more intense than that obtained from the soybean.

The methods of studying the action of lipases have been numerous, and the differences in results obtained by different investigators may be attributed, in part at least, to this cause. Since the action of lipase on fats and oils is relatively slow, many investigators have used ethyl butyrate, triacetin, and other simple esters as a substrate in their study of the action of this enzyme. From the standpoint of plant physiology, however, the study of the hydrolyzing action of the lipases on the fats and oils is more desirable, since these compounds are the ones normally acted upon by these enzymes in the digestive process in plants.

The method used by Haley and Lyman (1921) and Longenecker and Haley (1935) in studying the action of lipase is as follows: Place 0.1 g. of lipase powder, 1.0 g. olive oil, and 0.6 cc. of hydrochloric acid, varying in concentration from 0.02 to 0.2 per cent, in a test tube. The contents are thoroughly mixed and placed in the incubator at 38°C. for 24 hr., using toluene as an antiseptic. The order in which the ingredients are added in making up the digestive mixture is of much importance. Thus Haley and Lyman found that if the acid is added to the enzyme material before the oil, complete loss of the lipase is apt to occur. After the period of incubation the mixture is washed from the test tube with 50 per cent alcohol into wide-mouth titration bottles. The resulting mixture is then titrated with 0.1 *N* sodium hydroxide in 50 per cent alcohol using phenolphthalein as an indicator. The degree of hydrolyzation of the oil is determined by the amount of sodium hydroxide required for the neutralization of the fatty acids formed in excess of that required to neutralize the controls.

Nicloux (1904 to 1906) made extensive studies concerning the lipolytic activities of the castor bean in a manner quite different from that pursued by other investigators. By mechanical means he separated the cytoplasm of the ground material from the aleurone grains and other cell contents. The cytoplasmic material extracted in this manner had the property of hydrolyzing fats. It acted on the fats in the same manner as enzymes and followed all the laws of enzyme action. He termed the active matter in the cytoplasmic material "lipaseidine" and claimed that it was destroyed by water as soon as it was no longer protected by fats. It seems very probable that Nicloux was working with the lipase of the castor bean, which had been obtained in a different manner from that which is generally followed.

Kirsh (1935) found that the molds, *Penicillium oxalicum* and *Aspergillus flavus*, when grown on a bran-soybean medium, produced a water-soluble enzyme capable of hydrolyzing olive oil. The production of this lipase was greatest when the fungus was incubated at 28°C. for 3 to 4 days during sporulation.

b. Factors Influencing the Action.—The influence of the acidity of the medium upon the action of lipase has been extensively studied. The early investigators on this subject noted in the germination of oily seeds that the hydrolysis of oils took place slowly at first and then increased rapidly. This led to the conclusion that for rapid hydrolysis by lipase a certain amount of free acid is necessary. This conclusion was verified in many cases, since when a small amount of free acid was added at the beginning of an experiment the hydrolysis of the fat was rapid from the first and was soon completed. Considerable contradiction, however, existed in the literature in regard to the effect of acids upon the hydrolysis of fats and oils by lipase. These contradictions are due primarily to the failure of the investigators to take into account the two following facts: (1) that lipase in the seeds in many cases exists in the zymogen condition and (2) that after the zymogen is once activated the enzyme is rapidly inactivated by acids unless oil is present. Armstrong (1905) and Armstrong and Gosney (1913) found that any acid is effective in activating lipase, but the enzyme prepared with a weak acid such as acetic is distinctly superior to that obtained by the use of a stronger acid. They found that aspartic, glutamic, and succinic acids were very efficient in activating lipase preparations. In this regard it is also of interest that Falk and Nelson (1912) found that glycine, phenylalanine, and other amino acids as well as polypeptides aided the hydrolysis of methyl acetate, ethyl butyrate, and olive oil and that this action was to a certain extent selective in character. The above observations are significant, since the compounds mentioned occur in relatively large amounts in germinating seeds at a very early stage.

The effect of various concentrations of hydrochloric acid on the hydrolysis of olive oil by castor-bean lipase that had been activated in its preparation by 1 per cent acetic acid is shown by the following data, which were taken from the work of Haley and Lyman (1921). In this experiment 0.1 g. of lipase powder, 1.0 g. of olive oil, and 0.6 cc. of hydrochloric acid were mixed and incubated for 24 hr. at 38°C.

HCl 0.6 cc., per cent	Extent of hydrolysis NaOH used in titration, cubic centimeters	Fat hydrolyzed, per cent
0.00	1.0	3
0.02	2.2	6
0.04	16.5	49
0.06	18.2	54
0.08	24.6	73
0.10	24.6	73
0.12	27.2	79
0.14	30.6	90
0.16	29.7	88
0.18	28.3	84
0.20	27.6	81

They found that the optimum pH for castor-bean lipase activity was 5.0 and that lipolytic activity ceased entirely at pH 3.0. Tanka (1910) considered that the lipase of the castor-oil bean is contained in the resting seed as a zymogen and that the acid, found by some to be necessary for the activity of the extracts, is of use only for the conversion of the zymogen into enzyme, which in reality is most active in a neutral medium. In this regard the observations of Falk and Hamlin (1913) in respect to the effect of manganous sulphate on the acceleration of the activity of castor-bean lipase preparation should be noted. They considered that the acceleration of lipase activity is due to the fact that the inactive zymogen of lipase in the castor bean is converted into the active enzyme by an oxidation reaction for which the presence of an "oxygen carrier" or catalytic agent is necessary. Thus manganous sulphate does not accelerate directly the action of the enzyme present, but, by aiding the conversion of the inactive zymogen into active enzyme, it increases the total amount of enzyme present or replaces the enzyme which may become inactive on account of hydrolysis. It was shown by Falk (1913) that solutions of methyl and ethyl alcohol and acetone exerted an inhibitory action on the hydrolysis of ethyl butyrate by castor-bean lipase preparation, the amount of inhibition increasing with the concentration. Solutions of glucose and glycerol showed no inhibiting effects except in concentrated solutions. As compared with aqueous solutions, decreased activities of lipase were shown in the presence of all the univalent salts of the chlorides and nitrates of barium, calcium, and magnesium, of sodium oxalate, and of dilute solutions of sodium sulphate. Increased activities were shown by lipase in the presence of dilute solutions of the chlorides of barium and calcium, of more concentrated solutions of sodium sulphate and magnesium sulphate, and of the chlorides and sulphates of manganese. Theis, Long, and Brown (1929) noted that the activity of the lipase of the flax seed was retarded by the presence of potassium iodide, potassium chloride, potassium nitrate, sodium chloride, lithium chloride, and magnesium sulphate.

Armstrong and Gosney (1913) considered that the fatty acids and glycerol formed in the hydrolysis of oil by lipase inhibit the interaction of enzyme and oil, but there are few data in this regard.

In this connection the reverse action of lipase on its substrate—the formation of glycerides from the glycerol and acids—should be considered. Taylor (1906) using triacetin as a substrate considered that this reverse action of castor-bean lipase is one of very low velocity and may be disregarded in ordinary tests. The hydrolytic reaction of lipase, however, is never complete and there is a definite point of equilibrium in the reaction. The synthetic action of lipase has been discussed in Chap. X.

The enzyme lipase when prepared in the powdered form is very resistant to heat and may be heated when dry to 100°C. without injury. Falk (1917) found that when lipase extractions in water were heated to 100°C. for a few minutes they were completely inactivated. The same preparations when heated dry at 100 to 110°C. lost from 50 to 80 per cent of their activity. The temperature range of lipase activity is about 23 to 42°C. with the optimum temperature in the vicinity of 38°C.

The degree of the emulsification of the fats and fatlike materials is an important one in determining the lipolytic action of lipase. The lipase powder of castor bean and soybean is apparently effective in bringing about emulsification. The addition of ether or petroleum ether to certain fatty mixtures has been found greatly to facilitate the hydrolytic action of lipase, due, evidently, to the solution of the fats. The amount of water present in the digestive mixture is also an important factor. The rate at which interaction takes place is dependent presumably on the conditions at the colloid surfaces, and Armstrong and Gosney (1913) considered that in the case of lipase this interaction must be supposed to take place at or between the surfaces separated, at the most, by a thin film of water. Falk (1917) considered that the inactivation of esterase and lipase preparations by acids, bases, neutral salts, alcohols, acetone, esters, and heat leads to the hypothesis that the active enzyme grouping in these substances possesses the enol-lactim structure —C(OH) = N— which becomes inactive by tautomerization to the keto-lactam structure, —CO—NH—.

4. The Proteases of Plants.—The proteases of one type or another are apparently universally distributed in all plants and plant parts. As a general rule, they are more difficult to prepare for study than the carbohydrate enzymes, and their action proceeds much more slowly. Even the most active of the proteolytic enzymes require from several hours to several days to produce an appreciable amount of digestion products under laboratory conditions as contrasted with only a few minutes required by diastase or invertase to transform starch into sugar or cane sugar into the invert form. The stage to which the proteolytic action has proceeded as well as the amount of digestion products formed is also difficult to determine, so that much of the work that has been done with plant proteases has been only qualitative in character.

The common qualitative methods that have been the most generally used are to test the enzyme mixture for tryptophane, to examine it for leucine or tyrosine crystals, to test for peptone by the biuret color reaction, or to note the general dissolving action of the enzyme. Some of the quantitative methods that have been used are (*a*) the determination by weight of the amount of coagulable protein that remains in the solution, (*b*) the determination of the total nitrogen of the digestion products, (*c*) the measurement of the increased amino nitrogen by the Van Slyke method, (*d*) the determination of the increase in the electrical conductivity, (*e*) the determination of the changes in optical activity, (*f*) the determination of the extent of protein hydrolysis from the number of free carboxyl groups formed (Sörensen's method, 1908), and (*g*) the use of the biuret and tryptophane color reactions in a quantitative way by noting the differences in color intensities. Sherman and Neun (1916) considered that the determination of the total nitrogen or the amino nitrogen of the digestion products is the most accurate and delicate means of measuring proteolysis. Some of the methods for detecting the degree of proteolytic action will be discussed in detail when some of the enzymes are considered.

a. Historical.—Vines (1909) considered that the delivery of Sir Joseph Hooker's presidential address at the British Association in 1874 and the publication of Darwin's book on "Insectivorous Plants" in the following year may be taken as the starting point of the scientific investigations of proteolysis in plants. Hooker found that if cubes of the white of eggs were immersed in the pitchers of *Nepenthes* for 24 hr. their surfaces were more or less dissolved or gelatinized and pieces of fibrin totally dissolved. He was not certain, however, whether this action was due to the juices secreted by the pitchers or to the action of bacteria. Tait (1875), however, considered that digestive enzymes of a peptic nature occurred in these plants and prepared the enzyme in crude form.

Von Gorup-Besanez (1874, 1875, 1876) appears to have been the first to examine seeds for proteolytic enzymes. Using the glycerin method of extraction, he obtained protease preparations from the resting seeds of hemp, flax, and vetch and from germinating barley. He failed to find enzymes of this type in the ungerminated seeds of barley, lupine, and corn. In 1887 Green found a proteolytic enzyme in the seeds of lupine. This enzyme worked in an acid medium and converted fibrin into peptone, leucine, and tyrosine. He considered that it existed in the seed in the form of a zymogen and was transformed into the active state by acid. In 1890 the same author discovered that a tryptic enzyme was developed in the castor bean during germination. This enzyme was capable of splitting fibrin with the formation of peptone and crystal bodies including tyrosine. He considered that this enzyme also existed in zymogen form in the seed. Neumeister (1894) found positive tests for proteases in barley, beet, poppy, corn, and wheat seedlings but negative tests in many others. Fernback and Hubert (1900) and Weis (1900) showed that the germinating barley of malt contained a proteolytic enzyme. Finally, the work of Fermi and Buscalioni (1899), who were the first to make a systematic examination of a large number of plants, showed that proteases occur in a great diversity of plants and plant parts and give strong evidence to the present conception that proteases are of almost universal occurrence in plants.

b. Kinds.—The proteolytic enzymes are generally grouped into three classes: (1) the pepsins, (2) the trypsins, and (3) the erepsins.

1. *The Pepsins or Peptases.*—A pepsin or peptase is a proteolytic enzyme that hydrolyzes protein no further than to the form of proteoses or peptones. It does not act on proteoses or peptones whether they are produced by its own digestion or supplied to it in the artificial form. Enzymes of this type occur in the gastric juice of all normal animals. It was considered by the early investigators that many of the proteolytic enzymes of plants were of the nature of pepsin, but later investigations have proved that they were mistaken and that enzymes of the pepsin type occur only rarely in plants.

The only case in which pepsin has apparently been proved to occur in plants is that of *Drosera,* which was studied by White (1910). She studied the leaves of the four species of this plant, and, with the best methods so far known for enzyme extraction, the only proteolytic enzyme that could be obtained was one which had the characteristics of a pepsin, since the end product under well-controlled experiments of digestion was always peptone. Her method of procedure is given here because it may be used as a model for the extraction of other plant proteases and the study of their reaction.

The leaves were cut from the plant and all traces of foreign matter were removed from them. They were then washed in cold boiled water and again in a strong solution of chloroform, which acts as an antiseptic. The leaves were then chopped into minute pieces with a sterilized knife and the fragments weighed and put into a bottle containing about 100 cc. of lukewarm boiled water and 30 drops of chloroform. The bottle was shaken vigorously for 2 hr., when its contents were filtered. To the filtrate was added half its volume of a saturated solution of ammonium sulphate, which was found to be more efficient in the precipitation of this enzyme than alcohol. The precipitate thus obtained was filtered off on a filter paper that had been previously sterilized with boiling water and was dried in a sulphuric acid desiccator. When almost dry the precipitate was scraped off the filter paper with a sterilized knife and dissolved in cold boiled water. A measured quantity of this solution was then placed in test tubes, and the material to be tested for digestion added. One of the test tubes was boiled and another left unboiled. About 20 drops of chloroform was then added, and the contents were well shaken. The ends of the test tubes were plugged with cotton and placed in an oven at 35°C. After 30 to 50 hr. the tubes were removed from the incubator and tested for the activity of the enzyme.

Quintanilha (1926) found that *Drosophyllum lusitanicum* digests proteins by an enzyme of the pepsin type which is secreted for the most part by the sessile glands. The stalked glands serve largely in capturing the prey and indirectly stimulate the secretion of enzymes by the sessile glands. Hopkins (1929) reported that a protease and a peptidase could be obtained by a water extraction of green malt. Stern and Stern (1932) demonstrated a peptic and a tryptic enzyme in the secretions of *Nepenthes hibberdii* and *N. mixta*.

2. *The Trypsins or Tryptases.*—The term "trypsin" is given to an enzyme that not only hydrolyzes proteins to proteoses and peptones but also splits these up further into amino acids. The protein may be completely hydrolyzed into amino acids by an enzyme of this type or only partly so, since in some cases the hydrolysis is not complete, some polypeptides remaining as a residue. The first enzyme of the trypsin type to be identified in plants was papain, first studied by Wurtz and Bouchut (1879), whose tryptic behavior was first definitely determined by Martin (1884 to 1885). The discovery by Green (1887, 1890) of a tryptic enzyme in the germinating seeds of lupine and the castor bean, the investigations by Chittenden (1894) of bromelin in the pineapple, and the study of the pitcher liquid of *Nepenthes* by Vines (1897, 1898) definitely established that enzymes of the trypsin type are widespread in plants. We shall now consider in detail some of the plant trypsins.

(*a*) *Papain.*—This enzyme has been studied more than any other protease of the plant kingdom. It is elaborated by the papaw (*Carica papaya*), a plant that is native to the Caribbean, Gulf of Mexico, and South American regions, whence it has spread to many parts of the world. This enzyme is secreted into the milky latex that is characteristic of this plant and is distributed in its roots, stem, leaves, and fruit. The enzyme has been designated variously "papain," "papayotin," "papaytin," or "papayacin." It is obtained by collecting the latex from incisions made in the plant parts and drying it in the sun. This dried preparation is reduced to a powder and may be obtained on the drug market.

The proteolytic properties of the latex of this plant have long been known, and Vines (1909) noted that statements concerning its digestive action are recorded as early as 1750. It was observed that if meat was steeped in this liquid for a short time it became very tender. Its digestive action on the mucous membrane of the intestines of swine that had eaten the fruit was also observed. The latex was first scientifically investigated by Wurtz and Bouchut (1879) and Wurtz (1880). They extracted the latex with distilled water and added to this extract ten times its volume of alcohol. The precipitate that was formed by this treatment was collected on a filter and dried. To the white powder thus formed they gave the name "papain" and regarded it as the digestive enzyme of the latex. Sen (1931) found that the yield of papain increases as the fruit develops until it reaches a maximum when the fruit is full grown but not yet ripe. A plucked fruit exudes no papain. The first milky juice exuded after lancing gives the largest yield and best quality of papain. Martin (1884, 1885) proved the formation of leucine and tyrosine in the course of the digestion of fibrin and albumin by papain and thus considered that it behaved as a trypsin. Later Chittenden (1892) reported the formation of large proportions of peptone together with small amounts of leucine and tyrosine from the digestion of coagulated egg white, fibrin, and raw and cooked meats by the action of this enzyme. These observations were substantiated by Chittenden, Mendel, and McDermott (1898), who showed that the chief products of digestion in the case of papain were albumose and peptone, and later these observations were again confirmed by Mendel and Underhill (1901). In 1902 Vines found by means of the tryptophane test that papain actively digests peptone in neutral solution, more actively in the presence of acid (0.5 per cent citric), and less actively in the presence of alkali (0.5 per cent sodium carbonate).

Ringer and Grutterink (1927) observed that the maximal digestion by papain occurred at pH 2.5 and 11.3, the optimum varying with the type of protein used. Small quantities of electrolytes had a restraining influence on the activity of this enzyme in both an acid and an alkaline medium. In later experiments, Vines (1903, 1905) suggested that papain might be a mixture of two proteases, basing his opinion on the behavior of the enzyme toward different antiseptics. He found that chloroform, sodium fluoride, thymol, salicylic acid, toluene, and formalin did not inhibit the peptonizing action of papain, but that they impeded further proteolysis in the formation of tryptophane. He found that hydrocyanic acid was the only antiseptic in the presence of which papain split off any considerable amount of tryptophane. It is of interest to note that several of the earlier workers who observed leucine and tyrosine as digestive products of this enzyme used hydrocyanic acid as an antiseptic. Mendel and Blood (1910) considered that the extreme differences in the rate at which papain accomplishes the earlier and later steps in digestion furnish strong evidence that it is a mixture of at least two enzymes, although conclusive proof that this is the case has not been furnished.

The properties of papain were studied in considerable detail by Mendel and Blood (1910). They observed that the digestion of peptone by papain, in presence of most of the common antiseptics used in digestion experiments, is very slow judged by the production of tryptophane. In the presence of 0.15 per cent hydrocyanic acid, however, hydrolysis is rapid. This accelerated effect is not limited to the hydrolysis of peptone but is also shown in the digestion of raw and coagulated egg white, fibrin, and edestin, whether the measure of digestion is the appearance of tryptophane, leucine, and tyrosine or the rate of solution of insoluble protein. It was also found that hydrogen sulphide in saturation also produces an acceleration of digestion comparable to that effected by hydrocyanic acid. Brill and Brown (1922) found that dilute sodium chloride showed a slightly activating effect followed by an inhibitory effect in more concentrated solutions. Sodium carbonate, sodium bicarbonate, calcium chloride, and magnesium sulphate had no marked influence, potassium chloride and sodium citrate showed marked activating influence, while acetic acid and lactic acid showed strong inhibitory effects.

The behavior of papain at relatively high temperatures has received considerable attention. Chittenden (1892) noted that in acid solution, papain digested more meat protein at 70°C. than at any lower temperature. According to Delezenne and Mouton (1906) and Pozerski (1909), papain digests proteins of egg white and serum so rapidly at 80 to 90°C. that if a suitable mixture of enzyme and uncoagulated protein faintly acidified is heated to boiling over a flame, scarcely any coagulum is obtained. This rapid digestion by papain at high temperatures was verified by Mendel and Blood (1910). Since at 40°C., a temperature which is generally considered favorable for enzyme action, the proteins are not measurably digested by papain, during short periods of time, the question arises as to the cause of the rapid rate of digestion at the higher temperatures. The rapid rate of digestion by papain at these relatively high temperatures is apparently due to the fact that it is not so easily destroyed by heat as other enzymes, and that the acceleration of the rate of action by heat more than compensates for the rate of destruction of the enzyme, so that for short periods under favorable conditions, the rate of digestion may be very high. This assumption is strengthened by the observations of Pratt (1915), who stated that at 70°C. the activity of the enzyme in the presence of a large amount of the enzyme is not greatly weakened but that with decreasing percentages of the enzyme, the loss in activity becomes more marked. Finally, Pratt found that, if a papain solution is heated rapidly to 100°C., allowed to boil 5 sec., and immediately cooled, it loses all its proteolytic activities.

Several methods for the determination of the activity of papain are given here in brief in order to give the student a general idea of the procedure that has been followed in studying this enzyme. Details, however, in this regard may be obtained by consulting the literature that has been mentioned in the preceding discussion. Mendel and Blood (1910) in the study of the digestion of peptone by papain used the following method: 3 cc. of 5 per cent peptone in 1 per cent sodium chloride were mixed with 3 cc. of 1 per cent papain in 1 per cent sodium chloride solution. Enough hydrocyanic acid was added to make a 0.15 per cent solution. Chloroform, 0.5 per cent; thymol, 0.5 per cent; sodium fluoride, 1 per cent; or several drops of toluene were also used as antiseptics. The mixture was digested in glass-stoppered bottles at 40°C. for 17 hr. It was tested at the end of the experiment for tryptophane by adding saturated bromine water drop by drop to 2-cc. portions of the digest.

The digestion of uncoagulated egg white by this enzyme was studied after the following manner: To 15 cc. of an egg-white solution prepared by diluting slightly beaten white of egg with three volumes of 1 per cent salt solution and filtering, 1 cc. of 1 per cent papain solution was added. This was made up to 30 cc., antiseptics were added after the manner mentioned above, and the digestion was allowed to proceed at 40°C. for 17 hr. The undigested protein was precipitated by adding 30 cc. of a 10 per cent solution of trichloracetic acid and heating for 5 min. in a water bath at 100°C. to coagulate the proteins completely and dissolve any albumoses. The mixture was then filtered while hot through a dried weighed filter paper, washed free from acid with water, and dried to constant weight. The amount of protein in the original mixture of egg white and papain was determined in a blank by the trichloracetic acid method.

Pratt (1915) prepared a papain solution by dissolving 0.75 g. of powdered papain in 150 cc. of distilled water. Although papain is not completely soluble in water, the active principle is dissolved upon being kept for 30 min. at 40°C., so that upon filtering a clear solution is obtained. Pratt used milk as nearly free from butter fat as possible. Into 150-cc. flasks were measured 25 cc. of milk, and to this was added water, varying from 5 to 25 cc., and sufficient papain solution in each case to make the total addition of water and papain solution 25 cc. After the enzyme solution was added, the contents of the flasks were thoroughly mixed by shaking, after which the flask was placed at 40°C. for 30 min. The flasks were then cooled by ice water until their contents could be examined. The contents of each flask were washed into 500-cc.

beakers, sufficient water being used to make the volume up to 75 cc. The undigested protein was precipitated by slowly adding 0.5 cc. of copper sulphate solution followed by 5 cc. of glacial acetic acid, the solution being vigorously stirred during the precipitation. After the precipitate had settled it was collected and washed upon weighed ashless paper and dried to constant weight at 100°C. The weight of protein digested by the papain was calculated by subtracting from similar determinations made on blanks to which no enzyme was added. Duplicate analyses in this manner agreed within 2 per cent. No antiseptic was used for such short periods of incubation.

(*b*) *Bromelin.*—This tryptic enzyme occurs in large quantities in the juice of the pineapple (*Ananas sativa*) and in other plants of the family *Bromeliaceae.* This enzyme was discovered by V. Marcano of Venezuela, according to a brief note published by Russell (1891) in the *Bulletin of Pharmacy.* Russell suggested the name "bromelin" for the enzyme after the natural order to which the plants containing it belong. This enzyme has been studied almost exclusively in the pineapple and was first scientifically investigated by Chittenden and his pupils (1891, 1894). The juice of the pineapple is acid, the acidity being equal to that of a solution of hydrochloric acid of about 0.45 per cent. The fresh juice is strongly proteolytic and its protein digesting power is manifested in an acid, neutral, or slightly alkaline medium, but in general it acts most energetically in a neutral medium. Ambros and Harteneck (1929) found that the activity of bromelin of the pineapple decreased as the fruit ripened. This enzyme from the ripe pineapple may be activated by hydrocyanic acid or by juice from the unripe fruit. An activator of bromelin is apparently present in the unripe pineapple.

When blood fibrin is warmed at 40°C., or thereabouts, with filtered pineapple juice, the fibrin swells up and then quickly disintegrates and in part dissolves. For studying the proteolytic power of pineapple juice under different conditions, Chittenden used the following procedure: About 100 cc. of filtered pineapple juice was warmed at 40°C. for a given period of time with 10 g. of moist, freshly coagulated egg albumin that had been completely freed from all soluble matter by washing with water. When the period of digestion was completed, the undissolved matter was collected in a weighed filter, washed with water, and dried at 110°C. to a constant weight. By subtracting the weight of the insoluble residue so obtained from the weight of dry albumin, equivalent to the moist albumin used in the experiment, the amount of protein matter converted into the soluble form was ascertained. In this manner, it was found, for example, that after 3½ hr. in one experiment 34.5 per cent of the protein was rendered soluble in the juice of natural acidity and 40 per cent in the juice that had been neutralized. This enzyme produces in digestion proteoses, peptones, tyrosine, and leucine, which may be detected by proper means.

The temperature relations of bromelin are interesting. Chittenden (1894) observed that neutral pineapple juice was capable of digesting more protein at 60°C. than under like conditions at 40°C., but that warming the enzyme solution alone at 60°C. for 15 min. diminished the proteolytic power of the enzyme 50 per cent. This suggested that the products of digestion protect the enzyme from the destructive action of high temperatures, since, when the neutralized juice is heated to 70 to 80°C. for 15 min. in the absence of digestive products, it is rapidly destroyed. It was observed by Pozerski (1909) that at high temperatures the action of bromelin was very rapid, behaving in this regard similarly to papain, the results being due apparently to the same causes as are mentioned under that topic.

Chittenden (1894) precipitated the enzyme from the juice by saturation with sodium chloride, magnesium sulphate, and ammonium sulphate and he considered the product obtained from sodium chloride to be superior to that obtained with the other salts. Effront (1917) stated that bromelin may be prepared by adding two volumes of alcohol to the pineapple juice and filtering off the precipitate, which contains little or no enzyme. To the filtrate thus obtained, five volumes of 95 per cent ethyl alcohol are added, and the precipitate formed, which contains the enzyme, is collected, dried, and pulverized for use.

Impure preparations of bromelin are strongly autodigestive in either an acid or an alkaline medium, such digestion, according to Caldwell (1905), beginning when the breaking up of protein impurities has been completed and proceeding to the total destruction of the enzyme. Bromelin, however, when prepared in a relatively pure condition is not at all autodigestive, so that the presence of some protein in the juice is apparently a prerequisite for such action. Caldwell (1905) obtained by the following method a preparation of this enzyme which contained only very slight traces of protein: The dialyzed sodium chloride precipitate was dissolved in a small amount of water and reprecipitated by the addition of 95 per cent alcohol. This precipitate was again dissolved in water and again precipitated by adding crystals of ammonium sulphate. A little of the associated protein was left behind at every precipitation, and five repetitions of the process gave a preparation containing only slight traces of protein. Precipitation was much hastened by placing the solutions at 4°C. After being dried upon the water bath at 40°C., the preparation was completely soluble in water and was not autodigestive in any medium even after prolonged standing.

(c) *Other Plant Trypsins.*—In 1880 Bouchut discovered a tryptic enzyme in the juice of the stem, leaves, and fruit of the common fig (*Ficus carica*) to which Mussi (1890) gave the name "cradina." Green (1887, 1890, 1892) found enzymes of the trypsin type in the germinating seeds of the lupine and castor-bean seedlings and in the

Kachree gourd (*Cucumis utilissimus*), while Butkewitsch (1900, 1901) observed tryptic enzymes in the germinating seeds of *Lupinus angustifolius* and *Lupinus luteus*. Vines (1902) found the liquid of the pitchers of *Nepenthes* contained a tryptic enzyme and later (1903) found similar enzymes in the juice of the cucumber and melon and in the bulbs of the tulip and hyacinth. The early observations of vegetable trypsins were, with but few exceptions, in seedlings and storage organs. In 1919 Fisher examined the leaves of numerous plants for the presence of trypsins, using finely powdered legumin as a substrate after the following manner: 10 g. of ground fresh leaves were placed with 3 g. of legumin in 250 cc. of water in a flask with a layer of toluene as an antiseptic. The flasks were tightly corked and placed in an incubator at 37°C. for 3 days. The material was filtered and the residue thoroughly washed with water, until the volume was 400 cc. A 40-cc. portion was then transferred to a flask, decolorized by shaking with alumina cream, filtered, and the residue thoroughly washed. The filtrate was then tested by Sorensen's method to determine the extent of protein hydrolysis as follows: To the filtrate was added 15 cc. of a fresh solution consisting of 50 cc. of commercial formaldehyde, 25 cc. of absolute alcohol, and 10 cc. of a thymol phthalein solution. (The thymol phthalein solution consisted of 0.5 g. of thymol phthalein dissolved in 1,000 cc. of 93 per cent alcohol.) Fifth-normal barium hydroxide was then run in until a distinctly green or blue color was obtained which matched that obtained by similar treatment of the control flask. The results show that the leaves of barley, oats, corn, rye, red clover, alfalfa, vetch, beans, peas, buckwheat, white mustard, and others contain enzymes of the trypsin type that are capable of hydrolyzing legumin. The reaction, however, is relatively slow as compared with the hydrolysis of peptone by the same leaf extract. In 3 days the amount of legumin hydrolyzed by the various leaf materials only amounted to from 1.5 to 9.6 per cent. Enzymes of a tryptic nature thus seem to be widely distributed in plants and plant parts. Their action is apparently relatively slow, but this may be due to the fact that the conditions under which they are placed in the laboratory may not be comparable to the conditions that prevail in the cells in which they normally act. Mounfield (1936) found that the aqueous extract of sprouted wheat contained a protease that showed an optimum activity at a pH of 4.1 for the decomposition of edestin at 40°C.

3. *The Erepsins or Ereptases.*—In 1901 Cohnheim described and gave the name "erepsin" to the enzyme formed in the mucous membrane of the small intestine which actively digests peptone, prolamins, polypeptides, and casein to the amino acids but does not act upon the higher proteins. Vines (1903) obtained evidence that various parts of widely different species of plants contain enzymes that resemble erepsin in their reaction. He based his conclusion on his observation that many plant extracts split off tryptophanes rapidly from peptone but entirely fail to hydrolyze fibrin as indicated by any apparent solution or by the formation of tryptophane. Independently of Vines, Javillier (1903) found that *Lolium perenne* contained among other enzymes one that hydrolyzes peptone into products that no longer give the biuret reaction. It has since been shown that erepsins are almost universally distributed in plants and plant parts. They have been found in the embryo of wheat, in green peas, in the expressed juice of the melon, cucumber, and tomato, in the rind of the apple and orange, in the juice of grape, in the leaves

of lettuce, cabbage, spinach, barley, oats, corn, rye, clover, alfalfa, vetch, bean, peas, buckwheat, mustard, in the potato tuber and artichoke, in the onion and bulbs of the hyacinth and tulip, and in the roots of turnip, tomato, carrot, and beet, in the leaves of various seedlings, and in many other plants and plant parts.

The erepsin of cabbage was studied in considerable detail by Blood (1910). She prepared the enzyme after the following manner: The leaves were ground and then pressed and the juice so obtained was dialyzed for 40 hr. against running water, with toluene as an antiseptic. The clear juice obtained by filtering the dialysate was saturated with ammonium sulphate and left in the cold room over night. The precipitate was then washed with saturated ammonium sulphate and dissolved in water. This solution was filtered and the filtrate dialyzed against running water, with toluene for an antiseptic, until free from ammonium sulphate, which required 6 days. A preparation of this type can be kept for a considerable period of time without loss of enzymic action.

In the digestive experiments, Blood followed the following procedure: To 5 cc. of 5 per cent peptone in 1 per cent sodium chloride solution 5 cc. of the enzyme solution was added and made to a volume of 12 cc. This was then digested in the incubator at 40°C. for 17 hr., using toluene as an antiseptic. To test for digestion, 2-cc. portions were removed, acidified with acetic acid when necessary, and treated with bromine water drop by drop until a maximum color was obtained.

The erepsin of cabbage obtained and tested in this manner split tryptophane and tyrosine from commercial peptones, clotted milk, and liquefied gelatin. It did not digest fibrin, edestin, or coagulated egg white in neutral, acid, or alkaline solution. It was active over a considerable range of acidity and alkalinity.

5. The Coagulases of Plants. *a. The Rennets or Rennins.*—Rennet is an enzyme which when introduced into milk causes coagulation, the milk becoming gelatinous and compact. The formation of this milk clot is due to the alteration of the casein of the milk. Rennet is secreted by the gastric glands of animals and is associated in relatively large amounts with animal pepsin.

The enzyme rennet or rennin is apparently widespread in the plant kingdom and is similar to if not identical with that found in the animal body. Experimental evidence indicates that, in the majority of cases at least, it is always closely associated with proteolytic enzymes. The occurrence of rennet in the plant kingdom was known as early as the sixteenth century. It was at that time known by certain tribes of Lapland and by the peasants of the Alps that the leaves of the bitterwort (*Pinguicula vulgaris*) had the power to curdle milk and the leaves were used by them for that purpose. It was also known in England, about that time, that the stem and leaves of the yellow bedstraw (*Galium verum*) coagulated milk, and until recently, at least, this plant was used in cheese making in certain parts of England.

When the proteases of plants were discovered, it was found that in many cases they possessed the power of curdling milk. Thus papain, bromelin, the trypsin of the castor bean and the ereptase of cabbage all have this power, which is evidently due to rennins accompanying them. The most extensive studies of plant rennins have been made by Gerber (1907 to 1912), and the student is referred to his works for a detailed study of this enzyme.

Rennin has been found in the juice of the stem, leaves, and fruit of the fig, in the juice of the papaw, in the brown algae, and in the seeds of *Datura stramonium*, *Pisum sativum*, *Lupinus hirsutus*, and others. In some of the seeds, it occurs apparently in the zymogen state. This enzyme was found by Gerber to be present in the *Cruciferae*, in the *Ranunculaceae*, in the *Rubiaceae*, in the *Compositae*, in the *Euphorbiaceae*, and others.

As an example of the methods of isolation and study of this enzyme the work of Lea (1883), who studied the rennin of *Withania coagulans*, may be cited. He found that a 5 per cent sodium chloride solution at 38°C. gave the best extraction of the enzyme from the seeds. The active principle is soluble in glycerin and can be extracted from the seeds by this means. This enzyme loses its activity if boiled in water for a minute or two. Alcohol precipitates the enzyme from its solution, and the precipitate after being washed with alcohol may again be dissolved without losing its coagulating power. When a normal clot is formed by this rennin, the reaction of the clot remains neutral or faintly alkaline. The clot is thus a true one and is not due to the action of acid and resembles in appearance the clot formed by animal rennin.

b. The Pectases.—The enzymes of this group coagulate pectic bodies with the formation generally of gelatinous calcium pectate. The presence of calcium salts is apparently necessary for the action of the pectases and it has been found that pectic gels can be formed in the absence of the enzyme, provided the necessary conditions are present.

G. The Formation of Enzymes in Plants

Two types of enzymes are distinguished in plants, the classification of these two types being based on the relation of their place of origin to the place of their activity. Most of the enzymes of plants function in the cells in which they are formed and are called "intracellular" or "endocellular" enzymes. Some plant parts produce enzymes that function outside the cells that produce them, and such enzymes are commonly termed "extracellular enzymes." Enzymes of this type are secreted, for the most part, by specialized cells that have a more or less glandular appearance. The study of the formation of extracellular enzymes in plants has been confined almost entirely to the secretion of extracellular enzymes by insectivorous plants and to the germinating seeds of barley, wheat, corn, and other cereal grains.

The secretion of enzymes by certain cells of insectivorous plants received considerable attention from early investigators who demonstrated that these cells excreted enzymes into the liquid in the "pitchers" of *Nepenthes* and similar plants or to the exterior as in the case of *Drosera* or sundew. They found that these enzymes were secreted and digestion of food brought about only when the secreting cells were stimulated in some way or another.

A discussion of the observations of Hepburn (1918) in his studies of the liquid of *Nepenthes* will suffice to show the general status of our present knowledge concerning the secretion of enzymes by insectivorous plants. He examined the liquid in the pitchers of 14 species and hybrids of *Nepenthes,* always studying it prior to the opening of the pitcher. Through an opening he stimulated the glands of the inner wall of the pitcher by stroking with a camel's-hair brush or by placing several round, solid, glass beads therein and shaking the pitcher at intervals during one or more days. After stimulation by the brush or the insertion of the beads, cotton plugs were inserted in the openings of the pitchers and the liquid removed for study the following day. Hepburn studied especially the action of the proteolytic enzymes secreted by the pitchers and found that the liquid from the stimulated pitchers produced a more rapid digestion than did that from the non-stimulated pitchers. The latter exerted proteolytic action only in the presence of acid and failed to produce this action in its absence. The liquid from the stimulated pitchers exerted proteolytic action in either the presence or the absence of an acid. Hepburn concluded that increased proteolytic activity due to stimulation might be caused by one or more of the following results: (1) by changing the hydrogen-ion concentration, thus rendering conditions more favorable for the action of proteases already present; (2) by causing the activation of a zymogen already present; and (3) by producing an increased secretion of proteases by the glands of the pitcher. Hepburn showed conclusively that the liquid taken from the young unopened pitchers was sterile and that the proteolytic action of the liquid is due to a protease and not to bacterial action. Holter and Linderstrom-Lang (1933) found two proteases in *Drosera rotundifolia.* One of these was secreted by the glandular hairs and showed a maximum activity at pH 3.2; the other was an endoenzyme in the leaf tissues and showed its optimum activity at pH 4.3.

In order to discuss the secretion of enzymes by the germinating seeds of the *Gramineae*, it is necessary to have a knowledge of the arrangement and structure of the various seed parts. The structure of the barley grain has been described in detail by Brown and Morris (1890), and that of the corn to some extent by Torrey (1902) and Sargant and Robertson (1905). The general structure of the seeds of the grains and grasses is approximately the same, so that the structure of the corn grain to be herein considered may be taken as representative of this group of seeds.

In Fig. 31 it is seen that a grain of corn consists of an endosperm and embryo surrounded by several coats and the pericarp. The endosperm occupies the greater portion of the seed and partly surrounds the embryo. The endosperm consists for the most part of large cells filled with starch grains, part of which are embedded in a matrix of protein matter. Just beneath the coats of the grain and completely encircling the outer part of the endosperm is a layer of columnar cells filled with protein and termed the "aleurone layer." The embryo is on the furrowed, flattened side of the grain. It is thickest at the end attached to the cob and gradually slopes to a point reached at about three-fourths to four-fifths the length of the grain. The embryos consist of the young plant and the scutellum. The young plant or plantlet consists of the plumule and radicle with the connecting hypocotyl. The scutellum is a shieldlike expansion of the hypocotyl and makes up the greater part of the bulk of the embryo. It is considered by some to be the homologue of the cotyledon and serves as a special organ for absorbing the food from the endosperm and transferring it to the developing plantlet.

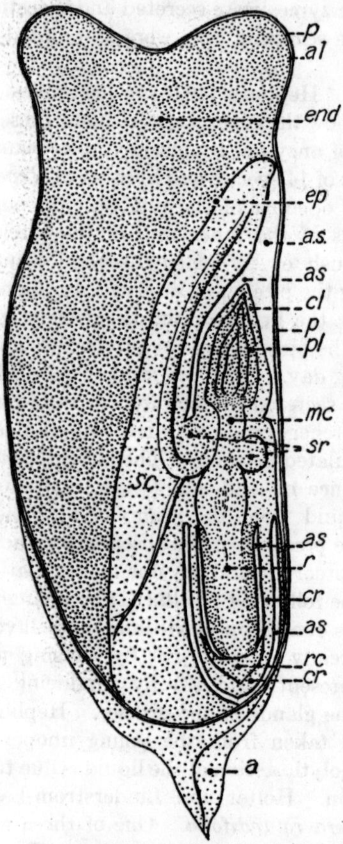

Fig. 31—Longitudinal section of a corn grain. *end*, endosperm. *sc*, scutellum. *p*, pericarp. *al*, aleurone layer. *ep*, epithelial layer. *as*, air space. *cl*, coleoptile. *pl*, plumule. *mc*, mesocotyl. *sr*, initials of secondary roots. *r*, radicle. *rc*, root cap. *cr*, coleorhiza. *a*, point of attachment to cob.

The surface of the scutellum that is in contact with the endosperm consists of a layer of columnar cells which is termed the "epidermal" or "epithelial" layer of the scutellum. In the case of corn, this epithelial layer dips down at frequent intervals into the endosperm, thus producing a greater surface for secretion. These convolutions of the epithelial layer, however, are not present in most of the other members of the grain family (Sargant and Robertson, 1905). These epithelial cells are about three times as long as broad and have one end resting on the scutellar parenchyma and the other in close contact with the endosperm. The protoplasmic contents of the epithelial cells stand in marked contrast to those of the other cells of the scutellum in being finely granulated, semitransparent, and possessing prominent nuclei (Fig. 32).

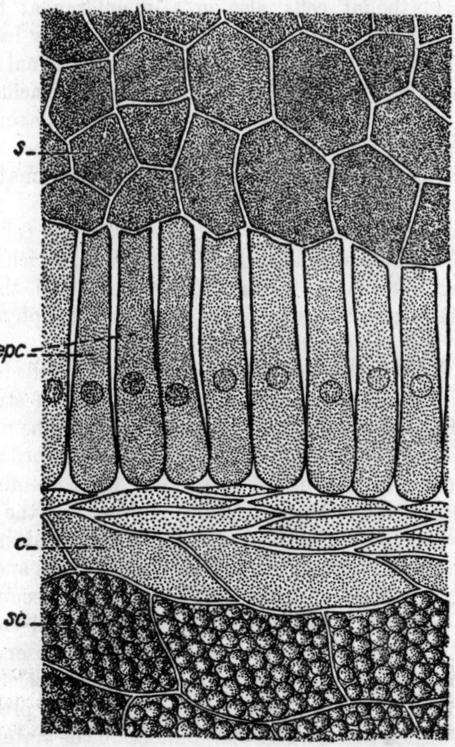

FIG. 32.—Section through the scutellum, epithelial layer, and endosperm of the corn grain. *s*, scutellum. *epc*, epithelial cells. *c*, flattened cells of the endosperm. *sc*, starch cells of the endosperm.

Avery (1930) discussed the analogy of the different parts of the seeds of corn, oats, and wheat to the various organs and portions of organs in the adult plants.

Within a few hours after the seeds of barley, corn, or other grains are moistened and placed under favorable conditions for germination, the protoplasm of the epithelial cells undergoes marked changes, becoming much coarser in structure, the granulations increasing in size and number and clouding the cell contents so that the nucleus which is conspicuous in the resting stage of the seed cannot readily be observed. This cloudiness reaches its maximum in from 24 to 36 hr. and shows little change in most cases until the endosperm is depleted, after which the cells again become hyaline. In the case of the date seed, however, the epithelial cells clear long before the endosperm is digested (Reed, 1904). The epithelial cells also greatly enlarge at the beginning of germination, so that between the first and third day in the germination of corn they enlarge to three to four times their original size. Soon after the above-mentioned activities appear in the epithelial layer, the cell walls of the cells of the endosperm nearest to the scutellum begin to dissolve and the starch grains therein show evidence of pitting, while temporary starch appears as grains in the parenchymatous tissue of the scutellum bordering upon the epithelial cells.

All investigators are agreed that the epithelial cells are capable of forming cytase, diastase, and probably proteases, which are excreted into the adjoining endosperm. Pozen (1934) reported that the enzymes cytase, amylase, protease, peptidase, oxidase, and phytase are secreted by the embryo of barley during germination.

The cytological changes that occur in the cells of the epithelial layer during the formation of enzymes have been studied by Torrey (1902) and Reed (1904). Torrey considered that the nucleus is the seat of this enzyme formation. He noted in the case of corn that at the beginning of germination the nuclei contained dark, staining granules that exuded into the cytoplasm and finally collected at the wall next to the endosperm where they disappeared. Immediately after this dissolution, the first activity of enzymes is noted in the cell walls and starch grains of the endosperm. Torrey thus considered these accumulations at the base of the epithelial cells to be deposits of actual enzyme substance. Reed (1904), however, was unable to confirm the observations of Torrey relative to the extrusion of solid matter from the nucleus but noted that the chromatin of the nuclei increased as germination progressed while the nucleoli diminished in size. In this connection the statements of Horning and Petrie (1927) in regard to the function of mitochondria as mentioned in Chap. I should again be mentioned. They considered that the mitochondria of the epithelial cells migrate into the endosperm, carrying on their surfaces the enzymes that act upon the food reserves contained therein.

The function of the aleurone layer has also received considerable attention (Fig. 33). Beyerinck (1895) considered that this layer secreted maltase; Green (1899), Haberlandt (1890), and Brown and Escombe (1898) concluded that it secreted cytase in the case of barley; while Puriewitsch (1897) and Linz (1896) came to the opposite conclusion. There is much evidence, however, that the aleurone layer has no enzymic secretory powers. The cells that compose it are relatively thick walled and undergo apparently little change in their contents until the endosperm is entirely depleted. No erosion of the starch grains or dissolution of the cell walls occurs next to the aleurone layer except as these changes move out from the scutellum. From thousands of observations on barley grains, Mann and Harlan (1915) concluded that the aleurone layer of that seed exercises no secretory power at all during germination. They considered that all the enzymes formed in the seed during germination are secreted by the epithelial layer. They considered that the aleurone layer may act as a protective layer to the endosperm and embryo and that the nitrogenous material in these cells might serve as a supply of nitrogen for the young plant after it had full power to manufacture its own carbohydrates. The origin of the aleurone layer has been investigated by Jodidi and Peklo (1929) and should be mentioned here in a discussion of its function. From certain cytological and biochemical observations they concluded that symbiotic fungi produce the aleurone layer in the case of English rye grass, wheat, and barley. This is an entirely new line of thought and should be investigated further. Schander (1934) found that the germination of rice and other cereals was greatly impaired if the aleurone layer was removed by the polishing of the grains.

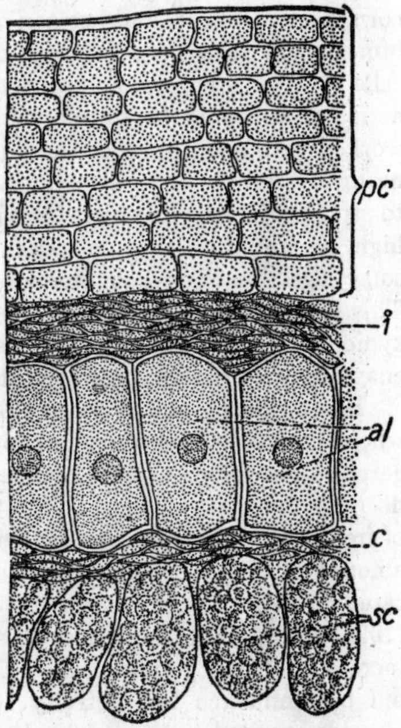

FIG. 33.—Section through the outer portion of a grain of corn. *pc*, pericarp. *i*, integuments. *al*, aleurone layer. *c*, flattened cells containing some protein. *sc*, starch cells containing mostly starch but also some protein.

Although all investigators have agreed that the epithelial cells of the scutellum secrete enzymes, there has been much dispute as to the extent to which these cells supply the enzymes concerned in the digestion of the reserves in the endosperm.

It has been found that embryos of many of the *Gramineae* can be grafted onto other endosperms or placed in contact with starch preparations and still develop and function normally by digesting and absorbing their food from the substratum upon which they are placed. On this account and from certain observations on the behavior of endosperms, Brown and Morris (1890), Brown and Escombe (1898), and Pond (1906) concluded that the endosperm has no power at all of self-digestion. On the other hand, Krabbe (1890), Grüss (1893 to 1897), Hansteen (1894), Puriewitsch (1897), Paton, Nanji, and Ling (1924), and others have reported observations that contradict these conclusions. The work of Bruschi (1908) showed the cause for the contradictory results that had been obtained in this regard. He found that the starchy endosperm of corn, barley, wheat, and rye can digest itself in the absence of the scutellum though to a very different degree. The vitality of the endosperm cells of various species and varieties differs greatly, so that the enzymic action that would be developed will vary greatly. If an investigator worked with a set of seeds in which the vitality was very low, he would naturally observe little or no digestion of the endosperm. If he happened to study a variety in which the vitality of the endosperm cells remained high, he would observe considerable self-digestion. Bruschi found that some digestion may occur in endosperms that have lost all their vitality. This is apparently due to the fact that the cells contain proenzymes or zymogens that exist after the death of the cells and can form active enzymes after soaking in water at ordinary temperatures.

Bach, Oparin, and Wähner (1927) reported that the dormant seeds of wheat contain active enzymes although in minute quantities. During germination these enzymes increase rapidly, attain a maximum, and then decrease in amount during the last phases of germination. The presence of free oxygen is necessary for their formation. A similar increase in the amount of enzymes is observed during the ripening of the seed, but a rapid decrease occurs toward the end of ripening. Tascher and Dungan (1928) found that the diastatic activity of the corn seed and seedling increased during germination. The stage at which corn was harvested did not influence this activity to any appreciable extent. The vigor of seed cannot thus be explained as due to differences in diastatic activity but is due apparently to the greater quantity of reserves.

The diastatic activity or power of wheat flour is an important factor in its use in baking. A considerable amount of work has been done to find the cause of the marked fluctuations of this power in various flours. Swanson (1935) stated that the diastatic activity varies in different classes of wheat. It was found to be highest in durum wheats. Soft winter wheats as a group have a lower diastatic activity than hard winter wheats. Those wheats grown under very dry conditions are lower in this activity than those grown under more moist conditions. The diastatic activity is not increased by wetting until the moisture is sufficient to start germination. He considered that the diastatic enzymes in the endosperm, and consequently in the flour, probably exist in the form of proenzymes which may be activated by water. The amount of such enzymes present probably depends on conditions prevailing during kernel formation and ripening. The amount of diastatic enzymes produced by the epithelial layer is increased during germination so that flour from malted wheat is rich in these enzymes. The water added in tempering wheat, however, does not affect this diastatic activity. Swanson showed that the greatest amount of diastase was produced in the germ end of the grain during germination. His observations were:

Part analyzed	White wheat		Red wheat	
	Sugar content, mg.	Diastatic activity, mg.	Sugar content, mg.	Diastatic activity, mg.
Check ungerminated seed	68	240	50	277
Whole germinated seed	415	1050	565	1750
Germ end of germinated seed	720	1800	775	1225
Brush end of germinated seed	130	750	340	850

Bailey and Sherwood (1935) in a discussion of the biochemistry of breadmaking stated that during the dough mixing the diastatic enzymes therein become active and hydrolyze the starch into fermentable sugars. The amylase of wheat flour is of the beta type. Malted wheat flour has its α-amylase greatly increased in malting, while the β-, or saccharogenic, amylase remains constant. The addition of 1 per cent malted flour to high or low diastatic flours effects an increase in sugar production of 100 per cent in some cases. Several hypotheses have been proposed to account for this accelerated saccharogenesis. The first is that the dextrinogenic action of the α-amylase may result in a new substrate which the β-amylase can more readily convert into maltose. The second is that the malted flour may contain active proteases that function in liberating amylases from protein complexes with which they are associated. The third is that the malted wheat flour may contribute a substrate that is more readily hydrolyzed than the native starch of the normal flour. The diastatic activity of flours is influenced by the variety of wheat, the fineness of the starch particles, and the degree of hydration of the starch.

The effect of the water content and temperature upon the secretion of diastase in the barley grain was studied by Pickler (1919). The grains were placed under certain conditions of temperature and humidity until the absorption of water had reached an equilibrium. A certain portion of each grain sample was then taken, dried and pulverized to a powder, and the action of each sample of powder on a 0.2 per cent solution of starch paste noted. It was found that the temperature changes made little difference in the rate of secretion of the enzyme, but that the changes in water content exerted a marked effect. This may be illustrated by the following concrete example: At 10°C. the water content of two samples of seed was 11 and 29.9 per cent, respectively. The former had a diastatic activity of 36.25, while the latter had an activity of 24.25. That is, it required 36.25 hr. for a diastase sample from the seed with a water content of 11 per cent to digest a given amount of starch paste, while it required only 24.25 hr. for a diastase sample from the seed with a water content of 29.9 per cent to digest the same amount of starch paste. At 20°C. with water contents of 11.5 and 30.9 per cent, respectively, the diastatic activities were 36.5 and 23.1. These results show that the water content is a very important factor in determining the rate of formation of diastase by the scutellum of the barley grain.

IV. A COMPARISON OF DIGESTION IN PLANTS AND ANIMALS

The process of digestion in plants and animals is similar in that, for the most part, plants digest the same foods as animals. These foods are digested by similar enzymes and the products of digestion are the same. As a general rule, the process of digestion in animals is more rapid than in plants.

The process of digestion in plants is different from that in animals primarily in regard to its location. In the higher animals digestion occurs in certain definite specialized organs, while in plants, with but few exceptions, it does not occur in any special organs but may take place in any part of the plant body.

Digestion in plants is, for the most part, intracellular, occurring within the cells which produce the enzymes that act upon the food contained therein. The only exceptions are the digestion of some food by insectivorous plants and of the reserve foods in the endosperms of the *Gramineae* and date seed by the enzymes secreted by the epithelial cells of the scutellum and the absorbing portions of the date embryo.

Digestion in animals occurs in practically all cases outside the cells and is termed "extracellular digestion." Thus in the higher animals digestion occurs in the alimentary tract and is brought about by enzymes excreted therein by cells bordering upon it or by special glands connected with it. Also, in the case of unicellular animals as the amoebae, which simply wrap themselves around food particles and digest them, the digestive process is really an extracellular one.

Bibliography

ACHARYA, C. N., 1933: Investigations on the development of prussic acid in cholam (*Sorghum vulgare*), *Indian J. Agr. Sci.*, **3**: 851–869; *Exp. Sta. Rec.*, **71**: 312–313.

ALEXANDER, J., 1934: Enzymes, vitamins and the zone of maximum colloidality, *Sci.*, **80**: 79–80.

———, 1935: The nature of enzymes, *Sci.*, **81**: 44–45.

AMBARD, L., E. PELBOIS, and M. BRICKA, 1920: Similitude de l'hydrolyse du sucre par les acides et de l'hydrolyse de l'amidon par l'amylase. Étude de certaines réactions mono-moléculaire, *Bull. Soc. Chim. Biol.*, **2**: 42–63.

———, 1920, 1921: Fixation de l'amylase par l'amidon cru et l'empois d'amidon, *C. R. Soc. Biol.*, **83**: 1458–1460; **84**: 230–232.

———, 1921: Sur l'amylase. Son dosage, mécanisme de la digestion amylolytique, *Bull. Soc. Chim. Biol.*, **3**: 51–65.

———, 1923: De l'amylase. Liaison du ferment et des substances qu'il digère, *Bull. Soc. Chim. Biol.*, **5**: 693–716.

AMBROS, O., and A. HARTENECK, 1929: Über natürliche Aktivierung von Proteasen pflanzlicher Milchsäfte, *Z. physiol. Chem.*, **181**: 24–41.

APPLEMAN, C. O., 1911: Physiological behavior of enzymes and carbohydrate transformations in after-ripening of the potato tuber, *Bot. Gaz.*, **52**: 306–315.

ARMSTRONG, H. E., 1905: Studies on enzyme action. Lipase, *Proc. Roy. Soc.*, B, **76**: 606–608.

——— and E. ORMEROD, 1906: Studies on enzyme action. Lipase II, *Proc. Roy. Soc.*, B, **78**: 376–385.

———, E. F. ARMSTRONG, and E. HORTON, 1908: Studies on enzyme action. XII, The enzymes of emulsin, *Proc. Roy. Soc.*, B, **80**: 321–331.

——— and H. W. GOSNEY, 1913: Studies on enzyme action. Lipase III, *Proc. Roy. Soc.*, B, **86**: 586–600.

——— and ———, 1915: Studies on enzyme action. Lipase IV, The correlation of synthetic and hydrolytic activity, *Proc. Roy. Soc.*, B, **88**: 176–189.

AVERY, G. S., 1930: Comparative anatomy and morphology of embryos and seedlings of maize, oats and wheat, *Bot. Gaz.*, **89**: 1–40.

BACH, A., A. OPARIN, and R. WÄHNER, 1927: Untersuchungen über den Fermentgehalt von reifenden, ruhenden und keimenden Weizensamen, *Biochem. Z.*, **180**: 363–370.

BAENS, L., F. M. YENKO, A. P. WEST, and H. M. CURRAN, 1934: Tannin content of Philippine barks and woods, *Philippine J. Sci.*, **55**: 177–190.

BAILEY, C. H., and R. C. SHERWOOD, 1935: Biochemistry of bread making, *Ind. and Eng. Chem.*, **27**: 1426–1430.

BAILEY, E. M., 1912: Biochemical and bacteriological studies on the banana, *J. Am. Chem. Soc.*, **34**: 1706–1730.

BAKER, J. L., and H. F. E. HULTON, 1921: Amylases of the cereal grains. Rye, *J. Chem. Soc., London*, **119**: 805–809.

——— and ——— 1929: Amylases of the cereal grains—oats, *J. Chem. Soc., London*, **1929**: 1655–1660.

BALLS, A. K., 1931: Recent advances in enzyme chemistry: the mechanism of peptide hydrolysis, *Sigma Xi Quart.*, **19**: 98–112.

BALY, E. C. C., and E. S. SEMMENS, 1924: The selective photochemical action of polarised light, *Proc. Roy. Soc.*, B, **97**: 250–253.

——— and ———, 1925: Selective action of polarized light upon starch grains, *Nature*, **116**: 817.

BARANETZKY, J., 1878: "Die stärkebildenden Fermente in den Pflanzen," Felix, Leipzig.

BARENDRECHT, H. P., 1913: Enzyme-action, facts and theory, *Biochem. J.*, **7**: 549–561.

BARTHOLOMEW, E. T., 1914: Concerning the presence of diastase in certain red algae, *Bot. Gaz.*, **57**: 136–147.

BARTON, A. W., 1920: The lipolytic activity of the castor and soybean, *J. Am. Chem. Soc.*, **42**: 620–632.

BAYLISS, W. M., 1925: "The Nature of Enzyme Action," mon., Longmans, Green and Company, New York, 200 pp.

BERCZELLER, L., and J. FREUD, 1922: Über die Wirkung der Halogene auf Diastasen, *Biochem. Z.*, **139**: 476–481.

BERGMANN, M., and W. F. ROSS, 1935: On proteolytic enzymes. VIII, The proteolytic systems of papain, *J. Biol. Chem.*, **111**: 659–666.

BEYERINCK, M. W., 1895: Ueber Nachweis und Verbreitung der Glukase, das Enzym der Maltose, *Cent. Bakt. u. Parasitenkunde*, II, **1**: 221–229, 265–271, 329–342.

BLAGOWESTSCHENSKI, A., 1926: Über die synthetische Wirkung der pflanzlichen Proteasen, *Biochem. Z.*, **168**: 1–6.

BLOOD, A. F., 1910: The erepsin of the cabbage, *J. Biol. Chem.*, **8**: 215–225.

BOIS, E., and A. NADEAU, 1935: Contribution à l'étude d'*Acer saccharum*, *Nat. Canadien*, **62**: 106–112.

BOUCHUT, E., 1880: Sur un ferment digestif contenu dans le suc de figuier, *C. R. Acad. Sci. Paris*, **91**: 67–68.

BOURQUELOT, E., 1893: Inulose et fermentation alcoolique indirect de l'inuline, *C. R. Soc. Biol.*, **5**: 481–483.

———, 1893: Inulase et fermentation alcoolique indirecte de l'inuline, *C. R. Acad. Sci. Paris*, **116**: 1143–1145.

———, 1893: Remarques sur les ferments solubles sécrétés par l'*Aspergillus niger* et le *Penicillium glaucum*, *C. R. Soc. Biol.*, **5**: 653–654.

———, 1903: Généralities sur les ferments solubles qui déterminent l'hydrolyse des polysaccharides, *C. R. Acad. Sci. Paris*, **136**: 762–764.

BRADLEY, H. C., and E. KELLERSBERGER, 1912: The problem of enzyme synthesis. III, Diastase and starch of plant tissue, *J. Biol. Chem.*, **13**: 425–429.

BRASSE, L., 1884: Sur la présence de l'amylase dans les feuilles, *C. R. Acad. Sci. Paris*, **99**: 878–879.

———, 1885: Action de la diastase du malt sur l'amidon cru, *C. R. Acad. Sci. Paris*, **100**: 454–456.

BRAUN, K., and E. BEHRENDT, 1903: Beitrag zur fermentative Spaltung der Fette, *Ber. chem. Ges.*, **36**: 1142–1145, 1900–1911.

BRILL, H. C., and R. E. BROWN, 1922: The digestive properties of Philippine papaïn, *Philippine J. Sci.*, **20**: 185–191.

BROWN, H. T., and J. HERON, 1879: Contributions to the history of starch and its transformations, *J. Chem. Soc., London*, **35**: 596–654.

——— and G. H. MORRIS, 1890: Researches on the germination of some of the *Gramineae*, *J. Chem. Soc., London*, **57**: 458–528.

——— and ——— 1893: A contribution to the chemistry and physiology of foliage leaves, *J. Chem. Soc., London*, **63**: 604–677.

——— and F. ESCOMBE, 1898: On the depletion of the endosperm of *Hordeum vulgare* during germination, *Proc. Roy Soc.*, **63**: 3–25.

BRUSCHI, D., 1908: Researches on the vitality and self digestion of the endosperm of some *Graminaceae*, *Ann. Bot.*, **22**: 449–463.

BUNKER, J. W. M., and E. G. E. ANDERSON, 1928: Polarized light and starch hydrolysis, *J. Biol. Chem.*, **77**: 473–488.

BUTKEWITSCH, W., 1900: Ueber das Vorkommen proteolytischer Enzyme in gekeimten Samen und über ihre Wirkung, *Ber. bot. Ges.*, **18**: 185–189.

———, 1901: Über das Vorkommen eines proteolytischen Enzyms in gekeimten Samen und über seine Wirkung, *Z. physiol. Chem.*, **32**: 1–53.

———, 1908: Zur Frage über die Umwandlung der Stärke in den Pflanzen und über den Nachweis der amylolytischen Enzyme, *Biochem. Z.*, **10**: 314–344.

CALDWELL, J. S., 1905: The effect of toxic agents upon the action of bromelin, *Bot. Gaz.*, **39**: 409–419.

CHITTENDEN, R. H., E. P. JOSLIN, and F. S. MEARA, 1891: On the ferments contained in the juice of the pineapple together with some observations on the composition and proteolytic action of the juice, *Trans. Conn. Acad. Arts and Sci.*, **8**: 283–308.

———, 1892: Papoid-digestion, *Trans. Conn. Acad. Arts and Sci.*, **9**: 297–332.

———, 1894: The proteolytic action of bromelin—the ferment of pineapple juice, *J. Physiol.*, **15**: 249–310.

———, L. B. MENDEL, and H. E. MCDERMOTT, 1898: Papaïn proteolysis with some observations on the physiological action of the products formed, *Am. J. Physiol.*, **1**: 256–276.

CHRZASZCZ, T., and A. JOSCHT, 1917: Über die Verschiebung einzelner amylolytischer Kräfte der Malzamylase und deren Verhalten beim Aufbewahren in Gegenwart verschiedener Reagentien, *Biochem. Z.*, **80**: 211–241.

———, 1923: Einfluss der Temperatur auf die Wirkung der Amylase. Die Wirkung der verzuckernden Kraft der Amylase, *Biochem. Z.*, **142**: 417–439.

———, Z. BIDZINSKI, and A. KRAUSE, 1925: Über den Einfluss der Wasserstoffionkonzentration auf die Dextrinierung der Stärke durch gereinigte Malzamylase, *Biochem. Z.*, **160**: 155–171.

CLARK, R. H., F. L. FOWLER, and P. T. BLACK, 1931: The activation of amylase, *Trans. Roy. Soc. Canada*, Sec. 3, **25**: 99–105.

COHNHEIM, O., 1901: Die Umwandlung des Eiweiss durch die Darmwand, *Z. physiol. Chem.*, **33**: 451–465.

COLIN, M. H., 1915: Sur la distribution de l'invertine dans les tissus de la betterave, aux différentes époques de la végétation, *C. R. Acad. Sci. Paris*, **160**: 777–779.

COMPTON, A., 1921: Studies in the mechanism of enzyme action. I, Role of the reaction of the medium in fixing the optimum temperature of a ferment, *Proc. Roy. Soc.*, B, **92**: 1–6.

CONNSTEIN, W., E. HOYER, and H. WARTENBERG, 1902: Ueber fermentative Fettspaltung, *Ber. chem. Ges.*, **35**: 3988–4007.

CREIGHTON, M., and N. M. NAYLOR, 1933: A study of the starch-digesting and the sugar forming enzymes of wheat, *Iowa State Col. J. Sci.*, **7**: 253–260.

CUISINIER, L., 1885: Une nouvelle matière sucrée diastasque la Cerélose et pour sa fabrication, *French Patent* 171958, Oct. 30.

CZAPEK, F., 1903: Antifermente im Pflanzenorganismus, *Ber. bot. Ges.*, **21**: 229–242.

———, 1905: The anti-ferment reaction in tropistic movements of plants, *Ann. Bot.*, **19**: 75–98.

DAISH, A. J., 1916: The distribution of maltase in plants. II, The presence of maltase in foliage leaves, *Biochem. J.*, **10**: 49–55.

———, 1916: The distribution of maltase in plants. III, The presence of maltase in germinated barley, *Biochem. J.*, **10**: 56–76.

DAVIS, A. R., 1915: Enzyme action in the marine algae, *Ann. Mo. Bot. Gard.*, **2**: 771–836.

DAVIS, W. A., 1916: The distribution of maltase in plants. I, The function of maltase in starch degradation and its influence on the amyloclastic activity of plant materials, *Biochem. J.*, **30**: 31–48.

DEAN, A. L., 1903: Experimental studies on inulase, *Bot. Gaz.*, **35**: 24–35.

———, 1905: On proteolytic enzymes. I, *Bot. Gaz.*, **39**: 321–339.

———, 1905: On proteolytic enzymes. II, *Bot. Gaz.*, **40**: 121–134.

DELEZENNE, C., and H. MOUTON, 1906: Sur l'allure anomale de quelques protéolyses produites par la papaïne, *C. R. Soc. Biol.*, **60**: 68–70.

———, ———, and E. Pozerski, 1906: Sur la digestion brusque de l'ova-albumine et du sérum sanguin par la papaïne, *C. R. Soc. Biol.*, **60**: 309–312.

Denny, F. E., 1930: Increasing amylase activity of potato juice by the addition of potassium cyanide, *abst., Am. J. Bot.*, **17**: 1050.

———, 1931: The effect of thiocyanates upon amylase activity. I, Potato amylase, *Contr. Boyce Thompson Inst.*, **3**: 277–286.

———, 1931: The effect of potassium cyanide upon the amylase activity of potato juice, *Contr. Boyce Thompson Inst.*, **3**: 297–308.

———, 1932: Direct versus indirect effects upon potato amylase by chemicals which induce sprouting of dormant tubers, *Contr. Boyce Thompson Inst.*, **4**: 53–63.

———, 1933: Effect of potassium thiocyanate and ethylene-chlorhydrin upon amylase activity, *Contr. Boyce Thompson Inst.*, **5**: 441–450.

Doby, G., and R. P. Hibbard, 1927: Nutrient ions of plants and the ion activation of plant enzymes, *J. Biol. Chem.*, **73**: 405–416.

——— and J. Burger, 1932: Potato amylase, *Fermentforschung*, **13**: 201–211; *Chem. Abst.*, **26**: 4078.

——— and L. Brázay, 1932: The amylase of sugar beet leaves, *Fermentforschung*, **13**: 212–227; *Chem. Abst.*, **26**: 4078.

——— and E. Szladits, 1932: Enzymes and salt ions. III, Saccharogenic amylase of leaves of different fertilized potatoes, *Z. physiol. Chem.*, **206**: 177–186; *Exp. Sta. Rec.*, **70**: 754.

Doby, P., 1915: Über Pflanzenenzyme. IV, Die Invertase der Kartoffelblätter, *Biochem. Z.*, **71**: 495–500.

Duggar, B. M., and A. R. Davis, 1914: Enzyme action in *Fucus vesiculosis*, *Ann. Mo. Bot. Gard.*, **1**: 419–426.

Effront, J., 1905: Sur le développement de l'amylose pendant la germination des graines, *C. R. Acad. Sci. Paris*, **141**: 626–628.

———, 1917: "Biochemical Catalysts in Life and Industry. Proteolytic Enzymes." English translation by S. C. Prescott. John Wiley & Sons, Inc., New York.

———, 1922: Sur les propriétés distinctives des amylases de différentes provenances, *C. R. Acad. Sci. Paris*, **174**: 18–21.

Emmerling, O., 1902: Ueber die Eiweissspaltung durch Papayotin, *Ber. chem. Ges.*, **35**: 695–700.

Englis, D. T., and H. A. Lunt, 1925: Effect of the concentration of potassium salts in soil media upon the carbohydrate metabolism of plants. The diastatic activity of the nasturtium, *Soil Sci.*, **20**: 459–463.

——— and L. Gerber, 1929: A study of diastase activity in plants: The effect of phosphates in the soil media, *Soil Sci.*, **28**: 221–223.

——— and C. D. Zannis, 1930: The effect of ethylene upon the activity of diastase and invertase, *J. Am. Chem. Soc.*, **52**: 797–802.

Fales, H. A., and J. M. Nelson, 1915: The effect of sodium chloride upon the action of invertase, *J. Am. Chem. Soc.*, **37**: 2769–2786.

Falk, K. G., and J. M. Nelson, 1912: Studies on enzyme action. I, Some experiments with the castor bean lipase, *J. Am. Chem. Soc.*, **34**: 735–745.

——— and ———, 1912: Studies on enzyme action. II, The hydrolytic action of some amino acids and polypeptides of certain esters, *J. Am. Chem. Soc.*, **34**: 828–845.

——— and M. L. Hamlin, 1913: Studies on enzyme action. III, The action of manganous sulfate on castor bean lipase, *J. Am. Chem. Soc.*, **35**: 210–219.

———, 1913: Studies on enzyme action. V, The action of neutral salts on the activity of castor bean lipase, *J. Am. Chem. Soc.*, **35**: 601–616.

——, 1913: Studies on enzyme action. VI, The specificity of lipase action, *J. Am. Chem. Soc.*, **35**: 616–624.

——, 1913: Studies on enzyme action. IX, Extraction experiments with the castor bean lipase, *J. Am. Chem. Soc.*, **35**: 1904–1915.

—— and K. Sugiura, 1915: Studies on enzyme action. XII, The esterase and lipase of castor beans, *J. Am. Chem. Soc.*, **37**: 217–230.

——, 1915: Studies on enzyme action. XIII, The lipase of soybeans, *J. Am. Chem. Soc.*, **37**: 649–653.

——, 1917: Studies on enzyme action. XIV, Further experiments on lipolytic actions, *J. Biol. Chem.*, **31**: 97–123.

——, G. McGuire, and E. Blout, 1919: Studies on enzyme action. XVII, The oxidase, peroxidase, catalase, and amylase of fresh and dehydrated vegetables, *J. Biol. Chem.*, **38**: 229–244.

—— and ——, 1921: Studies on enzyme action. XIX, The sucrolytic actions of bananas, *J. Gen. Physiol.*, **3**: 595–611.

—— and ——, 1922: Studies on enzyme action. XXI, Banana gel and banana sucrose, *J. Biol. Chem.*, **54**: 655–671.

——, 1935: The mechanism of enzyme actions, *Sci.*, **81**: 471–475.

Feist, K., 1908: Die Spaltung des Amygdalin unter dem Einfluss von Emulsin, *Archiv. Pharm.*, **246**: 206, 509.

Fermi, C., and Dr. Buscalioni, 1899: Die proteolytischen Enzyme im Pflanzenreiche, *Cent. Bakt.*, II, **5**: 24–27, 63–67, 91–95, 125–135, 146–158.

Fernbach, A., and L. Hubert, 1900: Sur la diastase proteolytique du malt, *C. R. Acad. Sci. Paris*, **130**: 1783–1785.

Filipowicz, B., 1931: Influence of proteins and protein derivatives on the enzymic hydrolysis of starch by malt diastase, *Biochem. J.*, **25**: 1874–1884.

Fisher, D. F., C. P. Harley, and C. Brooks, 1930: The influence of temperature on the development of water core, *Proc. Am. Soc. Hort. Sci.*, **27**: 276–280.

Fisher, E. A., 1919: Contributions to the study of the vegetable proteases. I, Introductory, *Biochem. J.*, **13**: 124–134.

Frankel, E. M., 1917: Studies on enzyme action. XV, Factors influencing the proteolytic activity of papain, *J. Biol. Chem.*, **31**: 201–215.

Freeman, G. G., and R. H. Hopkins, 1936: The mechanism of degradation of starch by amylases. I, Nature of the early fission products, *Biochem. J.*, **30**: 442–445.

—— and ——, 1936: The mechanism of degradation of starch by amylases. II, Kinetics of action of α- and β- amylases on starch, its components and partial degradation products, *Biochem. J.*, **30**: 446–450.

—— and ——, 1936: The mechanism of degradation of starch by amylases. III, Mutarotation of fission products, *Biochem. J.*, **30**: 451–456.

Fuller, H. J., 1931: Some effects of ultra-violet radiation upon plant enzymes, abst., *Am. J. Bot.*, **18**: 895.

——, 1932: Some effects of radiations from a mercury vapor arc in quartz upon enzymes, *Ann. Mo. Bot. Gard.*, **19**: 505–531.

Gardiner, W., 1897: The histology of the cell wall with special reference to the mode of connection of cells, *Proc. Roy. Soc.*, **62**: 100–112.

Gerber, C., 1907: La présure des *Crucifères*, *C. R. Soc. Biol.*, **62**: 1223–1225.

——, 1907: Action du phosphate neutre de sodium sur la coagulation du lait de vache par les présures végétales, *C. R. Soc. Biol.*, **63**: 640–642.

——, 1907: Action du phosphate neutre de potassium sur la coagulation du lait de vache par les présures végétales, *C. R. Soc. Biol.*, **63**: 642–644.

——, 1907: La présure des *Crucifères*, *C. R. Acad. Sci. Paris*, **145**: 92–94.

———, 1907: La présure des *Rubiacées, C. R. Acad. Sci. Paris,* **145**: 284–286.

———, 1907: Les agents de la coagulation du lait contenus dans le suc du Mûrier de Chine (*Broussonetia papyrifera*), *C. R. Acad. Sci. Paris,* **145**: 530–532.

———, 1908: Action des acides sur la coagulation du lait par les présures végétales, *C. R. Acad. Sci. Paris,* **146**: 1111–1114.

———, 1908: Suc présurants des *Renonculacées, C. R. Soc. Biol.,* **64**: 522–523.

———, 1909: La présure du papayer.—Son action sur le lait bouilli aux diverses températures, *C. R. Soc. Biol.,* **66**: 227–229.

———, 1909: Relations entre les ferments présurants et les ferments proteolytiques végétaux. Leur rôle dans la plante, *C. R. Soc. Biol.,* **67**: 332–334.

———, 1909: Méthode générale de préparation des présures végétales, *C. R. Soc. Biol.,* **66**: 890–892.

———, 1909: Action comparée des présures végétales sur la peptone et la caséine. I, Type *Composées.* II, Algues brunes, *C. R. Soc. Biol.,* **66**: 1122–1125, 1125–1127.

———, 1909: Activité présurante des divers organes des *Composées, C. R. Congr. Soc. Sav. Rennes,* **1909**: 152–155.

———, 1909: Coagulation du lait cru par la présure du Papayer (*Carica papaya*), *C. R. Acad. Sci. Paris,* **148**: 497–500.

———, 1909: Répartition de la présure dans les membres et tissus végétaux, *C. R. Acad. Sci. Paris,* **148**: 992–994.

———, 1912: Relations entre l'activité présurante du latex du *Euphorbes* et l'espèce considérée ou la partie du végétal considérée. Résistance de cette présure à la chaleur, *C. R. Soc. Biol.,* **73**: 578–580.

———, 1912: Action des sels neutres sur la caséification du lait par la présure du latex des *Euphorbes, C. R. Soc. Biol.,* **73**: 582–584.

Glick, D., and C. G. King, 1933: The protein nature of enzymes. An investigation of pancreatic lipase, *J. Am. Chem. Soc.,* **55**: 2445–2449.

Glimm, E., and W. Sommer, 1927: Beitrag zur Reinigung der Malzamylase, *Biochem. Z.,* **188**: 290–325.

Gore, H. C., and S. Józsa, 1932: Sugar formation by diastatic enzymes of flour, *Ind. and Eng. Chem.,* **24**: 99–102.

——— and ———, 1932: Diastatic enzymes in certain foods, *Ind. and Eng. Chem.,* **24**: 102.

———, 1936: Action of amylases on starch, *Ind. and Eng. Chem.,* **28**: 86–88.

Green, J. R., 1887: On the changes in the proteids in the seed which accompany germination, *Phil. Trans. Roy. Soc.,* B, **178**: 39–61.

———, 1887: On the germination of the tuber of the Jerusalem artichoke (*Helianthus tuberosus*), *Ann. Bot.,* **1**: 223–236.

———, 1888: Vegetable rennet, *Nature,* **38**: 274–276.

———, 1890: On the germination of the seed of the castor-oil plant, *Proc. Roy. Soc.,* **48**: 370–392.

———, 1892: On the occurrence of vegetable trypsin in the fruit of *Cucumis utilissimus, Ann. Bot.,* **6**: 195–202.

———, 1893: On vegetable ferments, *Ann. Bot.,* **7**: 83–137.

———, 1894: Researches on the germination of the pollen grain and the nutrition of the pollen tube, *Phil. Trans. Roy. Soc.,* B, **185**: 385–409.

———, 1894: The influence of light on diastase, *Ann. Bot.,* **8**: 370–373.

———, 1897: On the action of light on diastase and its biological significance, *Phil. Trans. Roy. Soc.,* B, **188**: 167–190.

———, 1899: "The Soluble Ferments and Fermentation," Cambridge University Press, 480 pp.

GRIFFIN, E. G., and J. M. NELSON, 1916: The influence of certain substances on the activity of invertase, *J. Am. Chem. Soc.*, **38**: 722–730.

GRÜSS, J., 1893: Ueber den Eintritt von Diastase in das Endosperm, *Ber. bot. Ges.*, **11**: 286–292.

———, 1894: Ueber das Verhalten des diastatischen Enzyms in der Keimpflanze, *Jahrb. wiss. Bot.*, **26**: 379–437.

———, 1895: Die Diastase im Pflanzenkörper, *Ber. bot. Ges.*, **13**: 2–13.

———, 1896: Beiträge zur Physiologie der Keimung, *Landw. Jahrb.*, **25**: 385–452.

———, 1897: Ueber die Secretion des Schildchens, *Jahrb. wiss. Bot.*, **30**: 645–664.

HABERLANDT, G., 1890: Die Kleberschicht des Gras-Endosperms als Diastase ausscheidendes Drüsengewebe, *Ber. bot. Ges.*, **8**: 40–48.

HAEHN, H., and H. SCHWEIGART, 1923: Zur Kenntnis der Kartoffelamylase, *Biochem. Z.*, **143**: 516–526.

HALEY, D. E., and J. F. LYMAN, 1921: Castor bean lipase, its preparation and some of its properties, *J. Am. Chem. Soc.*, **43**: 2664–2670.

HANES, C. S., 1932: Studies on plant amylases. I, The effect of starch concentration upon the velocity of hydrolysis by the amylase of germinated barley, *Biochem. J.*, **26**: 1406–1421.

HANSTEEN, B., 1894: Ueber die Ursachen der Entleerung der Reservestoffe aus Samen, *Flora*, **79**: 419–429.

HARADA, T., 1931: Preparation of *Aspergillus oryzae* enzymes, *Ind. and Eng. Chem.*, **23**: 1424–1427.

HARLEY, C. P., D. F. FISHER, and M. P. MASURE, 1931: A starch splitting enzyme in apple tissues, *Proc. Am. Soc. Hort. Sci.*, **28**: 561–565.

HARRIS, M. R., and W. L. GOSS, 1934: A seedling disease of sorghum and Sudan grass, *Calif. Sta. Month. Bull.*, **23**: 109–118.

HENRI, V., 1902: Théorie générale de l'action de quelques diastases, *C. R. Acad. Sci. Paris*, **135**: 916–919.

——— and A. LALOU, 1903: Action de l'émulsine sur la salicine et l'amygdaline. Théorie de l'action de l'émulsine, *C. R. Acad. Sci. Paris*, **136**: 1693–1694.

——— and M. NICLOUX, 1904: Influence des proportions d'huile et d'acide sur la vitesse de saponification par la lipaséidine, *C. R. Soc. Biol.*, **57**: 175–177.

HEPBURN, J. S., 1918: Biochemical studies of the pitcher liquor of *Nepenthes*, *Proc. Am. Phil. Soc.*, **57**: 112–130.

———, E. Q. ST. JOHN, F. M. JONES, and W. F. BAKER, 1922: Studies of the North American *Sarraceniaceae*, *J. Biol. Chem.*, **50**: *Proc.* XLVI.

HILTNER, R. S., 1900: The fatal effect of green sorghum, *Neb. Sta. Bull.* 63.

HOGOUNENQ, L., and J. LOISELEUR, 1925: Sur la constitution des diastases proteolytique et le mécanisme de leur actions, *Bull. Soc. Chim. Biol.*, **7**: 955–973.

HOLTER, H., and K. LINDERSTROM-LANG, 1933: Beiträge zur enzymatischen Histochemie. III, Ueber die Proteinasen von *Drosera rotundifolia*, *Z. physiol. Chem.*, **214**: 222–240.

HOPKINS, R. H., 1929: The proteolytic enzymes of green malt. I, Adsorption and elution, *Biochem. J.*, **23**: 1022–1029.

———, G. F. COLE, and J. W. GREEN, 1933: Some observations on barley diastase, *J. Inst. Brewing*, **39**: 487–493; *Biol. Abst.*, **8**: 1409.

HORNING, E. S., and A. H. K. PETRIE, 1927: The enzymatic function of mitochondria in the germination of cereals, *Proc. Roy. Soc.*, B, **102**: 188–206.

HORTON, E., 1921: On the use of taka-diastase in estimating starch, *Jour. Agr. Sci.*, **11**: 240–257.

HOYER, E., 1904: Ueber fermentative Fettspaltung, *Ber. chem. Ges.*, **37**: 1436–1447.

———, 1907: Ueber fermentative Fettspaltung, *Z. physiol. Chem.*, **50**: 414–435.

HUBER, H., 1929: Über den Zustand und die Rolle der Gerbstoffe in der Pflanze, *Jahrb. wiss. Bot.*, **70**: 278–327; *Biol. Abst.*, **5**: 2669.

HUDSON, C. S., 1908: The inversion of cane sugar by invertase. I, II, *J. Am. Chem. Soc.*, **30**: 1160–1166, 1564–1583.

———, 1909: The inversion of cane sugar by invertase. III, *J. Am. Chem. Soc.*, **31**: 655–664.

——— and H. S. PAINE, 1910: The inversion of cane sugar by invertase. IV, The influence of acids and alkalies on the activity of invertase, *J. Am. Chem. Soc.*, **32**: 774–779.

——— and———, 1910: The inversion of cane sugar by invertase. V, The destruction of invertase by acids, alkalis and hot water, *J. Am. Chem. Soc.*, **32**: 985–989.

———, 1910: The inversion of cane sugar by invertase. VI, A theory of the influence of acids and alkalis on the activity of invertase, *J. Am. Chem. Soc.*, **32**: 1220–1222.

——— and H. S. PAINE, 1910: The inversion of cane sugar by invertase. VII, The effect of alcohol on invertase, *J. Am. Chem. Soc.*, **32**: 1350–1357.

———, 1910: The quantitative determination of cane sugar by the use of invertase, *J. Ind. Eng. Chem.*, **2**: 143–146.

———, 1914: The inversion of sucrose by invertase. VIII, An improved method for preparing strong invertase solutions from top or bottom yeast, *J. Am. Chem. Soc.*, **36**: 1566–1571.

——— and H. S. PAINE, 1914: The inversion of sucrose by invertase. IX, Is the reaction reversible? *J. Am. Chem. Soc.*, **36**: 1571–1581.

HUERRE, R., 1909: Sur la maltase du maïs, *C. R. Acad. Sci. Paris*, **148**: 300–302, 505–507.

———, 1909: Influence de la réaction du milieu sur la activité des maltases du maïs, *C. R. Acad. Sci. Paris*, **148**: 1121–1123.

———, 1909: Sur la maltase du sarrasin, *C. R. Acad. Sci. Paris*, **148**: 1526–1528.

HUTCHINSON, A. H., and M. R. ASHTON, 1933: The effect of radiant energy on diastase activity, *Can. J. Res.*, **9**: 49–64.

JACOBSON, C. A., and A. HOLMES, 1914: Alfalfa investigations. V, Enzymes present in alfalfa, *J. Am. Chem. Soc.*, **36**: 2170–2182.

JAMES, W. O., and M. CATTLE, 1933: Studies on the physiological importance of the mineral elements in plants. VI, The influence of potassium chloride on the rate of diastatic hydrolysis of starch, *Biochem. J.*, **27**: 1805–1809.

JAVILLIER, M., 1903: Sur quelques ferments proteolytiques associés à la présure chez les végétaux, *C. R. Acad. Sci. Paris*, **136**: 1013–1015.

JODIDI, S. L., and J. PEKLO, 1929: Symbiotic fungi of cereal seeds and their relation to cereal proteins, *J. Agr. Res.*, **38**: 69–93.

JONES, W. N., 1925: Polarized light and starch grains, *Ann. Bot.*, **39**: 651–653.

JOSLYN, M. A., and M. SHERRILL, 1933: Inversion of sucrose by invertase at low temperatures, *Ind. and Eng. Chem.*, **25**: 416–417.

JÓZSA, S., and H. C. GORE, 1932: Development of diastatic enzymes of malt and flour. Effects of certain salts, carbohydrates, and papain, *Ind. and Eng. Chem.*, **24**: 95–98.

KASTLE, J. H., and M. CLARK, 1903: On the occurrence of invertase in plants, *Am. Chem. J.*, **30**: 422–427.

KAYSER, E., 1891: Note sur les ferments de l'ananas, *Ann. Inst. Pasteur*, **5**: 456–463.

KELLERMAN, K. F., 1903: The effects of various chemical agents upon the starch converting power of taka diastase, *Bull. Torrey Bot. Club*, **30**: 56–70.

KERSTAN, G., 1934: The physiological significance of the glucosides in *Aesculus* and *Salix*, *Planta*, **21**: 677–698; *Chem. Abst.*, **28**: 6772.

Kertesz, Z. I., 1931: Discharge of saccharase from mycelium of *Penicillium glaucum*, *Plant Physiol.*, **6**: 249–264.

Kirsh, D., 1935: Lipase production by *Penicillium oxalicum* and *Aspergillus flavus*, *Bot. Gaz.*, **97**: 321–333.

Kizel, A., 1915: The effect of the reaction of the medium on the activity of inulase of *Aspergillus niger*, *Isv. Imp. Akad. Nauk.* (*Bull. Acad. Imp. Sci.*) *Petrograd*, **6**: 1077–1092; *Exp. Sta. Rec.*, **37**: 203.

Knudson, L., 1920: The secretion of invertase by plant roots, *Am. J. Bot.*, **7**: 371–380.

Koga, T., 1923: Zur Frage der Differenzierung tierischer und pflanzlicher Diastasen, *Biochem. Z.*, **142**: 159–164.

Kohl, F. G., 1908: Über die Reversibilität der Enzymwirkungen und den Einfluss äusserer Faktoren auf die Enzyme (Invertase, Maltase), *Beih. bot. Cent.*, **23**: 64*b*–64*o*.

Kosmann, M. C., 1877: Recherches chimiques sur les ferments contenus dans les végétaux et sur les effets produits par l'oxydation du fer sur les matières organiques, *Bull. Soc. Chim.*, **27**: 251–256.

Krabbe, G., 1890: Untersuchungen über das Diastaseferment unter specieller Berücksichtigung seiner Wirkung auf Stärkekörner innerhalb der Pflanzen, *Jahrb. wiss. Bot.*, **21**: 521–561.

Krauch, C., 1879: Beiträge zur Kenntniss der ungeformten Fermente im Pflanzenreich, *Landw. Versuchs-Stat.*, **23**: 77–104.

Kuhn, R., D. B. Hand, and M. Florkin, 1931: Über die Natur der Peroxydase, *Z. physiol. Chem.*, **201**: 255–266.

Lea, S., 1883: On a "Rennet" ferment contained in the seeds of *Withania coagulans*, *Proc. Roy. Soc.*, **36**: 55–58.

Ling, A. R., and D. R. Nanji, 1923: On the presence of maltase in germinated and ungerminated barley, *Biochem. J.*, **17**: 593–596.

Lintner, C. J., 1885: Studien über Diastase, *J. Prak. Chem.*, **34(2)**: 378–394.

Linz, F., 1896: Beiträge zur Physiologie der Keimung von *Zea mais*, *Jahrb. wiss. Bot.*, **29**: 267–319.

Longenecker, H. E., and D. E. Haley, 1935: Ricinus lipase, its nature and specificity, *J. Am. Chem. Soc.*, **57**: 2019–2021.

Lothrop, R. E., and H. S. Paine, 1931: Diastatic activity of some American honeys, *Ind. and Eng. Chem.*, **23**: 71–74.

Macht, D. I., and J. H. Hill, 1925: The influence of polarized light on yeast and bacteria, *Proc. Soc. Exper. Biol. Med.*, **22**: 474–475.

———, 1928: Effect of polarized light on plants, *abst.*, *Am. J. Bot.*, **15**: 621.

Maestrini, D., 1923: Contributo alla conoscenza degli enzimi. IX, Sulla resistenza all' invecchiamento di alcun enzimi dell'orzo germoglato, *Atti R. Accad. Lincei Roma Rendiconti Cl. Sci. Fis. Mat. e Nat.*, **32**: 397–398; *Bot. Abst.*, **13**: 178.

Mann, A., and H. V. Harlan, 1915: Morphology of the barley grain with reference to its enzyme secreting areas, *U. S. Dept. Agr. Bull.*, **183**: 1–32.

Maquenne, L., and E. Roux, 1906: Recherches sur l'amidon et sa saccharification disastasique, *Ann. Chem. et Phys.*, 8^{e}, **9**: 179–220.

Martin, S. H. C., 1884: Papaïn-digestion, *J. Physiol.*, **5**: 213–230.

———, 1885: The nature of papaïn and its action on vegetable proteid, *J. Physiol.*, **6**: 336–360.

Martinand, V., 1907: Recherche de l'invertine ou sucrase et du saccharose dans les divers organes de la Vigne et dans quelque fruits, *C. R. Acad. Sci. Paris*, **144**: 1376–1379.

MASLOW, H. L., and W. C. DAVIDSON, 1926: The effect of hydrogen ion concentration upon the starch liquefying activity of the amylase of *Aspergillus oryzae*, *J. Biol. Chem.*, **68**: 83–93.

MATHEW, A. P., and T. H. GLENN, 1911: The composition of invertase, *J. Biol. Chem.*, **9**: 29–56.

McGINTY, R. A., 1919: Diastase activity in relation to stage of development and carbohydrate content of the tuber *Solanum tuberosum*, *Ann. Mo. Bot. Gard.*, **6**: 223–251.

McGUIRE, G., and K. G. FALK, 1919: The saccharogenic actions of potato juice, *J. Gen. Physiol.*, **2**: 215–227.

——— and ———, 1923: Studies on enzyme action. XXIII, The spontaneous increase in sucrase activity of banana extracts, *J. Am. Chem. Soc.*, **45**: 1539–1551.

McNAIR, J. B., 1932: Some properties of plant substances in relation to climate of habitat-volatile oils, saponins, cyanogenetic glucosides, and carbohydrates, *Am. J. Bot.*, **19**: 168–193.

MENDEL, L. B., and F. P. UNDERHILL, 1901: Observations on the digestion of proteids with papaïn, *Trans. Conn. Acad. Arts and Sci.*, **11**: 1–14.

———, 1902: Observations on vegetable proteolytic enzymes, with special reference to papaïn, *Am. J. Med. Sci.*, **124**: 310–318.

——— and A. F. BLOOD, 1910: Some peculiarities of the proteolytic activity of papaïn, *J. Biol. Chem.*, **8**: 177–213.

MICHAELIS, L., and M. ROTHSTEIN, 1920: Zur Theorie der Invertasewirkung, *Biochem. Z.*, **110**: 217–233.

MICHEL-DURAND, E., 1928–1930: Physiological investigations on tannins, *Rev. Gén. Bot.*, **40**: 705–734 (1928); **41**: 35–48, 106–118, 142–153, 237–251, 307–336, 388–399, 441–464, 513–528, 582–592, 637–652, 700–720, 772–783 (1929); **42**: 46–63, 115–128, 164–184, 233–253, (1930); *Chem. Abst.*, **27**: 3238.

———, 1929: "Recherches sur les composés tanniques," Librairie générale de l'enseignement, Paris, 293 pp., 11 Figs.

———, 1932: Origin of tannins from proteins and carbohydrates, *Rev. Gén. Bot.*, **44**: 161–214; *Chem. Abst.*, **27**: 3238.

MIEHE, H., 1923: Über die Lebensdauer der Diastase, *Ber. bot. Ges.*, **41**: 263–268.

MILLER, E. R., 1929: The chemical nature of enzymes, *Sci.*, **70**: 356.

MOUNFIELD, J. D., 1936: The proteolytic enzymes of sprouted wheat, *Biochem. J.*, **30**: 549–557.

MURRY, D. R. P., 1933: The activation of papain by cyanide and other substances. I, *Biochem. J.*, **27**: 541–556.

MUSSI, DR., 1890–1891: Cradina, a proteolytic enzyme in the fig (*Ficus carica*), abst., *Pharm. J.*, 3 ser., **21**: 560–561.

NAVEZ, A. E., and B. B. RUBENSTEIN, 1928: Starch hydrolysis as affected by polarized light, *J. Biol. Chem.*, **80**: 503–513.

———, 1930: On the alleged effect of polarized light on films of starch, *Sci.*, **72**: 13.

——— and B. B. RUBENSTEIN, 1932: Starch hydrolysis as affected by light, *J. Biol. Chem.*, **95**: 645–660.

NAYLOR, N. M., M. SPENCER, and M. HOUSE, 1925: The preparation and properties of amylase from germinated wheat and rye, *J. Am. Chem. Soc.*, **47**: 3037–3039.

NEIDIG, R. E., 1914: The survival of amylase in dried fodders, *J. Am. Chem. Soc.*, **36**: 1312–1314.

NELSON, J. M., and S. BORN, 1914: A study of the chemical constitution of invertase, *J. Am. Chem. Soc.*, **36**: 393–403.

——— and E. G. GRIFFIN, 1916: Adsorption of invertase, *J. Am. Chem. Soc.*, **38**: 1109–1115.

——— and W. C. Vosburgh, 1917: Kinetics of invertase action, *J. Am. Chem. Soc.*, **39**: 790–811.

——— and D. I. Hitchcock, 1921: The activity of adsorbed invertase, *J. Am. Chem. Soc.*, **43**: 1956–1961.

——— and ———, 1921: Uniformity in invertase action, *J. Am. Chem. Soc.*, **43**: 2632–2655.

——— and F. Hollander, 1923: Uniformity in invertase action, *J. Biol. Chem.*, **58**: 291–305.

——— and G. Bloomfield, 1924: Some characteristics of invertase action, *J. Am. Chem. Soc.*, **46**: 1025–1043.

——— and O. Bodansky, 1925: Mutarotation as a factor in the kinetics of invertase action, *J. Am. Chem. Soc.*, **47**: 1624–1638.

——— and C. Hemperly, 1933: Co-ferments and banana respiration, *J. Am. Chem. Soc.*, **55**: 1102–1106.

Neumeister, R., 1894: Ueber das Vorkommen und die Bedeutung eines eiweisslösenden Enzyms in jugendlichen Pflanzen, *Z. Biol.*, **30**: 447–463.

Newcombe, F. C., 1898: Cellulose-enzyme, *Bot. Cent.*, **73**: 105–108.

———, 1899: Cellulose-enzymes, *Ann. Bot.*, **13**: 49–81.

Nicloux, M., 1904: Étude de l'action lipolytique du cytoplasma de la graine de ricin, *C. R. Acad. Sci. Paris*, **138**: 1288–1290.

———, 1904: Sur le pouvoir saponifiant de la graine de ricin, *C. R. Soc. Biol.*, **56**: 702–704; *C. R. Acad. Sci. Paris*, **138**: 1175–1177.

———, 1904: Étude de l'action lipolytique du cytoplasma de la graine de ricin, *C. R. Soc. Biol.*, **56**: 839–843.

———, 1904: La propriété lipolytique du cytoplasma de la graine de ricin n'est pas due à un ferment soluble, *C. R. Acad. Sci. Paris*, **138**: 1352–1354; *C. R. Soc. Biol.*, **56**: 868–870.

———, 1904: Mécanisme d'action du cytoplasma (lipaseïdine) dans la graine en voie de germination: Réalisation synthétique in vitro de ce mécanisme, *C. R. Acad. Sci. Paris*, **139**: 143–145.

———, 1904: Mécanisme d'action du cytoplasma "lipaseïdine" dans la graine en voie de germination réalisation synthétique en vitro de ce mécanisme, *C. R. Soc. Biol.*, **57**: 84–86.

———, 1905: La saponification des corps gras, *Rev. Gén. des Sciences*, 16e année, No. 23, pp. 1029–1037.

———, 1906: Studies on enzyme action—Lipase, *Proc. Roy. Soc.*, B, **77**: 454–455.

Nordh, G., and E. Ohlsson, 1932: Amylases in resting and germinating seeds. I, Barley, *Z. physiol. Chem.*, **204**: 89–100; *Chem. Abst.*, **26**: 3003.

Ohlsson, E., 1922: Sur l'existence de deux ferments amylolytique dans la diastase du malt, *C. R. Soc. Biol.*, **87**: 1183–1184.

———, 1926: On the two components of malt diastase, *C. R. trav. lab. Carlsberg*, **16**: 1.

———, 1930: Über die beiden Komponenten der Malzdiastase, besonders mit Rücksicht auf die Mutarotation der bei der Hydrolyse der Stärke gebildeten Produkte, *Z. physiol. Chem.*, **189**: 17–63.

——— and C. E. Uddenberg, 1933: Amylases in resting and germinating seeds. II, Rye, *Z. physiol. Chem.*, **221**: 165–173; *Chem. Abst.*, **28**: 504–505.

——— and O. Edfeldt, 1933: Amylases in resting and germinating seeds. III, Oats, *Z. physiol. Chem.*, **221**: 174–179; *Chem. Abst.*, **28**: 505.

Olsson, U., 1921: Über Vergiftungserscheinungen an Amylasen, *Z. physiol. Chem.*, **117**: 91–145.

Oparin, A., and S. Risskina, 1932: Über die Aktivität der Amylase in den Blättern der Zukerrübe, *Biochem. Z.*, **252**: 8–15.

OSBORNE, T. B., 1895: The chemical nature of diastase, *J. Am. Chem. Soc.*, **17**: 587–604.

——— and G. F. CAMPBELL, 1896: The chemical nature of diastase. II, *J. Am. Chem. Soc.*, **18**: 536–542.

OSBORNE, W. A., 1898: Beiträge zur Kenntniss des Invertins, *Z. physiol. Chem.*, **28**: 399–425.

O'SULLIVAN, C., and F. W. TOMPSON, 1890: Invertase: A contribution to the history of an enzyme or unorganized ferment, *J. Chem. Soc.*, **57**: 834–931.

OTIS, C. H., 1930: A source of diastase, *Sci.*, **71**: 220.

PAINE, H. S., and R. T. BALCH, 1925: Application of enzymes to beet sugar factory control, *Ind. and Eng. Chem.*, **17**: 240–246.

———, C. F. WALTON, and M. S. BADOLLET, 1925: Industrial applications of invertase, *Ind. and Eng. Chem.*, **17**: 445–450.

PALLADIN, V. I., and E. M. POPOVA, 1924: On the origin of diastase in plants, *Bull. App. Bot. Plant-breeding*, **13**: 355–369 (Russian); *Bot. Abst.*, **14**: 1448.

PALLADIN, W., and H. POPOFF, 1922: Über die Entstehung der Amylase und Maltase in den Pflanzen, *Biochem. Z.*, **128**: 487–494.

PATON, F. J., D. R. NANJI, and A. R. LING, 1924: On the hydrolysis of the endosperm of *Phytelephas macrocarpa* by its own enzymes, *Biochem. J.*, **18**: 451–454.

PATON, J. B., 1921: Pollen and pollen enzymes, *Am. J. Bot.*, **8**: 471–501.

PELOUZE, J., 1855: Mémoire sur la saponification des huiles sous l'influence des matières qui les accompagnent dans les graines, *C. R. Acad. Sci. Paris*, **40**: 605–611.

PICKLER, W. E., 1919: Water content and temperature as factors influencing diastase formation in the barley grain, *Plant World*, **22**: 221–238.

PINCUSSEN, L., 1923: Fermente und Licht. I, Diastase. II, Urease, *Biochem. Z.*, **134**: 459–469, 470–475.

POLAK, F., and A. TYCHOWSKI, 1928: Über die Umwandlung der α-Diastase in β-Diastase, *Biochem. Z.*, **192**: 463–478.

POND, R. H., 1906: The incapacity of the date endosperm for self-digestion, *Ann. Bot.*, **20**: 62–78.

POZEN, M. A., 1934: Enzymes in brewing, *Ind. and Eng. Chem.*, **26**: 1127–1133.

POZERSKI, E., 1909: Contribution à l'étude physiologique de la papaïne, *Ann. Inst. Pasteur*, **23**: 321–359.

———, 1909: Digestion brusque produite par la bromeline. Comparaison avec la papaïne, *Ann. Inst. Pasteur*, **23**: 341–346.

PRATT, D. S., 1915: Papaïn. Its commercial preparation and digestive properties, *Philippine J. Sci.*, A, **10**: 1–37.

PRUNET, A., 1892: Sur le mécanisme de la dissolution de l'amidon dans la plante, *C. R. Acad. Sci. Paris*, **115**: 751–754.

PURIEWITSCH, K., 1897: Physiologische Untersuchungen über die Entleerung der Reservestoffbehälter, *Jahrb. wiss. Bot.*, **31**: 1–76.

QUINTANILHA, A., 1926: O proglema das plantas carnivoras. Estudo cito-fisiológico da digestão no *Drosophyllum lusitanicum*, *Bol. Soc. Broteriana* (Portuguese), **4**: 44–129; *Biol. Abst.*, **2**: 874.

REED, H. S., 1904: A study of the enzyme-secreting cells in the seedlings of *Zea mais* and *Phoenix dactylifera*, *Ann. Bot.*, **18**: 267–287.

RICHAND, A., 1900: "Recherches physiologique sur l'inulase et sur l'inuline," thèse 8°, Carre et Naud, Paris, 95 pp.

RINGER, W. E., and B. W. GRUTTERINK, 1927: Einfluss der Reaktion auf die Eiweissverdauende Kraft des Papains. II, *Z. physiol. Chem.*, **164**: 112–142.

ROBERTSON, R. A., J. C. IRVINE, and M. E. DOBSON, 1909: A polarimetric study of the sucroclastic enzymes in *Beta vulgaris*, *Biochem. J.*, **4**: 258–273.

ROBINSON, M. E., 1930: Cyanogenesis in plants, *Biol. Rev. and Biol. Proc. Cambridge Phil. Soc.*, **5**: 126–141; *Biol. Abst.*, **5**: 2675.

RUSSELL, J. B., 1891: Bromelin, *Bull. Pharm.*, **5**: 77.

SANDBERG, M., and O. M. HOLLY, 1932: Note on myrosin, *J. Biol. Chem.*, **96**: 443–447.

SARGANT, E., and A. ROBERTSON, 1905: The anatomy of the scutellum in *Zea mais*, *Ann. Bot.*, **19**: 115–124.

SCHANDER, H., 1934: The significance of the aleurone layer in *Oryza* and other *Gramineae*, *Z. Bot.*, **27**: 433–515; *Chem. Abst.*, **29**: 489.

SCHENKER, R., 1921: Zur Kenntnis der Lipase von *Aspergillus niger*, *Biochem. Z.*, **120**: 164–196.

SCHMITZ, H., 1920: Enzyme action in *Echinodontium tinctorium*, *J. Gen. Physiol.*, **2**: 613–616.

SCHULTZ, A. S., and Q. LANDIS, 1932: Vegetable amylases. Study of diastase action in the absence of maltose, *J. Am. Chem. Soc.*, **54**: 211–220.

SEMMENS, E. S., 1926: Hydrolysis of starch grains by light polarized by small particles, *Nature*, **117**: 821–822.

———, 1926: Some further notes on the hydrolysis of starch grains under polarized light, *Plant Physiol.*, **1**: 201–202.

———, 1932: Hydrolysis in green plants by moonlight, *Nature*, **130**: 243.

SEN, H. D., 1931: A study on the extraction of papain, the active digestive principle from *Papaya*, *J. Agr. Sci.*, **21**: 209–219.

SHERMAN, H. C., E. C. KENDALL, and E. D. CLARK, 1910: Studies on amylases. I, An examination of methods for the determination of diastatic power, *J. Am. Chem. Soc.*, **32**: 1073–1087.

——— and M. D. SCHLESINGER, 1913: Studies on amylases. V, Experiments upon the purification of the amylase of malt, *J. Am. Chem. Soc.*, **35**: 1617–1624.

——— and A. O. GETTLER, 1913: Studies on amylases. VII, The forms of nitrogen in amylase preparations from the pancreas and from malt, as shown by the Van Slyke method, *J. Am. Chem. Soc.*, **35**: 1790–1794.

——— and A. W. THOMAS, 1915: Studies on amylases. VIII, The influence of certain acids and salts upon the activity of malt amylase, *J. Am. Chem. Soc.*, **37**: 623–643.

——— and M. D. SCHLESINGER, 1915: Studies on amylases. IX, Further experiments upon the purification of malt amylase, *J. Am. Chem. Soc.*, **37**: 643–648.

——— and ———, 1915: Studies on amylases. X, Comparison of certain properties of pancreatic and malt amylase preparations, *J. Am. Chem. Soc.*, **37**: 1305–1319.

——— and A. P. TANBERG, 1916: Experiments upon the amylase of *Aspergillus oryzae*, *J. Am. Chem. Soc.*, **38**: 1638–1644.

——— and J. C. BAKER, 1916: Experiments upon starch as substrate for enzyme action, *Am. J. Chem. Soc.*, **38**: 1885–1904.

——— and D. E. NEUN, 1916: An examination of certain methods for the study of proteolytic action, *J. Am. Chem. Soc.*, **38**: 2199–2216.

——— and J. A. WALKER, 1917: Influence of certain electrolytes upon the course of the hydrolysis of starch by malt amylase, *J. Am. Chem. Soc.*, **39**: 1476–1493.

———, A. W. THOMAS, and M. E. BALDWIN, 1919: Influence of hydrogen-ion concentration upon enzymic activity of three typical amylases, *J. Am. Chem. Soc.*, **41**: 231–235.

———, F. WALKER, and M. L. CALDWELL, 1919: Action of enzymes upon starches of different origin, *J. Am. Chem. Soc.*, **41**: 1123–1129.

——— and ———, 1919: Influence of aspartic acid and asparagin upon the enzymic hydrolysis of starch, *J. Am. Chem. Soc.*, **41**: 1866–1873.

——— and M. WAYMAN, 1921: Effect of certain antiseptics upon the activity of amylases, *J. Am. Chem. Soc.*, **43**: 2454–2461.

——— and F. WALKER, 1921: The influence of certain amino acids upon the enzyme hydrolysis of starch, *J. Am. Chem. Soc.*, **43**: 2461–2469.

——— and M. L. CALDWELL, 1921: A study of the influence of arginine, histidine, tryptophane and cystine upon the hydrolysis of starch by purified pancreatic amylase, *J. Am. Chem. Soc.*, **43**: 2469–2476.

——— and ———, 1922: Influence of amino acid in protecting amylase from inactivation by mercury, *J. Am. Chem. Soc.*, **44**: 2923–2926.

——— and———, 1922: Influence of lysine upon the hydrolysis of starch by purified pancreatic amylase, *J. Am. Chem. Soc.*, **44**: 2926–2930.

——— and N. M. NAYLOR, 1922: Influence of some organic compounds upon the hydrolysis of starch by salivary and pancreatic amylases, *J. Am. Chem. Soc.*, **44**: 2957–2966.

———, A. W. THOMAS, and M. L. CALDWELL, 1924: The isoelectric point of malt amylase, *J. Am. Chem. Soc.*, **46**: 1711–1717.

———, M. L. CALDWELL, and M. ADAMS, 1927: Establishment of the optimal hydrogen-ion activities for the enzymic hydrolysis of starch by pancreatic and malt amylases under varied conditions of time and temperature, *J. Am. Chem. Soc.*, **49**: 2000–2005.

———, ———, and H. H. BOYNTON, 1930: A quantitative study of the influence of acetate and of phosphate on the activity of malt amylase, *J. Am. Chem. Soc.*, **52**: 1669–1672.

———, ———, and S. E. DOEBBELING, 1934: Further studies upon the purification and properties of malt amylase, *J. Biol. Chem.*, **104**: 501–509.

SIGMUND, W., 1890: Ueber fettspaltende Fermente im Pflanzenreiche, *Monats. Chem. Wien*, **11**: 272–276.

———, 1892: Beziehungen zwischen fettspaltenden und glycosidspaltenden Fermente, *Sitzungsber. Akad. Wiss. Wien*, **101**: 549–559.

SJÖBERG, K., 1922: Beiträge zur Kenntnis der Amylase in Pflanzen. I, Über die Bildung und das Verhalten der Amylase in lebenden Pflanzen, *Biochem. Z.*, **133**: 218–294.

———, 1922: Beiträge zur Kenntnis der Amylase in Pflanzen. II, Die Temperaturempfindlichkeit der Amylase von *Phaseolus vulgaris*, *Biochem. Z.*, **133**: 294–330.

———, 1923: Beiträge zur Kenntnis der Amylase in Pflanzen. III, *Biochem. Z.*, **142**: 274–279.

SLADE, H. B., 1903: Prussic acid in sorghum, *J. Am. Chem. Soc.*, **25**: 55–59.

SÖRENSEN, S. P. L., 1908: Enzymstudien, *Biochem. Z.*, **7**: 45–101.

STERN, K. G., and E. STERN, 1932: Über die Proteinasen insectivorer Pflanzen, *Biochem. Z.*, **252**: 81–96.

STONE, W. E., 1896: The carbohydrates of wheat, maize, flour and bread and the action of enzymic ferments upon starches of different origin, *U. S. Dept. Agr. Off. Exp. Sta. Bull.* 34.

STOWARD, F., 1912: On the influence exercised by certain acids on the inversion of saccharose by sucrase, *Biochem. J.*, **6**: 131–140.

SULLIVAN, B., and M. A. HOWE, 1933: Lipases of wheat. I, *J. Am. Chem. Soc.*, **55**: 320–324.

SUMNER, J. B., 1926: The isolation and crystallization of the enzyme urease, *J. Biol. Chem.*, **69**: 435–441.

———, 1933: The chemical nature of enzymes, *Sci.*, **78**: 335.

SWANSON, C. O., and J. W. CALVIN, 1913: A preliminary study of the conditions which affect the activity of the amylolytic enzymes in wheat flour, *J. Am. Chem. Soc.*, **35**: 1635–1640.

———, 1921: Hydrocyanic acid in Sudan grass and its effect on cattle. *J. Am. Soc. Agron.*, **13**: 33–36.

———, 1935: Some factors which affect the diastatic activity in wheat, *Cereal Chem.*, **12**: 89–107.

TAIT, L., 1875: Insectivorous plants, *Nature*, **12**: 251–252.

TAKAMINE, J., and O. KOKICHI, 1920: The properties of a specially prepared enzymic extract, polyzime, comparing its starch liquefying power with malt diastase, *J. Am. Chem. Soc.*, **42**: 1261–1265.

TANKA, Y., 1910: The action of acids in the enzymic decomposition of oil by castor seeds, *J. Col. Eng. Tokyo*, **5**: 25–42. Quoted by Bayliss, 1925.

———, 1912: The preparation of lipase-powder acting in neutral medium, *J. Col. Eng. Tokyo*, **5**: 125–136.

TASCHER, W. R., and G. H. DUNGAN, 1928: Seedling vigor and diastatic activity of dent corn as related to composition of endosperm and stage of maturity, *J. Am. Soc. Agron.*, **20**: 133–141.

TAUBER, H., 1936: "Experimental enzyme chemistry," Burgess Pub. Co., Minneapolis, Minn., 118 pp.

TAYLOR, A. E., 1906: On the action of lipase, *J. Biol. Chem.*, **2**: 87–105.

TEODORESCO, E. C., 1914: Température mortelle pour quelques diastases d'origine animale et végétale, *Rev. Gén. Bot.*, **25**: 599–630.

THATCHER, R. W., and G. P. KOCH, 1914: The quantitative extraction of diastases from plant tissues, *J. Am. Chem. Soc.*, **36**: 759–770.

———, 1915: Enzymes of apples and their relation to the ripening process, *J. Agr. Res.*, **5**: 103–116.

———, 1921: "The Chemistry of Plant Life," McGraw-Hill Book Company, Inc., New York, 268 pp.

THEIS, E. R., J. S. LONG, and C. E. BROWN, 1929: Studies in the drying oils. XII, Changes in linseed oil, lipase and other constituents of the flaxseed as it matures, *Ind. and Eng. Chem.*, **21**: 1244–1248.

THOMAS, A. W., 1917: A noteworthy effect of bromides upon the action of malt amylase, *J. Am. Chem. Soc.*, **39**: 1501–1503.

TORREY, J. C., 1902: Cytological changes accompanying the secretion of diastase, *Bull. Torrey Bot. Club.*, **29**: 421–435.

TYSDAL, H. M., 1934: Determination of hardiness in alfalfa varieties by their enzymatic responses, *J. Agr. Res.*, **48**: 219–240.

VINES, S. H., 1891: On the presence of a diastatic ferment in green leaves, *Ann. Bot.*, **5**: 409–412.

———, 1897, 1898, 1901: The proteolytic enzyme of *Nepenthes*. I, II, III, *Ann. Bot.*, **11**, 563–584; **12**: 545–555; **15**: 563–573.

———, 1902: Tryptophane in proteolysis, *Ann. Bot.*, **16**: 1–22.

———, 1903: Proteolytic enzymes in plants. I, II, *Ann. Bot.*, **17**: 237–264, 597–616.

———, 1904–1906, 1908–1910: The proteases of plants. I, II, III, IV, V, VI, VII, *Ann. Bot.*, **18**: 289–317; **19**: 149–162, 171–187; **20**: 113–122; **22**: 103–113; **23**: 1–18; **24**: 213–222.

VINSON, A. E., 1907: The function or invertase in the formation of cane and invert sugar dates, *Bot. Gaz.*, **43**: 393–407.

———, 1908: The endo- and ektoinvertase of the date, *J. Am. Chem. Soc.*, **30**: 1005–1020.

VON GORUP-BESAÑEZ, E., 1874: Ueber das Vorkommen eines diastatischen und peptonisirenden Fermentes in den Wickensamen, *Ber. chem. Ges.*, **7**: 1478–1480.

—, 1875: Weitere Beobachtungen über diastatische und peptonbildende Fermente im Pflanzenreiche, *Ber. chem. Ges.*, **8**: 1510–1516.

——— and H. Will, 1876: Fortgesetzte Beobachtungen über peptonbildende Fermente im Pflanzenreiche, *Ber. chem. Ges.*, **9**: 673–678.

Vosburgh, W. C., 1921: Some errors in the study of invertase action, *J. Am. Chem. Soc.*, **43**: 1693–1705.

Waksman, S. A., 1920: A method of testing the amylolytic action of the diastase of *Aspergillus oryzae*, *J. Am. Chem. Soc.*, **42**: 293–299.

Waldschmidt-Leitz, E., 1933: The chemical nature of enzymes, *Sci.*, **78**: 189–190.

Ward, M., 1888: A lily disease, *Ann. Bot.*, **2**: 319–383.

Weis, F., 1900: Ueber das proteolytische und ein eiweisscoagulirendes Enzym in keimender Gerste (Malz), *Z. physiol. Chem.*, **31**: 79–97.

White, J., 1909: The ferments and latent life of resting seeds, *Proc. Roy. Soc.*, B, **81**: 417–442.

———, 1910: The proteolytic enzyme of *Drosera*, *Proc. Roy. Soc.*, B, **83**: 134–139.

Wierzchowski, Z., 1913: Studien über die Einwirkung von Maltase auf Stärke, *Biochem. Z.*, **56**: 209–219.

———, 1913: Über das Auftreten der Maltase in Getreidearten, *Biochem. Z.*, **57**: 125–131.

Willstätter, R., 1922: Über Isolierung von Enzymen, *Ber. chem. Ges.*, **55**: 3601–3623.

———, J. Graser, and R. Kuhn, 1922: Zur Kenntnis des Invertins, *Z. physiol. Chem.*, **123**: 1–78.

Wolff, J., 1916: Sur une substance coagulant l'inuline et l'accompagnant dans les tissus végétaux, *C. R. Acad. Sci. Paris.*, **162**: 514–516.

Wurtz, A., 1879: "Recherches cliniques et chimiques sur la papaïne," Paris.

——— and E. Bouchut, 1879: Sur le ferment digestif du *Carica papaya*, *C. R. Acad. Sci. Paris*, **89**: 425–429.

———, 1880: Sur la papaïne. Nouvelle contribution à l'histoire des ferments solubles, *C. R. Acad. Sci. Paris*, **91**: 787–791.

Young, V. H., 1918: Some factors affecting inulase formation in *Aspergillus niger*, *Plant World*, **21**: 75–87, 114–133.

Zeile, K., and H. Hellström, 1930: Über die aktive Gruppe der Leberkatalase, *Z. physiol. Chem.*, **192**: 171–192.

———, 1931: Über die aktive Gruppe der Katalase. II, *Z. physiol. Chem.*, **195**: 39–48.